EXPONENTS

Definition: If n is a natural number and b is a nonzero real number, then:

(1) $b^n = \overbrace{b \cdot b \cdot b \cdots \cdots b}^{n \text{ factors}}$ (2) $b^0 = 1$ (3) $b^{-n} = \dfrac{1}{b^n}$

(4) $b^{1/n}$ is defined according to the following table:

n	$b > 0$	$b < 0$	$b = 0$
Even	$b^{1/n}$ is the positive nth real root of b $-b^{1/n}$ is the negative nth real root of b	Not defined	0
Odd	$b^{1/n}$ is the nth real root of b		

(5) $b^{m/n} = (b^{1/n})^m$

(6) $\sqrt[n]{b} = b^{1/n}$

Simplifying Radicals

An algebraic expression containing radicals is simplified if all four of the following conditions are satisfied:

1. When the radicand is written in completely factored form, there is no factor raised to a power greater than the index of the radical.
2. No radical appears in a denominator.
3. No fraction (or negative exponent) appears within a radical.
4. There is no common factor (other than 1) between the exponent of the radicand and the index of the radical.

Laws of Exponents

First Law: $b^m b^n = b^{m+n}$

Second Law: $(b^n)^m = b^{mn}$

Third Law: $(ab)^m = a^m b^m$

Fourth Law: $\left(\dfrac{a}{b}\right)^m = \dfrac{a^m}{b^m}$

Fifth Law: $\dfrac{b^m}{b^n} = b^{m-n}$

LOGARITHMS

Definition: $y = \log_b x$ is equivalent to $x = b^y$

$\log x$ means $\log_{10} x$ and $\ln x$ means $\log_e x$

Change of Base:

$$\log_b x = \frac{\log x}{\log b} \quad \text{or} \quad \frac{\ln x}{\ln b}$$

Laws of Logarithms

I. $\log_b AB = \log_b A + \log_b B$

II. $\log_b \dfrac{A}{B} = \log_b A - \log_b B$

III. $\log_b A^n = n \cdot \log_b A$

IV. $\log_b 1 = 0$

V. $\log_b \dfrac{1}{A} = -\log_b A$

SEQUENCES AND SERIES

Arithmetic sequence: $a_n = a_1 + (n-1)d$

Arithmetic series: $A_n = \dfrac{n}{2}(a_1 + a_n)$ or $A_n = \dfrac{n}{2}[2a_1 + (n-1)d]$

Geometric sequence: $g_n = g_1\, r^{n-1}$ for $n \geq 1$

Geometric series: $G_n = \dfrac{g_1(1 - r^n)}{1 - r}$ and $G_\infty = \dfrac{g_1}{1 - r}$ for $|r| < 1$

Intermediate Algebra
For College Students
Second Edition

Other Brooks/Cole Titles by the Same Authors

Trigonometry for College Students, Second Edition
KARL J. SMITH

Introduction to Symbolic Logic
KARL J. SMITH

Beginning Algebra for College Students, Second Edition
KARL J. SMITH AND PATRICK J. BOYLE

Study Guide for Beginning Algebra for College Students, Second Edition
KARL J. SMITH AND PATRICK J. BOYLE

Study Guide for Intermediate Algebra for College Students, Second Edition
KARL J. SMITH AND PATRICK J. BOYLE

Algebra and Trigonometry
KARL J. SMITH AND PATRICK J. BOYLE

College Algebra, Second Edition
KARL J. SMITH AND PATRICK J. BOYLE

Analytic Geometry: A Refresher
KARL J. SMITH

Precalculus Mathematics: A Functional Approach
KARL J. SMITH

The Nature of Modern Mathematics, Third Edition
KARL J. SMITH

Basic Mathematics for College Students
KARL J. SMITH

Arithmetic for College Students
KARL J. SMITH

Intermediate Algebra
For College Students

Second Edition

KARL J. SMITH

Santa Rosa Junior College

PATRICK J. BOYLE

Santa Rosa Junior College

Brooks/Cole Publishing Company
Monterey, California

Contemporary Undergraduate Mathematics Series
ROBERT J. WISNER, EDITOR

Brooks/Cole Publishing Company
A Division of Wadsworth, Inc.

Printed in the United States of America

10 9 8 7 6 5 4 3

Library of Congress Cataloging in Publication Data

Smith, Karl J.
  Intermediate algebra for college students.

  Includes index.
  1. Algebra.   I. Boyle, Patrick J.
II. Title.
QA154.2.S57   1982   512.9   81–15539
ISBN 0–8185–0468–4   AACR2

ACQUISITION EDITOR: *Craig Barth*
PRODUCTION SERVICE: *Phyllis Niklas*
PRODUCTION COORDINATORS: *Cece Munson, Joan Marsh*
INTERIOR DESIGN: *Janet Bollow*
COVER ART: *Ron Grauer*
ILLUSTRATIONS: *Carl Brown*
TYPESETTING: *Kingsport Press*

To children:
Me and Shannon,
Cathris, Cindy, Connie, and Cori

Preface

In writing this second edition we've incorporated the suggestions of the reviewers and many users who've written to us. While retaining the philosophy that mathematics can be enjoyable, and at the same time serious and practical, we paid particular attention in this edition to making it easy for the student to use this text. We have included the following features:

1. There are more examples and less exposition than in the first edition.
2. Examples are clearly set apart from the rest of the text.
3. All problems are keyed directly to examples; problems in this edition follow the examples more closely than they did in the first edition.
4. Important ideas are enclosed in boxes; important terms are shown in boldface type.
5. The margin is restricted to the following uses:
    a. Noting the most important ideas for the student.
    b. Referencing the student to a previous idea (especially referring to a previous example to help the student when working the problems).
    c. Historical Notes to give some of the human side of mathematics. These are not just biographical notes, but give some personal aspects to make it clear that mathematicians are human.

The development of topics follows the usual pattern. However, with the large number of books available, the instructor must select a book that offers some special features, or has a particular emphasis, which is appropriate for the students taking a definite course. This edition has retained those features that we feel are most needed for the type of student taking this course. Recent developments in business management, behavioral and social sciences, biological science, and many other fields have completely changed the population of college mathematics classes. More and more students are finding that they need a background in math to handle their major fields of study. Many good students have not had good records in math and yet find themselves faced with one or more required math courses, such as this one. With these students in mind, we have written a book with the following features:

1. The problem sets contain many routine, easy problems that are useful for drill. Problems are given as matched pairs and are divided into A and B problems according to increasing difficulty.

Mind Boggler problems are provided for those students who are interested in trying them.

2. Special emphasis is given to graphing and graphs.

3. Inequalities are treated along with equalities throughout the book.

4. Logarithms are examined as functions rather than as a means of making computations.

5. We recognize the importance of calculators and encourage their proper use. Calculator problems appear throughout the book, and they are marked with the symbol so they can be easily recognized.

6. A complete and very thorough presentation of word problems is presented. The transition from verbal to algebraic statements and back to verbal solutions is thoroughly explained throughout the text, offering students a chance to get away from the vicious circle of having to understand word problems to do them and having to do them to understand them. A variety of topics are included in the word problems, covering several fields. We hope the word problems will provide something of interest for every reader, but we've made sure that each word problem is self-contained and doesn't require "outside" knowledge.

7. A *Study Guide for Intermediate Algebra for College Students,* Second Edition, has been developed to help students with some of the more difficult concepts and to give them additional practice with problems. It provides a review for each chapter and an extensive self-test. An instructor's manual is also available with solutions to all the problems in the text (naturally, answers to odd-numbered problems and all review problems are given in the back of the text itself).

We would like to thank Craig Barth, Phyllis Niklas, Cece Munson, Joan Marsh, and the rest of the staff at Brooks/Cole for their support and encouragement while we were working on this book. Also, special thanks go to Robert J. Wisner and the other reviewers of the manuscript: Nancy S. Angle, University of Colorado, Denver; Carole Bauer, Triton College; Dale E. Boye, Schoolcraft College; Roger Breen, Florida Junior College; Elizabeth Dougherty, Louisiana State University; Ferdinand Haring, North Dakota State University; Steven Hatfield, Marshall University; David A. Horwitz, California Polytechnic University; Stephanie E. Jorgensen, Oregon State University; Gordon Roberts, Shoreline Community College; and Jerry Swisher, College of the Sequoias. We would also like to thank Gloria Langer for checking all the problems in the book.

Special thanks to our wives, Linda and Theresa, for their support while working on this book.

Karl J. Smith and Patrick J. Boyle

Contents

*Sections 6.3, 6.5, and 6.6 are the only sections from Chapter 6 required for the study of Chapter 7.

CHAPTER **10**

Exponential and Logarithmic Functions   331

CHAPTER **11**

Sequences, Series, and the Binomial Theorem   373

Appendix A   415

Appendix B   421

Appendix C   449

Index   455

Intermediate Algebra
For College Students
Second Edition

Introductory Concepts

Contents

1.1   Sets of Numbers

Algebra is a study of the general properties of numbers and operations on numbers. This first chapter reviews the terminology and symbolism that we will use in this study. We begin by listing four examples of **sets** of numbers, since they are what algebra is all about.

Natural Numbers: $N = \{1, 2, 3, 4, 5, \ldots\}$

Integers: $I = \{\ldots, -3, -2, -1, 0, 1, 2, 3, \ldots\}$

Even Integers: $E = \{\ldots, -4, -2, 0, 2, 4, \ldots\}$

Prime Numbers: $P = \{2, 3, 5, 7, 11, 13, 17, 19, 23, \ldots\}$

A capital letter may be used to name a set. The set of natural numbers will often be referred to by the letter N, and the letter I will be used to refer to the set of integers. One method of designating a set is to enclose a list of its **members, or elements,** in braces, { }, and to use three dots, if needed, to indicate that the numbers continue in the pattern shown. Since there is no last element listed, there are infinitely many numbers in the set. The set is said to be an **infinite set.** All elements of a **finite set** may be listed. To show that 5 is a natural number, we write $5 \in N$, which means "5 is an element of N." Similarly, $-2 \notin N$ means "-2 is not an element of N." Symbols used to represent unspecified elements of a given set are called **variables.** For example, $x \in E$ means "x is an element of E"; that is, x is an even integer. A set with no members is called the **empty set,** or **null set,** and is labeled $\emptyset$.

Notice that all the elements of N are also in I. Because of this, N is said to be a **subset** of I, or $N \subseteq I$, or "N is contained in I." The idea is clearer if you picture the sets as regions in a diagram. Diagrams used to illustrate the relationships among sets are called **Venn diagrams.** The Venn diagram in Figure 1.1 shows N contained inside I, and both are contained in the set of all numbers.

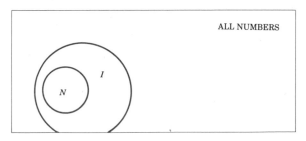

Figure 1.1

A **number line** is often used to display a set of numbers. A point on the line is designated to represent 0 and is called the **origin.** The points to the right of 0 are associated with the positive numbers, and the points to the left of 0 correspond to the negative numbers. Each number may be represented as a point on the line.

Example 1   Display the set $\{-3, -1, 1, 3, 5\}$ on a number line.

Solution

A number line is a convenient means of ordering numbers. If a lies to the right of b on a number line, then a **is greater than** b, written $a > b$. For example, $5 > 3$ or $0 > -1$. The positive numbers are to the right of 0, and we say that any positive number x is greater than 0, or $x > 0$. If a is to the right of b, then b is to the left of a, and we say that b **is less than** a, or $b < a$. For example, $3 < 5$, $-1 < 0$, and $x < 0$ if x is a negative number. The symbols of comparison are summarized below.

$a = b$	a is equal to b
$a \neq b$	a is not equal to b
$a > b$	a is greater than b
$a \geq b$	a is greater than or equal to b
$a < b$	a is less than b
$a \leq b$	a is less than or equal to b
$a \ngtr b$	a is not greater than b
$a \nless b$	a is not less than b

The expressions $a \ngtr b$ and $a \nless b$ are not used very often, since they are equivalent to $a \leq b$ and $a \geq b$, respectively.

As an alternative to listing the elements in a set, we may specify a set by **set-builder notation**. The set $\{1, 2, 3\}$ is the set of natural numbers less than 4. Using set-builder notation, this same set is specified by

All n such that n is in N and n is less than 4

$$\boldsymbol{S = \{n \mid n \in N, \quad n < 4\}}$$

Note that each symbol can be read as a word or phrase to make a complete statement.

$$S = \{n \mid n \in N, \quad n < 4\} = \{1, 2, 3\}$$

Several statements can be made about S: $S \subseteq N$, $S \subseteq I$, $1 \in S$, $2 \in S$, $3 \in S$, $4 \notin S$, and S is finite.

Historical Note

A fraction was often called a *broken number;* hence, the term *whole number* for a counting number. This terminology is due to the origin of the word *fraction,* which comes from the Latin *frangere,* meaning "to break." Many symbols are employed to denote fractions. The slant line, or *solidus,* is often seen, as in 3/4 or 7/12. The symbol was first proposed by the English mathematician Augustus DeMorgan in the *Encyclopedia Metropolitana* (1845). G. G. Stokes took up its use in 1880 and his contemporary, Cayley, wrote to him "I think the 'solidus' looks very well indeed . . . ; it would give you a strong claim to be President of the Society for the Prevention of Cruelty to Printers."

One set that is built from I is the set of **rational numbers.** Rational numbers are obtained by dividing two integers; that is, rational numbers are fractions. Since rational numbers are fractions, or **Q**uotients, we call the set Q.

All quotients a over b — such that — a and b are in I — and — b is not 0

$$Q=\left\{\frac{a}{b}\,\middle|\, a,\ b\in I,\quad b\neq 0\right\}$$

If $b=1$, then $\frac{a}{b}$ is an integer, so the integers are a subset of the rationals: $I\subseteq Q$

Every rational number may be expressed as a repeating or a terminating decimal. A number that can be expressed as a nonrepeating, nonterminating decimal is called an **irrational number.** The set containing all rational and irrational numbers is called the set of **real numbers** and is indicated by R. Figure 1.2 shows an expanded Venn diagram including Q and R.

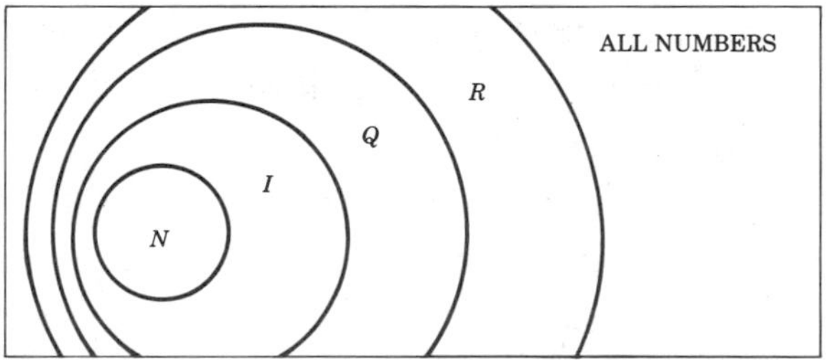

Figure 1.2

In Examples 2–4 list the elements of the given set.

Example 2 $S=\{n\,|\,3<n\leq 5,\quad n\in I\}$

Solution This specifies that n is an integer between 3 and 5, including 5, so you have

$S=\{4, 5\}$ □

Example 3 $T=\{x|x\leq 12,\quad x \text{ is an odd prime number}\}$

Solution This states that x is a prime number no larger than 12. Since the primes are 2, 3, 5, 7, 11, 13, . . . , and 2 is even:

$T=\{3, 5, 7, 11\}$ □

Example 4   Place the elements of the sets listed below in a Venn diagram.

$A = \{1, 2, 3, 4\}$
$B = \{b \mid b \text{ is positive and even, } \quad b < 7\}$
C is the set of prime numbers less than 7

Solution $A = \{1, 2, 3, 4\}$
$B = \{2, 4, 6\}$
$C = \{2, 3, 5\}$

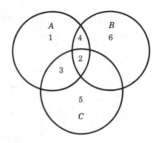

Order of Operations

It is often necessary to classify expressions as **sums, differences, products,** or **quotients.** With a single operation, the classification is easy:

$3 + 5$ Sum
$12 - 8$ Difference
$6 \cdot 9$ Product
$7 \div 2$ Quotient

But what if an expression has more than one operation? In

$2 + 3 \cdot 4$

is addition performed first?

$2 + 3 \cdot 4 = 5 \cdot 4 = 20$

Or is multiplication performed first?

$2 + 3 \cdot 4 = 2 + 12 = 14$

Both answers can't be correct, so we must have some agreement about how these operations are to be performed. To avoid confusion and ambiguity, we make the following agreement, which is called the **order-of-operations convention.**

ORDER-OF-
OPERATIONS
CONVENTION

Order-of-Operations Convention

First perform all multiplications and divisions as they occur from left to right. Then perform all additions and subtractions from left to right.

We classify an expression according to the *last* operation performed when simplifying an expression. For example, $2 + 3 \cdot 4$ is classified as a sum, since addition is performed last; $2 + 3 \cdot 4$ is the *sum* of 2 plus the product of 3 and 4.

In Examples 5–8 use the order-of-operations convention to simplify the expression, and classify each as a sum, difference, product, or quotient.

Example 5 $5 + 6 \cdot 4 = 5 + \mathbf{24}$
$$= \mathbf{29}$$

Sum   □

Example 6 $6 + 9 \div 3 - 2 \times 3$

Solution   In algebra, we generally avoid the use of $\times$ and $\div$ symbols for multiplication and division. Instead, we use the dot or parentheses for multiplication and fractional notation for division wherever possible. Thus, the given expression would normally be written as

$$6 + \frac{9}{3} - 2(3) = 6 + \mathbf{3} - \mathbf{6} \qquad \text{Multiplications and divisions first}$$
$$= \mathbf{9} - 6 \qquad\qquad \text{Additions and subtractions next}$$
$$= \mathbf{3}$$

Difference   □

Example 7 $5 + 8 \div 4 \times 2 - 6$

Solution   Work this yourself before reading further. Did you get 0? If you did, you multiplied first. Remember, multiplications *and* divisions are done from left to right *as they occur. Then,* do additions and subtractions from left to right *as they occur*. The correct answer is 3. Now study the solution:

$$5 + 8 \div 4 \times 2 - 6 = 5 + \frac{8}{4}(2) - \mathbf{6}$$
$$= 5 + 2(2) - 6$$
$$= 5 + 4 - 6$$
$$= \mathbf{9} - 6$$
$$= \mathbf{3}$$

Difference   □

Example 8 $27 \div 9 \cdot 3 - 6 + 3$

Solution $27 \div 9 \cdot 3 - 6 + 3 = \dfrac{27}{9}(3) - 6 + 3$

$$= 3(3) - 6 + 3$$
$$= 9 - 6 + 3$$
$$= 3 + 3$$
$$= 6$$

Sum   □

Symbols of Inclusion

You are probably familiar with number tricks where you are asked to "think of a number. . . ." After performing several operations, the puzzler tells you your number from the result. Consider the following set of directions: "Take your age, add 7, multiply by 5, subtract 10, multiply by 4, and finally subtract 100."

If you just write the individual operations, you get

Age, add 7, times 5, take away 10, times 4, take away 100

$$x \quad + 7 \quad \cdot \quad 5 \quad - \quad 10 \quad \cdot \quad 4 \quad - \quad 100$$

But what the puzzler had in mind was

$[(x + 7)(5) - 10](4) - 100$

This is a different order of operations, and to make that clear we use certain *symbols of inclusion:* **parentheses** ( ), **brackets** [ ], and **braces** { }. These symbols indicate that the operations enclosed are performed first. For example, if you are 19 years old, then $x = 19$, and

$$[(19 + 7)(5) - 10](4) - 100 = [(26\,(5) - 10](4) - 100$$
$$= [130 - 10](4) - 100$$
$$= [120](4) - 100$$
$$= 480 - 100$$
$$= 380$$

Drop the final 0 to get 38, and take half. The age is 19.

By changing the symbols of inclusion, we could obtain different results from the same operations performed in different orders. The examples that follow use the same numbers and operations, but with different orders of operation implied by the symbols of inclusion.

In Examples 9–13 simplify the expression, and classify each as a sum, difference, product, or quotient.

Example 9 $8 + 12 \div 2 = 8 + \dfrac{12}{2}$

$$= 8 + 6$$
$$= 14$$

Sum   □

Example 10 $(8 + 12) \div 2$

Solution   Fractional form is used as a grouping symbol to write this in usual algebraic form:

$$\frac{8 + 12}{2} = \frac{20}{2}$$
$$= 10$$

Quotient   □

Example 11 $\{19 + [(7)(5) - 10]\}4 - 10 = \{19 + [35 - 10]\}4 - 10$
$$= \{19 + 25\}4 - 10$$
$$= \{44\}4 - 10$$
$$= 176 - 10$$
$$= 166$$

Difference   □

Example 12 $[(19 + 7)(5)] - [(10)(4) - 10] = [(26)(5)] - [40 - 10]$
$$= [130] - [30]$$
$$= 100$$

Difference   □

Example 13 $19 + \{(7)(5) - [(10)(4) - 10]\} = 19 + \{35 - [40 - 10]\}$
$$= 19 + \{35 - 30\}$$
$$= 19 + 5$$
$$= 24$$

Sum   □

Problem Set 1.1

A   *Specify each set in Problems 1–10 by listing the elements. Display each set of numbers on a number line.*

See Examples 1–4.   **1.** $\{v | v$ is an English letter, v is always a vowel$\}$
2. $\{r | r$ is a robot, r is featured in *Star Wars*$\}$

3. $\{p|p$ is a former American president, p is living$\}$
4. $\{h|h$ is a U.S. national holiday, h is in July$\}$

Recall that N is the set
of natural numbers.

5. $\{r|r < 17, \quad r \in N, \quad r$ is prime$\}$
6. $\{s|s \leq 20, \quad s \in N, \quad s$ is not prime$\}$
7. $\{t|t < 10, \quad t$ is even, t is positive$\}$
8. $\{u|u > -12, \quad u$ is odd, u is negative$\}$
9. $\{v|7 \leq v \leq 19, \quad v \in N, \quad v$ is not prime$\}$
10. $\{w|0 \leq w \leq 10, \quad w \in N, \quad w$ is odd, w is prime$\}$

Use the order-of-operations convention in Problems 11–20 to simplify each expression. Classify each as a sum, difference, product, or quotient.

See Examples 5–8.

11. $2 + 3 \cdot 4$ 12. $2 \cdot 3 - 4$
13. $4 + 8 \div 2$ 14. $8 \div 4 + 2$
15. $3 \times 2 - 8 \div 4$ 16. $4 \div 2 + 5 \times 3$
17. $15 + 3 \cdot 2 - 12 \div 3$ 18. $25 + 24 \div 6 + 5 \cdot 7$
19. $5 + 2 \cdot 3 + 12 - 5 \cdot 3$ 20. $17 + 4 \cdot 12 - 2 \cdot 6 + 3$

B *Compute the result in Problems 21–30. Notice that the numbers and operations are the same and in the same order; the only changes are in the symbols of inclusion. Classify each as a sum, difference, product, or quotient.*

See Examples 9–13.

21. $3 + [(9 \div 3) \cdot 2] + [(2 \cdot 6) \div 3]$ 22. $[(3 + 9) \div (3 \cdot 2)] + [(2 \cdot 6) \div 3]$
23. $(3 + 9) \div [(3 \cdot 2 + 2 \cdot 6) \div 3]$ 24. $(3 + 9 \div 3 \cdot 2) + (2 \cdot 6 \div 3)$
25. $[(3 + 9) \div 3 \cdot 2 + 2] \cdot (6 \div 3)$ 26. $[(3 + 9 \div 3) \cdot 2] + (2 \cdot 6 \div 3)$
27. $[(3 + 9) \div (3 \cdot 2) + 2] \cdot 6 \div 3$ 28. $3 + (9 \div 3) \cdot (2 + 2 \cdot 6 \div 3)$
29. $3 + \{[(9 \div 3) \cdot (2 + 2)] \cdot (6 \div 3)\}$ 30. $[(3 + 9) \div 3] \cdot 2 + [(2 \cdot 6) \div 3]$

For Problems 31 and 32, place the elements of sets A, B, and C in the Venn diagram shown, so as to illustrate their relationship. Note that some elements will be in more than one set, and they should be positioned accordingly.

See Example 4.

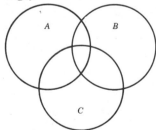

31. $A = \{2, 3, 5, 6\}$
    $B = \{n|4 \leq n < 8, \quad n \in N\}$
    C is the set of odd integers between 0 and 8
32. $A = \{n|n$ is even, $0 \leq n \leq 7\}$
    $B = \{n|n$ is a perfect square, $0 \leq n \leq 10\}$
    C is the set of multiples of 3 from 0 to 12, inclusive

33. In the text we simplified

$$2 + 3 \cdot 4$$

Push the following buttons on your calculator:

$\boxed{2}\ \boxed{+}\ \boxed{3}\ \boxed{\times}\ \boxed{4}\ \boxed{=}$

  a. If your calculator does not have an equal sign, it uses *RPN logic.*

  b. If your calculator gives the answer 14, it uses *algebraic logic.* That is, it works arithmetic problems according to the order-of-operations convention.

  c. If your calculator gives the answer 20, it uses *arithmetic logic.* If your calculator is arithmetic, *you* will have to remember to use the order-of-operations convention and press the keys

$\boxed{3}\ \boxed{\times}\ \boxed{4}\ \boxed{+}\ \boxed{2}\ \boxed{=}$

in order to simplify this expression. Classify your calculator, and keep this is mind when you use it.

Here are a couple of problems for which a calculator is necessary. When you finish each calculation, turn the machine upside down to read the answer to the question. Be careful of the order of operations.

You may have noticed that many of the numerals in an electronic calculator display appear as letters of the alphabet when inverted. For instance, when

710.77345

is turned upside down, it becomes

ShELL·OTL

34. How did Joe College decide he'd get the calculator he needed for Chem Lab?

    Answer: $[(197)(13.29 + 11.79) + .14](19)$

35. What did Betty Coed have to say about her new pocket calculator?

    Answer: $\{[(16)(15)]83\}277$

Mind Bogglers *Insert symbols of inclusion into the following expression so as to obtain each of the values in Problems 36–39.*

$$9 + 12 \div 3 + 4 \div 2 + 1 \cdot 2$$

  36. 2   **37.** 8   **38.** 11   **39.** 12

1.2 Properties of Real Numbers

9

8

7

6

5

4

3

2

1

___

Add the numbers in the margin, quickly.

If you started adding at the top of the list and went through one at a time, then you were working far too hard. It is much easier to *rearrange* and *regroup* to take advantage of certain combinations.

$$9 + 1 + 8 + 2 + 7 + 3 + 6 + 4 + 5 = ?$$
$$(9 + 1) + (8 + 2) + (7 + 3) + (6 + 4) + 5 = ?$$
$$10 + 10 + 10 + 10 + 5 = \mathbf{45}$$

So, ten, twenty, thirty, forty, forty-five does it. If you look for a shortcut, frequently you can find one, and computation can be simplified. Why can you do this? Can you always add in any order? Doesn't the order-of-operations convention apply? Yes it does, but when the operations are all addition (or multiplication), the order in which you add doesn't affect the sum. This property of real numbers is called the **commutative property,** and addition and multiplication are commutative for all real numbers.

COMMUTATIVE
PROPERTY

> **Commutative Property**
>
> For all real numbers a and b,
>
> $\quad ab = ba \qquad$ and $\qquad a + b = b + a$

The word *commutative* may be remembered more easily if you connect it with the commuter going back and forth to the city. The word *associative* may be easier to remember if you connect it with the associations we make with people. Friendships, groups, and cliques associate people instead of numbers.

As well as reordering the numbers in the above example, we regrouped the numbers. That is,

$$9 + 8 + 7 + 6 + 5 + 4 + 3 + 2 + 1$$
$$= 9 + 1 + 8 + 2 + 7 + 3 + 6 + 4 + 5 \qquad \text{Reordered}$$
$$= (9 + 1) + (8 + 2) + (7 + 3) + (6 + 4) + 5 \qquad \text{Regrouped}$$

By regrouping, we cause the operations to be performed in an order other than that dictated by the standard convention. Real numbers may be regrouped for addition (or for multiplication) because of the **associative property** of addition (or multiplication). We say that the reals are associative for addition and for multiplication.

ASSOCIATIVE
PROPERTY

> **Associative Property**
>
> For all real numbers a, b, and c,
>
> $\quad (ab)c = a(bc) \qquad$ and $\qquad (a + b) + c = a + (b + c)$

The Distributive Property

Both the commutative and associative properties apply to a single operation at a time. The **distributive property** relates the operations of addition and multiplication. Consider 4 times 5:

$$4(5) = 20$$

You know 4(5) is 20, and 5 is 3 + 2, so 4(3 + 2) must also be 20. Can you multiply before adding to obtain the same result?

$$4(3 + 2) = 4(3) + ?$$
$$= 12 + ?$$

The missing number must be 8 in order to obtain the correct result of 20:

$$4(3 + 2) = 4(3) + 4(2)$$
$$= 12 + 8$$
$$= 20$$

The distributive property distributes multiplication over addition; that is, it enables you to multiply a number times a sum by multiplying both terms by the number and then adding. We say that multiplication is distributive over addition for the real numbers. The distributive property enables you to change a basic product to a basic sum.

DISTRIBUTIVE
PROPERTY

Distributive Property

For all real numbers a, b, and c,

$$a(b + c) = ab + ac \qquad \text{or} \qquad (b + c)a = ba + ca$$

The commutative, associative, and distributive properties are basic keys to algebra. The distributive property, in particular, will be continually applied and reapplied to new situations.

Example 1 Use the given property to complete each statement.

a. Commutative property:

$3 \cdot 4 = ?$

$3 \cdot 4 = 4 \cdot 3$

b. Associative property:

$2(3 \cdot 4) = ?$

$2(3 \cdot 4) = (2 \cdot 3)4$

c. Commutative property:

$3(xy) = ?$

$3(xy) = 3(yx)$ or $(xy)3$

d. Distributive property:

$2(3 + 4) = ?$

$2(3 + 4) = 2(3) + 2(4)$

e. Commutative property (for addition):   **f.** Distributive property:

$2(3+4)=?$ $(2+a)b=?$

$2(3+4)=2(4+3)$ $(2+a)b=2b+ab$ □

Properties of Zero and One

The numbers 0 and 1 are very special real numbers. They perform unique functions in the system of real numbers, and many techniques of algebra rely upon their special properties.

ADDITIVE IDENTITY
(ZERO)

MULTIPLICATIVE
IDENTITY (ONE)

> **Identity Property**
>
> There is a unique real number 0, called the **additive identity,** such that
>
> $$a+0=a$$
>
> for any real number a.
>
> There is a unique real number 1, called the **multiplicative identity,** such that
>
> $$1 \cdot a = a$$
>
> for any real number a.

The properties of real numbers can be employed to establish further results. Statements that are derived from elementary results such as these are called **theorems.** For instance: *The product of 0 and any real number is 0* is a logical result of the basic properties. Let's see why.

Certainly,

$$ab=ab$$

Then we can say

$ab=a(\boldsymbol{b+0})$ Since $b=b+0$

$ab=a \cdot \boldsymbol{b} + a \cdot \boldsymbol{0}$ Distributive property

$ab=ab+a \cdot \boldsymbol{0}$

Since the additive identity property states that there is a unique number 0, such that

$$ab=ab+\boldsymbol{0}$$

the numbers $a \cdot 0$ and 0 must be the same number, so

$$a \cdot 0 = 0$$

and

$$a \cdot 0 = 0 \cdot a \qquad \text{Commutative property}$$

Therefore, $a \cdot 0 = 0 \cdot a = 0$ for any real number a.

The identity elements 0 and 1 are also the keys to inverse operations. Later we will see how this leads to subtraction of integers, division of integers, and the procedures for solving equations. In general, the properties of inverses may be stated as follows:

ADDITIVE INVERSE
(OPPOSITE)

MULTIPLICATIVE
INVERSE
(RECIPROCAL)

> **Property of Inverses**
>
> For every real number a, there is a unique real number $-a$, called the **additive inverse** (or **opposite**) of a such that
>
> $$a + (-a) = 0$$
>
> For every nonzero real number a, there is a unique real number $\dfrac{1}{a}$, called the **multiplicative inverse** (or **reciprocal**) of a such that
>
> $$a\left(\frac{1}{a}\right) = 1$$

Again, the stated property has many logical results. One such theorem is basic to solving many equations. The so-called **zero-product theorem** states that if $a \cdot b = 0$, then either $a = 0$ or $b = 0$. That is, if a product is 0, then at least one of its factors is 0. To see why this is true, consider the given statement $a \cdot b = 0$, and then:

If $a \neq 0$,	If $b \neq 0$,
$\left(\dfrac{1}{a}\right) a \cdot b = \left(\dfrac{1}{a}\right) 0$	$a \cdot b \left(\dfrac{1}{b}\right) = 0 \left(\dfrac{1}{b}\right)$
$1 \cdot b = 0$	$a \cdot 1 = 0$
$b = 0$	$a = 0$

Thus, if $a \cdot b = 0$, then either $a = 0$ or $b = 0$. Also, if $a = b = 0$, then $a \cdot b = 0 \cdot 0 = 0$.

Example 2 Use the given property to complete each statement.

    a. Identity property: **b.** Identity property:

        $x + 0 = ?$ $1 \cdot y = ?$

        $x + 0 = x$ $1 \cdot y = y$

c. Inverse property: d. Identity property:

$1 + (-1) = ?$ $x + y \cdot 0 = ?$

$1 + (-1) = 0$ $x + y \cdot 0 = x + 0$

$= x$ □

The Property of Closure

If $a + b = b + a$, then $a + b$ and $b + a$ must both name the same number. In making this statement, we have assumed that $a + b$ is always equal to some number. This assumption is the **closure property.**

CLOSURE PROPERTY

Closure Property

For all real numbers a and b,

$a + b$ and ab are unique real numbers

A set of numbers is **closed** for an operation if whenever the operation is performed on numbers from that set, the resulting number is also in the given set. For example, the sum of two even numbers is also even, so the even numbers are closed for addition. Adding two odd numbers does not always produce an odd number, so the odd numbers are not closed for addition.

The natural numbers are closed for addition and multiplication but not for subtraction. To find a set that is also closed for subtraction, a larger set must be considered. This larger set—the integers—includes the natural numbers, 0, and the negative integers. The integers are closed for addition, multiplication, and subtraction. Larger and larger sets can be built, each closed for an additional operation as well as all operations of the previous set. To have closure for division (except by 0), the rational numbers are needed. But there are other operations remaining, so still larger sets are needed. Taking square roots creates a need for irrational numbers, so all irrational numbers are combined with the rational numbers to obtain the real numbers. This set is closed for addition, multiplication, subtraction, nonzero division, and taking roots of nonnegative numbers.

Example 3 Show that the set {0, 1} is closed for multiplication.

Solution Consider all possible products:

$0 \cdot 0 = 0 \qquad 0 \cdot 1 = 0 \qquad 1 \cdot 0 = 0 \qquad 1 \cdot 1 = 1$

All answers are in the set, so {0, 1} is closed for multiplication. □

Example 4 Determine whether the set {0, 2} is closed for addition.

Solution $0 + 0 = 0$ $0 + 2 = 2$ $2 + 0 = 2$ $2 + 2 = 4$

Since 4 is not an element of the set, {0, 2} is not closed for addition.   □

Example 5 Classify each as an example of the commutative, associative, distributive, identity, or inverse property.

a. $2(3 + 4) = 2(4 + 3)$
Commutative property
(for addition)

b. $2(3 + 4) = (3 + 4)2$
Commutative property
(for multiplication)

c. $2(3 + 4) = 2(3) + 2(4)$
Distributive property

d. $2[3 + 4 + (-4)] = 2[3 + 0]$
Inverse property (for addition)

e. $2(3 + 0) = 2(3)$
Identity property (for addition)

f. $2 \cdot 0 = 0$
None (an application of the theorem $a \cdot 0 = 0 \cdot a = 0$ for all real a)   □

Problem Set 1.2

A *In Problems 1–20 use the given property to complete each statement.*

See Examples 1 and 2.

1. Commutative property: $3 \cdot x = ?$
2. Commutative property: $3 + x = ?$
3. Identity property: $y + 0 = ?$
4. Identity property: $1 \cdot y = ?$
5. Associative property: $x + (y + z) = ?$
6. Associative property: $(xy)z = ?$
7. Inverse property: $5 + (-5) = ?$
8. Inverse property: $\frac{1}{5}(5) = ?$
9. Commutative property: $ab = ?$
10. Commutative property: $a + b = ?$
11. Associative property: $(a + 2) + b = ?$
12. Associative property: $2(ab) = ?$
13. Distributive property: $2(a + b) = ?$
14. Distributive property: $(a + 2)b = ?$
15. Inverse property: $x + (-x) = ?$
16. Identity property: $0 + x = ?$
17. Distributive property: $4a + 4b = ?$
18. Distributive property: $ab + 4b = ?$
19. Commutative property: $0 + b = ?$
20. Commutative property: $a(b + c) = ?$

Determine whether each set given in Problems 21–30 is closed for the specified operation.

See Examples 3 and 4.
21. {0, 1} for addition   **22.** {0, 1} for subtraction
23. {0, 1} for multiplication   **24.** {0, 1} for division
25. The set of odd numbers for multiplication
26. The set of even numbers for multiplication
27. The set of odd numbers for addition
28. The set of even numbers for addition
29. The set of negative numbers for addition
30. The set of positive integers for division

B   *In Problems 31–50 classify each as an example of the commutative, associative, distributive, identity, inverse property, or none of these.*

See Example 5.

31. $ab = ba$ **32.** $a + b = b + a$

33. $(ab)c = a(bc)$ **34.** $(a + b) + c = a + (b + c)$

35. $a(b + c) = ab + ac$ **36.** $(a + b)c = ac + bc$

37. $a + 0 = a$ **38.** $a \cdot 1 = a$

39. $a + (-a) = 0$ **40.** $a\left(\dfrac{1}{a}\right) = 1$

41. $3 + (4 + 5) = 3 + (5 + 4)$ **42.** $(4 + 5) + 3 = 3 + (4 + 5)$
43. $3(4 \cdot 5) = 3(5 \cdot 4)$ **44.** $3(4 \cdot 5) = (4 \cdot 5)3$
45. $3(4 + 5) = 3(4) + 3(5)$ **46.** $3(5) + 4(5) = (3 + 4)5$
47. $3 + 4 \cdot 0 = 3 + 0$ **48.** $3 \cdot 1 + 4 = 3 + 4$
49. $3 + 4 \cdot 5 = 3 + 5 \cdot 4$ **50.** $3 \cdot 4 + 5 = 5 + 3 \cdot 4$

Mind Boggler   **51.** In the English language, some groupings of words are associative and others are not. For example, the words

CITY BUS SCHEDULE

are associative, since a

(CITY BUS) SCHEDULE

means the same thing as a

CITY (BUS SCHEDULE)

On the other hand, the words

LIGHT BROWN JACKET

are not associative, since a

(LIGHT BROWN) JACKET

is not the same as a

LIGHT (BROWN JACKET)

Decide which of the following groups of words are associative:

a. RED TAG SALE   b. RED HOT MAMA
c. NO HIT GAME   d. REAL HIGH PRICES
e. LONG PASS PLAY   f. WHITE SAIL BOAT
g. HIGH RISE BUILDING   h. BOX OFFICE SMASH
i. DARK BLUE SEDAN   j. FANCY DRESS BALL

1.3 Operations with Integers

The set of integers includes positive and negative integers as well as 0. Certain pairs of integers are related to the inverse property for addition. We call $(+3)$ and (-3) *opposites*, because

$$(+3) + (-3) = 0$$

If opposites are plotted on a number line, as in Figure 1.3a, you can see that they are the same distance from the origin, but on opposite sides. The distance a number is from 0 is called its **absolute value.** The absolute value of a number n is always nonnegative and is indicated by the symbol $|n|$ (see Figure 1.3b).

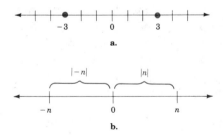

Figure 1.3

Is $-n$ a negative number? Not necessarily. If n is negative, its opposite is positive (see Figure 1.4), and if n is 0, then $-0 = 0$.

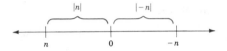

Figure 1.4

There are many ways to define absolute value, but the most useful definition utilizes the concept of opposites.

ABSOLUTE VALUE

Absolute Value

$$|n| = \begin{cases} n & \text{if } n \geq 0 \\ -n & \text{if } n < 0 \end{cases}$$

The absolute value of a number is that number if the number is nonnegative, and it is the opposite of that number if the number is negative.

Example 1

a. $|3| = 3$ Since $3 \geq 0$

b. $|-5| = -(-5) = 5$ Since $-5 < 0$

c. $|0| = 0$

d. $|-3| = 3$

e. $|n| = |-n|$ For every real number n ☐

Addition and Subtraction of Integers

We can use the idea of absolute value to help define the operations on integers. Knowledge of these operations and the properties of the last section allows a great deal of computation with numerical quantities and simplification of algebraic expressions. The procedure for adding two integers is summarized in Figure 1.5.

A **flowchart** is a device used to illustrate decision-making processes. The diamond shape is used to indicate choices.

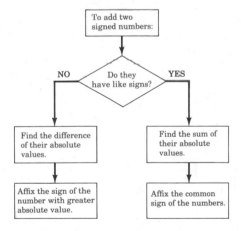

Figure 1.5 Addition of Integers

In Examples 2–5 find each sum.

Example 2 $(-5) + (-7) = -(5 + 7)$ Like signs; add

         $= -12$ Common sign   ☐

Example 3 $(+8) + (-11) = -(11 - 8)$ Unlike signs; subtract

$= -3$ Sign of the larger (-11) □

Example 4 $(-6) + (+9) = 9 - 6$ Unlike signs; subtract

$= +3$ Positive   □

Example 5 $(+3) + (+4) = 3 + 4$ Add

$= +7$ Positive   □

The idea of opposites allows us to define the subtraction of numbers.

SUBTRACTION

> **Subtraction**
>
> $a - b = a + (-b)$
>
> Subtracting a number is equivalent to adding its opposite.

Since subtraction is defined as a sum, there is no need for a separate statement on the procedure for subtracting integers. Each subtraction can be rewritten as addition and the procedure for addition followed.

In Examples 6–9 find each difference.

Example 6 $(-6) - (-9) = (-6) + (+9)$ Add opposite

$= (9 - 6)$ Unlike signs; subtract

$= +3$ □

Example 7 $(+8) - (-3) = (+8) + (+3)$ Add opposite

$= (8 + 3)$ Like signs; add

$= +11$ □

Example 8 $(-5) - (+7) = (-5) + (-7)$ Add opposite

$= -12$ See Example 2   □

Example 9 $(-5) - (-7) - (-6) + (-8) - (+9)$

$= (-5) + (+7) + (+6) + (-8) + (-9)$ Add opposites

$= (-5) + (-8) + (-9) + (+7) + (+6)$ Now regroup

$= (-22) + (+13)$ Add like signs

$= -9$ □

Multiplication and Division

Figure 1.6 summarizes the procedure for multiplying two integers.

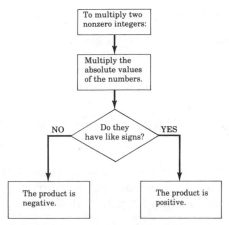

Figure 1.6 Multiplication of Integers

In Examples 10–13 find each product.

Example 10 $(-3)(2) = -6$ Unlike signs; product is negative

Note: The 2 is assumed to be positive, since no sign appears.   ☐

Example 11 $(-7)(-5) = 35$ Like signs; positive product   ☐

Example 12 $(6)(-8) = -48$ Unlike signs; negative product   ☐

Example 13
$$(-2)(-3)(-5) = [(-2)(-3)](-5)$$
$$= 6(-5)$$
$$= -30 \qquad ☐$$

Multiplication can now be used to define the opposite of a number in a more useful form.

OPPOSITE

> **Opposite**
> $$-n = (-1)n \qquad \text{for all real } n$$
> The opposite of a real number is -1 times that number.

Just as the inverse property for addition led to the idea of opposites, the inverse property of multiplication leads to the idea of reciprocals.

RECIPROCAL

> **Reciprocal**
> $$\frac{1}{n} \text{ is the reciprocal of } n$$

Note that 0 has no reciprocal, since $\frac{1}{0}$ is undefined.

DIVISION

Division

$$\frac{a}{b} = a \cdot \frac{1}{b} \qquad b \neq 0$$

Dividing by a number is equivalent to multiplying by its reciprocal.

Similar to the case of subtraction, division requires no special rules, since it is defined as a product. If a quotient is rewritten as a product, then the procedure for multiplication can be followed.

In Examples 14 and 15 find each quotient.

Example 14

$$(-12) \div 4 = (-12)\left(\frac{1}{4}\right) \qquad \text{Multiply by reciprocal}$$

$$= -\left(\frac{12}{4}\right)$$

$$= -3 \qquad \square$$

Example 15

$$(-18) \div (-3) = (-18)\left(-\frac{1}{3}\right) \qquad \text{Multiply by reciprocal}$$

$$= \frac{18}{3}$$

$$= 6 \qquad \square$$

You can combine operations in a single expression, but always keep in mind the order of operations. Cautious calculation with negative quantities and careful attention to signs will certainly minimize errors.

In Examples 16–18 compute the answer.

Example 16

$$\frac{(-4)(9)}{(-3)(-6)} = \frac{-36}{18} \qquad \text{Multiply first}$$

$$= -2 \qquad \square$$

Example 17

$$2 - 3(6-1) = 2 + (-3)[6 + (-1)] \qquad \text{Rewrite as addition}$$
$$= 2 + (-3)[5] \qquad \text{Inside [ ] first}$$
$$= 2 + (-15) \qquad \text{Then multiply}$$
$$= -13 \qquad \text{Finally, add} \qquad \square$$

Example 18

$$\frac{(-3)[5-(-3)]}{-6}-(-7)=\frac{(-3)[5+3]}{-6}+7$$

$$=\frac{(-3)[8]}{-6}+7$$

$$=\frac{-24}{-6}+7$$

$$=4+7$$

$$=11 \qquad \square$$

Problem Set 1.3

A *Perform the indicated operations in Problems 1–70, and evaluate each expression.*

See Example 1.
1. $|+4|$ 2. $|-6|$
3. $|-9|$ 4. $|0|$
5. $|3-5|$ 6. $|5-3|$
7. $|3|-|5|$ 8. $|5|-|3|$
9. $|3|+|-5|$ 10. $|-3|+|5|$

See Examples 2–5.
11. $(+2)+(-6)$ 12. $(-2)+(+6)$
13. $(-8)+(+7)$ 14. $(+8)+(-7)$
15. $(-3)+(-9)$ 16. $(+3)+(+9)$
17. $(+4)+(-1)$ 18. $(-4)+(-1)$
19. $(-3)+(-5)$ 20. $(-7)+(-4)$

See Examples 6–9.
21. $(-3)-(-5)$ 22. $(-7)-(-4)$
23. $3-(-5)$ 24. $7-(-4)$
25. $(+4)-(-1)$ 26. $(-4)-(-1)$
27. $(-3)-(-9)$ 28. $(+3)-(+9)$
29. $(-8)-7$ 30. $8-(-7)$
31. $(+2)-(-6)$ 32. $(-2)-(+6)$
33. $|-8-2|$ 34. $|-3-6|$
35. $|9-(-7)|$ 36. $|-9-(-7)|$
37. $-5+(-6)-|-4|$ 38. $-2+(-5)-|-8|$
39. $(-1-7)-(-4+6)$ 40. $(-9+5)-(-4-3)$

See Examples 10–13.
41. $(+2)(-6)$ 42. $(-2)(+6)$
43. $(-8)(+7)$ 44. $(-8)(-7)$
45. $(-3)(-9)$ 46. $(+3)(-9)$
47. $(+4)(-1)$ 48. $(-4)(-1)$
49. $|(-3)(-5)|$ 50. $|(-7)(-4)|$
51. $|(-3)(5)|$ 52. $|(7)(-4)|$

53. $(-2)(4)(-3)$ 54. $(-3)(-5)(-2)$
55. $(-3)(-5)(+4)$ 56. $(+2)(-7)(+3)$

See Examples 14 and   57. $(+12) \div (-6)$ 58. $(-12) \div (+6)$
15.   59. $(-24) \div (-4)$ 60. $(-24) \div (-6)$

B

See Examples 16–18.   61. $\dfrac{(-3)(-4)(5)}{(-10)(-6)}$ 62. $\dfrac{(-6)(7)(-4)}{(-8)(-3)}$

63. $2 \cdot 3 - (-4)(5)$ 64. $3 \cdot 4 - (-2)(-5)$
65. $2[3 - (-4)] + 5$ 66. $3[4 - (-2)](-5)$
67. $2 - [3(-4) + 5]$ 68. $[3 \cdot 4 - (-2)](-5)$

69. $\dfrac{5 - (-7)}{-6} - 3$ 70. $\dfrac{3 - 9}{-2} + 1$

Mind Boggler   71. Three people are playing a game and betting on each round. After three rounds, each has $24. On each round, the loser must double the money of the two winners. If each player loses once, how much did each start with?

1.4   Algebraic Expressions

Any meaningful combination of numbers, variables, and signs of operations is called an **algebraic expression.** A **polynomial** is an algebraic expression that may be written as a sum (or difference) of terms. A **term of a polynomial** contains multiplication only. For example, $2x = 2 \cdot x$, $3x^2 = 3 \cdot x \cdot x$, $y = 1 \cdot y$, and $4x^2y = 4 \cdot x \cdot x \cdot y$ are the terms of the polynomial $2x + 3x^2 + y + 4x^2y$. Single numbers or variables are also considered polynomials; that is, $2x + 3x^2$, $y + 4x^3y + 1$, $5xy^2$, and 9 are all polynomials. Quotients of polynomials are called **rational expressions.**

Any factor in a term is said to be the **coefficient** of the remaining factors of the term. In the term $4x^2y$, 4 is the coefficient of x^2y, $2x$ is the coefficient of $2xy$, and xy is the coefficient of $4x$. The number 4 is called the **numerical coefficient** of the term $4x^2y$, and generally the word *coefficient* means the numerical coefficient unless otherwise stated. If a term has identical factors, an **exponent** is used to indicate the number of times the factor is used. In $4x^2y$, $x^2 = x \cdot x$, and in general, if n is a natural number,

$$x^n = \overbrace{x \cdot x \cdot x \cdot \cdots \cdot x}^{n \text{ factors}}$$

Exponents are used to classify polynomials. The **degree** of a term in one variable is the exponent of the variable. The degree of a term with more than one variable is the sum of the exponents of the variables. Thus, $3x^2$ is degree 2; $5y^3$ is degree 3; $4x^2y$ is degree 3, since the exponent of y is understood to be 1; and $2x^2y^3$ is degree 5. A nonzero constant has degree 0. The degree of a polynomial is the degree of the highest-degree term. Thus, $3x^2 + 5y^3 + 4x^2y + 2x^2y^3$ is a polynomial of degree 5. Terms that differ only in their numerical coefficients are called **like terms** or **similar terms,** and are necessarily of the same degree. Like terms can be combined by an application of the distributive property. Combining like terms yields an equivalent expression that is simpler than the original expression.

In Examples 1–4 combine like terms.

Example 1
$$3x + 4x - 2x = 3x + 4x + (-2x)$$
$$= [3 + 4 + (-2)]x$$
$$= 5x \qquad \qquad \square$$

Example 2
$$6xy^2 - xy^2 - 3xy^2 = 6xy^2 + (-xy^2) + (-3xy^2)$$
$$= [6 + (-1) + (-3)]xy^2$$
$$= 2xy^2 \qquad \qquad \square$$

Example 3
$$2x - 3y + 2 - 3x + 5y - 8 + x = 2x - 3x + x - 3y + 5y + 2 - 8$$
$$= 2x + (-3x) + x + (-3y) + 5y + 2 + (-8)$$
$$= [2 + (-3) + 1]x + (-3 + 5)y + [2 + (-8)]$$
$$= 0x + 2y + (-6)$$
$$= 2y - 6 \qquad \qquad \square$$

Example 4
$$(4x^2 + 2) - (5x - 3) - (4x - x^2)$$
$$= (4x^2 + 2) + \{-[5x + (-3)]\} + \{-[4x + (-x^2)]\} \qquad \text{Add opposites}$$
$$= (4x^2 + 2) + (-1)[5x + (-3)] + (-1)[4x + (-x^2)] \qquad -n = (-1)n$$
$$= 4x^2 + 2 + (-5x) + 3 + (-4x) + x^2 \qquad \text{Multiply}$$
$$= 4x^2 + x^2 + (-5x) + (-4x) + 2 + 3 \qquad \text{Reorder terms}$$
$$= 5x^2 + (-9x) + 5 \qquad \text{Combine}$$
$$= 5x^2 - 9x + 5 \qquad \qquad \square$$

Evaluating Algebraic Expressions

The equality symbol is used when two quantities are exactly the same. That is, if we write $x = a$, we mean that x and a name the same number; x may be replaced by a in any expression and the value of that expression will remain unchanged. For example, for $2x + 3$ where $x = -5$,

$$2x + 3 = 2(-5) + 3$$
$$= -10 + 3$$
$$= -7$$

To evaluate an expression means to replace the variables with values and to simplify the resulting expression. A variable is replaced by the same number every time that the variable occurs.

Example 5 Find the value of $x - 2y + xz$ if $x = -1$, $y = 2$, and $z = -3$.

Solution $x - 2y + xz = (-1) - 2(2) + (-1)(-3)$ Substitute given values
$$= -1 - 4 + 3$$ Simplify
$$= -2$$ □

Example 6 Evaluate $x[y - (1 - x)] + z$ for $x = 4$, $y = 5$, and $z = -3$.

Solution $x[y - (1 - x)] + z = 4[5 - (1 - 4)] + (-3)$
$$= 4[5 - (-3)] + (-3)$$
$$= 4[5 + 3] + (-3)$$
$$= 4[8] + (-3)$$
$$= 32 + (-3)$$
$$= 29$$ □

Problem Set 1.4

A *Simplify each expression in Problems 1–20 by combining like terms.*

See Examples 1 and 2.

1. $2a + 3a$
2. $5b + 4b$
3. $9x - x$
4. $y + 4y$
5. $a + 5a$
6. $7b - b$
7. $3x + 5x + 8x$
8. $2y + 5y + 6y$
9. $2x - 7x + 9x$
10. $3y - 6y + 8y$
11. $x - 3x - 6x + 4x$
12. $2y - y - 3y + 5y$
13. $2xy - xy + 4xy$
14. $5xy - 2xy - 4xy$
15. $x^2y + 3x^2y - 7x^2y$
16. $xy^2 - 5xy^2 + 2xy^2$
17. $2a + 3b - 4a + 5b$
18. $3h - 4k - 5h + 6k$
19. $7x + 4 - 3x + 5$
20. $3z - 5 + 4z - 2$

Evaluate each expression in Problems 21–30 for $x = -1$, $y = 2$, and $z = -3$.

See Example 5.

21. $x + y + z$
22. $x + y - z$
23. $x - 3y - z$
24. $x - y + 3z$
25. $x - 2(y + z)$
26. $x - (y - 2z)$
27. $x - (yz - 2z)$
28. $x - (3y + yz)$
29. $xy - yz + 4xz$
30. $xy + 5y - xyz$

B *Simplify each expression in Problems 31–40.*

See Examples 3 and 4.

31. $(x + y - z) + (2x - 3y + z)$
32. $(r - s - t) + (2r + s - 3t)$
33. $(m + 2n) - (2m - n)$
34. $(2p - q) - (2p + q)$
35. $(2x + y + 3) - (x - y + 4)$
36. $(v + w - 5) - (2v - 3w + 4)$
37. $(x^2 - 1) - (2 - x) + (x^2 - x)$
38. $(y^2 - y) + (y - 3) - (y - y^2)$
39. $(3m - m^2) - (5 - m) - (3m - 2)$
40. $(n^2 - 7) - (3n + 4) - (n - 2n^2)$

Evaluate each expression in Problems 41–50 for a $=-2$, b $=3$, and c $=-5$.

See Example 6.

41. $ab^2 + c^2$
42. $a^2 - b^2c$
43. $(ab)^2 + ab^2 + a^2b$
44. $(bc)^2 - bc^2 - b^2c$
45. $a(b-c) - (a-b)$
46. $(a-b)c - (c-b)$
47. $(|a| + b) - (-a + |c|)$
48. $5a - |4b + 3c|$
49. $|a| + b^3 - c^2$
50. $a^4 + b^2 - c^2$

1.5 Review Problems

All answers to Review Problems are given in the back of the book so that you can check your progress. The numbers in parentheses refer to the section in which the problem was discussed.

Fill in the word or words that make the statements in Problems 1–10 complete and correct.

(1.1) **1.** All the elements of a _____ set may be listed.

(1.1) **2.** {. . . , −3, −2, −1, 0, 1, 2, 3, . . .} is the set of _integers_ .

(1.2) **3.** The _____ property assures that the order in which we add does not affect the sum.

(1.2) **4.** The _____ property enables us to change a basic product to a basic sum.

(1.3) **5.** The _____ of a real number is always nonnegative.

(1.3) **6.** Subtracting a number is equivalent to adding its _____ .

(1.3) **7.** $\dfrac{1}{n}$ is the _____ of n.

(1.4) **8.** Any factor in a term is said to be the _____ of the remaining factors.

(1.4) **9.** If a term has identical factors, an _____ is used to indicate the number of times the factor is used.

(1.4) **10.** Terms that differ only in their numerical coefficients are called _____ .

(1.1) **11.** Specify each set by listing the elements.
   a. {$a|a$ is one of the states in the United States, a begins with the letter A}
   b. {$b|b \leq 8$, b is even, b is nonnegative}
   c. {$c|4 < c < 9$, $c \in N$}

(1.1) **12.** Compute and classify as a sum, difference, product, or quotient.
   a. $2 + 6 \div 2 \cdot 3 + 2$
   b. $(2+6) \div (2 \cdot 3 + 2)$
   c. $(2 + 6 \div 2) \cdot 3 + 2$

(1.2)   **13.**   Use the given property to complete each statement.
        a.   Associative property: $(ab)c = ?$
        b.   Commutative property: $0 + b = ?$
        c.   Distributive property: $ab + ac = ?$

(1.2)   **14.**   Is the set $\{3,\ 6,\ 9,\ 12,\ 15,\ \ldots\}$ closed for the operation of addition?

(1.2)   **15.**   Classify each as an example of the associative, commutative, distributive, identity, or inverse property.
        a. $a + b = b + a$
        b. $1 \cdot b = b$
        c. $ac + bc = (a + b)c$

(1.3)   **16.**   Perform the indicated operations and classify.
        a. $-2 - (-4) + 6 - 8$
        b. $(-1)(-2)(-3)(4)$
        c. $1 - (-3)(5) - 7$

(1.3)   **17.**   Perform the indicated operations and classify.
        a. $\dfrac{(-6)(-5)(7)}{(-2)(21)}$
        b. $[(-2)(3) - (-4)](-5)$
        c. $|(-2)[8 + (-5)]|$

(1.4)   **18.**   Simplify.
        a. $4a + 3a - 5a$
        b. $a + 2b - 3a - b$
        c. $c + 4 + 3c - 5$

(1.4)   **19.**   Evaluate each expression for $a = -3$, $b = 5$, and $c = -7$.
        a. $a - b - c$
        b. $a - (b - c)$
        c. $a^2 b - c^2$

(1.4)   **20.**   Simplify.
        a. $(a + b + 3) + (2a - b - 5)$
        b. $(b + 2c - 4) - (2b - 3c + 4)$
        c. $(c^2 - 3) - (c + 5) + (2c + c^2)$

CHAPTER

2

Linear Equations and Inequalities in One Variable

Contents

2.1   Solving Linear Equations

A statement of equality is called an **equation.** The statement may be true, it may be false, or it may depend on the values of the variable. If the equation is always true, as in $x = x + 0$, it is called an *identity*. If the equation is always false, it is called a *contradiction*. The equation $x = x + 1$ is a contradiction, since it is false for all values of x. If the equation depends on the values of the variable, it is called a **conditional equation.** For example, $x + 1 = 5$ is true if $x = 4$ and false otherwise. The values that make the conditional equation true are said to **satisfy** the equation and are called the **solutions** or **roots** of the equation. The number 4 is the root or solution of $x + 1 = 5$.

When we speak of equations, we generally mean conditional equations. Our goal is to be able to determine the numbers that satisfy a given conditional equation, so we look for ways to make the solutions or roots more obvious. Two equations with the same solutions are called **equivalent equations.** We try to get successively simpler equivalent equations until the solution is obvious. The following basic properties are used to create equivalent equations.

ADDITION
PROPERTY
OF EQUALITY

> Given an equation, if the same number or algebraic expression is added to or subtracted from both sides, the resulting equation is equivalent.

MULTIPLICATION
PROPERTY OF
EQUALITY

> Given an equation, if both sides are multiplied or divided by any nonzero number, the resulting equation is equivalent.

These properties are used to **isolate the variable** on one side of the equation, as illustrated in the examples below. Substituting the solution into the original equation will verify that it satisfies the equation.

In Examples 1–5 solve the equation. (To solve *an equation means to find its roots.)*

Example 1 $x - 5 = 7$

Solution
$$x - 5 = 7$$
$$x - 5 + 5 = 7 + 5 \qquad \text{Add 5 to both sides}$$
$$x = \mathbf{12} \qquad \text{Simplify}$$

The solution is 12.

Check: $12 - 5 \overset{?}{=} 7$
$$7 = 7 \checkmark$$

$\square$

Example 2 $6y = 72$

Solution $6y = 72$

$$\frac{6y}{6} = \frac{72}{6} \qquad \text{Divide both sides by 6}$$

$$y = \mathbf{12} \qquad \text{Simplify}$$

The solution is 12.

Check: $6(12) \overset{?}{=} 72$

$$72 = 72 \checkmark$$

□

Example 3 $7 - 2z = 1$

Solution $7 - 2z = 1$

$$7 - 7 - 2z = 1 - 7 \qquad \text{Subtract 7 from both sides}$$

$$-2z = -6 \qquad \text{Simplify}$$

$$\frac{-2z}{-2} = \frac{-6}{-2} \qquad \text{Divide both sides by } -2$$

$$z = \mathbf{3} \qquad \text{Simplify}$$

The solution is 3.

Check: $7 - 2(3) \overset{?}{=} 1$

$$7 - 6 \overset{?}{=} 1$$

$$1 = 1 \checkmark$$

□

Example 4 $4x = 20 - x$

Solution $4x = 20 - x$

$$4x + x = 20 - x + x \qquad \text{Add } x \text{ to both sides}$$

$$5x = 20 \qquad \text{Simplify}$$

$$\frac{5x}{5} = \frac{20}{5} \qquad \text{Divide both sides by 5}$$

$$x = \mathbf{4} \qquad \text{Simplify}$$

The solution is 4.

Check: $4(4) \overset{?}{=} 20 - 4$

$$16 = 16 \checkmark$$

□

Example 5 $4(s + 1) - 3 = 15 - 3s$

Solution $4(s + 1) - 3 = 15 - 3s$

$$4s + 4 - 3 = 15 - 3s \qquad \text{Eliminate parentheses}$$

$$4s + 1 = 15 - 3s \qquad \text{Simplify}$$
$$4s + 3s + 1 = 15 - 3s + 3s \qquad \text{Add } 3s \text{ to both sides}$$
$$7s + 1 = 15 \qquad \text{Combine like terms}$$
$$7s + 1 - 1 = 15 - 1 \qquad \text{Subtract 1 from both sides}$$
$$7s = 14 \qquad \text{Simplify}$$
$$\frac{7s}{7} = \frac{14}{7} \qquad \text{Divide both sides by 7}$$
$$s = 2 \qquad \text{Simplify}$$

The solution is 2.

Check: $\quad 4(2 + 1) - 3 \overset{?}{=} 15 - 3(2)$
$$12 - 3 \overset{?}{=} 15 - 6$$
$$9 = 9 \checkmark \qquad \square$$

You will soon learn to make the needed steps easily and to check your results mentally. The next four examples illustrate how your work should look after you have some practice in solving equations.

In Examples 6–9 solve the equations.

Example 6 $5x(7 - 3) + 15 = 14x + x - 5$
$$20x + 15 = 15x - 5$$
$$5x = -20$$
$$x = -4 \qquad \square$$

Example 7 $5(y + 2) + 6 = 3(2y) + 5(3y)$
$$5y + 10 + 6 = 6y + 15y$$
$$5y + 16 = 21y$$
$$16 = 16y$$
$$1 = y \qquad \square$$

Example 8 $x - 8(x + 1) = 3(1 - x) + 1$
$$x - 8x - 8 = 3 - 3x + 1$$
$$-7x - 8 = 4 - 3x$$
$$-4x = 12$$
$$x = -3 \qquad \square$$

Example 9 $2(4 - 3x) + 3(x - 2) = 4(3x - 2) - 5(2x - 1)$
$$8 - 6x + 3x - 6 = 12x - 8 - 10x + 5$$
$$-3x + 2 = 2x - 3$$
$$5 = 5x$$
$$1 = x \qquad \square$$

Problem Set 2.1

A *Solve the equations in Problems 1–48.*

See Examples 1–4.

1. $2x = 8$
2. $3y = 6$
3. $4v - 24 = 0$
4. $6w + 18 = 0$
5. $\dfrac{r}{2} = 6$
6. $\dfrac{s}{3} = 12$
7. $t + 3 = 7$
8. $u + 5 = 12$
9. $v - 4 = 1$
10. $w + 3 = 2$
11. $x + 7 = -2$
12. $y - 9 = -11$
13. $2x - 1 = 9$
14. $3y + 2 = 11$
15. $19 = 3w + 4$
16. $13 = 5z - 2$
17. $6m + 14 = 32$
18. $15 + 4n = 7$
19. $2p - 7 = 13$
20. $7q + 2 = 16$
21. $5r + 11 = 6$
22. $3s - 2 = -14$
23. $3 + 4t = -5$
24. $2 - 6u = -4$
25. $7 - 3x = 4$
26. $12 - 7x = 5$
27. $21 - 2y = 13$
28. $8 - 3y = 20$
29. $12 = 2 - 5z$
30. $18 = 4 - 7z$

B

31. $2s - 3 = s + 2$
32. $3t + 4 = 2t - 1$
33. $14 + a = 3a - 2$
34. $2b - 1 = 13 - 5b$
35. $2x + 7 = x + 5$
36. $3x - 7 = 4x - 9$
37. $5y - 14 = 19 - 6y$
38. $6y - 19 = 6 + y$
39. $9 - 7z = 12z - 10$
40. $8 + 5z = 2z - 7$

See Examples 5–9.

41. $x + 3(2 - x) = 6x - 2$
42. $6x = 2(14 - 3x) - 2x$
43. $x + 3(2x - 1) = 5(1 + x) - 6$
44. $3(y - 2) + y = 7(2y + 1) - 3$
45. $1 + 2(3x + 1) = 2(x - 1) + 5x$
46. $5(2x - 1) - 5 = 3(x + 2) - x$
47. $5(2x - 1) - 3(4 - 3x) = 4(5x - 3) - 6(3 - 2x)$
48. $3(3x + 2) - 5(2x - 1) = -3(3 - 5x) - (1 + 7x) + 3$

Mind Bogglers

49. Find at least three ways to use exactly three threes and standard mathematical symbols to represent 30.
50. Jo Cool drives three miles to class each morning. She must average 30 miles per hour in order to arrive on time. One morning she begins on time but is delayed by heavy traffic. She averages only ten miles per hour in the first mile. What must Jo average for the remaining two miles to arrive on schedule?

2.2 Word Problems and Equations

Consider the following problem: "Driving from Buffalo to Utica, it is 180 miles across northern New York state. On this route, you first pass Rochester and then Syracuse before reaching Utica. It is ten miles farther from Buffalo to Rochester than from Syracuse to Utica, and ten miles farther from Rochester to Syracuse than from Buffalo to Rochester. How far is it from Rochester to Syracuse?" Does the problem have a solution? Can algebra be used to solve it? What do you do first? You may begin to answer these questions by examining the problem in some logical manner. Remember that you can't solve a problem you don't understand. It must make sense before mathematics can be applied to it.

Historical Note

The Englishman W. K.
Clifford, in *Common
Sense in the Exact
Sciences* (1885), made
an interesting
comment that relates
to our work with word
problems. "We may
always depend upon it
that algebra, which
cannot be translated
into good English and
sound common sense,
is bad algebra."

Start at the beginning of the problem, and make a sketch of the situation, as shown in Figure 2.1. The cities are located in the order sketched on the line, but how can that fact give us an equation? To have an equation, you must find an equality. What quantities are equal? The distances from Buffalo to Rochester, Rochester to Syracuse, and Syracuse to Utica must add up to the distance from Buffalo to Utica. That is, the sum of the parts must equal the whole distance—so start there. Use words at this stage and keep everything in terms of the quantities in the problem. Don't be too eager to use algebra yet.

Buffalo — Rochester — Syracuse — Utica

B R S U

Figure 2.1

$$\left(\begin{smallmatrix}\text{DISTANCE}\\ B\text{ TO }R\end{smallmatrix}\right) + \left(\begin{smallmatrix}\text{DISTANCE}\\ R\text{ TO }S\end{smallmatrix}\right) + \left(\begin{smallmatrix}\text{DISTANCE}\\ S\text{ TO }U\end{smallmatrix}\right) = \left(\begin{smallmatrix}\text{DISTANCE}\\ B\text{ TO }U\end{smallmatrix}\right)$$

Do you know the value of any quantity in the equation? The first sentence of the problem tells you the total distance is 180 miles, so

$$\left(\begin{smallmatrix}\text{DISTANCE}\\ B\text{ TO }R\end{smallmatrix}\right) + \left(\begin{smallmatrix}\text{DISTANCE}\\ R\text{ TO }S\end{smallmatrix}\right) + \left(\begin{smallmatrix}\text{DISTANCE}\\ S\text{ TO }U\end{smallmatrix}\right) = 180$$

Certain relationships between the other distances are known as well. Which is the smallest distance? The problem states that the distance from R to S is 10 miles longer than the distance from B to R, which is 10 miles longer than the distance from S to U. That information can be put into the equation:

$$\left(\begin{smallmatrix}\text{DISTANCE}\\ B\text{ TO }R\end{smallmatrix}\right) + \left(\begin{smallmatrix}\text{DISTANCE}\\ R\text{ TO }S\end{smallmatrix}\right) + \left(\begin{smallmatrix}\text{DISTANCE}\\ S\text{ TO }U\end{smallmatrix}\right) = 180$$

Replace this by:

$$\left(\begin{smallmatrix}\text{DISTANCE}\\ B\text{ TO }R\end{smallmatrix}\right) + \left(\begin{smallmatrix}\text{DISTANCE}\\ B\text{ TO }R\end{smallmatrix} + 10\right) + \left(\begin{smallmatrix}\text{DISTANCE}\\ S\text{ TO }U\end{smallmatrix}\right) = 180$$

Replace this by:

$$\left(\begin{smallmatrix}\text{DISTANCE}\\ S\text{ TO }U\end{smallmatrix} + 10\right) + \left(\begin{smallmatrix}\text{DISTANCE}\\ S\text{ TO }U\end{smallmatrix} + 10 + 10\right) + \left(\begin{smallmatrix}\text{DISTANCE}\\ S\text{ TO }U\end{smallmatrix}\right) = 180$$

Simplify

$$\left(\begin{smallmatrix}\text{DISTANCE}\\ S\text{ TO }U\end{smallmatrix} + 10\right) + \left(\begin{smallmatrix}\text{DISTANCE}\\ S\text{ TO }U\end{smallmatrix} + 20\right) + \left(\begin{smallmatrix}\text{DISTANCE}\\ S\text{ TO }U\end{smallmatrix}\right) = 180$$

Notice that there is only one quantity left in the equation that is unknown. *Now* is the time to introduce a variable and use algebra to find a solution for the equation. Then, you can answer the question posed in the problem. Let d represent the *distance* from S to U in miles:

$$(d + 10) + (d + 20) + d = 180$$
$$3d + 30 = 180$$
$$3d = 150$$
$$d = 50$$

The equation is solved. Does that mean that the answer to the problem is "$d = 50$"? No, the question asks for the distance from Rochester to Syracuse, which is $d + 20$. So now interpret the solution and answer the question: The distance from Rochester to Syracuse is 70 miles.

Notice that the solution to the problem needed primarily an understanding of the problem, and used algebra only after the facts were clearly outlined. To be certain that the answer makes sense in the original problem, the solution should always be checked.

$$60 + 70 + 50 \overset{?}{=} 180$$
$$180 = 180 \checkmark$$

Consider another example before we outline a general strategy.

Example 1   The sum of three consecutive odd integers is 111. Find the integers.

Solution   *Step 1.*   Read the problem.

          Step 2.   Restate the problem, and write out a verbal description.

$$\begin{pmatrix} \text{1ST ODD} \\ \text{INTEGER} \end{pmatrix} + \begin{pmatrix} \text{2ND ODD} \\ \text{INTEGER} \end{pmatrix} + \begin{pmatrix} \text{3RD ODD} \\ \text{INTEGER} \end{pmatrix} = \begin{pmatrix} \text{SUM OF THE} \\ \text{INTEGERS} \end{pmatrix}$$

          Step 3.   Evolve the equation to a single unknown. Think about three consecutive odd integers, such as 3, 5, and 7. The second is 2 more than the first and the third is 4 more than the first.

$$\begin{pmatrix} \text{1ST ODD} \\ \text{INTEGER} \end{pmatrix} + \begin{pmatrix} \text{1ST ODD} \\ \text{INTEGER} + 2 \end{pmatrix} + \begin{pmatrix} \text{1ST ODD} \\ \text{INTEGER} + 4 \end{pmatrix} = 111$$

          Step 4.   Choose a variable. Let $f = $ 1ST ODD INTEGER.

          Step 5.   Substitute the variable into the verbal equation and solve.

$$f + (f + 2) + (f + 4) = 111$$
$$3f + 6 = 111$$
$$3f = 105$$
$$f = 35$$
$$f + 2 = 37$$
$$f + 4 = 39$$

Step 6.   State the solution to the word problem in words.

   The integers are 35, 37, and 39.

It is wise to check your results. Recall that the problem asked for a sum of 111, so:

$$35 + 37 + 39 = 111 \checkmark \qquad \qquad \qquad \square$$

Study the following strategy for attacking word problems before attempting to solve the problems at the end of this section.

STRATEGY FOR
ATTACKING WORD
PROBLEMS

Strategy for Attacking Word Problems

Step 1.   *Read the problem.* Note what the problem is all about. Do not focus on the numbers in the problem but rather on processes. You can't work a problem you don't understand.

Step 2.   *Restate the problem.* Restate in as many ways as necessary to clarify the facts and relationships of the problem. Look for an equality. If you can't find equal quantities, you will never find an equation. Don't worry about the number of unknown quantities at this stage.

Step 3.   *Evolve the equation.* Don't rush this step; *evolve* is the key word. The discovery of a final equation with a single unknown should be the result of your understanding of the problem, not your algebraic skill.

Step 4.   *Choose a variable.* This choice should be a natural result of the process in Step 3. Don't force the choice of the variable to be the same as the quantity that is asked for in the question.

Step 5.   *Solve the equation.* This is the easy step. But be sure it's the right equation by checking the results in the original problem. Your solution should make sense.

Step 6.   *State an answer to the problem.* This is not necessarily the same as the solution to your equation. Give a word answer to the word problem. Pay attention to units of measure and other details of the problem.

If you follow the procedure outlined in the box, chances are you will be successful with a great many problems. Use this strategy to analyze even the simplest word problems, since the method you use to approach problems is a habit you'll acquire through use.

Example 2   A farmer must deliver 1,200 bushels of produce to town. He has two trucks. One carries 150 bushels and the other 115 bushels per load. If after two loads the larger truck breaks down, how many trips must the farmer make in the smaller truck?

— Careful reading (Technical?)

— Draw a diagram

Solution

$$\begin{pmatrix} \text{AMOUNT} \\ \text{CARRIED} \\ \text{BY LARGE} \\ \text{TRUCK} \end{pmatrix} + \begin{pmatrix} \text{AMOUNT} \\ \text{CARRIED} \\ \text{BY SMALL} \\ \text{TRUCK} \end{pmatrix} = \begin{pmatrix} \text{TOTAL} \\ \text{AMOUNT} \\ \text{TO BE} \\ \text{CARRIED} \end{pmatrix}$$

$$\begin{pmatrix} \text{CAPACITY} \\ \text{LARGE TRUCK} \end{pmatrix}\begin{pmatrix} \text{NO. OF} \\ \text{TRIPS} \end{pmatrix} + \begin{pmatrix} \text{CAPACITY} \\ \text{SMALL TRUCK} \end{pmatrix}\begin{pmatrix} \text{NO. OF} \\ \text{TRIPS} \end{pmatrix} = 1{,}200$$

$$(150)(2) + (115)\begin{pmatrix} \text{NO. OF} \\ \text{TRIPS} \end{pmatrix} = 1{,}200$$

Let t be the number of trips for the small truck:

$$300 + 115t = 1{,}200$$
$$115t = 900$$
$$t = \frac{900}{115} \approx 7.8$$

The farmer makes eight trips in the small truck.

Note that the answer is *not* 7.8 trips, since that would not get the farmer home after the eighth load was delivered to town. The root of the equation is not necessarily the answer to the problem. The root must be interpreted. So, it's important to state the answer in words. ☐

Example 3 A grocer mixes candy worth $1 a pound with some worth 75¢ a pound to get a mix that can be sold for 90¢ a pound. How many pounds of each must be used to get 50 pounds of the mix?

Solution The basic fact is that two things are mixed. The total value must be the same.

$$\begin{pmatrix} \text{VALUE} \\ \$1 \\ \text{CANDY} \end{pmatrix} + \begin{pmatrix} \text{VALUE} \\ 75¢ \\ \text{CANDY} \end{pmatrix} = \begin{pmatrix} \text{VALUE} \\ 90¢ \\ \text{MIX} \end{pmatrix}$$

VALUE = (AMOUNT) (RATE)

$$\begin{pmatrix} \text{POUNDS} \\ \$1 \\ \text{CANDY} \end{pmatrix}\begin{pmatrix} \text{PRICE} \\ \text{PER} \\ \text{POUND} \end{pmatrix} + \begin{pmatrix} \text{POUNDS} \\ 75¢ \\ \text{CANDY} \end{pmatrix}\begin{pmatrix} \text{PRICE} \\ \text{PER} \\ \text{POUND} \end{pmatrix} = \begin{pmatrix} \text{POUNDS} \\ 90¢ \\ \text{MIX} \end{pmatrix}\begin{pmatrix} \text{PRICE} \\ \text{PER} \\ \text{POUND} \end{pmatrix}$$

Substitute known quantities

$$\begin{pmatrix} \text{POUNDS} \\ \$1 \\ \text{CANDY} \end{pmatrix}(100) + \begin{pmatrix} \text{POUNDS} \\ 75¢ \\ \text{CANDY} \end{pmatrix}(75) = (50)(90)$$

Use a single unknown

$$\begin{pmatrix} \text{POUNDS} \\ \$1 \\ \text{CANDY} \end{pmatrix}(100) + \left[50 - \begin{pmatrix} \text{POUNDS} \\ \$1 \\ \text{CANDY} \end{pmatrix}\right](75) = 4{,}500$$

Let n be the number of pounds of $1 candy.

$$(n)(100)+(50-n)(75)=4{,}500$$
$$100n+75(50-n)=4{,}500$$
$$25n+3{,}750=4{,}500$$
$$25n=750$$
$$n=30$$
$$50-n=20$$

The grocer must use 30 pounds of $1 candy and 20 pounds of 75¢ candy. □

In the above example, the quantity (POUNDS 75¢ CANDY) was replaced by [50 − (POUNDS $1 CANDY)]. This step utilized a very common device for dividing a quantity into two parts. If you divide a sum of money with a friend, after the friend has taken his or her share, what remains is your share; that is,

$$\begin{pmatrix}\text{TOTAL}\\\text{AMOUNT}\end{pmatrix}-\begin{pmatrix}\text{FRIEND'S}\\\text{SHARE}\end{pmatrix}=\begin{pmatrix}\text{YOUR}\\\text{SHARE}\end{pmatrix}$$

If you are sharing $100 and your friend's share is x, then you are left with $100-x$. In Example 3, there was a total of 50 pounds of the candy mix. If you take the amount of $1 candy away, the remainder is the amount of 75¢ candy:

$$50-\begin{pmatrix}\text{POUNDS}\\\$1\\\text{CANDY}\end{pmatrix}=\begin{pmatrix}\text{POUNDS}\\75¢\\\text{CANDY}\end{pmatrix}$$

Problem Set 2.2

A *Fill in the blanks in Problems 1–10. Notice that the answers to the questions are given. The emphasis here is on the procedure.*

See Example 1.   **1.** The sum of three consecutive integers is 147. Find the integers.

$$\begin{pmatrix}\text{1ST}\\\text{INTEGER}\end{pmatrix}+\begin{pmatrix}\text{2ND}\\\text{INTEGER}\end{pmatrix}+\begin{pmatrix}\text{3RD}\\\text{INTEGER}\end{pmatrix}=(\text{SUM})$$

$$\begin{pmatrix}\text{1ST}\\\text{INTEGER}\end{pmatrix}+\begin{pmatrix}\text{1ST}\\\text{INTEGER}+1\end{pmatrix}+\begin{pmatrix}\underline{\quad\text{a.}\quad}\end{pmatrix}=147$$

Let $n = $ 1ST INTEGER.

$$\underline{\quad\textbf{b.}\quad} + \underline{\quad\textbf{c.}\quad} + \underline{\quad\textbf{d.}\quad} = 147$$
$$3n + 3 = 147$$
$$3n = \underline{\quad\textbf{e.}\quad}$$
$$n = \underline{\quad\textbf{f.}\quad}$$

The integers are 48, 49, and 50.

2. Find the first of three consecutive even integers if their sum is 420.

$$\left(\begin{array}{c}\text{1ST EVEN}\\\text{INTEGER}\end{array}\right) + \left(\begin{array}{c}\text{2ND EVEN}\\\text{INTEGER}\end{array}\right) + \left(\begin{array}{c}\text{3RD EVEN}\\\text{INTEGER}\end{array}\right) = (\text{SUM})$$

$$\left(\underline{\quad\textbf{a.}\quad}\right) + \left(\begin{array}{c}\text{1ST EVEN}\\\text{INTEGER}\end{array} + 2\right) + \left(\underline{\quad\textbf{b.}\quad}\right) = \underline{\quad\textbf{c.}\quad}$$

Let $e = $ 1ST EVEN INTEGER.

$$(\underline{\quad\textbf{d.}\quad}) + (\underline{\quad\textbf{e.}\quad}) + (\underline{\quad\textbf{f.}\quad}) = \underline{\quad\textbf{g.}\quad}$$
$$3e + 6 = \underline{\quad\textbf{h.}\quad}$$
$$3e = \underline{\quad\textbf{i.}\quad}$$
$$e = 138$$

The first even integer is 138.

Recall that for a rectangle,

AREA =
(LENGTH) (WIDTH)

PERIMETER =
2(WIDTH) + 2(LENGTH)

l That is,

$A = lw$
$P = 2w + 2l$

3. A rectangle is seven meters longer than it is wide. Find its width if the perimeter is thirty-four meters.

$$2(\text{WIDTH}) + 2(\text{LENGTH}) = (\text{PERIMETER})$$
$$2(\text{WIDTH}) + 2(\underline{\quad\textbf{a.}\quad} + 7) = \underline{\quad\textbf{b.}\quad}$$

Let $w = $ WIDTH of the rectangle.

$$2(\underline{\quad\textbf{c.}\quad}) + 2(\underline{\quad\textbf{d.}\quad}) = \underline{\quad\textbf{e.}\quad}$$
$$4w + 14 = \underline{\quad\textbf{f.}\quad}$$
$$4w = \underline{\quad\textbf{g.}\quad}$$
$$w = \underline{\quad\textbf{h.}\quad}$$

The width of the rectangle is five meters.

4. *Agriculture.* A rancher has 60 m of fencing and wishes to make an enclosure that is twice as long as it is wide. What will be the dimensions of the enclosure?

$$2(\text{WIDTH}) + 2(\text{LENGTH}) = (\text{PERIMETER})$$
$$2(\text{WIDTH}) + 2(\underline{\quad\textbf{a.}\quad}) = \underline{\quad\textbf{b.}\quad}$$

Let $w = $ WIDTH of the enclosure.

$$2w + 2(\underline{\quad\textbf{c.}\quad}) = \underline{\quad\textbf{d.}\quad}$$
$$6w = \underline{\quad\textbf{e.}\quad}$$
$$w = \underline{\quad\textbf{f.}\quad}$$

The enclosure will be 10 m by 20 m.

5. *Travel.* The drive from New Orleans to Memphis is 90 miles less than from Memphis to Cincinnati, but 150 miles more than from Cincinnati to Detroit. If the total highway distance is 1,140 miles on a New Orleans–Memphis–Cincinnati–Detroit trip, find the length of the Detroit–Cincinnati leg of the trip.

$$\left(\begin{array}{c}\text{NEW ORLEANS}\\\text{TO}\\\text{MEMPHIS}\end{array}\right) + \left(\begin{array}{c}\text{MEMPHIS}\\\text{TO}\\\text{CINCINNATI}\end{array}\right) + \left(\begin{array}{c}\text{CINCINNATI}\\\text{TO}\\\text{DETROIT}\end{array}\right) = \left(\begin{array}{c}\text{TOTAL}\\\text{DISTANCE}\end{array}\right)$$

$$\left(\begin{array}{c}\text{NEW ORLEANS}\\\text{TO}\\\text{MEMPHIS}\end{array}\right) + \left(\begin{array}{c}\text{NEW ORLEANS}\\\text{TO} \quad +\\\text{MEMPHIS} \quad \underline{\quad\text{a.}\quad}\end{array}\right) + \left(\begin{array}{c}\text{NEW ORLEANS}\\\text{TO} \quad -\\\text{MEMPHIS} \quad \underline{\quad\text{b.}\quad}\end{array}\right) = \quad \underline{\quad\text{c.}\quad}$$

Let d represent the distance from New Orleans to Memphis.

$$\underline{\quad\text{d.}\quad} + \underline{\quad\text{e.}\quad} + \underline{\quad\text{f.}\quad} = \underline{\quad\text{g.}\quad}$$

$$3d - 60 = \underline{\quad\text{h.}\quad}$$
$$3d = \underline{\quad\text{i.}\quad}$$
$$d = 400$$
$$d - 150 = 250$$

The highway distance is 250 miles from Cincinnati to Detroit.

6. *Travel.* The airline distance from Chicago to San Francisco is 1,140 mi more than the flight from New York to Chicago, and 540 mi less than the distance from San Francisco to Honolulu. What is the length of each leg of the 4,980 mi New York–Chicago–San Francisco–Honolulu flight?

$$\left(\begin{array}{c}\text{HONOLULU}\\\text{TO S.F.}\end{array}\right) + \left(\begin{array}{c}\text{S.F. TO}\\\text{CHICAGO}\end{array}\right) + \left(\begin{array}{c}\text{chicago}\\\text{NY}\ \underline{\text{a.}}\end{array}\right) = \left(\begin{array}{c}\text{TOTAL}\\\text{DISTANCE}\end{array}\right)$$

$$\left(\begin{array}{c}\text{S.F. TO}\\\text{CHICAGO}\end{array} + 540\right) + \left(\begin{array}{c}\text{S.F. TO}\\\text{CHICAGO}\end{array}\right) + \left(\begin{array}{c}x-1140\\\underline{\text{b.}}\end{array}\right) = \begin{array}{c}4980\\\underline{\text{c.}}\end{array}$$

Let S represent the air distance from San Francisco to Chicago.

$$\left(\underset{\text{d.}}{\underline{S+540}}\right) + S + \left(\underset{\text{e.}}{\underline{S-1140}}\right) = \underset{\text{f.}}{\underline{3S-600}}$$
$$3S - 600 = \underline{\quad\text{g.}\quad}$$
$$3S = \underline{\quad\text{h.}\quad}$$
$$S = \underline{\quad\text{i.}\quad}$$

New York to Chicago is 720 mi, Chicago to San Francisco is 1,860 mi, and San Francisco to Honolulu is 2,400 mi.

See Example 2.   7. *Business.* A stationery item is packed either one dozen or one hundred to a box. If 2,000 items are packed in 64 boxes, how many of each size box are used?

4980

540
yeso $(x+1140)$ x ?

H SF $\times$ C   NY

$X + 540 + X + X - 1140 = 4980$

$$\begin{pmatrix} \text{TOTAL IN} \\ \text{DOZEN-SIZE} \\ \text{BOXES} \end{pmatrix} + \begin{pmatrix} \text{TOTAL IN} \\ \text{HUNDRED-SIZE} \\ \text{BOXES} \end{pmatrix} = \begin{pmatrix} \text{TOTAL} \\ \text{PACKAGED} \end{pmatrix}$$

$$\begin{pmatrix} \text{NO. IN} \\ \text{EACH} \\ \text{DOZEN-SIZE BOX} \end{pmatrix}\begin{pmatrix} \text{NO. OF} \\ \text{DOZEN-SIZE} \\ \text{BOXES} \end{pmatrix} + \begin{pmatrix} \underline{\quad\text{a.}\quad} \end{pmatrix}\begin{pmatrix} \underline{\quad\text{b.}\quad} \end{pmatrix} = \underline{\quad\text{c.}\quad}$$

$$12(\underline{\quad\text{d.}\quad}) + 100(\underline{\quad\text{e.}\quad}) = \underline{\quad\text{f.}\quad}$$

Let $n = $ NO. OF DOZEN-SIZE BOXES.

$$12n + 100(\underline{\quad\text{g.}\quad}) = \underline{\quad\text{h.}\quad}$$
$$6{,}400 - 88n = \underline{\quad\text{i.}\quad}$$
$$-88n = \underline{\quad\text{j.}\quad}$$
$$n = \underline{\quad\text{k.}\quad}$$
$$64 - n = 14$$

There are 50 dozen-size boxes and 14 hundred-size boxes.

See Example 3. **8.** *Business.* Two fuels are mixed to obtain a blend that can sell for $2.54 per gallon. The retailer mixes fuels worth $2.70 and $2.45 per gallon. How much of each must be used to produce 2,500 gallons of the blend?

$$\begin{pmatrix} \text{VALUE OF} \\ \text{FUEL I} \end{pmatrix} + \begin{pmatrix} \text{VALUE OF} \\ \text{FUEL II} \end{pmatrix} = \begin{pmatrix} \text{VALUE OF} \\ \text{BLEND} \end{pmatrix}$$

$$\begin{pmatrix} \text{PRICE OF} \\ \text{FUEL I} \end{pmatrix}\begin{pmatrix} \text{VOLUME OF} \\ \text{FUEL I} \end{pmatrix} + \begin{pmatrix} \underline{\quad\text{a.}\quad} \end{pmatrix}\begin{pmatrix} \underline{\quad\text{b.}\quad} \end{pmatrix} = \begin{pmatrix} \text{PRICE OF} \\ \text{BLEND} \end{pmatrix}\begin{pmatrix} \underline{\quad\text{c.}\quad} \end{pmatrix}$$

$$2.70\begin{pmatrix} \text{VOLUME OF} \\ \text{FUEL I} \end{pmatrix} + 2.45\begin{pmatrix} \underline{\quad\text{d.}\quad} \end{pmatrix} = 2.54\begin{pmatrix} \underline{\quad\text{e.}\quad} \end{pmatrix}$$

$$2.70(2{,}500 - \underline{\quad\text{f.}\quad}) + 2.45(\underline{\quad\text{g.}\quad}) = \underline{\quad\text{h.}\quad}$$

Let $V = $ VOLUME OF FUEL II.

$$2.70(2{,}500 - V) + 2.45(V) = 6{,}350$$
$$\underline{\quad\text{i.}\quad} + 2.45V = 6{,}350$$
$$-0.25V = \underline{\quad\text{j.}\quad}$$
$$V = \underline{\quad\text{k.}\quad}$$
$$2{,}500 - V = 900$$

900 gallons of $2.70 fuel is blended with 1,600 gallons of $2.45 fuel.

9. *Finance.* Suppose $10,000 is divided between two investments that earn 10% and 12.5% over the year. If the year's earnings were $1,100, how much was invested at each rate?

The formula for simple interest with a yearly rate is

$$\begin{pmatrix} \text{EARNINGS} \\ \text{AT } 10\% \end{pmatrix} + \begin{pmatrix} \text{EARNINGS} \\ \text{AT } 12.5\% \end{pmatrix} = \begin{pmatrix} \text{TOTAL} \\ \text{EARNINGS} \end{pmatrix}$$

INTEREST = (PRINCIPAL) (RATE)

$$.10 \begin{pmatrix} \text{AMOUNT} \\ \text{INVESTED} \\ \text{AT } 10\% \end{pmatrix} + .125 \begin{pmatrix} \underline{\quad\text{a.}\quad} \end{pmatrix} = \begin{pmatrix} \underline{\quad\text{b.}\quad} \end{pmatrix}$$

$$.10 \begin{pmatrix} \text{AMOUNT} \\ \text{INVESTED} \\ \text{AT } 10\% \end{pmatrix} + .125 \begin{pmatrix} \underline{\quad\text{c.}\quad} - \underline{\quad\text{d.}\quad} \end{pmatrix} = \underline{\quad\text{e.}\quad}$$

Let $A =$ AMOUNT INVESTED AT 10%.

$$.10A + .125(10{,}000 - A) = 1{,}100$$
$$.10A + \underline{\quad\text{f.}\quad} = 1{,}100$$
$$-.025A = \underline{\quad\text{g.}\quad}$$
$$A = \underline{\quad\text{h.}\quad}$$
$$10{,}000 - A = \underline{\quad\text{i.}\quad}$$

$4,000 is invested at 12.5% and $6,000 at 10%.

10. *Industry.* Carbon steel contains 1% carbon and mild steel contains .1% carbon. How much carbon steel must be alloyed with a hundred tons of mild steel to obtain a construction steel that is .4% carbon?

$$\begin{pmatrix} \text{AMT CARBON} \\ \text{IN CARBON} \\ \text{STEEL} \end{pmatrix} + \begin{pmatrix} \text{AMT CARBON} \\ \text{IN MILD} \\ \text{STEEL} \end{pmatrix} = \begin{pmatrix} \text{AMT CARBON} \\ \text{IN CONSTR} \\ \text{STEEL} \end{pmatrix}$$

$$\begin{pmatrix} \text{\% CARBON} \\ \text{IN CARBON} \\ \text{STEEL} \end{pmatrix}\begin{pmatrix} \text{AMT} \\ \text{CARBON} \\ \text{STEEL} \end{pmatrix} + \begin{pmatrix} \text{\% CARBON} \\ \text{IN MILD} \\ \text{STEEL} \end{pmatrix}\begin{pmatrix} \text{AMT} \\ \text{MILD} \\ \text{STEEL} \end{pmatrix} = \begin{pmatrix} \underline{\quad\text{a.}\quad} \end{pmatrix}\begin{pmatrix} \underline{\quad\text{b.}\quad} \end{pmatrix}$$

$$\underline{\quad\text{c.}\quad}\begin{pmatrix} \text{AMT} \\ \text{CARBON} \\ \text{STEEL} \end{pmatrix} + \underline{\quad\text{d.}\quad}\begin{pmatrix} \underline{\quad\text{e.}\quad} \end{pmatrix} = \underline{\quad\text{f.}\quad}\begin{pmatrix} \underline{\quad\text{g.}\quad} + 100 \end{pmatrix}$$

Let $A =$ AMT CARBON STEEL used in the blend.

$$.01A + .001(100) = .004(A + 100)$$
$$.01A + .1 = .004A + .4$$
$$.006A = \underline{\quad\text{h.}\quad}$$
$$A = \underline{\quad\text{i.}\quad}$$

50 tons of carbon steel must be added.

B *Problems 11–30 are very similar to Problems 1–10. Use Problems 1–10 as models, and illustrate a technique for solution of each problem. Notice that since you are not asked for answers, they are shown as a check on your procedure.*

See Problem 1. **11.** The sum of three consecutive integers is 66. Find the integers.
Answer: The integers are 21, 22, and 23.

12. The sum of four consecutive integers is 102. Find the integers.
Answer: The integers are 24, 25, 26, and 27.

See Problem 2. **13.** The sum of three consecutive odd integers is 69. Find the first integer.
Answer: The first integer is 21.

14. What is the largest of three consecutive even integers if their sum is 72?
Answer: The largest integer is 26.

15. The sum of four consecutive odd integers is 100. Find the integers.
Answer: There are no such integers.

16. The sum of two consecutive integers is four more than the sum of the next two. Find the integers.
Answer: True for all integers.

See Problem 3. **17.** A rectangle is 2 centimeters longer than it is wide. If the perimeter of the figure is 36 centimeters, what is its width?
Answer: The width is 8 cm.

See Problem 4. **18.** *Agriculture.* A rectangular field is 10 meters longer than it is wide. If it has 88 meters of fencing enclosing it, what is the length of the longer side?
Answer: The longer side is 27 m.

See Problems 3 and 4. **19.** A square and a rectangle have equal perimeters. The width of the rectangle is three-fourths the side of the square and its length is 4 cm longer than the side of the square. Find the dimensions of the figures.

THINK
METRIC

Answer: The square is 16 cm on a side, and the rectangle is 12 by 20 cm.

20. The perimeter of a newspaper page is twice the perimeter of a page in a certain magazine. The length of the magazine page is 3 inches longer than it is wide. If the newspaper page is 7 inches wider and 12 inches longer than the magazine, what are its dimensions?
Answer: The newspaper is 15 by 23 in., and the magazine is 8 by 11 in.

See Problems 5 and 6. **21.** A college and the local movie theater are ten blocks apart. On his way from the college to the movies, Joe passes a sports arena first and then his dorm. It is a block farther from the college to the arena than from the arena to the dorm, and it's three blocks farther from his dorm to the theater than from the arena to the dorm. How far is it from the college to his dorm?
Answer: It is 5 blocks from the college to the dorm.

22. Traveling from Jenner to Guerneville along the Russian River, you pass through Duncan Mills and then Monte Rio before reaching Guerneville, a total distance of 13.8 miles. From Jenner to Duncan Mills is .4 mile farther than from Duncan Mills to Monte Rio, which is also .4 mile farther than from Monte Rio to Guerneville. How far is it between Monte Rio and Guerneville?

Answer: It is about 4.2 mi.

See Problem 7. **23.** *Business.* Sonic Stereo sold 1,200 cassettes during a big tape sale. The cassettes were sold singly or in packs of three, and for every single cassette sold there were five 3-packs sold. How many 3-packs were sold during the sale?

Answer: 375 3-packs were sold.

24. *Business.* A shipment of pushpins for bulletin boards contains 60,000 pins. The pins are packaged either 25 or 100 to a box, and there are 100 more of the larger packages. How many of each size package are included in the shipment?

Answer: There are 500 large packages and 400 small packages.

See Problem 8. **25.** *Business.* At the children's matinee, only one of every ten patrons is an adult. [*Hint:* This means that there are nine times as many children as adults.] Ticket prices are $1.50 for adults and 75¢ for children. If the receipts for a given Saturday afternoon totaled $321.75, how many children attended?

Answer: 351 children attended.

26. *Business.* The Art-z Theater had 244 admissions Friday evening. Prices are $2.50 for adults and $1.25 for students, and the total receipts were $550 that evening. How many adult tickets were sold?

Answer: 196 adult tickets were sold.

See Problem 9. **27.** *Finance.* Part of $1,500 is invested at 6%, and the remainder is invested at 8%. The combined investments will yield $119 interest the first year. How much is invested at each rate?

Answer: $50 is invested at 6% and $1,450 at 8%.

28. *Finance.* A total of $1,000 was invested for one year, part of it at 5% and the rest at 8%. If $74 interest was earned, how much was invested at 5%?

Answer: $200 was invested at 5% interest.

See Problem 10. **29.** *Nutrition.* Milk containing 10% butterfat and cream with 80% butterfat are mixed to produce half-and-half, which is 50% butterfat. How many gallons of each must be mixed to produce 140 gallons of half-and-half?

Answer: 60 gal of milk should be mixed with 80 gal of cream.

30. *Chemistry.* A chemist has two solutions of sulfuric acid. One is a 50% solution, and the other is a 75% solution. How many liters of each are necessary to produce 10 liters of a 60% solution?

Answer: 6 liters of 50% solution must be mixed with 4 liters of 75% solution.

Carefully analyze Problems 31–34. Restate the information and relationships until you are able to write an equation, and then solve and state an answer.

31. A bus was chartered for an outing. Each of the people who planned to go would be charged $7.50. However, if just 12 more people agreed to go, the bus would be full and the cost for each person would drop to $5.00. How many were originally planning to go?

32. A group plans to rent a ski lodge for a weekend. It will cost $16 per person unless nine more people are convinced to join the trip and fill the lodge. If the nine others come along, each person will pay only $10 toward the rent. How many people will the lodge accommodate?

33. Rich is hitchhiking back to school. He gets a ride immediately and rides at an average of 52 mph. After being dropped off, he walks the rest of the way at 4 mph. The total trip of 210 miles takes $4\frac{1}{2}$ hours. How much time did the walk take? How far did he walk?

34. Once a week, a sales representative drives 86 miles to see a client, but part of the journey is on a car ferry. She averages 48 mph on the road but only 8 mph on the ferry. If the total trip takes an average of two hours, how long is the ferry ride? How far does the ferry travel?

Mind Boggler

35. Matt Minde holds 240 shares of BOGGLE common stock. Its value has fluctuated wildly recently— from 59¢ to $4.87. A stockbroker tells Matt that there is a formula to help him decide what to do if he has an electronic calculator. The formula involves the "best advice" for dealing with such tricky stocks.

$$\begin{pmatrix} \text{STOCK} \\ \text{NAME} \end{pmatrix} = \left[\frac{\text{ADVICE}}{5(\text{LOW PRICE})} + \text{HIGH PRICE} \right] (\text{NO. OF SHARES})$$

Prices must be entered in dollars; the stock name is entered as 376608 (do you see why?), and the advice is read out by inverting the calculator (see Problem Set 1.1). What is the advice of the calculator? Is the calculator a "bull" or a "bear" in the market? [*Hint:* You must first "solve" for ADVICE. The calculator can't solve an equation; it can only evaluate **your** solution.]

2.3 Solving Linear Inequalities

An **inequality** is a statement of order. The inequality $3 > 1$ states that 3 is greater than 1, or 3 is to the right of 1 on the number line. Like an equation, the inequality may be an *identity,* a *contradiction,* or a **conditional inequality.** An identity such as $x < x + 1$ is true for all values of x. A contradiction like $x < x$ is false for every value of x. A conditional inequality such as $x < 2x + 1$ is true for some values of x and false for others. However, unlike an equation with a distinct root or solution, a

Figure 2.2

conditional inequality may have many solutions that satisfy it. The inequality $x > 3$ is satisfied by *any* number greater than 3—infinitely many values. The solution is often indicated on a number line, as illustrated in Figure 2.2. The circle, or "open point," at 3 is used to show that 3 itself is not included. The properties of order that are necessary to study inequalities are summarized in the box.

ADDITION
PROPERTY OF
ORDER

> Given an inequality, the same number may be added to or subtracted from both sides, leaving the order (or sense) of the inequality unchanged.

MULTIPLICATION
PROPERTY OF
ORDER

> Given an inequality, both sides may be multiplied or divided by the same positive number, and the order of the inequality will remain unchanged. The order of the inequality is *reversed* if both sides are multiplied or divided by a *negative* number.

Using these properties, you may operate on an inequality as you do on an equation, except when multiplying or dividing by negative quantities. To illustrate this similarity, here are some examples.

In Examples 1 and 2 solve each inequality, and graph the solution on a number line.

Example 1

$$4(s+1)+3 > 15$$
$$4s+4+3 > 15 \qquad \text{Multiply}$$
$$4s+7 > 15 \qquad \text{Simplify}$$
$$4s+7-7 > 15-7 \qquad \text{Subtract 7}$$
$$4s > 8$$
$$\frac{4s}{4} > \frac{8}{4} \qquad \text{Divide by 4}$$
$$s > 2$$

To check the solution, choose several numbers and substitute into the original inequality. You will find that numbers greater than 2 satisfy the inequality and numbers equal to or less than 2 do not.

Example 2

$$3(m+4)+5 > 5(m-1)-2$$
$$3m+12+5 > 5m-5-2 \qquad \text{Multiply}$$
$$3m+17 > 5m-7 \qquad \text{Simplify}$$
$$3m-\mathbf{5m}+17 > 5m-\mathbf{5m}-7 \qquad \text{Subtract } 5m$$
$$-2m+17 > -7$$
$$-2m+17-\mathbf{17} > -7-\mathbf{17} \qquad \text{Subtract } 17$$
$$-2m > -24$$
$$\frac{-2m}{-2} < \frac{-24}{-2} \qquad \begin{array}{l}\text{Divide by } -2; \text{ notice that the order} \\ \text{(or sense) of the inequality was reversed} \\ \text{because both sides were divided by } -2\end{array}$$
$$m < 12$$

The next example illustrates how your work should look. The extra steps and comments have been omitted.

Example 3

$$5(y-2)-6y \le 3(5y+2)$$
$$5y-10-6y \le 15y+6$$
$$-y-10 \le 15y+6$$
$$-16y \le 16$$
$$y \ge -1$$

The "closed point" at -1 is used to show that the end point *is included.*

The English language has many words for inequality: higher, lighter, wider, heavier, darker, shorter, and so on. Many problems involve inequalities, and you should approach these problems in the same manner as you do those involving equations.

Example 4 A car rental is $28.75 per day plus 22¢ per mile. If you must spend less than $46.00 per day for transportation, how many miles can you drive?

Solution

$$\left(\begin{array}{c}\text{RENTAL} \\ \text{FEE}\end{array}\right) \qquad\qquad < 46$$
$$\left(\begin{array}{c}\text{DAILY} \\ \text{COST}\end{array}\right) + \left(\begin{array}{c}\text{MILEAGE} \\ \text{CHARGE}\end{array}\right) \qquad < 46$$
$$28.75 + \left(\begin{array}{c}\text{CHARGE PER} \\ \text{MILE}\end{array}\right)(\text{MILES}) < 46$$
$$28.75 + \qquad (.22)(\text{MILES}) \qquad < 46$$

Let m be the number of *miles* driven.

$$28.75 + .22m < 46$$
$$.22m < 17.25$$
$$m < 78.40909$$

You may drive 78 miles or less.   □

Compound Statements

A **compound statement** imposes more than one condition on a quantity. The conditions are generally expressed as equations or inequalities. If we have two inequalities that apply simultaneously, we use the word *and*. The solution of the combined inequalities is whatever values they have in common and is called the **intersection** of their individual solutions. If we have two inequalities and one or the other applies—or if both apply— we use the word *or*. The solution of these two inequalities is all of the values of the individual solutions and is called the **union.**

If a person weighs more than 150 pounds *and* less than 200 pounds, this fact can be written as two inequalities, and their solutions can be graphed on number lines. That is, if w is the number of pounds in the weight, then $w > 150$ and $w < 200$. The graphs of these inequalities are shown in Figures 2.3a and 2.3b.

The points shared by the two solutions are the intersection of the sets and are the solution to the compound statement. The two may be combined into a single inequality, $150 < w < 200$, and we say that w is between 150 and 200 (see Figure 2.3c).

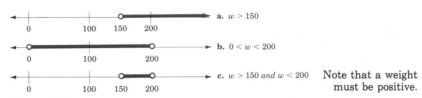

a. $w > 150$

b. $0 < w < 200$

c. $w > 150$ *and* $w < 200$ Note that a weight must be positive.

Figure 2.3

It may be necessary to keep the temperature of a certain mixture either above 100°F *or* below 60°F. That is, if t is the temperature, then $t > 100$ or $t < 60$. Figures 2.4a and 2.4b show the graphs of these two inequalities. Combining the points in Figure 2.4c—that is, taking all points from each graph—gives us the union of the two sets. Be careful! Note that $t > 100$ or $t < 60$ is *not* written as $60 > t > 100$, since this means $t > 100$ *and* $t < 60$, which is an empty set.

A compound inequality such as $150 < w < 200$ is called a **string of inequalities** and may be used to show the order of three or more quantities.

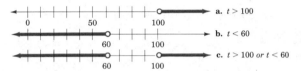

Figure 2.4

This string may be solved in a similar way to that used for other inequalities. In the following, notice that what is done to one member is done to all three members of the string.

Example 5 Joe College scores 65, 73, and 68 on his first three tests. What must he score on the last test in order to have an average of better than 75? What must he score to have an average between 65 and 75?

Solution Recall that an average is found by adding all the items involved and dividing by the number of items.

$$\text{AVERAGE} > 75$$

$$\frac{\text{TEST I} + \text{TEST II} + \text{TEST III} + \text{TEST IV}}{4} > 75$$

$$\text{TEST I} + \text{TEST II} + \text{TEST III} + \text{TEST IV} > 4(75)$$
$$65 + 73 + 68 + \text{TEST IV} > 300$$

Let s be the score on TEST IV.

$$65 + 73 + 68 + s > 300$$
$$206 + s > 300$$
$$s > 94$$

He must score over 94 on the last test to have an average of better than 75.

To answer the second part of the question, set up a compound inequality.

$$65 < \text{TEST AVERAGE} < 75$$

$$65 < \frac{65 + 73 + 68 + s}{4} < 75 \qquad \text{Recall the meaning of average}$$

$$65 < \frac{206 + s}{4} < 75$$

$4(65) <$	$206 + s$	$< 4(75)$	Multiply all parts by 4
$260 <$	$206 + s$	< 300	Simplify
$54 <$	s	< 94	Subtract 206 from all parts

He must score between 54 and 94 to keep his average between 65 and 75. □

Example 6　Solve and sketch the solution set.

$$-5 \le 2x - 1 \le 3$$
$$-4 \le 2x \le 4 \qquad \text{Add 1}$$
$$-2 \le x \le 2 \qquad \text{Divide by 2}$$

Example 7　Solve and sketch the solution set.

$$-5 \le 2 - 7x < 16$$
$$-7 \le -7x < 14 \qquad \text{Subtract 2}$$
$$1 \ge x > -2 \qquad \text{Divide by } -7; \text{ don't forget to change the}$$
$$-2 < x \le 1 \qquad \text{sense of the inequality}$$

Example 8　Solve and sketch the solution set.

$$2x < 3x + 1 < 2(x + 2)$$
$$2x < 3x + 1 < 2x + 4 \qquad \text{Simplify}$$
$$ 0 < x + 1 < 4 \qquad \text{Subtract } 2x; \text{ isolate the variable in}$$
$$\phantom{2x < 3x + 1 < 2x + 4 \quad} \text{one member of the string}$$
$$-1 < x < 3 \qquad \text{Subtract 1}$$

Example 9　Solve and sketch the solution set.

$$3(x - 2) < 4(x - 1) < 3x - 1$$
$$3x - 6 < 4x - 4 < 3x - 1 \qquad \text{Simplify}$$
$$-6 < x - 4 < -1 \qquad \text{Subtract } 3x$$
$$-2 < x < 3 \qquad \text{Add 4}$$

Problem Set 2.3

A *Solve the inequalities in Problems 1–30, and graph each solution on a number line.*

See Examples 1–3.

1. $3x > 12$
2. $7y < 21$
3. $2x \le -6$
4. $5y \ge -10$
5. $-4x > 20$
6. $-3y < -18$
7. $5 - x < 0$
8. $7 - y > 0$
9. $a + 7 \le 4$
10. $b + 6 \ge 1$
11. $h + 3 > 5$
12. $k - 2 < 3$
13. $2r - 1 < 9$
14. $3s + 2 > 8$
15. $5t - 7 \ge 8$
16. $7u - 5 \le 9$
17. $9 - 2v < 5$
18. $5 - 3w > 8$
19. $2 - x \ge 3x + 10$
20. $7 - 5y < 2y + 7$
21. $A > 3(1 + A)$
22. $3B > B + 19$
23. $2(C + 7) > 2 - C$
24. $5E + 4 < 3E - 6$
25. $3(3G - 2) > 4G - 3$
26. $4H - 1 > 3(H + 2)$
27. $5(4 + V) < 3(V + 1)$
28. $2 - 3W > 7(1 - W)$
29. $7(D - 2) + 5 \le 3(2 + D)$
30. $-3(F - 3) - 2 \le F + 3(F + 4)$

Solve the compound inequalities in Problems 31–40, and graph each solution on a number line.

See Examples 6–9.

31. $7 < x + 2 < 11$
32. $12 < 5 + y < 14$
33. $-2 < x - 1 < 3$
34. $-5 \le y - 2 \le 4$
35. $-8 \le 2x - 4 \le 6$
36. $-14 < 3y - 5 < 4$
37. $-4 \le 2x - 3 < 2$
38. $3 < 3y + 5 \le 6$
39. $9 < 1 - 2x < 15$
40. $-3 \le 1 - 2y \le 7$

B *Solve the inequalities in Problems 41–50, and graph the solutions on a number line.*

See Examples 1–3.

41. $4(x + 7) + 2 \le 2(4 - 3x) - x$
42. $6(y - 3) - 5y > 5(8 - y) + 2$
43. $3(x + 1) + 5(x - 4) \le 2(x - 2) - 5(2x + 1)$
44. $3(3y + 1) + 5(y - 4) \ge 3(y - 3) + 2(y - 1)$

See Examples 6–9.

45. $2n \le 3n + 2 \le 2n + 4$
46. $2n - 1 \le 5n - 2 \le 2n + 3$
47. $m - 7 \le 2(m + 4) \le m + 2$
48. $m - 3 < 2(2m + 3) < m + 3$
49. $2(x - 2) < 2(1 - 2x) < 2x + 5$
50. $7(y - 2) \le 6 - 5y \le 7(y + 3)$

Carefully analyze each of Problems 51–64. Restate the information and relationships until you are able to write an inequality, and then solve and state an answer.

See Example 4.

51. *Business.* A car rental is $31.10 per day plus 31.5¢ per mile. If your expense account allows less than $50 per day for transportation, how many miles can you drive?

52. *Business.* The charge for printing a poster is a $10 setup charge plus 15¢ per copy. If you have $25 or less available, how many posters can you afford to have printed?

53. *Business.* A sales representative is paid a salary of $200 plus a 10% commission on sales. How much must be sold if an income of at least $350 is expected?

54. *Business.* A car rental agency charges $29.00 per day plus 28¢ per mile. How many miles can you afford to drive if you must keep rental costs under $50 per day?

PRICE =
COST + MARKUP

The markup is usually given as a percentage of the cost of the item.

55. *Business.* The markup on a certain item must be at least 20% over a cost of $15.50. If a competitor is selling the item for $20, what price can be charged if the competitor is to be undersold?

56. *Business.* A certain dealer operates on a markup of at least 30%. A rival is selling a particular product for $149.50. If the product costs $110, what can the dealer charge to undersell the rival?

See Example 5.

57. *Sports.* A golfer shot 84, 91, 87, and 81 in four games. What must be scored in a fifth game in order to average in the low 80s (80–84)?

58. *Sports.* A bowler scores 146, 132, 153, 148, and 138 in five games. What must be bowled in the next game to attain an average between 145 and 150?

59. The sum of three consecutive even integers must be between 30 and 50. What are the permitted sets of integers?

60. The sum of four consecutive integers is between 65 and 80. What are the possibilities?

61. The sum of the first and the third of three consecutive even integers is not as large as the second integer. What values are possible for the first integer?

62. The sum of the first three of four consecutive integers is at least as large as twice the fourth. What are the possibilities for the initial number of the set?

63. *Finance.* A $10,000 legacy is to be invested. One part should safely earn 6%, and the rest will have a better yield of $8\frac{1}{2}\%$. How much should be invested in each to ensure an income of at least $700 per year?

64. *Business.* A craftsman uses both 55% and 70% silver alloys. How much of each should be used to obtain 100 grams of an alloy that is at least 60.7% silver?

Mind Boggler

65. The road from Rome passes through five small towns: Comb, Foam, Home, Nome, and Poem. Foam lies between Home and Poem. Home is further from Rome than Comb. Nome lies between Rome and Comb. Nome is not the first city on the route starting from Rome. Foam lies between Comb and Nome. Leaving Rome, in what order do you pass through the five hamlets?

2.4 Review Problems

Recall that all answers to Review Problems are given in the back of the book so that you can check your work.

Fill in the word or words that make the statements in Problems 1–10 complete and correct.

(2.1) **1.** Values that make a conditional equation true are said to _____ the equation.

(2.1) **2.** The _____ or _____ of an equation are the values that satisfy the equation.

(2.1) **3.** Two equations with the same solutions are called _____ _____.

(2.1) **4.** If both sides of a given equation are multiplied by any _____ number, the resulting equation is _____.

(2.2) **5.** Suppose $75 is divided between two people. If 1ST SHARE is the amount given one person, then the other person receives 2ND SHARE = _____ − _____.

(2.2) **6.** The second of two consecutive even integers is _____ more than the first.

(2.2) **7.** The area of a rectangle is the _____ of its length and width.

(2.3) **8.** An inequality is a statement of _____.

(2.3) **9.** The order of an inequality is reversed if it is multiplied or divided by a _____ _____.

(2.3) **10.** If two inequalities apply simultaneously, we find the _____ of the solutions of the two inequalities.

(2.1) *Solve the equations in Problems 11–14.*

11. $7x + 4 = -17$ **12.** $3(y - 1) = 5 - y$

13. $5(a - 5) + 2 = 3(a - 3)$ **14.** $3(2b - 3) + 6 = 1 - [-8 - 2(1 + 2b)]$

(2.2) **15.** *Agriculture.* A flower garden is enclosed by 54 feet of fencing. If the garden is rectangular and is 3 feet longer than it is wide, what are the dimensions of the plot?

(2.2) **16.** *Finance.* Suppose $1,700 is invested, part at 8% and the remainder at $14\frac{1}{2}\%$. If $201 interest is earned, how much is invested at each rate for the year?

(2.3) *Solve the inequalities in Problems 17–19, and graph each solution on a number line.*

17. $5x - 7 \geq 3$ **18.** $2y - 3[3 - (y - 2)] < y - 2(1 - y) + 1$

19. $-7 < 2z - 5 \leq 3$

(2.3) **20.** You score 82, 77, 90, and 75 on your first four quizzes. What must you score on the fifth quiz to have an average of better than 80?

CHAPTER
3

Linear Equations and Inequalities in Two Variables

Contents

3.1   Equations in Two Variables

In Chapter 2 our attention centered on equations and inequalities with only one variable. However, in mathematics, many situations exist in which one variable depends on the value of another variable. In this chapter we'll consider the solution of first-degree equations and inequalities with two variables.

Consider the equation

$$y = 3x - 2$$

For each value of x, there is exactly one value for y. We can construct a table by choosing arbitrary values for x and finding corresponding values of y:

x	0	1	2	-2	-5
y	-2	1	4	-8	-17

Step 1.   *You* choose a value for x.

Step 2.   Substitute into the equation.

Step 3.   Evaluate to find a corresponding value for y.

A table such as the one above is often represented as a set of *ordered pairs*. An **ordered pair** of numbers is a *pair* of numbers, written

$$(x, y)$$

where the *order* in which they are named is important. That is,

$$(4, 5) \neq (5, 4)$$

From the table above, we can write the following ordered pairs:

$$(0, -2), \quad (1, 1), \quad (2, 4), \quad (-2, -8), \quad (-5, -17)$$

This set of ordered pairs is derived from the equation

$$y = 3x - 2$$

and a new ordered pair can be added to the list for each new value for x.

The variable associated with the first component is called the **independent variable,** and the variable associated with the second component is called the **dependent variable.** In this book, the variable x will be used to represent a first component (the independent variable) and y will be used to represent a second component (the dependent variable). If other variables are used, such as h or V, the given ordered pair will indicate which is the independent variable and which is the dependent variable. That is, if you are given (h, V), then you know that h is the independent variable and V is the dependent variable.

Historical Note

The Arab mathematician al-Khowârizmî's text (ca. 825) entitled *Hisâb al-jabr w'al-mugâbalah* is the origin of the word *algebra*. The book was widely known in Europe through Latin translations. The word *al-jabr* or *al-ge-bra* became synonymous with equation solving. Interestingly enough, the Arabic word *al-jabr* was also used in connection with medieval barbers. The barber, who also set bones and let blood in those times, usually called himself an *algebrista*.

Example 1 For the equation

$$y = 5x - 2$$

find the value for the dependent variable, y, if we make the given choices for the independent variable, x. Write your answers as ordered pairs.

a. $x = 0$ $y = 5(0) - 2$ **b.** $x = 3$ $y = 5(3) - 2$
                       $= -2$ $= 13$

    Answer: (0, −2)   *Answer:* (3, 13)

c. $x = -1$ $y = 5(-1) - 2$ **d.** $x = a$ $y = 5a - 2$
                       $= -7$

    Answer: (−1, −7)   *Answer:* $(a, 5a - 2)$ □

Some ordered pairs will make the equation

$$y = 5x - 2$$

true, and some ordered pairs will make the equation false. For example, (−2, 0) makes the equation false, because

$$0 \neq 5(-2) - 2$$

The set of all ordered pairs that make an equation with two variables true is called the *solution set*.

SOLUTION SET   The **solution set** of an equation with variables x and y is the set of ordered pairs of real numbers (x, y) for which the equation is true.

Example 2 Which of the given ordered pairs belong to the solution set of the equation below?

$$3x + 2y = 1$$

a. (1, −1) $3(1) + 2(-1) \overset{?}{=} 1$ **b.** (2, −1) $3(2) + 2(-1) \overset{?}{=} 1$
                          $3 - 2 \overset{?}{=} 1$ $6 - 2 \overset{?}{=} 1$
                              $1 = 1$ $4 \neq 1$

    Answer: Belongs to solution set   *Answer:* Doesn't belong to
                                                 solution set   □

The set of possible replacements for the independent variable is usually limited to a given set of numbers. This set of possible replacements is called the *domain*. The domain is always either given or implied.

DOMAIN

> The **domain** is the set of replacements for the independent variable. If it is not stated, the implied domain is the set of all real numbers that make sense in the given equation or relation.

In Examples 3–6 state the domain for each equation.

Example 3 $y = 3x$

Solution   The domain is the set of all real numbers. ☐

Example 4 $y = 7x$

where x represents the number of people attending a performance at the Astrodome and y represents the income in dollars.

Solution   The domain is the set of integers between 0 (nobody attending) and 66,000 (absolute maximum capacity of the Astrodome). The domain must be whole numbers because fractional people don't make sense for this application.

☐

Example 5 $y = \dfrac{x}{3}$ where $0 < x < 3$

Solution   The domain is all real numbers between 0 and 3 because the domain is stated. ☐

Example 6 $y = \dfrac{3}{x}$

Solution   The domain is all nonzero real numbers because the equation doesn't make sense when $x = 0$. ☐

If the domain is small, sometimes we can find the solution set and state it as a set of ordered pairs.

In Examples 7 and 8 let the domain for the given equation be $\{-1, 0, 3\}$. Find the solution set.

Example 7 $2x + y = 1$

Solution   If $x = -1$, then: $2(-1) + y = 1$
$$-2 + y = 1$$
$$y = 3$$

If $x = 0$, then: $2(0) + y = 1$
$$y = 1$$

If $x = 3$, then: $2(3) + y = 1$
$$6 + y = 1$$
$$y = -5$$

Solution set: $\{(-1, 3), (0, 1), (3, -5)\}$ □

Example 8 $r + t = 0$ where (r, t) are the ordered pairs

Solution The ordered pair (r, t) means r is the independent variable, so the members of the domain are replacements for r.

If $r = -1$, then: $(-1) + t = 0$
$$t = 1$$

If $r = 0$, then: $0 + t = 0$
$$t = 0$$

If $r = 3$, then: $3 + t = 0$
$$t = -3$$

Solution set: $\{(-1, 1), (0, 0), (3, -3)\}$ □

We say that an ordered pair (x, y) *satisfies* an equation with variables x and y if the ordered pair is a member of the solution set. In Examples 7 and 8 we could state the solution sets because the domains were very limited. If the domains are large, we may focus on finding just *some* ordered pairs that satisfy the equation.

Example 9 Find three ordered pairs that satisfy the equation

$$2x - y = 3$$

Solution Let $x = 0$: When we say *let $x = 0$* or *let $x = 1$*, we mean that it is *your* choice of x. You can choose any value for x that is in the domain.

$$2(0) - y = 3$$
$$-y = 3$$
$$y = -3$$

Thus, $(0, -3)$ satisfies the equation.

Let $x = 1$:   Let $x = 2$:

$$2(1) - y = 3 \qquad 2(2) - y = 3$$
$$-y = 1 \qquad\qquad -y = -1$$
$$y = -1 \qquad\qquad y = 1$$

The ordered pairs $(1, -1)$ and $(2, 1)$ also satisfy the equation. □

Your goal in this chapter is to find the solution set of equations and inequalities with two first-degree variables. In this section, *some* ordered pairs that satisfy a given equation were found, and in the next section, *all* ordered pairs that satisfy the equation will be found.

Problem Set 3.1

A *For the equation*

$$y = 3x + 11$$

find the value for the dependent variable if you make the choice given for the independent variable in Problems 1–6.

See Example 1.   **1.** 0   **2.** 2   **3.** 5   **4.** −1   **5.** −3   **6.** −5

For the equation

$$y = -2x + 5$$

find the value for the dependent variable if you make the choice given for the independent variable in Problems 7–12.

7. 3   **8.** 0   **9.** 1   **10.** −2   **11.** −3   **12.** 10

Which of the given ordered pairs in Problems 13–18 belong to the solution set of the given equation?

See Example 2.   **13.** $x + 3y = 7$;   (−2, 3), (7, 0), (0, 7)
14. $y = 5x - 2$;   (1, 3), (−3, −17), (2, 8)
15. $4x - 3y = 5$;   (1, −3), (1, 3), (2, 1)
16. $2x - y = 4$;   (2 ,0), (3, −2), (0, 4)
17. $x = 3$;   (3, 4), (3, 0), (3, −2)
18. $y = 4$;   (3, 4), (0, 4), (−5, 4)

State the domain for each equation given in Problems 19–27.

See Examples 3–6.   **19.** $y = x + 5$ **20.** $x - 3y = 6$

21. $y = \dfrac{2}{x}$ **22.** $y = \dfrac{5}{x} + 6$

23. $y = 2x - 3$, $-7 < x < -2$
24. $y = 2x - 3$, $-7 < x < -2$, x is an integer
25. $y = 2x - 3$, $x < 10$, x is a natural number

Historical Note

The *Celsius* scale was originally called *centigrade*, but in 1948 the ninth General Conference on Weights and Measures adopted the name Celsius in honor of Anders Celsius, a Swedish scientist (1701–1744).

26. *Chemistry.*   The temperature, T (in degrees Celsius), for a certain experiment is varied according to the formula

$$T = t - 15$$

where (t, T) are the ordered pairs and t is the time of day (on a 24 hour clock) in hours past midnight.

27. *Physics.*   The maximum weight, W (in pounds), allowed in an elevator is

$$W = 200p$$

where (p, W) are the ordered pairs, p is the number of people in the elevator, and $W \leq 3{,}000$.

Let the domain be the set {0, 1, 2, 3}. Write the set of ordered pairs generated for each equation in Problems 28–35.

See Examples 7 and 8.

28. $2x - y = 3$ **29.** $x + 3y = 6$
30. $x - 2y = 4$ **31.** $5x + y = 3$
32. $2s + t = 3$,   where (s, t) are the ordered pairs
33. $m + 2n = 5$,   where (m, n) are the ordered pairs
34. $2p + 3q = 1$,   where (p, q) are the ordered pairs
35. $3p - 4W = 2$,   where (p, W) are the ordered pairs

B   *In Problems 36–49 find three ordered pairs that satisfy the equation.*

See Example 9.

36. $2x + 3y = 6$ **37.** $3x - 4y = 12$
38. $x - 3y = 15$ **39.** $5x - y = 10$
40. $x = 1$ **41.** $x = -2$
42. $y = -4$ **43.** $y = 0$
44. $3x - 2 = 2y + 1$ **45.** $5y + 1 = -1(2x - 3)$
46. Formula for the circumference, C, of a circle with radius r: $C = 2\pi r$,   where (r, C) are the ordered pairs
47. Formula for the area, A, of a circle with radius r: $A = \pi r^2$,   where (r, A) are the ordered pairs
48. Formula for the surface area, S, of a right circular cylinder with height equal to twice the radius r: $S = 4\pi r^2$,   where (r, S) are the ordered pairs
49. Formula for the volume, V, of a right circular cylinder with height equal to twice the radius r: $V = 2\pi r^3$,   where (r, V) are the ordered pairs

Mind Bogglers

50. A baker knows from experience that there is enough dough in the "holes" from four donuts to make one new donut. With the holes from 55 donuts, how many new complete donuts can be made? [*Hint:* Each new donut produces a new hole that can also be used.]
51. It is well known that $2 + 2 = 2 \times 2$. This can be symbolized by $x + y = xy$. If $x = y$, then 0 and 2 are the only solutions to this equation. But let's say that $x \neq y$. Find an ordered pair that satisfies this equation.

3.2   Graphing Lines

Infinitely many ordered pairs may satisfy a first-degree equation with two variables. In the last section, three ordered pairs of the solution sets of several equations were found. But continuing in this fashion to find others would be extremely tedious, and you could never find all the ordered pairs using this method. So, now we turn to graphical methods.

Historical Note

The Cartesian coordinate system is named in honor of the French mathematician René Descartes (1596–1665). Because of his frail health he was accustomed to staying in bed as long as he wished. Legend tells us that he thought of this coordinate system while he was lying in bed watching a fly crawl around on the ceiling of his room. He noticed that the path of the fly could be described if he knew the relation connecting the fly's distances from the walls.

Cartesian Coordinate System

Recall from elementary algebra that a **Cartesian coordinate system** is formed by drawing two perpendicular number lines, called **axes.** The point of intersection is called the **origin,** and the plane is divided into four parts called **quadrants,** which are labeled as shown in Figure 3.1.

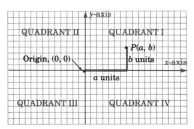

Figure 3.1 Cartesian Coordinate System

Point $P(a, b)$ in Figure 3.1 is found in the plane by counting a units from the origin in a horizontal direction (either positive or negative), and then b units (either positive or negative) in a vertical direction. The number a is sometimes called the **abscissa** and b the **ordinate** of the point P. Together, a and b are called the **coordinates** of the point P.

Example 1 Plot the following points, and then connect each point with the preceding one: $(-1, 0), (3, -2), (3, 0), (4, 0), (5, 2), (3, 2), (3, 8), (-4, 3), (3, 3), (3, 2), (-5, 2), (-3, 0), (3, 0)$

Solution The graph is shown in Figure 3.2.

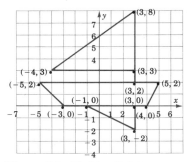

Figure 3.2 Plotting Points

Graphing a Line

Consider the following equation:

$$5x + 2y = 6$$

In the last section, you may have noticed that it was easier to find some ordered pairs (x, y) that make this equation true by first solving for y:

$$2y = -5x + 6$$

$$y = -\frac{5}{2}x + 3$$

Let $x = 0$:

$$y = -\frac{5}{2}(0) + 3$$

$$= 3 \qquad \text{This is the ordered pair } (0, 3).$$

Let $x = 2$:

$$y = -\frac{5}{2}(2) + 3 \qquad \begin{array}{l} \text{Notice that we choose values for } x \text{ that simplify the arithmetic.} \\ \text{This is why it helps to solve for } y \text{ first.} \end{array}$$

$$= -5 + 3$$

$$= -2 \qquad \text{This is the ordered pair } (2, -2).$$

Let $x = -2$:

$$y = -\frac{5}{2}(-2) + 3$$

$$= 5 + 3$$

$$= 8 \qquad \text{This is the ordered pair } (-2, 8).$$

Is this the entire solution set? If we plot these points as shown in Figure 3.3, we notice that a line can be drawn through these points. (Is this true of any three points?)

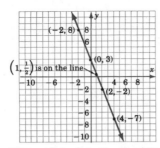

Figure 3.3 Solution Set of $5x + 2y = 6$

This is not a coincidence and *any* other coordinates that satisfy the equation, say $(1, \frac{1}{2})$, will also lie on the line. Not only that, but *any* other point on the line will satisfy the equation. For example, $(4, -7)$ is on the line, and we can check it in the equation:

$$5x + 2y = 6$$
$$5(4) + 2(-7) = 6$$
$$20 - 14 = 6$$
$$6 = 6$$

This relationship between the solution set of a first-degree equation with two variables and the graph of a line always holds. That is, we can speak of the *graph of an equation* or the *equation of a graph*.

GRAPH OF AN
EQUATION
OR
EQUATION OF A
GRAPH

By the **graph of an equation** or the **equation of a graph,** we mean:

1. Every point on the graph has coordinates that satisfy the equation.
2. Every ordered pair that satisfies the equation has coordinates that lie on the graph.

In particular, the graph of a first-degree equation is a line, and conversely, the equation of a line is a first-degree equation of the form

$$Ax + By + C = 0$$

where A, B, and C are numbers (A and B not both 0). For this reason, first-degree equations with two variables are called *linear equations*.

STANDARD FORM
OF EQUATION OF A
LINE

FIRST-DEGREE
EQUATION

LINEAR EQUATION

Standard Form of the Equation of a Line
  $Ax + By + C = 0$

where A, B, and C are real numbers (A and B not both 0) and (x, y) is any point on the line. This equation is called a:

1. **First-degree** equation in two variables, or
2. **Linear** equation in two variables.

Recall from geometry that two distinct points determine a line. Thus, the entire solution set of a first-degree equation with two variables can be represented graphically by plotting two points and then drawing the line passing through those points. However, it is usually desirable to plot a third point to guard against mistakes.

PROCEDURE FOR
GRAPHING A LINE
BY PLOTTING
POINTS

To Graph a Linear Equation with Two Variables:

1. Find two ordered pairs that satisfy the equation. These can be found by inspection or by choosing an x value (since it is the independent variable) and then finding the corresponding y value.
2. Plot these two points on a Cartesian coordinate system. Be sure to label the axes and choose an appropriate scale.
3. Draw the line passing through the two points. This line is a graph of the solution set.
4. *Check:* Find a third ordered pair that satisfies the equation, and then verify that this point lies on the line.

You can choose *any x*
value in the domain;
however, it is wise to
choose a value that
simplifies the
arithmetic.

In Examples 2–5 graph each linear equation.

Example 2 $y = \dfrac{1}{3}x + 2$

Solution   Choose values for x that make the arithmetic easy.

If $x = 0$, then $y = 2$.
If $x = 3$, then $y = 3$.

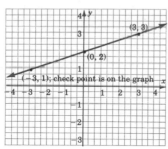

Figure 3.4   Graph of $y = \frac{1}{3}x + 2$

Check point: If $x = -3$, then $y = 1$.

Plot the points $(0, 2)$, $(3, 3)$, and $(-3, 1)$, and draw the graph as shown in Figure 3.4.   □

Example 3 $2x + 3y = 6$

Solution   If $x = 0$, then $y = 2$.
If $x = 3$, then $y = 0$.

The graph is shown in Figure 3.5.

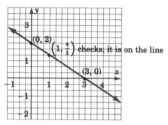

Figure 3.5   Graph of $2x + 3y = 6$

Check point: If $x = 1$, then $y = \frac{4}{3}$, which lies on the line.   □

Example 4 $x = y$

Solution   If $x = 0$, then $y = 0$.
If $x = 1$, then $y = 1$.
If $x = 2$, then $y = 2$.

Plot these points and draw the graph as shown in Figure 3.6. Notice that sometimes it is convenient to plot the check point right along with the other points when drawing the line. If the three points do not line up, then you have made a mistake, and you can go back and check your arithmetic, or else you can select a fourth point to see which three lie on the same line.

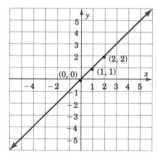

Figure 3.6   Graph of $x = y$ □

Example 5 $x = 2$

Solution   The y-coordinate can be any value; the only restriction is that the first coordinate is 2. Choose three points with 2 as the first component; for example: $(2, 0)$, $(2, 1)$, and $(2, -1)$. Plot these points and draw the graph as shown in Figure 3.7.

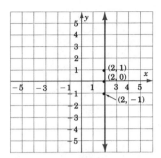

Figure 3.7 Graph of $x = 2$ ☐

In Examples 2–5 the domain was implied. It was the set of all real numbers, and this is indicated on the graphs in Figures 3.4–3.7 by arrows at the ends of the line segments.

Sometimes the domain is stated, as shown in Examples 6–8.

In Examples 6–8 graph each solution set.

Example 6 $x + y = 3$ where the domain is $\{-1, 2, 3\}$

Solution If $x = -1$, then $y = 4$.
If $x = \ \ 2$, then $y = 1$.
If $x = \ \ 3$, then $y = 0$.

Solution set: $\{(-1, 4), (2, 1), (3, 0)\}$

Plot these points as shown in Figure 3.8. Notice that you should not draw the line passing through these points for this problem, since the domain has only three values.

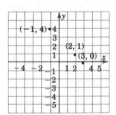

Figure 3.8 Graph with Limited Domain ☐

Example 7 $x + y = 3$ where $-1 \leq x \leq 3$

Solution Plot *any* three points to determine the line $x + y = 3$. *Then* draw the part of the line where x is between -1 and 3, *including* the end points. Since the end points are included, solid dots are drawn at the ends, as shown in Figure 3.9 (p. 68).

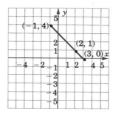

Figure 3.9 Graphing a Line Segment   □

Example 8 $x + 10y - 20 = 0$ where $10 < x < 60$

Solution   Plot *any* three points to determine the line $x + 10y - 20 = 0$. When restrictions are given, it is often convenient to use those values when finding points:

If $x = 10$, then: $10 + 10y - 20 = 0$
$$10y = 10$$
$$y = 1$$ This is the point (10, 1).

If $x = 60$, then: $60 + 10y - 20 = 0$
$$10y = -40$$
$$y = -4$$ This is the point (60, −4).

If $x = 0$, then: $0 + 10y - 20 = 0$
$$10y = 20$$
$$y = 2$$ This is the point (0, 2).

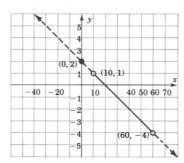

Figure 3.10 Graph of $x + 10y - 20 = 0$, where $10 < x < 60$

Draw the line determined by these three points (see Figure 3.10). Notice that it is *not* necessary that all three points satisfy $10 < x < 60$; you can use *any* three points to determine the line. (Also notice that it is not always convenient to let one square on your graph paper equal one unit.) Next, find the part of the line for which x is between 10 and 60, *excluding* the end points. This is indicated in Figure 3.10 by the open circles at the ends of the line segment.

Problem Set 3.2

A *Plot the points given in Problems 1–4.*

See Example 1.

1. **a.** $(4, 1)$ **b.** $(-3, 2)$ **c.** $(0, 3)$
  d. $(3, 0)$ **e.** $(-2, -5)$

2. **a.** $(2, -4)$ **b.** $(6, 1)$ **c.** $(-4, -3)$
  d. $(-6, 1)$ **e.** $(0, 0)$

Some consideration of scale is necessary when working Problems 3 and 4.

3. **a.** $(200, -100)$ **b.** $(-50, 500)$ **c.** $(650, 225)$
  d. $(-400, -350)$ **e.** $(0, 75)$

4. **a.** $(\frac{1}{6}, -\frac{1}{2})$ **b.** $(-\frac{1}{3}, \frac{3}{2})$ **c.** $(\frac{2}{3}, 0)$
  d. $(-\frac{5}{6}, -\frac{2}{3})$ **e.** $(\frac{1}{12}, \frac{11}{12})$

Palatable Plotting

Problems 5 and 6 are called *Palatable Plottings* because when you are finished with the graph, the result will be a picture.

5. Plot the following points on graph paper and connect each point with the preceding one: $(3, 5)$, $(0, 8)$, $(-3, 5)$, $(-3, 2)$, $(-6, -1)$, $(-6, -4)$, $(-3, -7)$, $(-3, -4)$, $(-6, -1)$. Starting again: $(0, 2)$, $(3, 5)$, $(3, 2)$, $(6, -1)$, $(6, -4)$, $(3, -7)$, $(0, -4)$, $(0, 2)$, $(-3, 5)$. Starting again: $(-3, -4)$, $(3, 2)$, $(6, -1)$, $(3, -4)$, $(-3, 2)$. Finally, draw segments from $(3, -4)$ to $(3, -7)$ and $(0, -4)$ to $(-3, -7)$.

6. Plot the following points on graph paper and connect each point with the preceding one: $(-10, -4)$, $(10, -4)$, $(0, -3)$, $(0, -2)$, $(9, -4)$, $(8, -4)$, $(0, -1)$, $(0, 0)$, $(7, -4)$, $(6, -4)$, $(0, 1)$, $(0, 2)$, $(5, -4)$, $(4, -4)$, $(0, 3)$, $(0, 4)$, $(3, -4)$, $(2, -4)$, $(0, 5)$, $(0, 6)$, $(1, -4)$, $(0, -4)$, $(0, 6)$, $(-1, -4)$, $(-2, -4)$, $(0, 5)$, $(0, 4)$, $(-3, -4)$, $(-4, -4)$, $(0, 3)$, $(0, 2)$, $(-5, -4)$, $(-6, -4)$, $(0, 1)$, $(0, 0)$, $(-7, -4)$, $(-8, -4)$, $(0, -1)$, $(0, -2)$, $(-9, -4)$, $(-10, -4)$, $(0, -3)$.

Graph each linear equation in Problems 7–32.

See Examples 2–5.

7. $y = x - 3$ **8.** $y = x + 4$
9. $y = 3x + 7$ **10.** $y = -2x - 3$
11. $y = \frac{1}{2}x + 3$ **12.** $y = \frac{2}{3}x - 4$
13. $2x + y = 1$ **14.** $x + 3y = 5$
15. $2x + 3y = 6$ **16.** $3x - 4y = 12$
17. $x - 3y - 15 = 0$ **18.** $5x - y - 10 = 0$
19. $2x + y - 4 = 0$ **20.** $y - 2x - 4 = 0$
21. $2x + y = 0$ **22.** $x + 2y = 0$
23. $x = y$ **24.** $2x = y$
25. $x = -4$ **26.** $y = 2$
27. $x = 1$ **28.** $x = -2$
29. $y = 0$ **30.** $x = 0$
31. $y + 2 = 0$ **32.** $x - 3 = 0$

B *Graph the lines given by the equations in Problems 33–38 with the restrictions indicated.*

See Examples 6–8.

33. $2x - y = -18$; where $-8 \le x \le -6$
34. $x + y = 15$; where $5 \le x \le 18$
35. $y + 3 = 0$; where $-9 \le x \le 5$

36. $3x - 5y - 60 = 0$; where $10 < x < 15$

37. $y = 2$; where $4 < x < 6$

38. $y = 0$; where $-2 < x < 2$

39. *Chemistry.* Fahrenheit and Celsius are related by the formula

$$°F = \frac{9}{5} °C + 32$$

Graph this relationship, where °C is chosen as the independent variable and $0 \le °C \le 100$.

Note: The assumption that this relationship is linear simplifies the work. The equation and graph allow for values of n that are not whole numbers even though the number of students must be a whole number.

40. *Business.* Suppose some market research shows that 300 students would buy a new type of pen if it were priced at $5 and that 1,500 would buy it if it were priced at $1. If we assume this relationship is linear, the equation representing this demand is

$$n = 1,800 - 300p$$

where n represents the number of pens sold and p is the price of the pen (in dollars). Graph this equation for $1 \le p \le 5$.

41. *Business.* A distributor of school supplies finds that he can supply 600 of the pens in Problem 40 if they sell for $1, but he can supply 2,600 if they sell for $5. The equation representing the supply is

$$n = 500p + 100$$

where n represents the number of pens supplied and p is the price of the pen (in dollars). Graph this equation for $1 \le p \le 5$.

Mind Bogglers

42.
  a. Let $y = 3x + b$. On the same coordinate axes, graph this equation where the values of b are the following: $b = 0$; $b = 2$; $b = 5$; $b = -3$; $b = -6$

  b. Let $y = -2x + b$. On the same coordinate axes, graph this equation where the values of b are the following: $b = 0$; $b = 3$; $b = 6$; $b = -4$; $b = -7$

  c. On the basis of parts a and b, what effect do you think the number b has on a given equation $y = mx + b$?

43.
  a. Let $y = mx + 3$. On the same coordinate axes, graph this equation where the values of m are the following: $m = 0$; $m = 2$; $m = 5$; $m = -3$; $m = -\frac{2}{3}$

  b. Let $y = mx - 4$. On the same coordinate axes, graph this equation where the values of m are the following: $m = 0$; $m = 3$; $m = -5$; $m = \frac{1}{2}$; $m = -\frac{2}{3}$

  c. On the basis of parts a and b, what effect do you think the number m has on a given equation $y = mx + b$?

3.3　Slope–Intercept

In this section we'll investigate some properties of lines. First, consider the standard form of the equation of a line:

$$Ax + By + C = 0$$

If $B \neq 0$, we can solve for y:

$$By = -Ax - C$$

$$y = -\frac{A}{B}x - \frac{C}{B}$$

Notice that if

$$m = -\frac{A}{B} \quad \text{and} \quad b = -\frac{C}{B}$$

then the first-degree equation in two variables x and y (with $B \neq 0$) can be written in the form

$$y = mx + b$$

This is a very useful way of writing the equation of a line.

y-Intercept

The points where a graph crosses the coordinate axes are usually easy to find, and they are often used to help sketch the curve. A **y-intercept** is a point where a graph crosses the y-axis, and consequently, it is a point with a first component of 0. An **x-intercept** is a point where a graph crosses the x-axis, and it has a second component of 0. The intercepts can be found as shown in Example 1.

Example 1 If $3x + 5y = 15$, find the intercepts.

Solution y-intercept: Let $x = 0$; then

$$3(0) + 5y = 15$$
$$5y = 15$$
$$y = 3$$

The y-intercept is the point $(0, 3)$.

x-intercept: Let $y = 0$; then

$$3x + 5(0) = 15$$
$$3x = 15$$
$$x = 5$$

The x-intercept is the point $(5, 0)$. □

The y-intercept is used more often than the x-intercept when graphing lines. Every nonvertical line has exactly one y-intercept, so we speak about *the* y-intercept of a line. In general, if

$$y = mx + b$$

and $x = 0$, then

$$y = m(0) + b$$
$$y = b$$

y-INTERCEPT

> The **y-intercept** of a line is the point where it crosses the y-axis. Given the line $y = mx + b$, we say the y-intercept is b. This means the graph crosses the y-axis at the point $(0, b)$.

In Examples 2–4 find the y-intercept of each line.

Example 2 $y = 5x + 7$

Solution $b = 7$ (by inspection), so the y-intercept is 7; this means that the line crosses the y-axis at the point $(0, 7)$ ☐

Example 3 $y = \dfrac{1}{2}x - 3$

Solution $b = -3$ (by inspection), so the y-intercept is -3 ☐

Example 4 $2x + 3y = 12$

Solution   First, solve for y:

$$3y = -2x + 12$$
$$y = -\frac{2}{3}x + 4$$

Then, by inspection, $b = 4$, so the y-intercept is 4. ☐

Slope

The symbol P_1 is read "P sub one," and P_2 is read "P sub two." The points (x_1, y_1) and (x_2, y_2) denote different points, and both are different from (x, y).

To find the significance of m, called the *slope of a line*, in the equation

$$y = mx + b$$

consider two points $P_1(x_1, y_1)$ and $P_2(x_2, y_2)$ on the line. Both of these points satisfy the equation:

$$y_1 = mx_1 + b \qquad y_2 = mx_2 + b$$

Subscripts are used to denote coordinates of known or given points, whereas (x, y) is used to denote an arbitrary point.

Solve each for b:

$$b = y_1 - mx_1 \qquad b = y_2 - mx_2$$

Since they both equal b, they are equal to each other, so we have

$$y_1 - mx_1 = y_2 - mx_2$$

Solve for m:

$$mx_2 - mx_1 = y_2 - y_1$$
$$m(x_2 - x_1) = y_2 - y_1$$
$$m = \frac{y_2 - y_1}{x_2 - x_1} \qquad x_2 \neq x_1, \text{ or we would be dividing by 0}$$

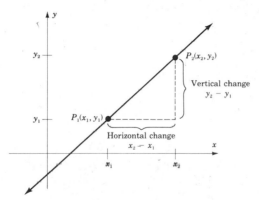

Figure 3.11 Slope

A graphical interpretation of m can be seen in Figure 3.11. Notice that $y_2 - y_1$ represents the **vertical change** between the points P_1 and P_2; this is sometimes called the **rise.** Also, $x_2 - x_1$ represents the **horizontal change,** sometimes called the **run.**

SLOPE

The **slope** of the line passing through $P_1(x_1, y_1)$ and $P_2(x_2, y_2)$ is denoted by m and is found by

$$m = \frac{y_2 - y_1}{x_2 - x_1} = \frac{\text{RISE}}{\text{RUN}} \qquad \text{where} \quad x_2 \neq x_1$$

In Examples 5–8 find the slope of each line:

Example 5 $y = \dfrac{1}{2}x - 3$

Solution   By inspection, $m = \frac{1}{2}$ □

Example 6 $4x + 2y + 3 = 0$

Solution   First, solve for y:

$$2y = -4x - 3$$
$$y = -2x - \dfrac{3}{2}$$

Then, by inspection, $m = -2$.   □

Example 7   Passing through $(4, 5)$ and $(1, 3)$

Solution
$$m = \frac{3-5}{1-4} = \frac{-2}{-3} = \frac{2}{3}$$ □

Example 8   Passing through $(-1, -2)$ and $(3, -3)$

Solution
$$m = \frac{-3 - (-2)}{3 - (-1)} = \frac{-1}{4}$$ □

SLOPE–INTERCEPT
FORM OF THE
EQUATION OF A
LINE

Slope-Intercept Form of the Equation of a Line

$y = mx + b$

where b represents the y-intercept $(0, b)$ and m represents the slope

---

Graphing a Line Using the Slope–Intercept Form

In the discussion of the standard equation of the line,

$$Ax + By + C = 0$$

the restriction $B \neq 0$ allowed us to solve for y. What happens if $B = 0$? Then the result is the following equation:

$$Ax + C = 0$$
$$Ax = -C$$

Since $A \neq 0$ (because if both $A = 0$ and $B = 0$, there could be no line), the equation has the form

$$x = h$$

for some constant h.

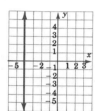

Figure 3.12
Graph of $x = -4$

You've seen before that this is a *vertical line*. For example,

$$x = -4$$

is shown in Figure 3.12. This line has *no y-intercept and its slope is undefined.* It is a special case that is considered separately from those lines that have the equation $y = mx + b$.

For all other lines, we can always solve for y and then sketch the line directly by noting its y-intercept and slope.

Example 9 Graph $y = \frac{2}{3}x - 4$.

Solution By inspection, $b = -4$ and $m = \frac{2}{3}$. First, plot the y-intercept $(0, -4)$, as shown in Figure 3.13a.

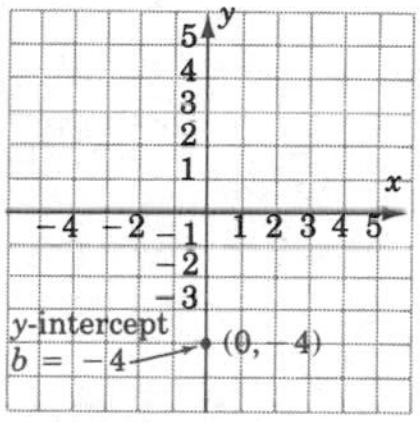

Figure 3.13a
First, Plot the y-Intercept

Starting from this point, plot the slope by writing m as a fraction and remembering that

$$m = \frac{\text{RISE}}{\text{RUN}}$$

This is shown in Figure 3.13b.

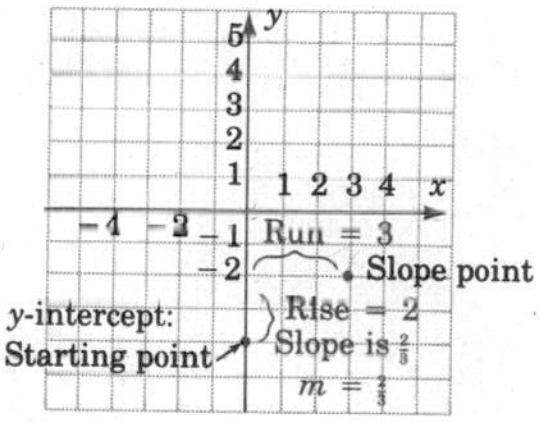

Figure 3.13b
Next, Count Out the Rise and Run to Find a Second Point, Called the *Slope Point*

Finally, draw the line passing through the two points—the y-intercept and the point found from the slope (see Figure 3.13c).

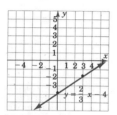

Figure 3.13c
Draw the Line Passing Through the Points

Here's a summary of the procedure illustrated by Example 9.

To Graph a Line Using the Slope–Intercept Method:

Step 1. Is there a y term? If not, then it is a vertical line; solve for x.

Step 2. Solve for y; by inspection determine the values for m and b.

Step 3. Plot the y-intercept, b.

Step 4. Plot the slope, m. *Start* at the y-intercept and write the slope as a fraction; recall that

$$m = \frac{\text{RISE}}{\text{RUN}}$$

Plot the point by counting out the rise and the run.

Step 5. Draw the line passing through the y-intercept and the point plotted from the slope.

PROCEDURE FOR
GRAPHING
A LINE:

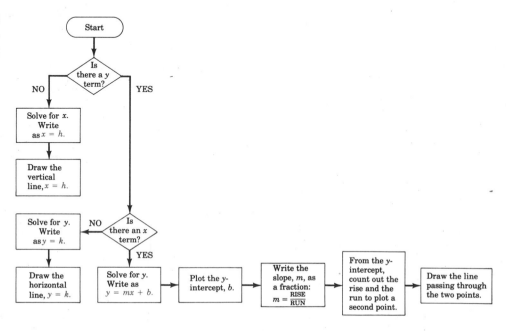

In Examples 10–13 plot each line using the slope–intercept method.

Example 10 $y = -\dfrac{2}{3}x + 3$

Solution   Notice that $b = 3$ and $m = -\frac{2}{3}$. The graph is shown in Figure 3.14. Notice that

$$m = -\frac{2}{3} = \frac{-2}{3} = \frac{2}{-3}$$

The result should be the same if we use

$$\frac{\text{DOWN 2: } (-2)}{\text{OVER 3: } (+3)} \quad \text{or} \quad \frac{\text{UP 2: } (+2)}{\text{BACK 3: } (-3)}$$

a vertical line doesn't have a slope or y intercept

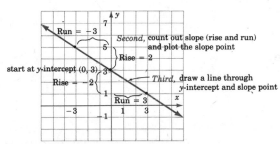

Figure 3.14   Graph of $y = -\frac{2}{3}x + 3$

Notice also that the x and y scales are the same. If the scales are the same, you can count *units* or *squares* when finding the slope point. Notice in Figure 3.14 that

$$\frac{\text{RISE}}{\text{RUN}} = \frac{2 \text{ units}}{-3 \text{ units}} = \frac{2 \text{ squares}}{-3 \text{ squares}} \qquad \square$$

Example 11 $y = 4x - 7$

Solution   Notice that $b = -7$ and $m = 4 = \frac{4}{1}$. The graph is shown in Figure 3.15. Notice from the graph that

$$\frac{\text{RISE}}{\text{RUN}} = \frac{-4}{-1} \quad \text{is the same as} \quad \frac{\text{RISE}}{\text{RUN}} = \frac{4}{1}$$

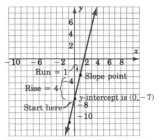

Figure 3.15   Graph of $y = 4x - 7$

What happens if you write the slope as shown below?

$$m = 4 = \frac{8}{2} = \frac{\text{RISE}}{\text{RUN}}$$

Will you obtain the same line if you use RISE $= 8$ and RUN $= 2$ for the slope?

□

Example 12 $x + 2y = 1$

Solution   First, solve for y:

$$2y = -x + 1$$

$$y = -\frac{1}{2}x + \frac{1}{2}$$

Notice that $b = \frac{1}{2}$ and $m = -\frac{1}{2}$. Don't let the fraction bother you; just change the scale, as shown in Figure 3.16. Notice that the rise is -1 unit and the run is 2 units. What happens if you count out a rise of -1 square ($-\frac{1}{2}$ unit) and a run of 2 squares (1 unit)? Will you obtain the same line?

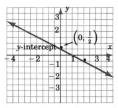

Figure 3.16   Graph of $x + 2y = 1$ □

Example 13 $3y - 6 = 0$

Solution   Solve for y:

$$3y = 6$$

$$y = 2$$

This can be written in the form

$y = mx + b$

as

$y = (0)x + 2$

Notice that $b = 2$ and $m = 0$. This equation makes a horizontal line, as shown in Figure 3.17.

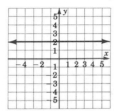

Figure 3.17 Graph of $3y - 6 = 0$ ☐

From Example 13, you can see that *horizontal lines have zero slope*. We've also seen that vertical lines don't have any slope at all; that is, the slope of a vertical line is undefined. You must be careful to make a distinction between a line that has *undefined slope* (a vertical line) and a line that has *zero slope* (a horizontal line).

HORIZONTAL LINES

Horizontal lines have the form

$y =$ Constant

and have zero slope.

VERTICAL LINES

Vertical lines have the form

$x =$ Constant

and have undefined slope.

Problem Set 3.3

A *In Problems 1–21 find the slope and y-intercept, if possible.*

See Examples 1–6.

1. $y = 2x - 3$
2. $y = -3x + 2$
3. $y = x + 2$
4. $y = x - 5$
5. $2x + y = 5$
6. $x + 2y = 8$
7. $2x + 3y = 4$
8. $4x - 3y = 6$
9. $2x + 3y = 600$
10. $x - 3y = 1,200$
11. $x + y + 3 = 0$
12. $x - y + 6 = 0$

13. $2x + 3y - 4 = 0$ 14. $x - 4y - 5 = 0$ 15. $x + 3y + 2 = 0$
16. $y = -3$ 17. $y = -2$ 18. $x = 1$
19. $x = 4$ 20. $y = 0$ 21. $x = 10$

Find the slope of the line passing through the points given in Problems 22–30.

See Examples 7 and 8.   22. $(1, 2), (3, 4)$ 23. $(4, 1), (3, 5)$ 24. $(4, 5), (8, 7)$
25. $(5, 4), (2, 1)$ 26. $(4, 3), (-8, 2)$ 27. $(1, -3), (2, -8)$
28. $(3, 5), (3, 9)$ 29. $(6, -2), (5, -2)$ 30. $(10, 200), (1, 2,200)$

Graph the lines in Problems 31–42 using the slope–intercept method.

See Examples 9–11.   31. $y = \dfrac{2}{3}x + 3$ 32. $y = \dfrac{1}{4}x - 2$ 33. $y = \dfrac{1}{2}x + 1$

34. $y = \dfrac{2}{5}x - 3$ 35. $y = -\dfrac{3}{4}x + 1$ 36. $y = -\dfrac{2}{5}x + 5$

37. $y = -\dfrac{2}{3}x - 3$ 38. $y = 3x - 1$ 39. $y = 3x + 3$

40. $y = -2x + 5$ 41. $y = -3x - 2$ 42. $y = -x - 1$

B   *Graph the lines in Problems 43–60 using the slope–intercept method.*

See Examples 12 and 13.
43. $2x + y = 3$ 44. $3x + y = -2$ 45. $x - y + 1 = 0$
46. $x + y - 1 = 0$ 47. $x + y + 3 = 0$ 48. $2x + 3y + 6 = 0$
49. $x - 3y + 2 = 0$ 50. $5x - 4y - 8 = 0$ 51. $5x - y = 0$
52. $4x + y = 0$ 53. $y + 1 = 0$ 54. $2y + 8 = 0$
55. $3y - 4 = 0$ 56. $2y + 3 = 0$ 57. $x + 1 = 0$
58. $x - 4 = 0$ 59. $2x - 5 = 0$ 60. $3x + 2 = 0$

Mind Bogglers   61. a. Graph $y = -\frac{3}{2}x + 4$.
   b. Draw any line that is parallel to the line you have drawn in part a.
   c. Find the equation of the line from part b in slope–intercept form.
   d. Repeat parts b and c for another line.
   e. Make a conjecture concerning the slopes of parallel lines.

62. a. Graph $y = -\frac{3}{4}x + 2$.
   b. Draw any line that is perpendicular to the line you have drawn in part a.
   c. Find the equation of the line from part b in slope–intercept form.
   d. Repeat parts b and c for another line.
   e. Make a conjecture concerning the slopes of perpendicular lines.

3.4 Equations of Lines

Now, suppose you are given a graph (or information about a graph) and you need to write an equation.

In Examples 1 and 2 find the equation of the line, and write your answer in standard form.

Example 1   *y*-intercept 3 and slope 4

Solution   We use $y = mx + b$ and note that $b = 3$ and $m = 4$, so

$$y = 4x + 3$$

To put this into standard form, subtract *y* from both sides:

$$4x - y + 3 = 0$$

Recall the standard form:
$Ax + By + C = 0$ □

Example 2   *y*-intercept −7 and slope $\frac{2}{3}$

Solution   We have $b = -7$ and $m = \frac{2}{3}$, so

$$y = \frac{2}{3}x - 7$$

Multiply both sides by 3:

$$3y = 2x - 21$$
$$2x - 3y - 21 = 0$$

If *A*, *B*, or *C* is a fraction, we usually multiply both sides by the denominator to eliminate fractions from the standard form of the equation. Also, if *A* is negative, we multiply both sides by (−1).   □

Instead of the *y*-intercept, suppose you are given any point (h, k) on the line and the slope, *m*. Then the equation

$$y = mx + b$$

is satisfied by the point (h, k):

Remember, if *any* point on the line is chosen, then the equation is satisfied.

$$k = mh + b$$

Solve for *b* (the unknown):

$$b = k - mh$$

Substitute into the original equation:

$$y = mx + (k - mh)$$
$$y - k = mx - mh$$
$$y - k = m(x - h)$$

This is called the **point–slope form** of the equation of a line.

POINT–SLOPE FORM
OF THE EQUATION
OF A LINE

Point–Slope Form of the Equation of a Line

$$y - k = m(x - h)$$

where (h, k) is a point on the line with slope *m*

In Examples 3 and 4 find the equation in standard form for each line.

Example 3   Passing through $(6, -3)$ with slope $-\frac{1}{2}$

Solution   Notice that $m = -\frac{1}{2}$, $h = 6$, and $k = -3$. Substitute into the point-slope form:

$$y - (-3) = -\frac{1}{2}(x - 6) \qquad \text{This is the equation. Now, put it into standard form.}$$

$$y + 3 = -\frac{1}{2}(x - 6)$$

$$2(y + 3) = -1(x - 6)$$
$$2y + 6 = -x + 6$$
$$x + 2y + 6 = 6$$
$$x + 2y = 0 \qquad\qquad \square$$

Example 4   Passing through $(5, 1)$ and $(-4, 3)$

Solution   First find the slope and then use the point–slope form.

$$m = \frac{3 - 1}{-4 - 5}$$

$$= \frac{2}{-9}$$

$$y - 1 = \frac{2}{-9}(x - 5)$$

$$(-9)(y - 1) = 2(x - 5)$$

$$-9y + 9 = 2x - 10$$

$$2x + 9y - 19 = 0 \qquad\qquad \square$$

Alternate solution   Use the slope $\frac{2}{-9}$ and the other point. We would obtain the same result if we used the point $(-4, 3)$, as shown below.

$$y - 3 = \frac{2}{-9}[x - (-4)]$$

$$(-9)(y - 3) = 2(x + 4)$$

$$-9y + 27 = 2x + 8$$

$$2x + 9y - 19 = 0$$

Table 3.1 summarizes the forms of linear equations used in this book. Study this table until you understand the uses and differences among the standard, slope–intercept, and point–slope forms.

Table 3.1
Summary of Forms of
Linear Equations

Standard Form		
Equation $Ax + By + C = 0$ of line	*Variables* (x, y) is any point on line A, B, C are any constants (A and B not both 0), but usually: A is not negative; A, B, and C are not fractions; and A, B, and ~~C~~ have no common factors	*When Used* Use this form when writing the equation of a line from given information about the graph. You will often be given the equation of a line to graph in this form, but it is *not* the most useful form from which to graph a line.

Slope–Intercept Form		
Equation $y = mx + b$	*Variables* (x, y) is any point on line m is slope b is y-intercept, $(0, b)$	*When Used* Use this form to graph a line. If you are given a linear equation to graph, you will often put it into this form before graphing so you can locate the slope and y-intercept by inspection. This form is also used when writing the equation of a line and you are given the slope and y-intercept.

Point–Slope Form		
Equation $y - k = m(x - h)$	*Variables* (x, y) is any point on line (h, k) is a *known* point on line m is slope	*When Used* Use this form when writing the equation of a line and you are given the slope and one point. This form is also used when you want the equation and are given two points. First find the slope using the two points; then use the slope with *either* of the given points.

Two important geometric properties of a line or line segment are found by looking at their slopes.

PARALLEL LINES

PERPENDICULAR
LINES

Two lines or line segments with slopes m_1 and m_2 are:

Parallel if $m_1 = m_2$

Perpendicular if $m_1 m_2 = -1$ where $m_1, m_2 \neq 0$

Example 5 Show that a line with slope $-\frac{2}{3}$ and another line with slope $1\frac{1}{2}$ are perpendicular lines.

Solution
$$m_1 = \frac{-2}{3} \quad \text{and} \quad m_2 = 1\frac{1}{2} = \frac{3}{2}$$

$$m_1 m_2 = \left(\frac{-2}{3}\right)\left(\frac{3}{2}\right)$$

$$= -1$$

The lines are perpendicular. □

Example 6 Let $A = (2, 3)$, $B = (6, 2)$, $C = (-3, -1)$, and $D = (1, -2)$. Show that line segment AB is parallel to line segment CD.

Solution   Slope of AB: Slope of CD:

$$m_1 = \frac{2 - 3}{6 - 2} \qquad m_2 = \frac{-2 - (-1)}{1 - (-3)}$$

$$= \frac{-1}{4} \qquad\qquad = \frac{-1}{4}$$

Since $m_1 = m_2$, the segments are parallel. □

Example 7 Find the equation of the line parallel to $3x + 4y - 7 = 0$ and passing through $(-2, 5)$.

Solution   First, find the slope of the given line:

$$3x + 4y - 7 = 0$$

$$4y = -3x + 7$$

$$y = -\frac{3}{4}x + \frac{7}{4}$$

The slope is $-\frac{3}{4}$.

Since the line you're looking for is parallel to the given line, its slope is the same; $m = \frac{-3}{4}$. It passes through $(-2, 5)$, so the point–slope form can be used to find the equation of the line:

$$y - k = m(x - h)$$

$$y - 5 = \frac{-3}{4}(x + 2)$$

$$4y - 20 = -3x - 6$$

$$3x + 4y - 14 = 0$$ □

Many relationships and applications are linear, and we'll look at several examples in the problem set at the end of this section. The basic procedure in applying linear equations requires the selection of independent and dependent variables, finding two points from the given information, and then writing the equation from these two points.

Example 8

It is known that the stretch of a spring is linear. Suppose you go to a hardware store and purchase a spring with a maximum length of 9 cm. With no weight, the stretch is 0. By experimenting, you find that if the spring is stretched 3 cm, the weight is 20 kg. Write an equation expressing this relationship, and then use the equation to find the weight if the spring is stretched 6.3 cm. Also, draw the graph of the points (s, w) showing that the maximum stretch is 9 cm.

Solution Write two ordered pairs from the given information: (0, 0) and (3, 20), where s is the stretch of the spring measured in centimeters and w is the weight measured in kilograms. The graph is shown in Figure 3.18.
First, notice that $0 \le s \le 9$.
To write the equation, find the slope:

$$m = \frac{20 - 0}{3 - 0}$$

$$= \frac{20}{3}$$

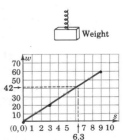

Figure 3.18

Next, use the point (0, 0) and $m = \frac{20}{3}$ in the point–slope form:

$$w - 0 = \frac{20}{3}(s - 0)$$

$$3w = 20s$$

$$20s - 3w = 0$$

If $s = 6.3$, then find w:

$$20(6.3) - 3w = 0$$

$$126 = 3w$$

$$42 = w$$

The weight is 42 kg when the stretch is 6.3 cm. ☐

Problem Set 3.4

A *In Problems 1–24 use the given information to write each equation in standard form and graph each line.*

See Example 1.
1. *y*-intercept 6; slope 5
2. *y*-intercept −2; slope 3

See Example 2.

3. y-intercept -3; slope -2
4. y-intercept -4; slope 4
5. y-intercept 4; slope $\frac{1}{2}$
6. y-intercept 5; slope $\frac{1}{3}$
7. y-intercept -1; slope $\frac{-2}{3}$
8. y-intercept 1; slope $-\frac{4}{5}$
9. y-intercept -2; slope $\frac{4}{5}$
10. y-intercept -1; slope $-\frac{3}{5}$

See Example 3.

11. Slope 2; passing through $(3, 3)$
12. Slope -1; passing through $(7, -2)$
13. Slope $\frac{2}{5}$; passing through $(5, -2)$
14. Slope $-\frac{2}{3}$; passing through $(-1, 5)$
15. Slope $-\frac{4}{5}$; passing through $(5, -1)$
16. Slope $\frac{1}{3}$; passing through $(-3, -2)$
17. Slope $-\frac{2}{3}$; passing through $(-6, -2)$
18. Slope $-\frac{4}{5}$; passing through the origin

See Example 4.

19. Passing through $(2, 3)$ and $(5, 7)$
20. Passing through $(-1, 3)$ and $(5, -5)$
21. Passing through $(-4, -1)$ and $(4, 3)$
22. Passing through $(6, -2)$ and $(-4, -3)$
23. Passing through $(-4, -1)$ and $(-3, -1)$
24. Passing through $(-5, -1)$ and $(-6, -5)$

In Problems 25–34 determine whether the lines with the given slopes are parallel, perpendicular, or neither.

See Examples 5 and 6.

25. $m_1 = \frac{4}{5}$; $m_2 = \frac{5}{4}$ **26.** $m_1 = \frac{-3}{2}$; $m_2 = \frac{2}{3}$
27. $m_1 = 2\frac{1}{2}$; $m_2 = \frac{5}{2}$ **28.** $m_1 = \frac{4}{8}$; $m_2 = \frac{1}{2}$
29. $m_1 = -1\frac{2}{3}$; $m_2 = \frac{3}{5}$ **30.** $m_1 = 3$; $m_2 = \frac{1}{3}$

31. m_1 is the slope of line segment AB and m_2 is the slope of line segment CD, where $A = (-1, 2)$, $B = (4, -1)$, $C = (-6, 4)$, and $D = (-1, 1)$
32. m_1 is the slope of line segment AB and m_2 is the slope of line segment CD, where $A = (3, 4)$, $B = (-1, 8)$, $C = (-3, 2)$, and $D = (0, 5)$
33. m_1 is the slope of line segment AB and m_2 is the slope of line segment CD, where $A = (5, 1)$, $B = (-3, 2)$, $C = (-3, 4)$, and $D = (-2, 12)$
34. m_1 is the slope of line segment AB and m_2 is the slope of line segment CD, where $A = (-5, 0)$, $B = (0, 3)$, $C = (2, 3)$, and $D = (7, 6)$

B *In Problems 35–48 write each equation in standard form and graph each line.*

See Examples 1–4.

35. y-intercept $\frac{4}{5}$; slope $-\frac{2}{5}$
36. y-intercept $-\frac{3}{4}$; slope $-\frac{1}{2}$
37. Passing through $(6, 4)$ and $(-1, 4)$
38. Passing through $(-2, -3)$ and $(-2, 5)$

$Y = 4$

39. *y*-intercept 4;   slope 0
40. *y*-intercept 0; slope 0
41. Slope undefined;   passing through the origin
42. Zero slope; passing through the origin

See Example 7.

43. Passing through $(4, 5)$;   parallel to $2x + y + 4 = 0$
44. Passing through $(-6, 2)$;   parallel to $3x - 2y - 5 = 0$
45. Passing through $(4, -3)$;   parallel to $x - 3y + 4 = 0$
46. Passing through $(-1, 4)$;   perpendicular to $x - 2y + 10 = 0$
47. Passing through $(1, 2)$;   perpendicular to $4x - 2y + 5 = 0$
48. Passing through $(-2, -3)$;   perpendicular to $3x - 5y - 2 = 0$

See Example 8; assume that no weight causes no stretch

49. *Physics.*   If a 10 kg weight stretches a certain spring 2 cm, write an equation expressing this relationship and then use the equation to find the weight of an object that stretches the spring 3.6 cm. Also, draw the graph of the points (s, w) if the maximum stretch is 10 cm.

THINK METRIC

50. *Physics.*   If a 250 kg weight stretches a certain spring 15 cm, write an equation expressing this relationship and then use the equation to find the weight of an object that stretches the spring 8.4 cm. Also, draw the graph of the points (s, w) if the maximum stretch is 21 cm.

51. *Sociology.*   The population of New York State in 1960 was roughly 16.8 million, and in 1970 it was about 18.2 million. Assuming that the increase continues linearly, write an equation relating population numbers and dates. Assume that the base year is 1950 ($x = 0$ represents 1950), as indicated in the graph shown in Figure 3.19.

Increases linearly means that the graph of the equation you are looking for is a line. Remember that this is a simplifying assumption.

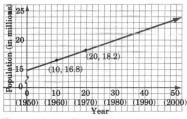

Figure 3.19 Population of New York State from 1950 to 2000

52. *Sociology.*   Use the results of Problem 51 to estimate the population of New York in 1990 and 2000.

53. *Business.*   The demand for a certain product is related to the price of that item. Suppose a new line of stationery is tested at two stores. It is found that 25 boxes are sold within a month if they are priced at $1.25, and 15 boxes priced at $2.00 are sold in the same time. Assuming that the demand is linear, write an equation expressing this relationship for p (the price), where $0 \le p \le 3$. Let n (the demand) be the dependent variable. Also, draw the graph.

Demand is linear means that the graph of the equation you are looking for is a line.

54. *Business.* An important factor that is related to the demand for a product is the supply. The amount of stationery in Problem 53 that can be supplied is also related to the price. At \$1.00 each, 15 boxes can be supplied; at \$2.00, 25 boxes can be supplied. Assuming that the supply is linear, write an equation expressing this relationship for p (the price), where $0 \le p \le 3$. Let n (the supply) be the dependent variable. Also, draw the graph.

55. In the last section we applied the formula

$$m = \frac{\text{RISE}}{\text{RUN}}$$

by saying that if the slope is $\frac{2}{3}$, then RISE $= 2$ and RUN $= 3$. In the equation

$$\frac{y}{x} = \frac{2}{3}$$

must it be true that $y = 2$ and $x = 3$? Explain your answer. Graph the relationship

$$\frac{y}{x} = \frac{2}{3}$$

Mind Boggler

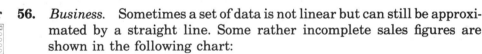

56. *Business.* Sometimes a set of data is not linear but can still be approximated by a straight line. Some rather incomplete sales figures are shown in the following chart:

Year	Sales (in thousands of dollars)
1965	160
1966	310
1975	220
1978	360
1980	450

Making 1950 the base year (that is, $1950 = 0$ years, $1965 = 15$ years, $1966 = 16$ years, and so on), plot these points on a coordinate system. The line that passes through $(12, 173)$ and $(28, 361)$ is called the *best-fitting line*. This is the line that "fits" the given points better than any other line that could be drawn. Write the equation of this line. Use the equation you've found to predict the sales in 1985, 1990, and 1995.

3.5 Linear Inequalities

We'll now extend the notion of a first-degree equation in two variables to include inequalities. A first-degree equation in two variables has a solution set that can be graphed as a line, and any line divides the plane into three parts. These parts are shown in Figure 3.20; they are the **half-planes** labeled I and II and the line itself, called the **boundary line.** The half-plane is called **closed** if the boundary line is included and **open** if it is not.

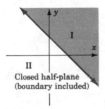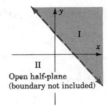

Closed half-plane
(boundary included)

Open half-plane
(boundary not included)

Figure 3.20 Half-Planes

Example 1 Graph the linear inequality

$$2x + 3y \leq 12$$

Solution Every linear inequality in two variables determines an associated linear equation that will form the boundary for the solution set of the inequality. This means that $2x + 3y \leq 12$ has the boundary line

$$2x + 3y = 12$$

Begin by graphing the boundary line. Solve for y: $y = -\frac{2}{3}x + 4$. So the y-intercept is $(0, 4)$ and the slope is $\frac{-2}{3}$. The graph of the boundary line is shown in Figure 3.21a.

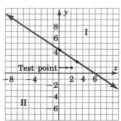

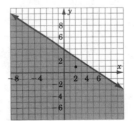

Figure 3.21a Graph of $2x + 3y = 12$ **Figure 3.21b** Graph of $2x + 3y \leq 12$

Next, decide whether the solution set is half-plane I or half-plane II. If one point in half-plane I makes the given inequality true, then all points in I will make it true. Conversely, if one point in half-plane I makes the given inequality false, then all points in half-plane I will make it false, and the solution is half-plane II. You can therefore choose *any* point not on the boundary line as a test point. For example, choose (2, 1).

Given: $2x + 3y \leq 12$
Test: $2(2) + 3(1) \leq 12$
$4 + 3 \leq 12$
$7 \leq 12$

True—the solution set is half-plane II.

The choice of (2, 1) was arbitrary. *Any* other point in half-plane II would have worked the same way, as shown below.

Test point: **(−4, −3)**   Test point: **(0, 0)**
Given: $2x + 3y \leq 12$ Given: $2x + 3y \leq 12$
Test: $2(-4) + 3(-3) \leq 12$ Test: $2(0) + 3(0) \leq 12$
$-8 + (-9) \leq 12$ $0 \leq 12$
$-17 \leq 12$ True
True

Notice that the arithmetic is easiest for the test point (0, 0). For this reason, if (0, 0) is not on the boundary, it is usually the point chosen as the test point. On the other hand, *any* point in half-plane I also can serve as a test point.

Test point: **(4, 5)**   Test point: **(1, 8)**
Given: $2x + 3y \leq 12$ Given: $2x + 3y \leq 12$
Test: $2(4) + 3(5) \leq 12$ Test: $2(1) + 3(8) \leq 12$
$8 + 15 \leq 12$ $2 + 24 \leq 12$
$23 \leq 12$ $26 \leq 12$
Not true   Not true

In this case, the test points chosen from half-plane I do not satisfy the given inequality, so the solution is the other half-plane, namely half-plane II. In any case, it is necessary for you to choose only one test point to determine the appropriate half-plane. For this example, half-plane II is the solution set and it is the shaded area shown in Figure 3.21b.   □

Notice that the solution set for Example 1 is the *closed* half-plane, since it *includes the boundary.* This is shown on the graph by using a solid line for the boundary. If the boundary is not included (when the inequality symbols are strictly < or >), then a dotted line is used to indicate the boundary.

Example 2   Graph: $150x - 75y < 1,875$

Solution   Graph the boundary line as a dotted line, since we're given a "strictly less than" relationship.

Boundary: $150x - 75y = 1{,}875$
$$-75y = -150x + 1{,}875$$
$$y = 2x - 25$$

Plot this line as shown in Figure 3.22. Choose some point not on the boundary, say $(0, 0)$, and substitute the coordinates of this point into the given *inequality:*

$$150(0) - 75(0) < 1{,}875$$

This is *true,* so the solution set is in the same half-plane as $(0, 0)$, as shown in Figure 3.22.

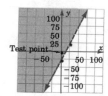

Figure 3.22   Graph of $150x - 75y < 1{,}875$

Let's summarize the procedure used in the preceding example.

PROCEDURE FOR
GRAPHING LINEAR
INEQUALITIES
WITH TWO
UNKNOWNS

The graph of a linear
inequality gives the
solution set.

To Graph a Linear Inequality

Step 1. Replace the inequality symbol with an equality symbol to find the boundary.

Step 2. Graph the line. If the inequality symbol is $\leq$ or $\geq$, draw a solid line (it is included in the solution set); if the inequality symbol is $<$ or $>$, draw a dotted line (it is not included in the solution set).

Step 3. Choose any point in the plane not on the line (the origin is a good choice when it is not on the boundary line).

Step 4. If the chosen point satisfies the given inequality, shade in that half-plane for the solution; if it does not satisfy the inequality, shade in the other half-plane for the solution.

In Examples 3–5 graph the linear inequalities.

Example 3 $y \geq 4$

Solution   Boundary: $y = 4$
Horizontal line; solid

Test $(0, 0)$: $0 \geq 4$
False; shade the other half-plane

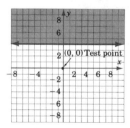

Figure 3.23   Graph of $y \geq 4$

Example 4 $x < -1$

Solution   Boundary: $x = -1$
This is parallel to the y-axis; dotted
Test $(0, 0)$: $0 < -1$
False; shade the other half-plane

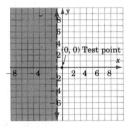

Figure 3.24   Graph of $x < -1$

Example 5 $x < y$

Solution   Boundary: $x = y$
Intercept 0, slope 1; dotted
Test $(2, 1)$: $2 < 1$
False; shade the other half-plane
Note that you can't choose $(0, 0)$ for this example, because $(0, 0)$ is on the boundary.

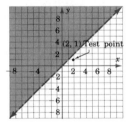

Figure 3.25   Graph of $x < y$

Problem Set 3.5

A *Graph the solution set of the inequalities in Problems 1–16.*

See Example 1.
1. $x + y \geq 2$
2. $x + y \leq 4$
3. $x - y < 3$
4. $x - y > 1$
5. $x - y \geq 6$
6. $x + y < 8$
7. $x + y \leq 9$
8. $x - y \leq 3$

See Example 2.
9. $x \geq 1$
10. $y \geq 2$
11. $x < 3$
12. $y > -4$
13. $x \geq 0$
14. $y \geq 0$
15. $x > y$
16. $x \leq y$

B *Graph the solution set of the inequalities in Problems 17–30.*

See Examples 1–3.
17. $2x - 3y \geq -6$
18. $2x - 7y > 14$
19. $3x + 2y < 6$
20. $3x - 2y > 10$
21. $x - 3y < 9$
22. $2x + 3y \geq 6$
23. $2x + y + 4 < 0$
24. $x + 2y - 3 \geq 0$
25. $x - 3y < 7$
26. $2x - 3y < 11$
27. $4x - 3y > 5$
28. $x + 2y \leq -3$
29. $260x - 1,040y > 11,250$
30. $.06x - .05y < 10,000$

3.6 Review Problems

Fill in the word or words to make the statements in Problems 1–5 complete and correct.

(3.1) 1. The variable associated with the first component of an ordered pair is called the _____ variable, and the variable associated with the second component is called the _____ variable.

(3.2) 2. The standard form of the equation of a line is _____ .

(3.3) 3. The place where a graph crosses the y-axis is called a _____ .

(3.5) 4. A line divides the plane into three parts; two _____ and the _____ .

(3.5) 5. A half-plane is said to be _____ if the boundary line is included and _____ if it is not.

Graph the solution set of each relationship given in Problems 6–14.

(3.3) 6. $2x + y = 5$
7. $3x - 2y = 1$
8. $y = \frac{2}{3}x + 4$
(3.5) 9. $4x + 3y > 12$
10. $x + 1 \geq y$
11. $x < 3$
(3.5) 12. $y + 2 \geq 0$
13. $x + 3y \leq 6$
(3.2) 14. $y - 2x = -1$ where $-2 \leq x < 4$

Find the equations in standard form of the lines described in Problems 15–19.

(3.4) 15. y-intercept -3; slope $\frac{2}{3}$

(3.4) **16.** Slope $-\frac{3}{2}$ and passing through $(-5, -3)$

(3.4) **17.** Passing through $(-5, -3)$ with undefined slope

(3.4) **18.** Passing through $(6, -1)$ and $(-2, 4)$

(3.4) **19.** y-intercept -3 and passing through $(2, -1)$

(3.5) **20.** *Business.* A manufacturer of calculator chips conducts a market survey and finds that if they sell a certain chip for \$1 they can sell 20,000, but if they sell the chip for \$7 they can sell only 2,000. Assuming that sales are linear, write an equation relating the independent variable, p (price), with the dependent variable, n (number of items). Graph this relationship for positive n and p.

CHAPTER

4

Polynomials and Factoring

Contents

4.1 Polynomials

Two numbers are multiplied to form a **product.** Each number is called a **factor** of the product. We will multiply polynomials to obtain another polynomial. Given a polynomial product, we'll attempt to obtain its factors by a process called **factoring.** Factoring is a valuable process with many applications.

First, several ideas should be reviewed. Recall that a **term** is an algebraic expression with multiplication only. A term, or the sum of two or more terms, is called a **polynomial.** Since polynomials may have a single term or many terms, it is standard practice to refer to a polynomial by the number of terms it contains. A polynomial with a single term is called a **monomial.** One with two terms is called a **binomial,** and one with three terms is a **trinomial.** Polynomials with still more terms could be named *quadnomial, pentanomial,* and so on, but these words are not commonly used.

Polynomials are often identified by the number of terms, but there are other ways to identify or classify polynomials. In the last chapter, you solved first-degree equations. The **degree of a term** is the exponent of the variable or the sum of the exponents of the variables if there are more than one. The **degree of a polynomial** is the degree of its highest-degree term. A nonzero constant has **degree 0.**

In Examples 1–6 name each polynomial by number of terms and degree.

Example 1 $x + 3$ Binomial, degree 1   □

Example 2 $x^2 - 3x + 4$ Trinomial, degree 2   □

Example 3 $x^4 - 2x$ Binomial, degree 4   □

Example 4 $a^2b - bc^3 + a^2c^3$ Trinomial, degree 5 a^2c^3 is degree 5, since $2 + 3 = 5$ □

Example 5 $5r^2t'$ Monomial, degree 3   □

Example 6 5   Monomial, degree 0   □

In Example 4 above, the term a^2b is third degree. It can also be described as second degree *in a* and first degree *in b.* Thus, a^2c^3 is a fifth-degree term *in a and c,* or second degree *in a* and third degree *in c.* A first-degree term is sometimes called **linear,** and a second-degree term is often called **quadratic.**

In Examples 7–9 describe the polynomial, its degree, and its variables.

Example 7 x^2y^3z Sixth-degree monomial in x, y, and z; second degree in x, third degree in y, and first degree in z □

Example 8 $r^3 + 2r^2 - 5$ Third-degree trinomial in r (implies that r is the only variable)   □

Example 9 $h^5k + 2hk^3 - h^2k^2$ Sixth-degree trinomial in h and k; fifth degree in h and third degree in k □

This classification process may be made complete by further specifying the coefficients and the domain of the variables. A **real polynomial** is a polynomial with coefficients that are restricted to real numbers. If the coefficients are restricted to some subset of the real numbers, then it is a real polynomial *over* that set. For example, if the coefficients must be integers, we refer to the polynomial **over the integers.**

In Examples 10–12 describe the polynomial completely.

Example 10 $x^2 + 3x - 2$ Second-degree trinomial in x over the integers   □

Example 11 $\frac{1}{4}x^2y - \frac{1}{2}xy$ Third-degree binomial in x and y over the rationals   □

Example 12 $x + 3y - \sqrt{2}$ First-degree trinomial in x and y over the reals   □

Exponents and Powers

The degree of a polynomial depends on the exponents, so consider the basic properties of exponents.

EXPONENT
BASE

$$b^x = \overbrace{b \cdot b \cdot b \cdot b \cdot \dots \cdot b}^{x \text{ factors}} \qquad \text{for } x \text{ a positive integer}$$

The **exponent** is the number of times the **base** is used as a factor.

If $b^x = a$, then x is the exponent, b is the base, and a is called the **power.** For example, 8 is the third power of 2, since $2^3 = 8$; that is, 8 is the power, 3 is the exponent, and 2 is the base.

Consider that $2^3 \cdot 2^4 = 8 \cdot 16 = 128 = 2^7$ or $3^2 \cdot 3^3 = 9 \cdot 27 = 243 = 3^5$. When you *multiply powers* of the same base, you *add exponents.*

FIRST LAW OF
EXPONENTS

First Law of Exponents

$b^x b^y = b^{x+y}$ To multiply powers of the same base, add the exponents.

In the same way, consider $8^2 = (2^3)^2$, but $8^2 = 64 = 2^6$. Thus, $(2^3)^2 = 2^6$. To raise a power to a power, *multiply the exponents.*

Second Law of Exponents

$(b^x)^y = b^{xy}$ To raise a power to a power, multiply the exponents.

A third law is needed to raise products to powers. For example, consider $(2 \cdot 3)^2 = 6^2 = 36$, which may also be written as $36 = 4 \cdot 9 = 2^2 \cdot 3^2$. Thus, $(2 \cdot 3)^2 = 2^2 \cdot 3^2$. We can state this third law generally:

$$\overbrace{(a \cdot b)^x = (a \cdot b) \cdot (a \cdot b) \cdot \cdots \cdot (a \cdot b)}^{x \text{ factors of } a \cdot b} \qquad \text{By definition}$$

$$= \underbrace{a \cdot a \cdot a \cdot a \cdots \cdot a}_{x \text{ factors of } a} \cdot \underbrace{b \cdot b \cdot b \cdot b \cdots \cdot b}_{x \text{ factors of } b} \qquad \text{By rearranging}$$

$$= a^x b^x \qquad \text{By definition}$$

Third Law of Exponents

$(ab)^x = a^x b^x$ To raise a product to a power, raise each factor to that power.

In Examples 13–16 simplify each expression.

Example 13 $(xy)^2 = x^2 y^2$ □

Example 14 $(a^2 b^3)^2 = (a^2)^2 (b^3)^2$
                              $= a^4 b^6$ □

Example 15 $(-x^2)^3 = (-x^2)(-x^2)(-x^2)$ Recall that $(-x)^2 \neq -x^2$.
                              $= -x^6$

or $(-x^2)^3 = [(-1)(x^2)]^3$
                $= (-1)^3 (x^2)^3$
                $= (-1)(x^6)$
                $= -x^6$ □

Example 16 $-(x^2)^3 = -(x^6)$
                              $= -x^6$ □

Note the distinction between quantities like -5^2 and $(-5)^2$, -4^3 and $(-4)^3$, or $(-2x^3)^2$ and $-(2x^3)^2$.

Example 17 Simplify.

a. $-5^2 = -(5 \cdot 5)$
   $= -25$

b. $(-5)^2 = (-5)(-5)$
   $= 25$

c. $-4^3 = -(4 \cdot 4 \cdot 4)$
   $= -64$

d. $(-4)^3 = (-4)(-4)(-4)$
   $= (-4)(16)$
   $= -64$

e. $(-3)^3 = (-3)(-3)(-3)$
   $= -27$

f. $-3^3 = -(3 \cdot 3 \cdot 3)$
   $= -27$

g. $(-2)^4 = (-2)(-2)(-2)(-2)$
   $= 16$

h. $-2^4 = -(2 \cdot 2 \cdot 2 \cdot 2)$
   $= -16$

Do you see the pattern in Example 17? You must be careful to distinguish raising a negative number to a power from taking the opposite of a power. Remember, the exponent does not include the negative sign unless it is enclosed in parentheses. That is, $(-x)^2 = (-x)(-x) = x^2$, but $-x^2 = -(x \cdot x)$.

Example 18 Simplify.

a. $-(2x^3)^2 = -(2)^2(x^3)^2$
   $= -(4)(x^6)$
   $= -4x^6$

b. $(-2x^3)^2 = (-2)^2(x^3)^2$
   $= (4)(x^6)$
   $= 4x^6$

c. $(-3x^4)(5x^2) = (-3)(5)(x^4)(x^2)$
   $= -15x^6$

d. $(-2r^2s^3t)^3 = (-2)^3(r^2)^3(s^3)^3(t)^3$
   $= -8r^6s^9t^3$

e. $-7x(-x^2)(2xy)^3 = -7x(-1)(x^2)(2^3)(x^3)(y^3)$
   $= (-7)(-1)(8)(x)(x^2)(x^3)(y^3)$
   $= 56x^6y^3$

f. $x^ax^bx = x^ax^bx^1$
   $= x^{a+b+1}$

g. $(x^a)^2(x^b)(x^3) = (x^{2a})(x^b)(x^3)$
   $= x^{2a+b+3}$

Problem Set 4.1

A *Write each of the expressions given in Problems 1–10 using exponents.*

See Definition.

1. $xxxxxx$
2. $yyyyy$
3. $xxyyyyyy$
4. $xxxxyyyyyy$
5. $2abbb$
6. $5aabb$

7. $3rrr - ssss$ **8.** $rrs + 2rss$

9. $-hhkkk - 7hkk$ **10.** $-5mmn + 3mnnnn$

Simplify the expressions in Problems 11–40 using the first three laws of exponents.

See Examples 13–17.

11. -7^2 **12.** $(-7)^2$

13. $(-3)^4$ **14.** -3^4

15. -2^3 **16.** $(-2)^3$

17. $-3(-2)^2$ **18.** $[(-3)(-2)]^2$

See Example 18.

19. $(-3y)^2$ **20.** $-(3y)^2$

21. $-x^2$ **22.** $(-x)^2$

23. $(-2y)^3$ **24.** $-(2y)^3$

25. z^2z^3 **26.** $(z^2)^3$

27. x^5x^2 **28.** y^3y^4

29. $(-y)^2(y^3)$ **30.** $-(-y)^3(y^2)$

31. $z^2(-z^3)^2$ **32.** $z^3(-z^2)^3$

33. $u^2(u^3v^2)$ **34.** $v^3(v^2u^3)$

35. $-(2z)(3z^2)$ **36.** $(5z)(-7z^3)$

37. $(x^2)^4(x^2)$ **38.** $(x^3)^2x^4$

39. $(2xy^2)(3x^3y)$ **40.** $(5x^2y^2)(9x^3y^3)$

See Examples 1–12.

Problems 41–54 give descriptions of polynomials. In each case, choose a polynomial that fits the decription from the list at the right and indicate your choice by the corresponding capital letter.

41.   Real polynomial in x and y that is third degree in y ✓

42.   Third-degree polynomial in x and y that is second degree in x I

43.   Quadratic binomial in x and y G

44.   Quadratic trinomial in x over the rationals

45.   Second-degree polynomial over the integers D

46.   Monomial that is second degree in x

47.   Linear monomial in x

48.   Zero-degree polynomial

49.   Linear binomial in x over the integers

50.   Linear polynomial in x and y

51.   Second-degree monomial in x and y

52.   Third-degree polynomial in x and y over the integers

53.   Fifth-degree polynomial that contains a third-degree term

54.   Fifth-degree polynomial that contains no linear term

A. $\frac{1}{2}$

B. $2x$

D. $\frac{1}{2}xy$

E. $2x^2y^2$ — 4th degree

F. $x + 2$

G. $\frac{1}{2}x^2 - \frac{1}{4}y^2$

I. $x^2y - \frac{1}{2}$

L. $x + y - \sqrt{2}$

N. $x^2 - \frac{1}{2}x + \frac{1}{4}$

R. $x^3 + y^2 - 2y$

S. $y^2 - 2y - 1$

T. $x^3y^2 + \frac{1}{3}x^3 - 3y$

V. $x^5 + 5xy^3 + y$

Y. $x^3y^2 + y^2x^2 - y^2$

B *Simplify each expression in Problems 55–70.*

See Example 18.

55. $(-3x)^2(-2xy)^3$ **56.** $(-xy)^3(-2x)^4$
57. $-(a^2b)(a^3b^2)(ab)$ **58.** $(-pq^2)(p^2q^3)(-p^3q^2)$
59. $(h^2k)^2(h^3k^2)$ **60.** $(ij^2)^3(i^3j^2)$
61. $-2x(-x^2y)(3xy)^2$ **62.** $-5y(xy^2)(-2x^2y)^3$
63. $y^2z(xyz^2)^3x^2y$ **64.** $(x^2y)(y^2z)^3xz^2$
65. $x^ax^bx^3$ **66.** $y^my^ny^2$
67. $(2x^n)(x^n)(-x)^2$ **68.** $(3x^m)(-x)^3(x^m)$
69. $(x^a)^b(x^c)(-x)^3$ **70.** $(x^r)^s(x^t)^2x$

$z^2 \cdot z^2 \cdot z^2 \cdots$

Mind Bogglers **71.** Use Problems 41–54 to complete the following algebra adage. Replace each number in parentheses by the capital letter that corresponds to the number clue.

Algebra Adage

(51)(42)(41)(46)(52)(45)(42)(53)(54)   (43)(42)(41)(46)(45)

(49)(50)(48)(41)(O)(52)   (53)(O)   (47)(46)(42)(44)(43).

72. Now that you have discovered the algebra adage in Problem 71, rephrase it as the common proverb it disguises.

73. There is a four-digit integer, N, with successive digits a, b, c, and d. This integer N is an interesting and powerful number, since $N = a^bc^d$. It contains no digit that is 0 or 1. What is N?

4.2 Operating with Polynomials

The distributive property is the key to products of polynomials. First, consider the product of a monomial and a binomial:

$$xy(2x+3y) = xy \cdot 2x + xy \cdot 3y$$
$$= 2xxy + 3xyy$$
$$= 2x^2y + 3xy^2$$

Recall that $a(b+c) = ab + ac$, where a is distributed over the sum $b+c$.

Now, let both factors be binomials and observe how the distributive property is used to find the product of two binomials:

$$(x+2)(x+3) = (x+2)(x) + (x+2)(3)$$
$$= x^2 + 2x + 3x + 6$$
$$= x^2 + 5x + 6$$

Now, multiply a binomial by a trinomial:

$$(x+2)(x^2-3x+2) = (x+2)x^2 + (x+2)(-3x) + (x+2)2$$
$$= x^3 + 2x^2 - 3x^2 - 6x + 2x + 4$$
$$= x^3 - x^2 - 4x + 4$$

Here, the factor $x + 2$ was distributed over the three terms of the trinomial. As you can see, it's possible to multiply any two polynomials by applying the distributive property. The following examples give several possibilities.

Example 1 $2x(x^2 - 1) = (2x)(x^2) - (2x)(1)$
$$= 2x^3 - 2x \qquad \square$$

Example 2 $(2x - 3)(x + 1) = (2x - 3)x + (2x - 3)1$
$$= (2x)x - (3)x + (2x)1 - (3)1$$
$$= 2x^2 - 3x + 2x - 3$$
$$= 2x^2 - x - 3 \qquad \square$$

Example 3 $(x + 2)(x^2 + x + 3) = (x + 2)x^2 + (x + 2)x + (x + 2)3$
$$= x^3 + 2x^2 + x^2 + 2x + 3x + 6$$
$$= x^3 + 3x^2 + 5x + 6 \qquad \square$$

Example 4 $(xy + 2z)(3xy^2 - 2xyz + z^2) = (xy + 2z)3xy^2 - (xy + 2z)2xyz + (xy + 2z)z^2$
$$= 3x^2y^3 + 6xy^2z - 2x^2y^2z - 4xyz^2 + xyz^2 + 2z^3$$
$$= 3x^2y^3 + 6xy^2z - 2x^2y^2z - 3xyz^2 + 2z^3 \qquad \square$$

Example 5 $(2x + 1)^3 = (2x + 1)(2x + 1)(2x + 1)$ Remember that $(2x + 1)^3$ is *not*
$$= (2x + 1)[(2x + 1)2x + (2x + 1)1] \qquad (2x)^3 + (1)^3.$$
$$= (2x + 1)[4x^2 + 2x + 2x + 1]$$
$$= (2x + 1)[4x^2 + 4x + 1]$$
$$= (2x + 1)4x^2 + (2x + 1)4x + (2x + 1)1$$
$$= 8x^3 + 4x^2 + 8x^2 + 4x + 2x + 1$$
$$= 8x^3 + 12x^2 + 6x + 1 \qquad \square$$

Historical Note

G. M. Mittag-Leffler (1846–1927) was a famous Swedish mathematician. However, he made many enemies while acquiring great wealth. When Alfred Nobel was establishing the Nobel prizes, he asked if there would be any chance of Mittag-Leffler winning a mathematics prize. Told he might, Nobel proclaimed "Let there be no Nobel prize in mathematics, then."

Binomial Products

In Example 2 the product of two binomials is a trinomial. This type of product is so common that we should examine the pattern closely. In the example four pairs of terms were multiplied when you expanded, using the distributive property:

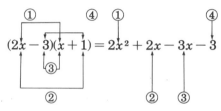

Look at the pattern you follow in obtaining the terms of the product. The first term (the leading term or the second-degree term) is the product of the variable terms of the binomials. The last term (the constant) is the product of the constants of the binomials. The first-degree term (middle term) is the sum of the products of the variable and constant terms from the two binomials. This pattern should provide a method for easily multiplying two binomials; it is sometimes referred to as **F.O.I.L.**, which stands for **F**irst, **O**utside, **I**nside, **L**ast. We concentrate first on two linear binomial factors whose product is a second-degree trinomial. A second-degree polynomial is called a **quadratic.**

In Examples 6–8 multiply the binomial factors.

Example 6 $(x+3)(x-5)$

Solution

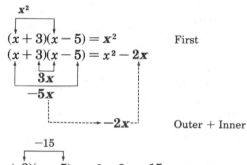

$$x^2$$

$$(x+3)(x-5)=x^2 \qquad \text{First}$$

$$(x+3)(x-5)=x^2-2x$$

$$3x$$
$$-5x$$

$$-2x \qquad \text{Outer + Inner}$$

$$-15$$

$$(x+3)(x-5)=x^2-2x-15 \qquad \text{Last}$$

Example 7 $(3x-4)(x-2)$

Solution

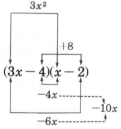

$$3x^2$$
$$+8$$
$$(3x-4)(x-2)$$
$$-4x$$
$$-10x$$
$$-6x$$

$$(3x-4)(x-2)=3x^2-10x+8$$

Example 8 $(5x+2)(4x-7)$

Solution

$$20x^2$$
$$-14$$
$$(5x+2)(4x-7)$$
$$8x$$
$$-27x$$
$$-35x$$

$$(5x+2)(4x-7)=20x^2-27x-14$$

Finding the product of two binomials is such a common operation that it will be helpful to develop speed and accuracy in its mental multiplication.

Combined Operations

In practice, many of the products just illustrated are combined into a single expression. Such an expression often looks menacing, but just keep in mind that you perform one operation at a time. Doing one thing at a time means the problem doesn't get harder, just longer. Note that in the following examples each step requires one idea and just one process at a time.

In Examples 9–11 simplify each expression.

Example 9

$(x + 2)(2x - 5) - x(x - 1)$ Multiply.
$= 2x^2 - x - 10 - x^2 + x$ Watch the signs!
$= x^2 - 10$ Combine like terms.   □

Example 10

$(x - 4)^2 - (x - 8)(x - 2)$ Multiply.
$= (x - 4)(x - 4) - (x - 8)(x - 2)$ Subtract.
$= x^2 - 8x + 16 - (x^2 - 10x + 16)$ Combine.
$= x^2 - 8x + 16 - x^2 + 10x - 16$
$= 2x$ □

Example 11

$(x + 1)^3 + 3x(x - 1)$ Deal with the cube first.
$= (x + 1)(x + 1)^2 + 3x(x - 1)$
$= (x + 1)(x^2 + 2x + 1) + 3x(x - 1)$
$= (x + 1)x^2 + (x + 1)2x + (x + 1)1 + 3x(x - 1)$ Use the distributive property.
$= x^3 + x^2 + 2x^2 + 2x + x + 1 + 3x^2 - 3x$ Multiply.
$= x^3 + 6x^2 + 1$ Combine.   □

Applications

Products have many applications, so the information in this section (together with that in the next section) is probably applied more often than all the rest of the material in this course. Many formulas that deal with products, such as those for area, volume, interest, and distance, are frequently used in everyday situations.

Example 12   The width of a rectangle is $w - 2$ and its length is $w + 9$. What is its area?

Solution   AREA = (LENGTH)(WIDTH)
$= (w + 9)(w - 2)$
$= w^2 + 7w - 18$

The area of the rectangle is $w^2 + 7w - 18$.   □

Example 13 If there are $1,000 - 2n$ items sold at a price of $5 + n$ dollars per item, what is the revenue from sales?

Solution

$$\text{REVENUE} = \left(\begin{array}{c}\text{PRICE}\\\text{PER ITEM}\end{array}\right)\left(\begin{array}{c}\text{NUMBER}\\\text{OF ITEMS}\end{array}\right)$$
$$= (5 + n)(1,000 - 2n)$$
$$= 5,000 + 990n - 2n^2$$

The revenue is $5,000 + 990n - 2n^2$ dollars. $\qquad\square$

Problem Set 4.2

A *In Problems 1–10 multiply by applying the distributive property.*

See Examples 1–5.

1. $2x(x^2 - 3x + 5)$
2. $3y(y^3 - 2y^2 - 7)$
3. $(x - 3)(x^2 - 3x + 7)$
4. $(y + 5)(y^2 + 6y - 8)$
5. $(2x + 5)(3x^2 - 4x + 9)$
6. $(3y - 4)(2y^2 + 5y - 6)$
7. $(x + 3)^3$
8. $(y - 4)^3$
9. $(x - 1)(2x + 3)^2$
10. $(y - 1)^2(2y + 3)$

Find the products in Problems 11–30, and then simplify, if possible.

11. $(3x^2)(5x^2)$
12. $(2x^3)(3x^3)$
13. $x^2y(2x^3y^5)$
14. $2xy^3(3x^4y^7)$
15. $4x^2(2x^3 - 3)$
16. $9x^3(x^4 - 2x)$
17. $2x(3x^2 - x + 1)$
18. $3y(y^2 - 4y + 5)$
19. $(x - 1)(x + 3)$

See Examples 6–8.

20. $(x - 2)(x + 4)$
21. $(x + 3)(x + 2)$
22. $(x + 4)(x + 3)$
23. $(x - 4)(y - 5)$
24. $(y - 4)(x - 6)$
25. $(2x + 3)(x - 5)$
26. $(2x - 5)(x + 7)$
27. $(3x - 1)(2x + 7)$
28. $(3x - 2)(4x + 1)$
29. $(2x + 5)(4x + 3)$
30. $(3x - 4)(5x - 2)$

See Example 12.
Recall that the area, A, of a rectangle is its length, l, times its width, w: $A = lw$

31. The width of a rectangle is $w - 5$ ft and the length is $2w + 4$ ft. What is the area of this rectangle?
32. What is the area of a rectangle $2a - 3$ ft wide and $3a + 4$ ft long?
33. The length of the side of a square is $5s - 2$ cm. What is the area of the square?

Recall that the area, A, of a square is its $(\text{SIDE})^2$: $A = s^2$

34. A square is $4c + 7$ cm on a side. What is its area?
35. Suppose $x - 3$ is the rate and $2x + 1$ is the time. What is the distance traveled?

DISTANCE = (RATE)(TIME)

36. Let $y + 5$ be the rate and $2y - 3$ be the time. What is the distance traveled?
37. *Agriculture.* If $3r + 5$ is the number of rows and $2r - 1$ is the number of trees in each row, what is the number of trees in the orchard? Assume that this is a rectangular arrangement.
38. The number of desks in each row is $4d + 3$. How many desks are there in a room of $2d - 1$ rows?

39. *Business.* Each apartment in a building rents for $150 - n$ dollars. What is the monthly income from $3n + 50$ units?

See Example 13. **40.** *Business.* There are $p + 10$ passengers on a flight that costs $450 - 7p$ dollars per passenger. What is the gross income from the flight?

B *In Problems 41–50 perform the indicated operations and simplify the polynomials obtained.*

See Examples 9–11.

41. $(x - 3)^2 - (x - 2)(x + 5)$ **42.** $(x - 3)(x - 5) - (x - 4)^2$

43. $(2x - 1)(3x + 1) + (x - 1)(x + 1)$ **44.** $(x - 2)(x + 2) - (3x - 1)(2x - 1)$

45. $(x - 2)(2x - 3) - (x - 1)(x - 6)$ **46.** $(3x + 2)(2x - 3) + (x + 2)(x + 3)$

47. $(x + y)(x + 2y) - (x - y)^2$ **48.** $(x - y)(x + y) + (2x - y)^2$

49. $(2x - 3y)(3x + 4y) + (x + 4y)(2x + 3y)$

50. $(3x - 5)(2x + 7) + (x - 12)(x + 1)$

51. The product of two consecutive integers is 62 less than the product of the next two integers. What is the second of the four integers?

52. The product of two consecutive odd integers is 208 more than the product of the preceding two odd integers. What is the third of these odd integers?

53. A rectangular field is 6 m narrower than it is long. If its width is reduced by 2 m and its length is increased by 3 m, the area is unchanged. Find the original dimensions of the field.

54. A rectangle is 2 cm longer than it is wide. However, if the length were 4 cm longer and the width were 2 cm shorter, the new rectangle would have the same area. Find the dimensions of the new figure.

Mind Boggler **55.** *Agriculture.* A farm hand is given the task of planting a new orchard. He is told to plant the seedlings in nine straight rows of five trees each. When he reaches the barn, he finds only 19 new seedlings. When he asks about more trees, he is assured that his instructions and the number of young trees are both correct. How does he plant the new orchard?

4.3   Division of Polynomials

To check multiplication, you can divide. If $5 \cdot 7 = 35$, then $\frac{35}{7} = 5$ and $\frac{35}{5} = 7$. This is also true for algebraic expressions and for polynomials in particular. In the previous section, we used the following example:

$$(x + 2)(x^2 + x + 3) = x^3 + 3x^2 + 5x + 6$$

This product implies the following quotient:

$$\frac{x^3 + 3x^2 + 5x + 6}{x + 2} = x^2 + x + 3$$

Long division can be used to verify this. The procedure calls for successive multiplications and subtractions, similar to the way you divide natural numbers.

$$\begin{array}{r} x^2 \\ x+2\overline{)x^3+3x^2+5x+6} \\ \underline{x^3+2x^2} \end{array}$$

First, multiply to duplicate the highest-degree term.

$$\begin{array}{r} x^2 \\ x+2\overline{)x^3+3x^2+5x+6} \\ \underline{x^3+2x^2} \\ x^2+5x \end{array}$$

Then subtract, to eliminate the highest-degree term, and bring down the next term.

$$\begin{array}{r} x^2+x+3 \\ x+2\overline{)x^3+3x^2+5x+6} \\ \underline{x^3+2x^2} \\ x^2+5x \\ \underline{x^2+2x} \\ 3x+6 \\ \underline{3x+6} \\ 0 \end{array}$$

Then repeat the process until you obtain a constant remainder.

Example 1 Divide: $\dfrac{x^3-3x-2}{x+1}$

Solution

$$\begin{array}{r} x^2-x-2 \\ x+1\overline{)x^3+0x^2-3x-2} \\ \underline{x^3+x^2} \\ -x^2-3x \\ \underline{-x^2-x} \\ -2x-2 \\ \underline{-2x-2} \\ 0 \end{array}$$

Note that the coefficient of x^2 is 0 in this example.

$$\frac{x^3-3x-2}{x+1}=x^2-x-2$$

□

So far, the remainder has been 0 in each example. But consider $\frac{17}{2}$, which does not have a zero remainder. Here, we write $\frac{17}{2}=8\frac{1}{2}$ or $8+\frac{1}{2}$. That is, $P/D=Q+R/D$, where P is a polynomial, D is a **divisor,** Q is a **quotient,** and R is the **remainder.**

Example 2 Divide: $\dfrac{2x^3+5x^2-6x-7}{x+1}$

Solution

$$\begin{array}{r} 2x^2 + 3x - 9 \\ x+1\overline{\smash{)}2x^3 + 5x^2 - 6x - 7} \\ \underline{2x^3 + 2x^2} \\ 3x^2 - 6x \\ \underline{3x^2 + 3x} \\ -9x - 7 \\ \underline{-9x - 9} \\ 2 \end{array}$$

$$\frac{2x^3 + 5x^2 - 6x - 7}{x+1} = 2x^2 + 3x - 9 + \frac{2}{x+1} \qquad \frac{P}{D} = Q + \frac{R}{D}$$

□

Example 3   Divide: $\dfrac{x^4 - 5x^2 + 6}{x^2 - x - 2}$

Solution

$$\begin{array}{r} x^2 + x - 2 \\ x^2 - x - 2\overline{\smash{)}x^4 + 0x^3 - 5x^2 + 0x + 6} \\ \underline{x^4 - x^3 - 2x^2} \\ x^3 - 3x^2 + 0x \\ \underline{x^3 - x^2 - 2x} \\ -2x^2 + 2x + 6 \\ \underline{-2x^2 + 2x + 4} \\ 2 \end{array}$$

$$\frac{x^4 - 5x^2 + 6}{x^2 - x - 2} = x^2 + x - 2 + \frac{2}{x^2 - x - 2}$$

□

Synthetic Division

If the divisor is of the form $x - k$, the long-division process can be shortened considerably. Since all variables can be aligned in columns of descending order, the variables may be omitted and the coefficients written alone.

$$\begin{array}{r} x^2 + 2x + 1 \\ x-2\overline{\smash{)}x^3 + 0x^2 - 3x - 2} \\ \underline{x^3 - 2x^2} \\ 2x^2 - 3x \\ \underline{2x^2 - 4x} \\ x - 2 \\ \underline{x - 2} \\ 0 \end{array} \qquad \begin{array}{r} 1 \quad 2 \quad 1 \\ 1-2\overline{\smash{)}1 \quad 0 \ -3 \ -2} \\ \underline{1 \ -2} \\ 2 \ -3 \\ \underline{2 \ -4} \\ 1 \ -2 \\ \underline{1 \ -2} \\ 0 \end{array}$$

Notice that when the division is rewritten below, the numerals in color are repeated in the quotient and the numerals in parentheses are also

Historical Note

Norbert Wiener (1894–1964), at M.I.T. for 40 years, was as eccentric as he was brilliant. He would forget that he had driven to a destination and would return by train. He would sleep through a colloquium talk only to awake at the end and ask pertinent questions. One day Wiener's students asked how to do a certain problem. He thought for a moment and simply wrote an answer on the board. The class was perplexed, but one brave soul asked whether there was another way to do the problem. Wiener thought again for a moment and replied "Why yes, there *is* another way." He then wrote the same answer on the board. His letter, *A Scientist Rebels,* published in the *Atlantic Monthly* in 1947, opened a public debate on the place of science and the scientist in the troubled world following Hiroshima and Nagasaki.

repetitions of the numerals directly above. If the repetitions are eliminated, the division may be written in a compact form as shown at the right:

$$
\begin{array}{r}
1 \quad 2 \quad 1 \\
1 -2\overline{)1 \quad 0 \;-3 \;-2} \\
\underline{1 \;-2} \\
2\,(-3) \\
\underline{2 \;-4} \\
1\,(-2) \\
\underline{1 \;-2} \\
0
\end{array}
\qquad
\begin{array}{r}
\underline{-2|} \quad 1 \quad 0 \;-3 \;-2 \\
\underline{-2 \;-4 \;-2} \\
1 \quad 2 \quad 1 \quad 0
\end{array}
$$

The compact form retains the essentials of the division. The top line contains the coefficients of the polynomial and the constant k of the divisor $x - k$. The bottom line contains the coefficients of the quotient and the remainder. The middle line retains the arithmetic of the successive multiplications and subtractions. The process is usually simplified one more step, since the same result is obtained if we replace -2 by 2 and add instead of subtract at each step:

$$
\begin{array}{r}
\underline{2|} \quad 1 \quad 0 \;-3 \;-2 \\
2 \quad 4 \quad 2 \\
\hline
1 \quad 2 \quad 1 \quad 0
\end{array}
$$

Notice the zigzag pattern of multiply–add, multiply–add, ...

The process in this form is called **synthetic division.** Synthetic division may be used to find the quotient (bottom line) of any polynomial (top line) and the divisor of the form $x - k$.

In Examples 4 and 5 use synthetic division to find the quotient and remainder (if any).

Example 4
$$\frac{x^4 + 6x^3 + 8x^2 - 6x - 9}{x + 3} = ?$$

Solution
$$
\begin{array}{r}
\underline{-3|} \quad 1 \quad 6 \quad 8 \;-6 \;-9 \\
-3 \;-9 \quad 3 \quad 9 \\
\hline
1 \quad 3 \;-1 \;-3 \quad 0
\end{array}
$$
Note that $x + 3 = x - (-3)$.

$$= 1x^3 + 3x^2 - 1x - 3 + 0$$
$$= x^3 + 3x^2 - x - 3 \qquad \square$$

Example 5
$$\frac{6x^3 - 7x^2 - 10}{x - 2} = ?$$
Remember to supply 0 coefficients for missing terms.

Solution $\underline{2|}$ 6   −7   0   −10
                           12   10   20
                 ─────────────────────────
                 6   5   10   10
                               $\dfrac{10}{}$

$$= 6x^2 + 5x + 10 + \frac{10}{x-2}$$ □

You now have a compact, quick method for dividing polynomials by certain binomials. Recall that in Example 1 the remainder was 0, and

$$\frac{x^3 - 3x - 2}{x + 1} = x^2 - x - 2$$

which can be written as

$$x^3 - 3x - 2 = (x + 1)(x^2 - x - 2)$$

That is, if the remainder is 0, the divisor and the quotient are *factors* of the polynomial.

Example 6   Determine whether the first expression is a factor of the second. If it is a factor, write the second in factored form.

a. $x + 2;$ $4x^3 - 15x + 2$

$\underline{-2|}$ 4   0   −15   2
                    −8   16   −2
        ──────────────────────
        4   −8   1   0

$$4x^3 - 15x + 2 = (x + 2)(4x^2 - 8x + 1)$$

b. $x + 3;$ $x^4 - 8x^2 - 9$

$\underline{-3|}$ 1   0   −8   0   −9
                    −3   9   −3   9
        ───────────────────────────
        1   −3   1   −3   0

$$x^4 - 8x^2 - 9 = (x + 3)(x^3 - 3x^2 + x - 3)$$

c. $x - 5;$ $2x^4 - 13x^3 + 13x^2 + 10x + 5$

$\underline{5|}$ 2   −13   13   10   5
                    10   −15   −10   0
        ──────────────────────────────
        2   −3   −2   0   5
                               └─Don't stop here!

The remainder is 5; hence, $x - 5$ is not a factor of $2x^4 - 13x^3 + 13x^2 + 10x + 5$.   □

Problem Set 4.3

A *Use long division in Problems 1–6. State the results in the form $Q + R/D$.*

See Examples 1 and 2.

1. $\dfrac{x^3 - 3x^2 + 5x - 2}{x - 1}$

2. $\dfrac{x^3 - 3x^2 + 5x - 2}{x + 1}$

3. $\dfrac{2x^3 + 3x^2 - 7x + 4}{x + 3}$

4. $\dfrac{3x^3 - 4x^2 + x - 9}{x - 2}$

5. $\dfrac{3x^4 - 20x^3 + 11x^2 + 30}{x - 6}$

6. $\dfrac{4x^4 + 10x^3 + 20x + 7}{x + 3}$

Use synthetic division in Problems 7–20. Determine in each problem whether the first expression is a factor of the second. If it is a factor, write the solution in factored form.

See Examples 4–6.

7. $x - 2;\quad x^3 + x^2 + x - 14$
8. $x - 1;\quad x^3 + x^2 + x - 3$
9. $x + 1;\quad x^3 + 1$
10. $x - 3;\quad x^3 - 27$
11. $x + 1;\quad x^4 + 1$
12. $x - 3;\quad x^5 - 32$
13. $x + 3;\quad 5x^3 + 12x^2 - 12x - 9$
14. $x - 2;\quad 7x^3 - 12x^2 - 12x + 80$
15. $x - 1;\quad 3x^4 - 2x^3 + 4x - 5$
16. $x + 2;\quad 2x^4 - 5x^2 + 4x - 4$
17. $x + 2;\quad x^4 - 3x^2 - 4$
18. $x - 3;\quad x^4 - 11x^2 + 18$
19. $x + 4;\quad 2x^5 + 7x^4 - 3x^3 + 4x^2 + x + 4$
20. $x + 4;\quad 2x^6 + 7x^5 - 3x^4 + 4x^3 + x + 4$

B *Use long division in Problems 21–30. State the results in the form $Q + R/D$.*

See Example 3.

21. $\dfrac{x^3 + 2x^2 + 2x + 2}{x^2 + x + 1}$

22. $\dfrac{x^3 + x^2 - x + 1}{x^2 - x + 1}$

23. $\dfrac{x^3 + x^2 - 5x - 2}{x^2 + 3x + 1}$

24. $\dfrac{2x^3 + x^2 - 2x + 1}{x^2 + 2x + 2}$

25. $\dfrac{9x^3 - 6x^2 + 1}{3x^2 - 3x + 1}$

26. $\dfrac{8x^3 - 12x^2 + 5}{4x^2 + 2x - 5}$

27. $\dfrac{6x^3 + x^2 - 6x + 1}{3x^2 + 2x - 1}$

28. $\dfrac{6x^3 - x^2 - 10x - 3}{2x^2 - x - 3}$

29. $\dfrac{x^4 + 3x^3 + 2x^2 + 5x - 4}{x^2 + 2x - 5}$

30. $\dfrac{2x^4 + 3x^3 + 4x^2 + 9x - 6}{x^2 + 3}$

Mind Bogglers
31. Find all the real roots of $x^6 + x + 6 = x^5 + 6x^4 + x^2$.
32. Consider the cubic, $3x^3 - 13x^2 + 16$.
   a. Find the value of the expression for $x = 1$, 2, and 3.
   b. Find the remainders after division by $x - 1$, $x - 2$, and $x - 3$.
   c. Compare the results in parts a and b and make a conjecture.
   d. Use your conjecture to find the value of the expression for $x = -2$, $x = 5$, and $x = -\frac{1}{2}$.

4.4 Factoring

The product is found by multiplying the factors. Can the factors be found if the product is known?

If you are told that there are 35 seats in a classroom arranged rectangularly in equal rows, how many rows of how many seats are in the room? There are five rows of seven seats or seven rows of five seats. Look for the factors of 35 to find the answer. This process—the reverse of multiplying—is called **factoring.**

Common Factors

To factor successfully, you must understand multiplication. Recall what is done when a monomial is a factor.

$$2x(3x^2 + x - 5) = (2x)3x^2 + (2x)x - (2x)5$$
$$= 6x^3 + 2x^2 - 10x$$

The monomial is multiplied by each term of the trinomial and hence is a factor of each. In looking for a **common monomial factor,** the monomial must be a factor of each term of the product.

In Examples 1–3 factor each expression.

Example 1 $3x^2 + 9x = (3x)(x) + (3x)(3)$
$= 3x(x + 3)$ ☐

Example 2 $4x^3 + 12x^2 - 6x = 2x(2x^2) + 2x(6x) - 2x(3)$
$= 2x(2x^2 + 6x - 3)$ ☐

Example 3 $10x^2y - 15xy^2 + 25x^2y^2 = 5xy(2x) - 5xy(3y) + 5xy(5xy)$
$= 5xy(2x - 3y + 5xy)$ ☐

If we find the *greatest factor* common to each term, or if no other factor can be found, we say the polynomial is **completely factored.**

Binomial Factors

Long multiplication gives a different view of the same product:

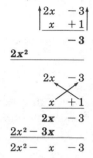

Consider the product of two binomials:

$$(2x - 3)(x + 1) = 2x^2 - 3x + 2x - 3$$
$$= 2x^2 - x - 3$$

If you understand where the terms of the product came from, you will find it easier to reverse the process. In the following discussion, we'll concentrate on a particular product, a second-degree polynomial in a single variable, like the one above. You can then see how this case applies to similar products.

First, examine the second-degree (or leading) term and the last term (or constant):

$$2x^2$$
$$-3$$
$$(2x - 3)(x + 1)$$

These terms are the products of the variable terms and the constants of the binomial factors.

Now, recall the origin of the first-degree (or middle) term of the product:

$$(2x - 3)(x + 1)$$
$$-3x$$
$$2x$$

This term is the sum of the products of the variable and constant terms in the binomial factors.

Now let's consider a product and reverse the multiplication procedure to determine the factors.

$$3x^2 + 13x - 10$$

First, find two factors whose product is $3x^2$. These determine the variable terms of the factors and hence the form of the factors:

$$(x \quad)(3x \quad)$$

Second, factor the constant term. These factors will yield all possible pairs of factors, which can be listed:

$(x + 2)(3x - 5)$	$(x + 1)(3x - 10)$
$(x - 2)(3x + 5)$	$(x - 1)(3x + 10)$
$(x + 5)(3x - 2)$	$(x + 10)(3x - 1)$
$(x - 5)(3x + 2)$	$(x - 10)(3x + 1)$

Third, check each to see which possibilities give the correct middle term:

$$(x + 5)(3x - 2) = 3x^2 + 13x - 10$$

We factor the polynomial by reversing our knowledge of multiplication. Not all examples are this easy, and indeed not all can be factored over the integers. If no possibility yields the correct middle term, the polynomial is **not factorable** over the integers. For example, $x^2 + x + 1$ must be of the form $(x \quad 1)(x \quad 1)$, but no possibility yields the correct product. Thus, $x^2 + x + 1$ is nonfactorable over the integers.

To Factor a Trinomial:

Find and remove any common monomial factors. Then:
1. Find the factors of the second-degree term and set up the binomials.
2. Find the factors of the constant term, and consider all possible binomials.
3. Determine the factors that yield the correct middle term.
4. If no pair of factors produces the correct full product, then the trinomial is not factorable using integers.

Example 4   Factor: $3x^2 + 7x + 2$

Solution   First, factor $3x^2$:

$(x \quad)(3x \quad)$

Second, factor 2:

$(x \quad 1)(3x \quad 2)$ Notice that the signs must be positive. Why?
$(x \quad 2)(3x \quad 1)$

Third, select the correct combination.

$(x + 2)(3x + 1) = 3x^2 + 7x + 2$ □

Example 5   Factor: $6x^2 - 13xy + 5y^2$ Now consider an example with two variables. The first step is the same.

Solution   First, factor $6x^2$:

$(x \quad)(6x \quad)$
$(2x \quad)(3x \quad)$

Second, factor $5y^2$:

$(x - y)(6x - 5y)$ Notice that you don't consider factors of 5 and y^2. Why? For in-
$(x - 5y)(6x - y)$ stance, $(x - y^2)(6x - 5)$ is not listed as a possibility.
$(2x - y)(3x - 5y)$
$(2x - 5y)(3x - y)$

Third, choose the correct combination.

$(2x - y)(3x - 5y) = 6x^2 - 13xy + 5y^2$ □

Applications

Products, as you have seen, have many applied uses. Factoring is also a very practical and useful process. If the product and a factor are known, you may find the other factor. If the area of a rectangle and its width are known, factoring will determine the length.

Example 6   The area of a rectangle is $3x^2 - x - 10$ square centimeters (written cm^2) and its width is $3x + 5$ cm. Find the length.

Solution   AREA = (LENGTH)(WIDTH)

$$3x^2 - x - 10 = (\text{LENGTH})(3x + 5)$$
$$= (x - 2)(3x + 5)$$

The length is $x - 2$ cm.   □

Example 7   If a vehicle travels at a constant rate of $2t + 3$ mph over a distance of $2t^2 + 5t + 3$ miles, then how many hours does it take?

Solution   DISTANCE = (RATE)(TIME)

$$2t^2 + 5t + 3 = (2t + 3)(\text{TIME})$$
$$= (2t + 3)(t + 1)$$

The time is $t + 1$ hours.   □

Problem Set 4.4

A   *Factor each polynomial in Problems 1–30.*

See Examples 1–3.

1. $2x^2 + 2$
2. $5y + 10x$
3. $3ab + 6b^2$
4. $4ab + 6a^2$
5. $x^3 + x^2 + x$
6. $y^4 + y^2 - y$
7. $6rs^2 + 9r^2s - 12rs$
8. $12r^3s - 18r^2s^2 + 24rs^3$

See Examples 4 and 5.

9. $x^2 + 3x + 2$
10. $y^2 + 4y + 3$
11. $y^2 - 5y + 6$
12. $z^2 - 6z + 8$
13. $z^2 - 2z - 35$
14. $x^2 - 11x - 42$
15. $2t^2 + 7t - 15$
16. $2s^2 + s - 10$
17. $3s^2 - 5s - 2$
18. $3t^2 - 8t - 3$
19. $6v^2 - 7v + 2$
20. $2w^2 + 7w + 3$
21. $8x^2y + 10xy - 3y$
22. $6x^3 + 11x^2 + 3x$
23. $2x^2 - 10x - 48$
24. $2x^2 + 20x - 48$
25. $2x^3 + x^2 - 21x$
26. $9x^2y + 15xy - 14y$
27. $12x^2 - 7x - 12$
28. $16y^2 - 16y - 12$ $4(4y^2 - 4y - 3)$
29. $12x^4 + 11x^3 - 15x^2$
30. $12x^4 - 11x^3 - 15x^2$

See Examples 6 and 7.

31. The area of a rectangle is $x^2 + 8x + 15$. What is the width if the length is $x + 5$?

32. A rectangle is $x + 3$ long. What is the width if the area is $x^2 + x - 6$?

33. A rectangular box is $w + 1$ cm deep and w cm wide. If the box has a volume of $w^3 + 5w^2 + 4w$ cm³, how long is it?

34. The volume of a rectangular box is $d^3 + 3d^2 + 2d$ cm³. If the depth is d cm and the length is $d + 2$ cm, then what is the width?

35. If you travel a distance of $2t^2 + 3t + 1$ km in $t + 1$ hours, what is your average rate?

36. If you travel $3r^2 - 5r - 2$ km at an average rate of $3r + 1$ km per hour, then how many hours does it take?

37. *Finance.* You invest $2p - 5$ dollars and receive $2p^2 + 3p - 20$ dollars in interest. What is the rate of interest?

38. *Finance.* You earn $(3r - 4)$ percent on a $6r^2 + 7r - 20$ dollar investment. How much is invested?

39. There are $6r^2 + 7r - 3$ seats in the auditorium, arranged rectangularly. If there are $2r + 3$ rows, then how many seats are in each row?

40. *Agriculture.* An orchard has $10t^2 + 17t + 3$ trees in $5t + 1$ rows. If the orchard is rectangular, how many trees are in each row?

B *Factor each trinomial in Problems 41–60, if possible.*

See Examples 4 and 5.

41. $8x^2 - 6x - 9$	**42.** $27x^2 - 6x - 8$
43. $24x^2 + 11x - 18$	**44.** $24x^2 + 6x - 45$
45. $6x^2 - 19x + 10$	**46.** $6x^2 - 17x + 12$
47. $16x^2 - 14xy - 15y^2$	**48.** $15x^2 - 4xy - 35y^2$
49. $14x^4 + 11x^2 - 15$	**50.** $18x^2y^2 + 3xy - 10$
51. $18x^2y^2 - 15xy^2 + 3y^2$	**52.** $14x^4 - 7x^3 - 21x^2$
53. $3x^4 + x^2y - 2y^2$	**54.** $5x^6 + 7x^3y - 6y^2$
55. $x^2y^2 - 2xyz + z^2$	**56.** $x^2y^2 - xyz - 2z^2$
57. $20x^2 - 9xyz + y^2z^2$	**58.** $18x^2 + 9xyz + y^2z^2$
59. $20x^2y^2 + 17x^2yz - 10x^2z^2$	**60.** $12x^2y^2 + 10x^2yz - 12x^2z^2$

Mind Boggler **61.** Factor each of the following without first multiplying:

  a. $(x + 3)^2 - 2(x + 3) - 3$
  b. $(x + y)^2 + 7(x + y) + 12$
  c. $(x - y)^2 + 13(x - y)z + 36z^2$
  d. $(x + 3)^2 - 5(x + 3)(x - 3) + 6(x - 3)^2$
  e. $(x + y)^2 + 3(x + y)(y - z) + 2(y - z)^2$

4.5 More on Factoring

All the quadratic polynomials of the previous section were factored using the same pattern. There are, however, a couple of special types that deserve special attention. These two will have several applications and will form the basis for processes in later topics. The first of these is also the most easily recognizable.

Difference of Squares

When you factored polynomials in the last section, the factors were binomials after an occasional monomial factor was first removed. There is only one case where two binomial factors produce a binomial instead of a trinomial. Consider the product with factors $(a + b)$ and $(a - b)$. Note that the middle term will be 0, so you obtain a binomial. This case is unique.

$$(a + b)(a - b) = a^2 - b^2$$
$$(x + 1)(x - 1) = x^2 - 1$$
$$(y + 2)(y - 2) = y^2 - 4$$
$$(z + 3)(z - 3) = z^2 - 9$$
$$(2x + 1)(2x - 1) = 4x^2 - 1$$
$$(3x + 4)(3x - 4) = 9x^2 - 16$$

The product in each case is the difference of two terms, and each of the terms is the square of one of the terms in the binomials. This distinctive case is called the **difference of squares,** and its factors are a sum and a difference.

DIFFERENCE OF SQUARES

Difference of Squares

$$a^2 - b^2 = (a + b)(a - b)$$

$$\left(\begin{smallmatrix}\text{FIRST}\\\text{NUMBER}\end{smallmatrix}\right)^2 - \left(\begin{smallmatrix}\text{SECOND}\\\text{NUMBER}\end{smallmatrix}\right)^2 = \left(\begin{smallmatrix}\text{FIRST}\\\text{NUMBER}\end{smallmatrix} + \begin{smallmatrix}\text{SECOND}\\\text{NUMBER}\end{smallmatrix}\right)\left(\begin{smallmatrix}\text{FIRST}\\\text{NUMBER}\end{smallmatrix} - \begin{smallmatrix}\text{SECOND}\\\text{NUMBER}\end{smallmatrix}\right)$$

Pairs of numbers that are the sum and difference of the same numbers are called **conjugates.** The product of a conjugate pair is a difference of squares.

Example 1 Factor, if possible.

a. $x^2 - 49 = (x)^2 - (7)^2$
$= (x + 7)(x - 7)$

b. $36y^2 - 1 = (6y)^2 - (1)^2$
$= (6y + 1)(6y - 1)$

c. $8z^2 - 50 = 2(4z^2 - 25)$
$= 2[(2z)^2 - (5)^2]$
$= 2(2z + 5)(2z - 5)$

d. $9r^2 + 64$
Not a difference and nonfactorable over the integers

e. $4v^2 - 9w^2 = (2v)^2 - (3w)^2$
$= (2v + 3w)(2v - 3w)$

f. $81x^2 - 125y^2$
125 is not a square of an integer ☐

Perfect Squares

A second special quadratic polynomial is the product of two identical binomial factors. The product has a distinctive form.

$$(a + b)(a + b) = (a + b)^2 = a^2 + 2ab + b^2$$
$$(x + 1)^2 = x^2 + 2x + 1$$
$$(y - 3)^2 = y^2 - 6y + 9$$
$$(2z + 1)^2 = 4z^2 + 4z + 1$$
$$(3t - 2r)^2 = 9t^2 - 12tr + 4r^2$$

The product in each case is a trinomial whose square terms are the squares of one of the terms of the binomials. The middle term is twice the product of the terms in the binomials. This case is called the **perfect square,** and its factors are identical.

PERFECT SQUARE

Perfect Square

$$a^2 + 2ab + b^2 = (a + b)^2$$

$$\left(\begin{array}{c}\text{FIRST}\\\text{NUMBER}\end{array}\right)^2 + \left(\begin{array}{c}\text{TWICE PRODUCT}\\\text{OF THE NUMBERS}\end{array}\right) + \left(\begin{array}{c}\text{SECOND}\\\text{NUMBER}\end{array}\right)^2 = \left(\begin{array}{c}\text{FIRST}\\\text{NUMBER}\end{array} + \begin{array}{c}\text{SECOND}\\\text{NUMBER}\end{array}\right)^2$$

Example 2 Factor, if the trinomial is a perfect square.

a. $x^2 + 12x + 36 = x^2 + 2(6x) + (6)^2$
$$= (x + 6)^2$$

b. $r^2 - 18r + 81 = r^2 + 2(-9r) + (9)^2$
$$= (r - 9)^2$$

c. $9y^2 + 30y + 25 = (3y)^2 + 2(15y) + (5)^2$
$$= (3y + 5)^2$$

d. $z^2 + 10z + 100 = (z)^2 + + (10)^2$ Middle term isn't twice 10 · z, so not a perfect square

e. $18h^2 - 60hk + 50k^2 = 2(9h^2 - 30hk + 25k^2)$
$$= 2[(3h)^2 + 2(-15hk) + (5k)^2]$$
$$= 2(3h - 5k)^2 \qquad \square$$

Quadratic-like Forms

Some polynomials, although they are of higher degree, *look like* the quadratics. That is, they have the form of the quadratics discussed in this section and the last. For instance, $x^4 - 9$ is a difference of squares, although it happens to be fourth degree:

$$x^4 - 9 = (x^2)^2 - (3)^2 \qquad \text{Recall that } (b^x)^y = b^{xy}.$$
$$= (x^2 + 3)(x^2 - 3)$$

Consider some other similar examples.

In Examples 3–5 factor, if possible.

Example 3 $a^6 - 4b^2 = (a^3)^2 - (2b)^2$ Difference of squares
$$= (a^3 + 2b)(a^3 - 2b)$$

Example 4 $x^6 + 6x^3 + 9 = (x^3)^2 + 2(3x^3) + (3)^2$ Perfect square
$$= (x^3 + 3)^2$$

Example 5 $x^4 - 5x^2 + 6 = (x^2)^2 - 5(x^2) + 6$ Binomial factors
$$= (x^2 - 2)(x^2 - 3)$$

Since the factors themselves can be quadratic, they can sometimes be factored further, as in the next example.

Example 6   **a.** $x^4 + 3x^2 - 4 = (x^2 - 1)(x^2 + 4)$ **b.** $x^4 - 81 = (x^2 + 9)(x^2 - 9)$
$$= (x + 1)(x - 1)(x^2 + 4)$$ $$= (x^2 + 9)(x + 3)(x - 3)$$
c. $x^4 - 13x^2 + 36 = (x^2 - 4)(x^2 - 9)$
$$= (x + 2)(x - 2)(x + 3)(x - 3)$$

Sum and Difference of Cubes

Of the higher-degree polynomials that may be factored, two are distinct and recognizable. Multiply the following, and observe the products:

$$(x + a)(x^2 - ax + a^2) = (x + a)x^2 - (x + a)ax + (x + a)a^2$$
$$= x^3 + ax^2 - ax^2 - a^2x + a^2x + a^3$$
$$= x^3 + a^3$$

$$(x - a)(x^2 + ax + a^2) = (x - a)x^2 + (x - a)ax + (x - a)a^2$$
$$= x^3 - ax^2 + ax^2 - a^2x + a^2x - a^3$$
$$= x^3 - a^3$$

Thus, there are two more recognizable factorable forms—the **sum of cubes** and the **difference of cubes**. Note, however, that the quadratic factor of these two forms may not be factored further.

SUM OF CUBES

DIFFERENCE OF
CUBES

> **Sum and Difference of Cubes**
> $$x^3 + a^3 = (x + a)(x^2 - ax + a^2)$$
> $$x^3 - a^3 = (x - a)(x^2 + ax + a^2)$$ compare by mult. back or division

In Examples 7–9 factor each expression.

Example 7 $x^3 - 8 = x^3 - 2^3$
$$= (x - 2)(x^2 + 2x + 4)$$

Example 8 $y^3 + 27z^3 = y^3 + (3z)^3$
$$= (y + 3z)(y^2 - 3yz + 9z^2)$$

$x^2 + a^2$

Example 9 $z^6 - 64 = (z^3)^2 - 8^2$

$= (z^3 - 8)(z^3 + 8)$

$= (z - 2)(z^2 + 2z + 4)(z + 2)(z^2 - 2z + 4)$

Note that $z^6 - 64$ is also a difference of cubes. Factor as a difference of cubes and compare.   □

A number of operations with polynomials may now be combined in a more complicated example. However, remember you can do only one thing at a time, so no one step will be that complicated. Consider the following example before tackling the problem.

Example 10   Perform the indicated operations, simplify, and then factor the simplified expression.

$6(x - 1)^2 + x(4x - 5) = 6(x^2 - 2x + 1) + x(4x - 5)$ First, square.

$= 6x^2 - 12x + 6 + 4x^2 - 5x$ Remove parentheses.

$= 10x^2 - 17x + 6$ Combine like terms.

$= (2x - 1)(5x - 6)$ Factor, if possible.   □

Problem Set 4.5

A   *In Problems 1–30 factor with integer coefficients, if possible.*

See Example 1.

1. $x^2 - 100$
2. $y^2 - 49$
3. $u^2 - 4v^2$
4. $9v^2 - w^2$

See Example 2.

5. $x^2 + 6x + 9$
6. $x^2 - 10x + 25$

See Examples 7–9.

7. $y^3 - 1$
8. $y^3 + 1$
9. $4z^2 - 9$
10. $9 - 4z^2$
11. $h^3 + 8$
12. $k^3 - 27$
13. $9r^2 - 6r + 1$
14. $25s^2 + 10s + 1$
15. $8t^2 - 98$
16. $27t^2 - 9$
17. $8t^3 - 64$
18. $27t^3 + 8$
19. $12h^2 + 12h + 3$
20. $6k^2 - 12k + 6$
21. $9x^2 - 12xy + 4y^2$
22. $4r^2 - 12rs + 9s^2$
23. $9s^3 - 121s$
24. $25x^3 - 25x^2 + 4x$
25. $9s^4 - 72s$
26. $x^4 + 125x$
27. $9x^4 + 42x^3 + 49x^2$
28. $64y^4 - 16y^2$
29. $9x^3 + 729$
30. $64y^3 - 8$

B   *Factor completely in Problems 31–40.*

See Examples 3–6.

31. $v^4 - 10v^2 + 9$
32. $v^4 - 8v^2 + 16$
33. $w^4 - 81$
34. $w^4 - 16$
35. $x^6 - 729$
36. $x^6 - 64$
37. $y^6 - 13y^4 + 36y^2$
38. $y^6 - 26y^4 + 25y^2$
39. $z^6 + 7z^3 - 8$
40. $z^6 - 26z^3 - 27$

Simplify the expressions in Problems 41–50, and then factor, if possible.

See Example 10.

41. $2(x^2 - 6) - x(x - 1)$ **42.** $3(x^2 - 5) + 2x(x - 1)$

43. $(2x + 1)(x - 1) - (x - 1)(x + 5)$ **44.** $2(x - 1)^2 - (x + 5)(x - 2)$

45. $(x + 3)(x - 6) + (x - 3)^2$ **46.** $(3x - 8)(x + 3) + (x + 3)(x - 7)$

47. $(5x + 6)(x - 1) + (x + 2)(x + 4)$ **48.** $(3x + 5)(x - 2) + (2x + 1)(3x + 2)$

49. $(2x - 1)(x + 4) + (3x + 2)(x + 5) + (x - 1)(x - 6)$

50. $(2x + 3)(x - 1) + (3x + 2)(x + 7) + (x - 2)^2$

4.6 Problems Involving Factoring

What do you do with factoring? For one thing, you use it to reduce fractions. In algebra it is used for the solution of equations and inequalities. The knowledge of factoring and one property of products is central to solving many polynomial problems. Consider the product $A \cdot B$. When is the product 0? When is it positive or negative? Here is a property of products that is just a restatement of the laws of signs for multiplication:

PROPERTY OF PRODUCTS

If $A \cdot B = 0$, then either A or B is 0.	If $A \cdot B < 0$, then A and B have opposite signs.	If $A \cdot B > 0$, then A and B have the same sign.

The same laws are stated a little more formally below.

If $A \cdot B = 0$, then $A = 0$ or $B = 0$ (or both).	If $A \cdot B < 0$, then $A < 0$ and $B > 0$, or $A > 0$ and $B < 0$.	If $A \cdot B > 0$, then $A > 0$ and $B > 0$, or $A < 0$ and $B < 0$.

Let's apply this property to equations first. Consider the following quadratic (or second-degree) equation:

$$5x = 3 - 2x^2$$

$$2x^2 + 5x - 3 = 0$$ First, bring all terms to one side of the equation.

$$(2x - 1)(x + 3) = 0$$ Factor the trinomial.

$$2x - 1 = 0 \quad \text{or} \quad x + 3 = 0$$ Apply the property of products.

$$2x = 1 \qquad\qquad x = -3$$ Solve the linear equations.

$$x = \tfrac{1}{2}$$

Solution: $\{\tfrac{1}{2}, -3\}$ State a solution set.

Notice that the quadratic is factored into linear factors, and the linear factors are set equal to 0. Then the resulting linear equations are solved in the usual way, and the solution set is the union of the solutions of the linear equations.

Consider an equation that involves a difference of squares:

$$x^2 - 16 = 0$$
$$(x + 4)(x - 4) = 0$$
$$x + 4 = 0 \quad \text{or} \quad x - 4 = 0$$
$$x = -4 \qquad\qquad x = 4$$

Solution: {−4, 4}

The roots are opposites; they have the same absolute value, but they're opposite in sign.

Consider an equation involving a perfect square:

$$x^2 - 8x + 16 = 0$$
$$(x - 4)^2 = 0$$
$$(x - 4)(x - 4) = 0$$
$$x - 4 = 0 \quad \text{or} \quad x - 4 = 0$$
$$x = 4 \qquad\qquad x = 4$$

Solution: {4}

The roots are equal, so an equation involving a perfect square has only one distinct root.

In Examples 1–3 solve by factoring.

Example 1

$$x^2 = 2x + 15$$
$$x^2 - 2x - 15 = 0 \qquad \text{Bring to one side}$$
$$(x + 3)(x - 5) = 0 \qquad \text{Factor}$$
$$x + 3 = 0 \quad \text{or} \quad x - 5 = 0 \qquad \text{Set equal to 0}$$
$$x = -3 \qquad\qquad x = 5 \qquad \text{Solve}$$

Solution: {−3, 5}   □

Example 2

$$2y^2 - 7y = 3 - 4y^2$$
$$6y^2 - 7y - 3 = 0$$
$$(2y - 3)(3y + 1) = 0$$
$$2y - 3 = 0 \quad \text{or} \quad 3y + 1 = 0$$
$$2y = 3 \qquad\qquad 3y = -1$$
$$y = \tfrac{3}{2} \qquad\qquad y = -\tfrac{1}{3}$$

Solution: {$\tfrac{3}{2}$, $-\tfrac{1}{3}$}   □

Example 3

$$3(z+1)(z+2) = z - (2z-3)(z+4)$$
$$3(z^2+3z+2) = z - (2z^2+5z-12)$$
$$3z^2+9z+6 = z - 2z^2 - 5z + 12$$
$$3z^2+9z+6 = -2z^2 - 4z + 12$$
$$5z^2+13z-6 = 0$$
$$(5z-2)(z+3) = 0$$

$$5z-2=0 \qquad \text{or} \qquad z+3=0$$
$$5z=2 \qquad\qquad\qquad z=-3$$
$$z=\tfrac{2}{5}$$

Several manipulations may be necessary to bring an equation to the proper form, but the same basic steps still apply.

Solution: $\{\tfrac{2}{5}, -3\}$ □

Inequalities

Historical Note

Robert Recorde (1510–1558) was the most influential textbook writer of his period in England. His algebra text *The Whetstone of Witte* (1557) contained the first use of our present symbol for equality. He reasoned that "noe 2 thynges can be moare equalle" than two parallel lines. Another Englishman, Thomas Harriot (1560–1621), was perhaps influenced by Recorde to use intersecting lines for the symbols $<$ and $>$, which he introduced for inequalities.

The procedure used for solving certain inequalities is similar to that used for quadratic equations. Factoring is the key. And again, the first step is to obtain a 0 on one side and then to factor, as shown in the following sample problem:

$$3 - 5x > 2x^2$$
$$-2x^2 - 5x + 3 > 0$$
$$(x+3)(-2x+1) > 0$$
$$(x+3)(1-2x) > 0$$

The values of the variable for which each of the factors is 0 are called **critical values.** In this sample, the critical values are -3 and $\tfrac{1}{2}$. However, for every other value of x, the factors are not 0. That is, the critical values divide the number line into intervals on which the factors are positive or negative. The critical value is -3 for the factor $x+3$, and it separates the number line into intervals on which $x+3$ is positive or negative:

Likewise, $\tfrac{1}{2}$ divides the number line for the factor $1-2x$:

The two factors may be shown together on a single number line in order to determine those intervals on which $-2x^2 - 5x + 3$ is positive or negative:

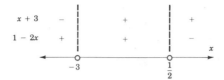

Now, the property of products can be applied to determine the sign of the product on each interval. In this example, look for the interval or intervals on which $(x + 3)(1 - 2x)$ is positive:

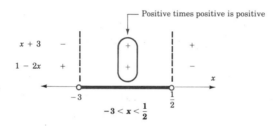

If the inequality had been $(x + 3)(1 - 2x) < 0$, you'd look, instead, for a negative product of the factors, which would produce a different solution:

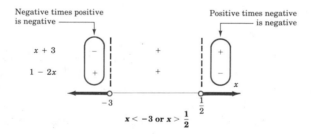

Let's now illustrate this method with several examples, and then summarize the procedure.

In Examples 4–7 solve and graph the solution on a number line.

Example 4 $3x^2 + 7x - 6 > 0$

                        $(3x - 2)(x + 3) > 0$ Factor

| | | | | |
3x − 2   —   —   +   Examine signs of factors

x + 3   —   +   +   Signs must be the same

$$x < -3 \text{ or } x > \frac{2}{3}$$

□

Example 5 $2x^2 < 5 - 3x$

$2x^2 + 3x - 5 < 0$ Bring to one side

$(2x + 5)(x - 1) < 0$

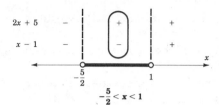

$-\dfrac{5}{2} < x < 1$

Examine signs of factors

Signs must be opposite

□

Example 6 $(x + 1)(x + 4)(2 - x) \leq 0$ How is $\leq$ different from $<$?

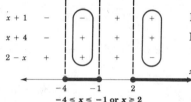

$-4 \leq x \leq -1 \text{ or } x \geq 2$

Examine factors

Look for odd number of negative signs (Why odd?)

□

Notice that for $\leq$ (or for $\geq$), the critical values are included. This is shown by drawing the critical values as solid points on the number line.

Example 7 $x^3 - 2x^2 - 35x > 0$

$x(x^2 - 2x - 35) > 0$

$x(x + 5)(x - 7 > 0$ Factor

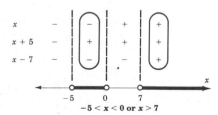

$-5 < x < 0 \text{ or } x > 7$

Examine signs

Look for even number of negative signs

□

SOLUTION OF
POLYNOMIAL
INEQUALITIES

To Solve a Polynomial Inequality:
1. Bring all nonzero terms to one side of the inequality.
2. Factor the expression.
3. Determine the critical values of the variable, and arrange them on a number line.
4. Examine the signs of the factors on the intervals between critical values.
5. Find those intervals on which there is a correct combination of signs for the given inequality.

Note that this method
applies only if the
polynomial is
factorable.

Problem Set 4.6

A   *Solve the equations in Problems 1–15 by factoring, and then check your solutions.*

See Examples 1–3.

1. $x^2 + 9x + 14 = 0$ 2. $x^2 - 8x + 15 = 0$
3. $x^2 + 5x = -6$ 4. $x^2 = 6x + 7$
5. $2x^2 = 3x + 2$ 6. $3x^2 + 2x = 1$
7. $3x^2 - 10 = 13x$ 8. $2x^2 - 9 = 3x$
9. $x^2 + 2x = 63$ 10. $x^2 + x = 72$
11. $1 - 5x + 6x^2 = 0$ 12. $12x^2 + 2 + 11x = 0$
13. $15x^2 - 4 = 17x$ 14. $42x^2 - 2 = 5x$
15. $15x^2 + 2x - 13 = 0$

Solve the inequalities in Problems 16–30, and graph each solution on a number line.

See Examples 4–7.

16. $(2x - 1)(3x + 2) < 0$ 17. $(2x + 3)(3x - 1) > 0$
18. $x^2 - 11x + 24 > 0$ 19. $x^2 - 7x + 10 < 0$
20. $x^2 + x - 20 \leq 0$ 21. $x^2 - x - 12 \geq 0$
22. $2x^2 - 3x - 2 > 0$ 23. $3x^2 - 2x - 1 < 0$
24. $3x^2 - 10 \leq 13x$ 25. $2x^2 - 9 \geq 3x$
26. $(1 - x)(x + 2)(x + 4) \geq 0$ 27. $(x - 5)(3 - x)(x + 1) \leq 0$
28. $(x + 1)(2x^2 - x - 1) < 0$ 29. $(1 - x)(3x^2 - 2x - 1) > 0$
30. $x^3 + 2x^2 + x > 0$

Fill in the word or words to make each statement in Problems 31–34 complete and correct.

31. If the product of several factors is equal to 0, then _____of the factors must be 0.

32. To solve a polynomial inequality, first _____ to one side.

33. The _____ of a factor is the value of the variable for which the factor is 0.

34. If the product of several factors is negative, then there must be _____ .

B *Solve the equations and inequalities in Problems 35–50, using the methods described in this section. Some expressions may first require simplification.*

See Examples 1–7.

35. $15x^2 = 11x + 12$

36. $21x^2 + 29x = -10$

37. $36x^2 + 11x = 12$

38. $8x^3 + 30x^2 = -27x$

39. $27x^3 < 6x^2 + 8x$

40. $2x^3 + x^2 \geq 55x$

41. $2(x^2 - 6) = x(x - 1)$

42. $3(x^2 - 1) = 2x(1 - x)$

43. $(2x + 1)(x - 1) < (x - 1)(x + 5)$

44. $2(x - 1)^2 > (x + 5)(x - 2)$

See Example 3.

45. $(x + 3)(6 - x) = (x - 3)^2 + 18$

46. $(3x - 8)(x + 3) \leq (x + 3)(7 - x)$

47. $(5x + 6)(1 - x) > (x + 2)(x + 4)$

48. $(3x + 5)(2 - x) = (2x + 1)(3x + 2)$

49. $(3x + 2)(x + 5) \leq (x + 4)(1 - 2x) + (x - 1)(x - 6)$

50. $(3x + 2)(x + 7) > (2x + 3)(1 - x) - (x - 2)^2 - x$

4.7 Further Applications of Factoring

As you have seen, if you are able to factor a polynomial, then you are able to solve the corresponding polynomial equation or inequality. The polynomials of the previous section were exclusively second-degree polynomials. Now consider some polynomials of higher degree and see how the same methods apply.

In Examples 1–4 solve by factoring.

Example 1

$$x^4 - 10x^2 + 9 = 0$$
$$(x^2 - 1)(x^2 - 9) = 0$$
$$(x + 1)(x - 1)(x + 3)(x - 3) = 0$$

$x + 1 = 0 \qquad x - 1 = 0 \qquad x + 3 = 0 \qquad x - 3 = 0$
$x = -1 \qquad\quad x = 1 \qquad\quad x = -3 \qquad\quad x = 3$

Solution: $\{-3, -1, 1, 3\}$

Example 2

$$x^3 - x = 0$$
$$x(x^2 - 1) = 0$$
$$x(x + 1)(x - 1) = 0$$

$x = 0 \qquad x + 1 = 0 \qquad x - 1 = 0$
$\qquad\qquad x = -1 \qquad\quad x = 1$

Solution: $\{-1, 0, 1\}$

Example 3

$$9y^4 + 4 = 13y^2$$
$$9y^4 - 13y^2 + 4 = 0$$
$$(9y^2 - 4)(y^2 - 1) = 0$$
$$(3y - 2)(3y + 2)(y - 1)(y + 1) = 0$$

$$y = \frac{2}{3} \qquad y = -\frac{2}{3} \qquad y = 1 \qquad y = -1$$

Solution: $\{-1, -\frac{2}{3}, \frac{2}{3}, 1\}$

Example 4 Solve $25x^3 > 4x$, and graph the solution on a number line.

Solution

$$25x^3 > 4x$$
$$25x^3 - 4x > 0$$
$$x(25x^2 - 4) > 0$$
$$x(5x - 2)(5x + 2) > 0$$

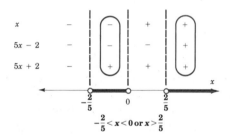

Notice that there is no largest solution. There is no smallest solution either, but 1 is the smallest integer that satisfies the inequality.

A physical application requiring these methods involves the height a projectile reaches after launch.

The height, h, that an object will reach in seconds is given by

$$h = rt - 16t^2$$

where r fps (feet per second) is the rate at which the object is initially propelled.

Note that when h and r are known, you have a quadratic in t. If the quadratic is factorable, you are able to solve the equation. Here are some examples.

Example 5 A stone is propelled upward at 112 fps. How long does it take it to reach 192 ft on the way up? On the way down?

Solution

$$h = rt - 16t^2$$
$$192 = 112t - 16t^2 \qquad \text{Given } h = 192 \text{ and } r = 112$$

$$16t^2 - 112t + 192 = 0$$
$$t^2 - 7t + 12 = 0 \qquad \text{Divide by 16}$$
$$(t - 3)(t - 4) = 0$$
$$t = 3 \quad \text{or} \quad t = 4$$

The stone reaches 192 ft after 3 seconds (on the way up) and 4 seconds (on the way down). □

Example 6   When will the stone in Example 5 be at a height of more than 160 ft?

Solution $h = rt - 16t^2$

First, the height must be more than 160:

$$160 < 112t - 16t^2$$
$$16t^2 - 112t + 160 < 0$$
$$t^2 - 7t + 10 < 0 \qquad \text{Divide by 16}$$
$$(t - 2)(t - 5) < 0$$

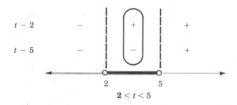

The stone will be above 160 ft between 2 seconds and 5 seconds after propulsion, or a total of 3 seconds. □

Problem Set 4.7

A   *For Problems 1–18 solve each equation for all rational solutions, and graph the solutions of the inequalities on a number line.*

See Examples 1–4.

1. $2B^2 - 18 \geq 0$
2. $16D^2 - 9 = 0$
3. $H^2 - 6H + 8 < 0$
4. $I^2 - 6I + 8 \leq 0$
5. $9L^2 + 24L + 16 = 0$
6. $9M^2 + 30M + 25 = 0$
7. $12Q^2 + 13Q < 35$
8. $20P^2 - 9P = 20$
9. $12U^2 = 35U - 25$
10. $8X^2 = 2X + 21$
11. $3A^3 + 4A^2 - 15A \geq 0$
12. $8E^3 - 27 = 4E^2 + 12E - 27$
13. $36N^4 + 4 = 25N^2$
14. $36C^4 + 25 = 229C^2$
15. $(R + 4)(16R^2 + 56R + 49) = 0$
16. $(4S^2 - 121)(9S^2 + 12S + 4) < 0$
17. $(4T + 5)^2 = 4(T - 1)(T + 1) + 3(T + 13)$
18. $(4V - 3)^2 = 4(V^2 + 4) + V$

B   *The following formula is used for Problems 19–22:* $h = rt - 16t^2$, *where h is the height an object will reach in t seconds if propelled upward at a rate of r feet per second.*

See Examples 5 and 6.

19. *Physics.* A rock is tossed upward at 64 fps. How long does it take the rock to reach 48 ft on the way up? On the way down?

20. *Physics.* A ball is hurled up at 92 fps. How long does it take to reach 60 ft on the way down?

21. *Physics.* An arrow is shot upward at 98 fps. When will the arrow be more than 55 ft above the ground?

22. *Physics.* A bullet is fired upward at 1,496 fps. For how long will the bullet be at least 5,040 ft high?

Recall that the area, *A*, of a rectangle is the base, *b*, times the height, *h* (or the length times the width):
$A = bh$

23. The base of a rectangle is 1 meter more than twice its height. If the area is 21 square meters, what are the dimensions of the figure?

24. Sixty-five square yards of carpet are laid in a rectangular room. The length is 2 yards less than three times the width. Give the dimensions of the room.

25. A large box is 3 feet tall and four times as long as it is wide. How long must it be if its surface area is at least 50 square feet?

26. An area is to be fenced. The length must be 5 ft more than the width and the total area must be more than 150 sq ft. What must be the length of the enclosure?

An open box may be constructed from a rectangular sheet of material, as shown in the margin. Square pieces are cut from the corners and the sides folded up to form the box. Problems 27–30 concern this type of box.

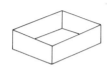

27. *Engineering.* How large a square sheet is needed to construct a box 4 cm deep with a volume of 144 cm³?

28. *Engineering.* A rectangular sheet, three times as long as it is wide, is used to construct a container 2 m deep. If the box contains 230 m³, what were the original dimensions of the sheet?

29. *Engineering.* How large a square should be cut from each corner of a 30 cm square sheet, if there is to be a surface area of 324 cm²?

30. *Engineering.* A square sheet 25 cm on a side is used to construct a box that must have 481 cm² of surface area. How large a square must be cut from each corner?

Mind Bogglers

31. Use Problems 1–18 to replace the number clues below and discover the algebra adage. Replace the roots of the equations by the corresponding variable. Choose the largest and/or the smallest integer solution for each inequality as the clue for its variable. Not all variables or roots are used in the adage.

Algebra Adage $(-\frac{10}{3})(3)(\frac{3}{2})$ $(-\frac{1}{4})(-1)(-4)(\frac{2}{3})(-3)(-\frac{4}{3})$

$(\frac{3}{2})(-2)(\frac{5}{3})(2)(-\frac{2}{3})(\bigcirc)(\frac{7}{4})$ $(\frac{3}{4})(4)(\frac{7}{3})(0)(-\frac{7}{4})(\frac{1}{4})(-5)$

(-3) $(-\frac{4}{3})(-3)(-\frac{3}{4})$ $(\frac{1}{4})(\bigcirc)$ $(-4)(\bigcirc)(-\frac{5}{3})(-3)(-\frac{1}{2})(-\frac{5}{2})(-1)$.

32. Paraphrase the algebra adage in Problem 31 as a well-known proverb or epigram.

4.8 Review Problems

Fill in the word or words that make the statements in Problems 1–10 complete and correct.

(4.1) **1.** A polynomial with two terms is called a _____.

(4.1) **2.** The exponent is the number of times the base is _____

_____ _____ _____.

(4.2) **3.** A second-degree polynomial is called a _____.

(4.3) **4.** $P/D = Q + R/D$, where P is a polynomial, D is a divisor, Q is the _____, and R is the _____.

(4.4) **5.** A _____ _____ _____ is a monomial that is a factor of each term of a polynomial.

(4.5) **6.** The product $(a+b)(a-b) = a^2 - b^2$ is called the

_____ _____ _____.

(4.5) **7.** The product $(x+a)(x^2 - ax + a^2)$ is a _____ of cubes.

(4.6) **8.** If $A \cdot B = 0$, then _____ or _____.

(4.6) **9.** If the product of several factors is greater than 0, then there must be _____.

(4.6) **10.** If _____, then A and B have the same sign.

(4.2) **11.** Find each product and simplify, if necessary.
  a. $3xy^2(x-2y)$
  b. $(y+5)(y-4)$
  c. $z(2z-1)(3z+5)$

(4.2) **12.** Find the area of a rectangle $w-1$ units wide and $3w+2$ units long.

(4.3) **13.** Determine whether $x-3$ is a factor of each polynomial, and if not, state the remainder.
  a. $x^3 - 2x^2 - 4x + 3$
  b. $3x^3 - 5x^2 - 10x + 4$
  c. $2x^4 - 5x^3 - 2x^2 - 4x + 3$

(4.4) **14.** Factor:
  a. $2xy - x^3y + 3xy^2$
  b. $y^2 - 9y + 14$
  c. $14z^2 + 3z - 5$

(4.4) **15.** If you travel $2t^2 - t - 6$ km in $t-2$ hours, what is your average rate?

(4.4) **16.** A rectangular box is d units deep and $d+2$ units wide. If the box has a volume of $d^3 + 7d^2 + 10d$ cubic units, how long is it?

(4.6)   **17.** Solve by factoring:
      a. $x^2 - 2x - 8 = 0$
      b. $2y^3 - 8y = 0$
      c. $4z^2 = 4z + 15$

THINK (4.7)   **18.** A large rectangular bin without a top is 4 m wide and twice as long
METRIC   as it is high. What are its dimensions if its surface area is 84 m²?

(4.5)   **19.** Factor:
      a. $25 - x^2$
      b. $y^3 - 8y^2 + 16y$
      c. $8z^3 + 27$

(4.6, 4.7)   **20.** Solve and graph each on a number line:
      a. $x^2 + 3x - 10 > 0$
      b. $6y^2 + 11y \leq 10$
      c. $2z^3 < 11z^2 - 9z$

CHAPTER

5

The Rationals

Contents

5.1 Rational Expressions

Rational Numbers

In algebra we work with various sets of numbers. The set of rational numbers arises quite naturally from the need for a set of numbers that is closed for addition, subtraction, multiplication, and nonzero division.

The set of integers, I, is closed for addition, since the sum of any two integers is an integer; for example,

$$(-5) + 2 = -3$$

The set I is closed for subtraction, since the difference of any two integers is an integer; for example,

$$(-5) - 2 = -7$$

The set I is closed for multiplication, since the product of any two integers is an integer; for example,

$$(-5) \times 2 = -10$$

The set I is *not closed* for division, since the quotient of integers is not necessarily an integer; for example,

$$(-5) \div 2 = ?$$

The set of rational numbers, Q, is used to fill this gap.

RATIONAL NUMBER

Rational Number

A number is called a **rational number** if it belongs to the set Q, defined by

$$Q = \left\{ \frac{a}{b} \,\middle|\, a \text{ is an integer and } b \text{ is a nonzero integer} \right\}$$

*Q is the set of quotients of integers; a is called the **numerator** and b is called the **denominator**.*

You are already familiar with the notation a/b, which is defined as

$$\frac{a}{b} = a\left(\frac{1}{b}\right)$$

Recall from Chapter 1 that multiplicative inverse means inverse for multiplication.

where $1/b$ is the **multiplicative inverse (reciprocal)** of b. Notice that the definition of rational numbers requires that $b \neq 0$, since 0 does not have a multiplicative inverse.

Equivalence Property of Rational Numbers

A given fraction can be written in different ways. Here are some examples of the many ways $\frac{1}{2}$ can be written:

$$\frac{5}{10}, \frac{8}{16}, \frac{-10}{-20}, \frac{786}{1,572}, \cdots$$

To determine whether two fractions represent the same number, we use the following important principle.

Equality of Rational Numbers

If a and c are integers and b and d are nonzero integers, then

$$\frac{a}{b} = \frac{c}{d}$$

if and only if

$$ad = bc$$

We can justify this property by multiplying both sides of the original equation by bd and simplifying:

Can you name the property used in each of these steps?

$$\frac{a}{b} = \frac{c}{d}$$

$$a\left(\frac{1}{b}\right) = c\left(\frac{1}{d}\right)$$

$$a\left(\frac{1}{b}\right)bd = c\left(\frac{1}{d}\right)bd$$

$$ad\left(\frac{1}{b}\right)b = bc\left(\frac{1}{d}\right)d$$

$$ad(1) = bc(1)$$

$$ad = bc$$

In a similar way, we can show that if $ad = bc$, then

$$\frac{a}{b} = \frac{c}{d} \qquad \text{if } b \neq 0, \, d \neq 0$$

Example 1 Which of the following fractions are equal?

a. $\frac{4}{5} \stackrel{?}{=} \frac{48}{60}$ $4(60) \stackrel{?}{=} 5(48)$ $240 = 240$
Answer: *Equal*

b. $\frac{2}{3} \stackrel{?}{=} \frac{22}{32}$ $2(32) \stackrel{?}{=} 3(22)$ $64 \neq 66$
Answer: *Not equal*

c. $\frac{a}{a-b} \stackrel{?}{=} \frac{-a}{b-a}$ $a \neq b$

$a(b-a) \stackrel{?}{=} (a-b)(-a)$
$ab - a^2 = -a^2 + ab$
Answer: *Equal*

Fundamental Property of Rational Numbers

The equivalence property of rational numbers leads us to the most important property of fractions; this property allows us not only to reduce fractions, but also to change the form of a fraction to carry out addition and subtraction.

FUNDAMENTAL
PROPERTY OF
RATIONAL
NUMBERS
This property allows
us to reduce fractions.

> **Fundamental Property of Rational Numbers**
> For any nonzero number x and any rational number a/b,
>
> $$\frac{ax}{bx} = \frac{a}{b}$$

This property follows from the equivalence property of rational numbers:

$$\frac{ax}{bx} = \frac{a}{b}$$

$$(ax)b = (bx)a \qquad \text{Can you supply reasons?}$$

$$abx = abx$$

This principle allows us to reduce fractions to lowest terms. We say that a fraction is **reduced** if the largest factor common to both numerator and denominator is 1. Thus, the key to reducing fractions is finding the factors of both numerator and denominator.

In Examples 2–4 simplify each expression

Example 2

$$\frac{45}{60} = \frac{3 \cdot 3 \cdot 5}{2 \cdot 2 \cdot 3 \cdot 5} \qquad \text{First, factor.}$$

$$= \frac{3 \cdot (3 \cdot 5)}{2 \cdot 2 \cdot (3 \cdot 5)} \qquad \text{This step is done mentally; } (3 \cdot 5) \text{ is the factor common to both numerator and denominator.}$$

$$= \frac{3}{4} \qquad \qquad \qquad \square$$

Example 3

$\dfrac{5}{3}$ This is in simplified form, since the largest factor common to both numerator and denominator is 1. $\square$

Example 4

$$\frac{45a^2bc^3}{60ab^3c^2} = \frac{3^2 \cdot 5 \cdot a^2 \cdot b \cdot c^3}{2^2 \cdot 3 \cdot 5 \cdot a \cdot b^3 \cdot c^2}$$

$$= \frac{3 \cdot a \cdot c \cdot (3 \cdot 5 \cdot a \cdot b \cdot c^2)}{2^2 \cdot b^2 \cdot (3 \cdot 5 \cdot a \cdot b \cdot c^2)}$$

$$= \frac{3ac}{4b^2} \qquad \qquad \qquad \square$$

Technically, in Example 4 we should say that $a \neq 0$, $b \neq 0$, and $c \neq 0$. In this book, we'll assume that all values for variables that cause division by 0 are excluded.

In Examples 5–7 simplify each expression.

Example 5
$$\frac{14x^2y^2z}{35y^2z} = \frac{2 \cdot 7 \cdot x^2 y^2 z}{5 \cdot 7 \cdot y^2 z}$$
$$= \frac{2x^2}{5}$$ □

Example 6
$$\frac{30(a+b)(x+y)^2}{66(a+b)^2(x+y)} = \frac{5 \cdot 6 \cdot (a+b) \cdot (x+y) \cdot (x+y)}{6 \cdot 11 \cdot (a+b) \cdot (a+b) \cdot (x+y)}$$
$$= \frac{5(x+y)}{11(a+b)}$$ □

Example 7
$$\frac{x-y}{y-x} = \frac{(x-y)(-1)}{(y-x)(-1)}$$ Multiply by 1 in the form $\frac{-1}{-1}$
$$= \frac{(x-y)(-1)}{-y+x}$$ Notice that $-y + x = x - y$.
$$= -1$$ □

Make a special note of this example. Frequently, one factor is the opposite of another (as $x - y$ and $y - x$ in this example). When a number is divided by its opposite, the result is -1. If you remember this, you can do a problem like this one directly, without intermediate steps.

Notice that we use diagonal lines to indicate a factor that is common to both numerator and denominator. When we write

$$\frac{(x+1)}{(x+1)}$$

we mean that we have

$$\frac{(x+1)}{(x+1)}$$

which is 1. Be careful, however, that you eliminate *factors* and *not terms*. The expression

$$\frac{x+1}{x-1}$$

can't be simplified further (the xs can't be eliminated because they are terms).

Example 8
$$\frac{\overset{3}{\cancel{18}}(x+2)\cancel{(x-3)}}{\underset{2}{\cancel{12}}\cancel{(3-x)}(x+2)} = \frac{-3}{2}$$

Notice how the work shown in this example has been reduced. Can you follow the steps? Compare this process with Example 7; notice that

$$\frac{x-3}{3-x} = -1$$ □

Example 9
$$\frac{(x+2)(x^2-9)}{(x^2+3x+2)(x+3)} = \frac{\cancel{(x+2)}\cancel{(x+3)}(x-3)}{(x+1)\cancel{(x+2)}\cancel{(x+3)}}$$
$$= \frac{x-3}{x+1}$$ □

As we have worked these examples, we've made a transition from rational numbers (Examples 2 and 3) to rational expressions. Notice that Examples 4–7 are not polynomials. However, they are polynomials divided by nonzero polynomials. Such expressions are called **rational expressions.**

RATIONAL EXPRESSION

> A **rational expression** is a polynomial divided by a nonzero polynomial.

Signs of a Rational Expression

The definition of rational numbers requires that in

$$\frac{a}{b}$$

a is an integer and b is a nonzero integer, so we often have cases involving positive and negative numerators and denominators. Suppose that p and q represent positive integers; then

$$\frac{p}{q} = \frac{-p}{-q} \quad \text{and} \quad \frac{-p}{q} = \frac{p}{-q}$$

Also, since the fraction itself can be negative,

$$\frac{p}{q} = -\frac{-p}{q} = -\frac{p}{-q} \quad \text{and} \quad \frac{-p}{q} = \frac{p}{-q} = -\frac{p}{q} = -\frac{-p}{-q}$$

Since all possibilities simplify to one of two forms, we formulate the following definition.

> **Standard Forms of a Fraction**
>
> If p and q represent positive integers, then the forms
>
> $$\frac{p}{q} \quad \text{and} \quad \frac{-p}{q}$$
>
> are called the **standard forms of a fraction.**

We can show that all fractional forms are equivalent to one of these standard forms by using the equivalence property of fractions. For example, the first one is justified by the following steps:

$$pq = pq$$
$$-pq = -pq$$
$$p(-q) = q(-p) \qquad \text{Can you supply the reasons for each step?}$$
$$\frac{p}{q} = \frac{-p}{-q}$$

Example 10 Write each fraction in standard form.

	Not in Standard Form	Standard Form		Not in Standard Form	Standard Form
a.	$\dfrac{-6}{-11}$	$\dfrac{6}{11}$	**b.**	$\dfrac{2}{-3}$	$\dfrac{-2}{3}$
c.	$-\dfrac{-7}{12}$	$\dfrac{7}{12}$	**d.**	$-\dfrac{5}{-8}$	$\dfrac{5}{8}$
e.	$-\dfrac{4}{9}$	$\dfrac{-4}{9}$	**f.**	$-\dfrac{-5}{-7}$	$\dfrac{-5}{7}$
g.	$\dfrac{5}{-x}$	$\dfrac{-5}{x}$	**h.**	$-\dfrac{pq}{-s}$	$\dfrac{pq}{s}$

With polynomials, the standard form can be slightly more obscure. We need to remember that

$$-(b - a) = a - b$$

From Example 1c, we know that

$$\frac{a}{a - b} = \frac{-a}{b - a} \qquad a \neq b$$

Either side of this equation is acceptable as standard form, although in most applications we prefer the form on the left.

Example 11   Write in standard form.

a. $\dfrac{x-y}{y-x} = -1$

b. $\overset{(-1)}{\dfrac{3w-3x}{sx-sw}} = \dfrac{3(w-x)}{s(x-w)}$

$\qquad\qquad\quad = \dfrac{-3}{s}$

c. $\dfrac{-mn-m^2}{n^2-m^2} = \dfrac{-m(n+m)}{(n-m)(n+m)}$

$\qquad\quad = \dfrac{-m}{(n-m)} \cdot \dfrac{(-1)}{(-1)}$

$\qquad\quad = \dfrac{m}{m-n}$ □

Problem Set 5.1

A   *Specify whether the pairs of fractions in Problems 1–10 are equal. Also, give values of the variables for which the rational numbers are not defined.*

See Example 1.

1. $\dfrac{5}{6} \overset{?}{=} \dfrac{455}{546}$

2. $\dfrac{23}{27} \overset{?}{=} \dfrac{92}{107}$

3. $\dfrac{-7}{9} \overset{?}{=} \dfrac{7}{-9}$

4. $\dfrac{-5}{-8} \overset{?}{=} \dfrac{5}{8}$

5. $\dfrac{a}{b} \overset{?}{=} \dfrac{-a}{-b}$

6. $\dfrac{-a}{b} \overset{?}{=} \dfrac{a}{-b}$

7. $-\dfrac{-a}{-b} \overset{?}{=} \dfrac{a}{b}$

8. $-\dfrac{-a}{\neg b} \overset{?}{=} \dfrac{a}{b}$

9. $\dfrac{x(a+b)}{x(c+d)} \overset{?}{=} \dfrac{a+b}{c+d}$

10. $\dfrac{x+2}{3-x} \overset{?}{=} \dfrac{x+2}{x-3}$

Write each fraction in Problems 11–19 in standard form.

See Example 10.

11. $-\dfrac{3}{-5}$

12. $-\dfrac{5}{6}$

13. $-\dfrac{-5}{-7}$

14. $\dfrac{-2}{-3}$

15. $-\dfrac{x}{5}$

16. $-\dfrac{-3x}{-y}$

17. $\dfrac{-3xy}{-2z}$

18. $\dfrac{2}{-y}$

19. $-\dfrac{x}{2-y}$

B   *Simplify each fraction in Problems 20–51.*

See Examples 2–9.

20. $\dfrac{12}{15}$

21. $\dfrac{21}{35}$

22. $\dfrac{63}{45}$

23. $\dfrac{33}{22}$

24. $\dfrac{-65}{75}$ **25.** $\dfrac{51}{-119}$ **26.** $\dfrac{76}{-95}$ **27.** $\dfrac{-60}{450}$

28. $\dfrac{-30}{550}$ **29.** $\dfrac{pq}{ps}$ **30.** $\dfrac{mpq}{mqt}$ **31.** $\dfrac{-p^3}{p^2}$

32. $\dfrac{p^2}{-p}$ **33.** $\dfrac{x}{-x^2}$ **34.** $\dfrac{x^3yz}{xyz}$ **35.** $\dfrac{14x}{21x^2}$

See Example 11a.   **36.** $\dfrac{21a^3bc}{7a^2bc}$ **37.** $\dfrac{26xy^2z}{13x^2yz^2}$ **38.** $\dfrac{a-b}{b-a}$ **39.** $\dfrac{s-t}{t-s}$

See Example 11b.   **40.** $\dfrac{3a-3b}{a-b}$ **41.** $\dfrac{m-n}{2m-2n}$ **42.** $\dfrac{p-q}{2q-2p}$ **43.** $\dfrac{6b-6a}{8a-8b}$

44. $\dfrac{(a+1)(a-2)(2a+3)}{(2a+3)(a-1)(a+1)}$ **45.** $\dfrac{(2b-1)(2b+1)(b-3)}{(3-b)(2b-1)(b+2)}$

46. $\dfrac{(c+1)^2(2c-1)}{c+1}$ **47.** $\dfrac{(d-1)^2(d+1)}{(d+1)^2(1-d)}$

See Example 11c.   **48.** $\dfrac{(x+y)^2(x-y)}{x^2-y^2}$ **49.** $\dfrac{x^2-y^2}{y^2-x^2}$

50. $\dfrac{(x^2-25)(2x+1)}{5-x}$ **51.** $\dfrac{(y^2-16)(y-3)}{(y-4)(3-y)}$

Mind Boggler   **52.** We have been careful not to use the word *cancellation* because it could lead to some incorrect assumptions. For example,

$$\frac{x^2+2}{y^2+2} \neq \frac{x^2}{y} \quad \text{and} \quad \frac{46}{36} \neq \frac{4}{3}$$

However, *sometimes* such "cancellation" does hold. For example,

$$\frac{16}{64} = \frac{1}{4} \quad \text{and} \quad \frac{19}{95} = \frac{1}{5}$$

Find one or two other fractions for which this strange "cancellation" holds true.

5.2   Operations with Rational Expressions

Multiplication and Division

The rules for multiplying and dividing rational expressions are the same as the rules for multiplication and division of fractions except that we let a and c represent any polynomials and b and d represent any nonzero polynomials.

MULTIPLICATION
AND DIVISION OF
RATIONAL
EXPRESSIONS

For any polynomials a and c, and nonzero polynomials b and d:

Multiplication $\dfrac{a}{b} \cdot \dfrac{c}{d} = \dfrac{ac}{bd}$

Division $\dfrac{a}{b} \div \dfrac{c}{d} = \dfrac{ad}{bc}$ For division, c must also be a nonzero polynomial.

In practice, the actual multiplication or division is **very easy, so your attention should be focused on simplifying the resulting rational expression. The key to multiplying and dividing rational expressions is finding the common factors.** To find common factors, first factor the numerator and denominator completely; then cancel the common factors to simplify.

Example 1

$$\frac{x^2-25}{x^2-9} \cdot \frac{x+3}{5-x} = \frac{(x-5)(x+5)(x+3)}{(x-3)(x+3)(5-x)}$$

We multiplied the fractions and at the same time factored the numerator and denominator.

$$= \frac{x+5}{(x-3)(-1)}$$

$$= \frac{x+5}{-x+3} \quad \text{or} \quad \frac{x+5}{3-x} \quad \text{or} \quad \frac{-x-5}{x-3} \qquad \square$$

Although any of these answers are acceptable, the last one is usually preferred because the denominator is in decreasing powers of the variable and also has a positive leading coefficient.

Example 2

$$\frac{x^2+7x+12}{x^2-16} \div \frac{x^2+x-6}{x-2} = \frac{x^2+7x+12}{x^2-16} \cdot \frac{x-2}{x^2+x-6}$$

$$= \frac{(x+4)(x+3)(x-2)}{(x-4)(x+4)(x-2)(x+3)}$$

$$= \frac{1}{x-4}$$

Remember that the diagonal lines don't mean "cancel out"; they represent 1. Thus, the numerator here is $1 \cdot 1 \cdot 1$ and the denominator is $(x-4) \cdot 1 \cdot 1 \cdot 1$.

$\square$

Example 3

$$\frac{x^3-8}{x^2-36} \cdot \frac{x^2-x-30}{x-2} \div \frac{x^2+2x+4}{x^2+9x+18}$$

$$= \frac{x^3-8}{x^2-36} \cdot \frac{x^2-x-30}{x-2} \cdot \frac{x^2+9x+18}{x^2+2x+4}$$ This is a mental step.

Historical Note

The sign ÷ as a symbol for division was adopted by John Wallis (1616–1703) and was used in Great Britain and the United States, but not on the European continent, where the colon (:) was used. In 1923 the National Committee on Mathematical Requirements stated: "Since neither ÷ nor :, as signs of division plays any part in business life, it seems proper to consider only the needs of algebra, and to make more use of the fractional form and (where the meaning is clear) of the symbol /, and to drop the symbol ÷ in writing algebraic expressions."*

* From *Report of the National Committee on Mathematical Requirements under the Auspices of the Mathematical Association of America, Inc.* (1923), p. 81.

$$= \frac{(x-2)(x^2+2x+4)(x-6)(x+5)(x+3)(x+6)}{(x-6)(x+6)(x-2)(x^2+2x+4)}$$

$$= (x+5)(x+3)$$

$$= x^2 + 8x + 15$$

After seeing that there are no additional common factors, you can complete the multiplication if you wish.

□

Addition and Subtraction

To add or subtract fractions you must pay attention to common denominators. For example,

$$\frac{3}{7} + \frac{2}{7} = \frac{5}{7}$$

Because $\frac{3}{7} = 3\left(\frac{1}{7}\right), \frac{2}{7} = 2\left(\frac{1}{7}\right)$, and

$$\frac{3}{7} + \frac{2}{7} = 3\left(\frac{1}{7}\right) + 2\left(\frac{1}{7}\right)$$

$$= (3+2)\left(\frac{1}{7}\right) \qquad \text{Use the distributive property.}$$

$$= 5\left(\frac{1}{7}\right)$$

$$= \frac{5}{7}$$

In general, whenever you have a common denominator,

$$\frac{a}{b} + \frac{c}{b} = \frac{a+c}{b} \qquad b \neq 0$$

If the fractions don't have common denominators, you must find a number called the **least common denominator (LCD)** and then rewrite the fractions using this LCD before adding.

LEAST COMMON DENOMINATOR (LCD)

> The **least common denominator (LCD)** of two or more fractions is the *smallest* natural number that is exactly divisible by the denominators of all of the fractions.

There is a rather straightforward procedure for finding the least common denominator. This procedure applies not only to denominators that are natural numbers, but to any polynomial denominators.

PROCEDURE FOR
FINDING THE LEAST
COMMON
DENOMINATOR

To Find the Least Common Denominator (LCD):

1. Completely factor each of the denominators and write the factorization using exponents.
2. Find the product of the representative of each factor, where the representative chosen is the one with the largest exponent.

In Examples 4–6 find the LCD for fractions having the given denominators.

Example 4 18, 30, and 40

Solution

$$18 = 2 \cdot 3^2$$
$$30 = 2 \cdot 3 \cdot 5$$
$$40 = 2^3 \quad \cdot 5$$
$$LCD = 2^3 \cdot 3^2 \cdot 5$$
$$= 360$$

Different factors are placed in different columns. Pick one representative of each different factor. The representative is the one with the largest exponent.

One way to find the complete factorization of a given number is to use a factor tree. Here's an example:

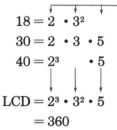

40
4 · 10 ← Any factorization of 40

2 · 2 · 2 · 5 ← Continue until all factors are prime

Example 5 $4xy, \quad 12x^2y, \quad 8xy^2$

Solution

$$4xy = 2^2 \cdot \quad x \cdot y$$
$$12x^2y = 2^2 \cdot 3 \cdot x^2 \cdot y$$
$$8xy^2 = 2^3 \cdot \quad x \cdot y^2$$
$$LCD = 2^3 \cdot 3 \cdot x^2 \cdot y^2$$
$$= 24x^2y^2$$

Example 6 $x^4 - 2x^3, \quad x^3 - 4x, \quad x^2 + 4x + 4$

Solution

$$x^4 - 2x^3 = x^3(x-2)$$
$$x^3 - 4x = x\ (x-2)(x+2)$$
$$x^2 + 4x + 4 = \qquad\qquad (x+2)^2$$
$$\downarrow \quad \downarrow \quad \downarrow$$
$$\text{LCD} = x^3(x-2)(x+2)^2 \qquad\qquad\qquad\qquad \square$$

To carry out the addition or subtraction of rational expressions, you first determine the LCD, and then multiply each fraction by 1. But the "1" is written as a fraction that contains the factors that are missing from the factored LCD. Thus, for

$$\frac{a}{b} + \frac{c}{d} \qquad b, d \neq 0$$

the LCD is *bd*, so multiply each fraction by 1:

$$\frac{a}{b}\left(\frac{d}{d}\right) + \frac{c}{d}\left(\frac{b}{b}\right) = \frac{ad}{bd} + \frac{bc}{bd}$$
$$= \frac{ad + bc}{bd}$$

(This is 1)

For subtraction, the fraction is written in standard form, and then you proceed as for addition:

$$\frac{a}{b} - \frac{c}{d} = \frac{a}{b} + \frac{-c}{d}$$
$$= \frac{ad - bc}{bd}$$

ADDITION AND SUBTRACTION OF RATIONAL EXPRESSIONS

For any polynomials *a* and *c*, and nonzero polynomials *b* and *d*:

Addition $\quad \dfrac{a}{b} + \dfrac{c}{d} = \dfrac{ad + bc}{bd}$

Subtraction $\quad \dfrac{a}{b} - \dfrac{c}{d} = \dfrac{ad - bc}{bd}$

The process of addition (or subtraction) of rational expressions is broken into five steps, as illustrated by the following examples.

In Examples 7–10 perform the indicated operations.

Example 7 $\dfrac{5}{18}+\dfrac{7}{30}-\dfrac{21}{40}$

Solution   **Step 1.** Find the LCD. In Example 4 we found the LCD for fractions having denominators of 18, 30, and 40; it is $2^3 \cdot 3^2 \cdot 5 = 360$.

$$\frac{5}{2 \cdot 3^2}=\frac{}{2^3 \cdot 3^2 \cdot 5}$$ ─Write LCD here, and repeat it for each fraction.

$$\frac{7}{2 \cdot 3 \cdot 5}=\frac{}{2^3 \cdot 3^2 \cdot 5}$$

$$\frac{-21}{2^3 \cdot 5}=\frac{}{2^3 \cdot 3^2 \cdot 5}$$ ─Write any subtractions as additions; write the fractions in standard form.

Step 2. Multiply each fraction by 1 written in a form that will give the LCD.

$$\frac{5}{2 \cdot 3^2} \cdot \frac{2^2 \cdot 5}{2^2 \cdot 5}=\frac{}{2^3 \cdot 3^2 \cdot 5}$$ Each of these is 1; notice that we have multiplied by those factors that are missing from the factored LCD.

$$\frac{7}{2 \cdot 3 \cdot 5} \cdot \frac{2^2 \cdot 3}{2^2 \cdot 3}=\frac{}{2^3 \cdot 3^2 \cdot 5}$$

$$\frac{-21}{2^3 \cdot 5} \cdot \frac{3^2}{3^2}=\frac{}{2^3 \cdot 3^2 \cdot 5}$$

Step 3. Multiply the fractions.

$$\frac{5}{2 \cdot 3^2} \cdot \frac{2^2 \cdot 5}{2^2 \cdot 5}=\frac{100}{2^3 \cdot 3^2 \cdot 5}$$ ─$5 \cdot 2^2 \cdot 5 = 100$; multiply numerator *and* denominator of *each* fraction

$$\frac{7}{2 \cdot 3 \cdot 5} \cdot \frac{2^2 \cdot 3}{2^2 \cdot 3}=\frac{84}{2^3 \cdot 3^2 \cdot 5}$$

$$\frac{-21}{2^3 \cdot 5} \cdot \frac{3^2}{3^2}=\frac{-189}{2^3 \cdot 3^2 \cdot 5}$$ Common denominators

Step 4. Complete the addition: $\dfrac{-5}{2^3 \cdot 3^2 \cdot 5}$ Add the numerators: $100 + 84 + (-189) = -5$

Step 5. Simplify the answer: $=\dfrac{-1}{2^3 \cdot 3^2}$

$$=\frac{-1}{72}$$

Example 8 $\dfrac{3}{4xy} + \dfrac{5}{12x^2y} - \dfrac{7}{8xy^2}$

Solution

$$\dfrac{3}{4xy} \cdot \dfrac{6xy}{6xy} = \dfrac{18xy}{24x^2y^2}$$

$$\dfrac{5}{12x^2y} \cdot \dfrac{2y}{2y} = \dfrac{10y}{24x^2y^2}$$

$$\dfrac{-7}{8xy^2} \cdot \dfrac{3x}{3x} = \dfrac{-21x}{24x^2y^2}$$

$$\dfrac{18xy + 10y - 21x}{24x^2y^2}$$

The five separate steps are carried out in compact form, as shown in this example. This LCD was found in Example 5.

☐

Example 9 $\dfrac{x}{x-1} + \dfrac{x-2}{1-x}$

Solution   Notice that $x - 1$ and $1 - x$ are opposites. That is, $x - 1 = (-1)(1 - x)$. To obtain a common denominator, you can multiply *either* fraction by $\dfrac{(-1)}{(-1)}$.

$$\dfrac{x}{x-1} \qquad = \dfrac{x}{x-1}$$

$$\dfrac{x-2}{1-x} \cdot \dfrac{(-1)}{(-1)} = \dfrac{-x+2}{x-1}$$

$$\dfrac{x-x+2}{x-1} = \dfrac{2}{x-1}$$

☐

Example 10 $\dfrac{4x^2}{x^2-2x} + \dfrac{8x}{4-x^2}$

Solution   *Step 1.* Factor the denominators to find the LCD. Ignore a factor of (-1) when finding the LCD; simply remember to multiply this fraction by $\dfrac{(-1)}{(-1)}$ when changing to the common denominator.

$$\dfrac{4x^2}{x(x-2)} = \dfrac{}{x(x-2)(x+2)}$$

$$\dfrac{8x}{(-1)(x-2)(x+2)} = \dfrac{}{x(x-2)(x+2)}$$

Step 2.   Find the missing factors to give the LCD.

$$\frac{4x^2}{x(x-2)}\cdot\frac{x+2}{x+2}=\frac{4x^3+8x^2}{x(x-2)(x+2)}\quad\leftarrow Step\ 3.\quad\text{Carry out the}$$
multiplication.

Found by looking for missing
factors

$$\frac{8x}{(-1)(x-2)(x+2)}\cdot\frac{(-1)x}{(-1)x}=\frac{-8x^2}{x(x-2)(x+2)}$$

Step 4.   Complete the addition.

$$\frac{4x^3}{x(x-2)(x+2)}$$

Step 5.   Simplify. Notice that you could have reduced the first fraction
in Step 1.

$$=\frac{4x^2}{(x-2)(x+2)}\qquad\qquad\square$$

Problem Set 5.2

A   *Find the LCD for fractions with the denominators given in Problems 1–8.*

See Examples 4–6.

1.   12, 15
2.   105, 20
3. $4xy,\ \ 24y^2$
4. $2x^2+x-1,\ \ 2x-1$
5. $x^2-9,\ \ 2x^2-5x-3$
6. $y^2-3y+2,\ \ y^2-5y+6$
7. $x^2-y^2,\ \ x-y,\ \ x+y$
8. $x^3-x^2-2x,\ \ x^2+2x+1,\ \ x^3-2x^2$

Perform the operations asked for in Problems 9–28. Leave your answers in the simplest form. Assume that all values of variables that cause division by 0 are excluded.

See Examples 1–3.

9. $\dfrac{75}{108}\cdot\dfrac{18}{125}$
10. $\left(\dfrac{3}{7}\cdot\dfrac{3}{5}\right)\div\dfrac{1}{2}$
11. $\dfrac{-2ab^2}{5c^3}\cdot\dfrac{25c^2}{4a^2b}$
12. $\left(\dfrac{12xy^2}{5z}\cdot\dfrac{-10xz^2}{2y^3}\right)\div4$
13. $(8x^2y+32xy^3-4xy)\div2xy$
14. $(6s^3t+18st^2-3st)\div3st$

See Examples 7–10.

15. $\dfrac{x}{12}+\dfrac{y}{15}$
16. $\dfrac{a}{105}-\dfrac{b}{20}$

17. $\dfrac{x}{12} - \dfrac{y}{20}$ 18. $\dfrac{a}{105} + \dfrac{b}{15}$

19. $\dfrac{3}{4xy} - \dfrac{5}{24y^2}$ 20. $\dfrac{6a}{7b} + 5$

21. $\dfrac{5}{x} + \dfrac{4}{5}$ 22. $\dfrac{a}{b} - 7$

23. $x + \dfrac{1}{x}$ 24. $y - \dfrac{6}{y}$

25. $\dfrac{2x-1}{2x^2+x-1} + \dfrac{3}{2x-1}$ 26. $\dfrac{4-x}{3-x} + \dfrac{6x}{x-3}$

27. $\dfrac{x-1}{18x^3} - \dfrac{x+2}{4x^2}$ 28. $\dfrac{p+4}{12p^2} - \dfrac{p+3}{18}$

B   *Perform the operations in Problems 29–54. Leave your answers in simplest form. Assume that all values of variables that cause division by 0 are excluded.*

See Examples 1–3 and 7–10.

29. $(x^2 - 25) \cdot \dfrac{2x+1}{x-5}$ 30. $(y^2 - 36) \div \dfrac{y+6}{y-1}$

31. $\dfrac{x^2-9}{x^2+8x+15} \cdot \dfrac{x^2+7x+10}{x^2-x-6}$ 32. $\dfrac{x^2-x-12}{x^2-2x-15} \div \dfrac{x^2+x-20}{x^2-25}$

33. $\dfrac{9x^2-1}{x^2-2x-8} \div \dfrac{3x+1}{x^2-16}$ 34. $\dfrac{25(3x^2-19x+20)}{2x+1} \cdot \dfrac{4x^2+4x+1}{5x^2-5x-100}$

35. $\dfrac{6}{2y-1} + \dfrac{3y-4}{1-2y}$ 36. $\dfrac{3m}{m-1} - \dfrac{2m-1}{1-m}$

37. $\dfrac{x}{(x+y)(x-z)} + \dfrac{y}{(x+y)(z-x)}$ 38. $\dfrac{2x+3}{(x-y)(x-z)} - \dfrac{3x+2}{(x-y)(z-x)}$

39. $\dfrac{2x+3}{x^2-9} + \dfrac{x-1}{2x^2-5x-3}$ 40. $\dfrac{2x}{16-x^2} + \dfrac{x+4}{x^2-3x-4}$

41. $\dfrac{4m-2}{m-n} + \dfrac{3n+1}{n-m}$ 42. $\dfrac{3x+1}{x-2} + \dfrac{2x+1}{x+1}$

43. $x + 3 + \dfrac{x}{x-4}$ 44. $y - 2 + \dfrac{y+3}{y+1}$

45. $\dfrac{x^2-4}{x^3-8} \div \dfrac{3x^2+5x-2}{x^2+2x+4}$ 46. $\dfrac{3x^2+2xy-y^2}{x^2+2xy+y^2} \cdot \dfrac{2x^2+9xy+4y^2}{3x^2+11xy-4y^2}$

47. $\dfrac{x^3-y^3}{y-x} \cdot \dfrac{(x+y)^2}{x^2+y^2}$ 48. $\dfrac{x^3+y^3}{x-y} \div \dfrac{(x+y)^2}{x^2-y^2}$

49. $\dfrac{1}{2y^2-7y-15} - \dfrac{2y+3}{y-5}$ 50. $\left(\dfrac{s+t}{s-t}\right)\left(\dfrac{s}{s-t} + \dfrac{t}{t-s}\right)$

51. $\left(\dfrac{m+1}{m-n}\right)\left(\dfrac{n}{m-n}+\dfrac{n-1}{n-m}\right)$ **52.** $\left(\dfrac{1}{x+h}-\dfrac{1}{x}\right)\div h$

53. $\left(\dfrac{1}{x+h}-\dfrac{1}{x^2}\right)\div h$ **54.** $\dfrac{(x+h)^3-x^3}{h}$

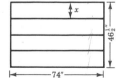

55. An outline sketch of a bookcase is shown in the figure (the dimensions given are outside measurements). The thickness of the wood used is $\frac{3}{4}$ inch. What is the clearance between the shelves (distance x) if they are equally spaced?

56. The bookcase in Problem 55 (outlined in the figure) is to be used to hold copies of *National Geographic*. If the average thickness is $\frac{5}{16}$ inch, how many copies will the bookcase hold?

57. A house plan calls for a scale of $\frac{1}{2}$ inch : 1 foot. The distance around an irregularly shaped room was measured on the plans and found to be $5\frac{3}{4}''$, $15\frac{1}{3}''$, $4\frac{5}{8}''$, and $7\frac{1}{4}''$. What will the perimeter of the actual room be in feet?

58. A farmer must fence the rectangular lot shown in the figure. The posts will be set $2\frac{1}{2}$ meters apart (from center of post to center of post).

40 m | ⎯⎯⎯⎯⎯ $127\frac{1}{2}$ m ⎯⎯⎯⎯⎯ |

    a. How many posts will be required for the entire lot?

    b. How many posts are needed to fence just one of the longer sides?

Mind Bogglers   **59.** Work this problem without using a calculator and without doing a lot of arithmetic:

$$\frac{4{,}351^2-4{,}347^2}{4{,}350\cdot4{,}353-4{,}351^2}$$

60. A man who owned 17 very rare stamps of equal value suddenly died. The lawyer read his will, which stated that the man's wife was to receive $\frac{1}{2}$ of the stamps, his oldest child $\frac{1}{3}$ of the stamps, and his youngest child $\frac{1}{9}$. The family was in a quandary about how to divide the stamp collection until the lawyer solved the problem by borrowing one additional stamp of the same kind from a museum. Now, he said, the wife will receive

$$\frac{1}{2}(18)=9 \text{ stamps}$$

the eldest will receive

$$\frac{1}{3}(18) = 6 \text{ stamps}$$

and the youngest will get

$$\frac{1}{9}(18) = 2 \text{ stamps}$$

TOTAL $= 17 \text{ stamps}$

Then the lawyer returned the stamp he had borrowed from the museum. Explain why the lawyer's solution was or was not correct.

5.3 Properties of Exponents

In Chapter 4 an exponent n was defined for n a natural number:

$$x^n = \overbrace{x \cdot x \cdot x \cdot \cdots \cdot x}^{n \text{ factors}}$$

Since n is the number of factors, the definition doesn't make sense unless n is a natural number. You have also studied three laws of exponents.

First Law of Exponents	$b^m \cdot b^n = b^{m+n}$
Second Law of Exponents	$(b^n)^m = b^{mn}$
Third Law of Exponents	$(ab)^m = a^m b^m$

Rational expressions cause us to consider another property of exponents that is similar to the third law. Consider

$$\left(\frac{x}{y}\right)^5 = \frac{x}{y} \cdot \frac{x}{y} \cdot \frac{x}{y} \cdot \frac{x}{y} \cdot \frac{x}{y} \qquad \text{Definition of exponent}$$

$$= \frac{xxxxx}{yyyyy} \qquad \text{Multiplication of rational expressions}$$

$$= \frac{x^5}{y^5} \qquad \text{Definition of exponent}$$

This leads to a fourth law of exponents.

Fourth Law of Exponents	$\left(\dfrac{a}{b}\right)^m = \dfrac{a^m}{b^m}$

We can generalize the definition of exponents so you can use them to work with rational expressions. We began this chapter by reducing fractions such as

$$\frac{x^7}{x^4} = \frac{x \cdot x \cdot x \cdot x \cdot x \cdot x \cdot x}{x \cdot x \cdot x \cdot x}$$
$$= x^3$$

Notice that $x^{7-4} = x^3$. Will this division property of powers always hold?

Example 1 $\dfrac{m^5}{m^4} = \dfrac{m \cdot m \cdot m \cdot m \cdot m}{m \cdot m \cdot m \cdot m} = m$ Notice that $\dfrac{m^5}{m^4} = m^{5-4} = m^1 = m.$ □

Example 2 $\dfrac{y^{57}}{y^{34}}$ It would be a waste of time to write this out as shown in Example 1. The numerator has 57 factors of y, and the denominator has 34 factors. All these will divide, leaving $57 - 34 = 23$ factors in the numerator. Thus,

$$\frac{y^{57}}{y^{34}} = y^{57-34} = y^{23}$$ □

Can you now write another property of powers, as indicated below?

$$\frac{b^m}{b^n} = b^{m-n} \qquad b \neq 0$$

Certainly this result works for the three preceding examples. But what if $m = n$? For example,

$$\frac{x^3}{x^3} = x^{3-3} = x^0$$

What is x^0? The original problem is the number x^3 divided by x^3, and any nonzero number divided by itself is 1. Thus, if the property

$$\frac{b^m}{b^n} = b^{m-n}$$

is to hold, then $x^0 = 1$. Also, consider the first property of exponents:

$$x^0 \cdot x^5 = x^{0+5} = x^5$$

This means

$$x^0 \cdot x^5 = x^5$$

which is true only if $x^0 = 1$. It seems that, if these properties are to hold, you should accept the following definition.

ZERO EXPONENT

> **Definition**
>
> $b^0 = 1$ $\qquad b \neq 0$

You've now seen that if $m \geq n$, then

$$\frac{b^m}{b^n} = b^{m-n}$$

What if $m < n$, as in the following example?

$$\frac{x^4}{x^7} = x^{4-7} = x^{-3}$$

But x^{-3} is not yet defined. Do you see why x^{-3} can't be defined by our original definition?

$$x^n = \overbrace{x \cdot x \cdot x \cdot \cdots \cdot x}^{n \text{ factors}}$$

If $n = -3$, then we would have

$$x^{-3} = \overbrace{x \cdot x \cdot x \cdot \cdots \cdot x}^{-3 \text{ factors}}$$

This doesn't make any sense at all, since you can't have (-3) factors. However, if it did mean something, what would it be? Consider

$$\frac{x^4}{x^7} = \frac{\cancel{x} \cdot \cancel{x} \cdot \cancel{x} \cdot \cancel{x}}{\cancel{x} \cdot \cancel{x} \cdot \cancel{x} \cdot \cancel{x} \cdot x \cdot x \cdot x}$$

$$= \frac{1}{x^3}$$

If this property of powers is to hold, then

$$x^{-3} = \frac{1}{x^3}$$

Consider the following definition.

NEGATIVE
EXPONENT

> **Definition**
>
> $b^{-n} = \dfrac{1}{b^n}$ $\qquad b \neq 0;\ n$ a natural number

Example 3   **a.** $10^{-3} = \dfrac{1}{10^3}$ **b.** $3x^{-3}y^2 = 3\left(\dfrac{1}{x^3}\right)y^2$

$= \dfrac{1}{1,000}$ $= \dfrac{3y^2}{x^3}$

$= .001$

c. $\dfrac{1}{s^{-5}} = \dfrac{1}{\frac{1}{s^5}}$ **d.** $\dfrac{5m^2t}{n^{-2}} = \dfrac{5m^2t}{\frac{1}{n^2}}$

$= 1 \cdot \dfrac{s^5}{1}$ $= 5m^2tn^2$

$= s^5$

    Notice in **Example 3** that the exponent of a *factor* will change sign if the factor is moved from the denominator to the numerator or from the numerator to the denominator. You must be careful when using this property because it only holds if it is a *factor* and not a term.

Example 4   Write each expression without using a negative exponent.

a. $\dfrac{7r^2s^{-3}}{t^{-4}} = \dfrac{7r^2t^4}{s^3}$ **b.** $\dfrac{12a^{-2}b^{-5}c^3}{18d^{-1}} = \dfrac{2c^3d}{3a^2b^5}$

c. $(-2)^{-2} = \dfrac{1}{(-2)^2}$ **d.** $-2^{-2} = -\left(\dfrac{1}{2^2}\right)$

$= \dfrac{1}{4}$ $= -\dfrac{1}{4}$

Compare **Examples 4c** and **4d**. Remember that the exponent applies only to the base and not to the negative sign, unless it is enclosed within parentheses.

    We summarize the above results in the boxes.

DEFINITION OF
EXPONENTS

> Let b be any nonzero real number, and let n be any natural number.
>
> $$b^n = \overbrace{b \cdot b \cdot b \cdot \,\cdots\, \cdot b}^{n \text{ factors}}$$
>
> $$b^0 = 1$$
>
> $$b^{-n} = \dfrac{1}{b^n}$$

LAWS OF
EXPONENTS

Let a and b be any nonzero real numbers, and let m and n be any integers.

First Law $\quad b^m \cdot b^n = b^{m+n}$
Second Law $\quad (b^n)^m = b^{mn}$
Third Law $\quad (ab)^m = a^m b^m$
Fourth Law $\quad \left(\dfrac{a}{b}\right)^m = \dfrac{a^m}{b^m}$
Fifth Law $\quad \dfrac{b^m}{b^n} = b^{m-n}$

You can combine these properties, as shown in the following examples, where all the variables are nonzero real numbers.

Example 5 Write your answers using only positive exponents. There is nothing wrong with leaving negative exponents in your answers. You are asked to use only positive exponents to give you more practice in manipulating exponents.

a. $(s^{-2}t)(s^2t^2) = s^{-2+2}t^{1+2}$
$= s^0 t^3$
$= t^3$

b. $\dfrac{10x^{-3}y^2}{5x^2y^{-3}} = \dfrac{10}{5}x^{-3-2}y^{2-(-3)}$
$= 2x^{-5}y^5$
$= \dfrac{2y^5}{x^5}$

c. $\left(\dfrac{s^{-3}}{t^4}\right)^{-2} = \dfrac{(s^{-3})^{-2}}{(t^4)^{-2}}$
$= \dfrac{s^6}{t^{-8}}$
$= s^6 t^8$

d. $\dfrac{8x^2y^{-2}z}{12x^3y^{-5}z^{-2}} = \dfrac{8}{12}x^{2-3}y^{-2-(-5)}z^{1-(-2)}$
$= \dfrac{2}{3}x^{-1}y^3z^3$
$= \dfrac{2y^3z^3}{3x}$

Compare Examples 5e and 5f, and notice how they differ.

e. $5^{-1} + 4^{-1} = \dfrac{1}{5} + \dfrac{1}{4}$
$= \dfrac{9}{20}$

f. $(5+4)^{-1} = 9^{-1}$
$= \dfrac{1}{9}$ □

Scientific Notation

One important use of integral exponents is in dealing with very large or very small numbers. Any rational number can be written as a product of a number between 1 and 10 and a power of 10. When this is done it is said to be in **scientific notation.**

Example 6 Write the following numbers in scientific notation.

a. $472 = 4.72 \times 10^2$ **b.** $93{,}000{,}000 = 9.3 \times 10^7$
c. $.0000012 = 1.2 \times 10^{-6}$ ☐

Notice that the number of places the decimal point is moved is the same as the exponent on the 10. In Example 6a, the decimal point in 4.72 is moved 2 places to the *right* (because of 10^2). In Example 6b the decimal point in 9.3 is moved 7 places to the *right* (exponent on 10 is +7). In Example 6c the decimal point in 1.2 is moved 6 places to the *left* (negative 6 exponent). You can verify this by actually doing the arithmetic:

$$10^{-6} = \frac{1}{10^6}$$
$$= \frac{1}{1{,}000{,}000}$$
$$= .000001$$

Then,

$$(1.2) \cdot (.000001) = .0000012$$

However, in practice, changing numbers into and out of scientific notation is done simply by moving the decimal point.

Example 7 Write the following numbers without using scientific notation.

a. $8.23 \times 10^5 = 823{,}000$ **b.** $5.01 \times 10^{-6} = .00000501$
c. $4.87 \times 10^{-4} = .000487$ ☐

When doing arithmetic involving numbers in scientific notation, group the powers of 10 so that you can use the laws of exponents. This will separate powers of 10 from other quantities and then you can perform the operations separately.

Example 8 Compute the result and leave your answer in scientific notation.

$$\frac{(6 \times 10^{-3})(4 \times 10^2)}{2 \times 10^4}$$

Solution

$$\left(\frac{6 \times 4}{2}\right)\left(\frac{10^{-3} \times 10^2}{10^4}\right) = 12(10^{-3+2-4})$$
$$= 12(10^{-5})$$
$$= (1.2 \times 10^1)(10^{-5})$$
$$= 1.2(10^1 \cdot 10^{-5})$$
$$= 1.2 \times 10^{-4}$$ ☐

Unit Analysis

In some scientific applications, units of measurement are associated with certain numbers by a convention known as **unit analysis.** That is, units of measurement are treated as algebraic variables in the calculations. For example, "square feet" is written ft² and is treated as the variable (ft) squared. "Two meters per second" is written 2 m/sec and is treated as the algebraic expression

$$\frac{2 \text{ m}}{\text{sec}}$$

with the number **2** multiplied by the unit **m** all divided by the unit **sec.**

Example 9 $\dfrac{15 \text{ ft}^2}{3 \text{ ft}} = 5 \text{ ft}$ Notice that the fraction $\frac{\text{ft}^2}{\text{ft}}$ has been "reduced" to ft.   □

Example 10 (10,000 kg) × (2 m/sec)²

Think of this as the following algebraic problem:

$$\frac{10{,}000 \text{ kg}}{1} \cdot \left(\frac{2 \text{ m}}{\text{sec}}\right)^2 = \frac{40{,}000 \text{ kg m}^2}{\text{sec}^2} \qquad \square$$

Example 11 $\dfrac{4 \text{ lb}}{2 \text{ in.} \times .001 \text{ in.}} = \dfrac{4 \text{ lb}}{.002 \text{ in.}^2}$

$$= 2{,}000 \text{ lb/in.}^2$$

or 2,000 pounds per square inch.   □

Problem Set 5.3

A *Perform the operations asked for in Problems 1–24. Write your answers without using negative exponents, and leave each answer in its simplest form. Assume that all variables are positive.*

See Examples 3–5.

1. $(x^2y)(x^{-2}y^3)$
2. $(a^2bc^3)(a^{-5}bc^{-2})$
3. $(m^2np^3)(m^{-1}n^{-3}p)$
4. 2^{-4}
5. -2^{-4}
6. $(-2)^{-4}$
7. $\left(\dfrac{1}{2}\right)^{-2}$
8. $-\left(\dfrac{1}{2}\right)^{-2}$
9. $\left(-\dfrac{1}{2}\right)^{-2}$
10. $2^{-1} + 3^{-1}$
11. $(2+3)^{-1}$
12. $(5+3)^{-2}$
13. $(5x^2y^{-3})^2$
14. $[4^3 + 2^5(3^2 + 4^4)]^0$
15. $(3x^{-2}y^3)^{-2}$
16. $\left(\dfrac{x^4y^{-2}}{x^2y^2}\right)^2$
17. $\left(\dfrac{a^5b}{a^2b^4}\right)^{-2}$
18. $\left(\dfrac{3s^{-2}t}{12st^2}\right)^{-1}$

19. $\dfrac{6x^{-3}y^2z^{-2}}{18xy^{-2}z^3}$ **20.** $\dfrac{15x^2y^3z^{-5}}{125x^5y^{-3}z^{-8}}$ **21.** $\dfrac{32a^{-3}b^2c}{8a^{-5}b^{-2}c^2}$

22. $(x+y)^{-1}$ **23.** $(x+y)^{-2}$ **24.** $x^{-2}+y^{-2}$

Write the numbers given in Problems 25–33 in scientific notation.

See Example 6.
25. 4,200   **26.** .00042   **27.** 10,000,000,000
28. 1,002,000,000 **29.** .0000000000613 **30.** .0000004132
31. 8.23   **32.** .00823   **33.** 823

Write the numbers given in Problems 34–42 without using scientific notation.

See Example 7.
34. 4.23×10^{-3} **35.** 2×10^{-6} **36.** 4.17×10^{-2}
37. 3×10^{12} **38.** 6.12×10^8 **39.** 5×10^{-2}
40. 5.23×10^0 **41.** 4.000201×10^{12} **42.** 8.461×10^2

B *Compute the results of Problems 43–52. Leave your answers in scientific notation.*

See Example 8.

43. $\dfrac{(5 \times 10^4)(8 \times 10^5)}{4 \times 10^6}$ **44.** $\dfrac{(6 \times 10^{-3})(7 \times 10^8)}{3 \times 10^7}$

45. $\dfrac{(2 \times 10^3)^2(6 \times 10^{-3})}{3 \times 10^{-5}}$ **46.** $\dfrac{(6 \times 10^5)(4 \times 10^{-8})^2}{32 \times 10^8}$

47. $\dfrac{(6 \times 10^7)(4.8 \times 10^{-6})}{2.4 \times 10^5}$ **48.** $\dfrac{(2.5 \times 10^3)(6.6 \times 10^8)}{8.25 \times 10^4}$

Hint for Problems 49–52: Write each number in scientific notation first. Then simplify.

49. $\dfrac{.00016 \times 500}{2,000,000}$ **50.** $\dfrac{15,000 \times .0000004}{.005}$

51. $\dfrac{4,500 \times .00001}{50 \times .0003}$ **52.** $\dfrac{.0348 \times .002}{.000058 \times .03}$

Simplify the expressions in Problems 53–61, treating the units of measure as algebraic variables.

See Examples 9–11.

53. $\dfrac{225 \text{ cm}^2}{25 \text{ cm}}$ **54.** $\dfrac{50 \text{ lb ft}}{4 \text{ ft}}$ **55.** $\dfrac{192 \text{ mi}^2}{12 \text{ mi}}$

56. $\dfrac{48 \text{ kg m/sec}^2}{6 \text{ kg}}$ **57.** $\dfrac{16 \text{ lb}}{64 \text{ lb/ft}^3}$ **58.** $98 \text{ lb} \times \dfrac{4 \text{ ft/sec}^2}{32 \text{ ft/sec}^2}$

59. $(4 \text{ kg} \times 9 \text{ m/sec}^2) - (2 \text{ kg} \times 9 \text{ m/sec}^2)$
60. $(5 \times 10^{-1}) \times (1.6 \times 10^3 \text{ kg}) \times (4 \text{ m}^2/\text{sec}^2)$
61. $\dfrac{(10^2 \text{ g} \times 4 \times 10^3 \text{ cm/sec}) - (2 \times 10^2 \text{ g} \times 2 \times 10^2 \text{ cm/sec})}{36 \times 10^2 \text{ cm/sec}}$

62. Traditionally, scientific measurements have been expressed in the metric system. Over the next several years the United States will be gradually changing to the metric system. One of the advantages of the metric system is the easy change from one unit of measurement to another. The basic units of measure are

Length: meter (m)
Capacity: liter (l)
Weight: gram (g)

The prefixes listed in the table are added to the three basic units to create the other units of measure. For example, *kilo* is added to *meter* to form *kilometer.* As you can see in the table, the metric system is based on powers of 10. Look at the following examples to discover a pattern of how to change from one metric unit to another.

Metric Prefix	Meaning
kilo	1,000 or 10^3
hecto	100 or 10^2
deka	10 or 10^1
(basic unit)	1 or 10^0
deci	.1 or 10^{-1}
centi	.01 or 10^{-2}
milli	.001 or 10^{-3}

1 meter = 10 decimeters
1 meter = 100 centimeters
1 meter = 1,000 millimeters

1 kilometer = 1,000 meters
1 kilometer = 10,000 decimeters
1 kilometer = 100,000 centimeters

1 kilogram = 10 hectograms
1 kilogram = 100 dekagrams
1 kilogram = 1,000 grams
1 kilogram = 10,000 decigrams
1 kilogram = 100,000 centigrams
1 kilogram = 1,000,000 milligrams

In your own words, explain how you change from one metric unit to another.

63. Using Problem 62, fill in the blanks.
   a. 1 liter = _____ deciliters
   b. 1 liter = _____ milliliters
   c. 1 liter = _____ kiloliters
   d. 1 kilometer = _____ millimeters
   e. 1 meter = _____ kilometers

64. Using Problem 62, fill in the blanks.
   a. 6.23 liters = _____ milliliters
   b. 4.5 meters = _____ centimeters
   c. 6 centimeters = _____ millimeters

d. 48 millimeters = _____ centimeters

e. 33 dekaliters = _____ hectoliters

65. Electronic calculators are now available to most of us. Several kinds have a key marked

$\boxed{\text{EE}}$ or $\boxed{\text{E Ex}}$

that allows you to enter a number in scientific notation. For example, to enter 4.83×10^{-6}, you first depress 4.83

$\boxed{4}\;\boxed{.}\;\boxed{8}\;\boxed{3}$

and then the

$\boxed{\text{EE}}$

key; the display will now read

4.83   00.

Next depress

$\boxed{6}$ and $\boxed{+/-}$

to obtain

4.83   −06.

This means 4.83×10^{-6}. Work Problems 43–45 on an electronic calculator.

66. Work Problems 46–48 on an electronic calculator.

Mind Bogglers

67. *Astronomy.* Our sun is so large that, if it were hollow, it could contain more than one million worlds the size of our earth. There are about 100 billion stars in the average galaxy, and the average star could hold 200 million suns the size of ours. There are at least 100 million galaxies in known space. How many planets the size of earth could fit in all those stars, if we assume that all the stars and galaxies are of average size?

68. *Finance.* The Indians sold Manhattan Island to the Dutch in 1626 for goods worth about $24. It has often been said that the Dutch took advantage of the Indians. However, suppose the Indians put the $24 in a savings account at 7% interest. The formula for calculating interest is

$A = P(1 + i)^n$

where A is the amount at present, P is the principal ($24 for this problem), i is the interest written as a decimal (.07 for this problem), and n is the number of years. For example, after 1 year,

$A = 24(1 + .07)^1$

$= 25.68$

After 2 years,

$$A = 24(1 + .07)^2$$
$$= 27.48$$

Show that the value of the money was more than $450,000,000,000 in 1976, and write your answer in scientific notation. (If you have a calculator, you should be able to make a closer estimate than $450 billion.)

 69. A sheet of notebook paper is approximately .003 inch thick. Tear the sheet in half so that there are two sheets. Place one on top of the other and tear them in half again so that there are four sheets. Repeat, so that there are eight sheets. If it were possible to continue in this fashion until the paper has been halved 50 times, how high would you guess the final pile would be? Having guessed, *compute* the height. [*Hint*: $2^{50} = 1,125,899,906,842,624$]

70. It has been said that you can determine the speed of a train on which you are a passenger by listening to the clickety-clack of the train. To do this, count the number of clickety-clacks in 20 sec. This number is the approximate speed of the train in miles per hour. Show how you can use this information to find the approximate length of each rail of track.

5.4 Rational Equations

We've already solved several types of equations, and now we consider equations that involve variables in one or more denominators. For example, the equation

$$\frac{x+1}{3x} = \frac{1}{x} - \frac{1}{3}$$

is called a **rational equation.** The procedure for solving rational equations is the same as for solving other equations, except that values of the variable that cause division by 0 are excluded from the solution set.

RATIONAL
EQUATION

A **rational equation** is an equation with at least one variable in a denominator.

PROCEDURE FOR
SOLVING A
RATIONAL
EQUATION

To Solve a Rational Equation:

Step 1. Exclude values that cause division by 0.

Step 2. Multiply both sides by the LCD and simplify.

Step 3. Solve the resulting equation.

Step 4. Check each member of the solution set to make sure it is not one of the excluded values; that is, the values in the solution set must not cause division by 0. Any value that is excluded in this manner is called an **extraneous root.**

In Examples 1–3 solve each rational equation.

Example 1 $\dfrac{x+1}{3x} = \dfrac{1}{x} - \dfrac{1}{3}$

Solution   *Step 1.*   Set each denominator equal to 0 and solve by inspection:

$$3x = 0 \qquad\qquad x = 0 \qquad\qquad \text{The denominator 3 is not 0.}$$
$$x = 0$$

Thus, $x \neq 0$.

Step 2. $(3x)\dfrac{x+1}{3x} = (3x)\left(\dfrac{1}{x} - \dfrac{1}{3}\right)$

$$x + 1 = 3x\left(\dfrac{1}{x}\right) - 3x\left(\dfrac{1}{3}\right)$$

$$x + 1 = 3 - x$$

Step 3. $2x + 1 = 3$

$$2x = 2$$

$$x = 1$$

Step 4.   The solution set is {1} because we checked $x = 1$ against the excluded value, $x \neq 0$.   □

Example 2 $\dfrac{3x}{x-4} + 4 = \dfrac{8-5x}{4-x}$

Solution   *Step 1.*   Set each denominator equal to 0 and solve:

$$x - 4 = 0 \qquad 4 - x = 0 \qquad \text{The denominator on the term 4}$$
$$x = 4 \qquad\qquad 4 = x \qquad \text{cannot be 0 since it is 1}$$

(remember that $4 = \frac{4}{1}$).

Write $x \neq 4$, since this is the only value of x that can cause any of the denominators to be 0. This step can be done by inspection.

Step 2. $(x-4)\dfrac{3x}{x-4} + (x-4)4 = (x-4)\left(\dfrac{8-5x}{4-x}\right)$ Notice: $\dfrac{8-5x}{4-x} = \dfrac{5x-8}{x-4}$.

Step 3.
$$3x + 4x - 16 = 5x - 8$$
$$7x - 16 = 5x - 8$$
$$2x = 8$$
$$x = 4$$

Step 4. We excluded 4 from the solution set (Step 1), so the solution set is empty. If we check $x = 4$ in the original equation, we have

$$\frac{3(4)}{4-4} + 4 = \frac{8-5(4)}{4-4}$$

$\underset{\text{Division by 0}}{\uparrow\qquad\uparrow}$

which is impossible. The number 4 is an extraneous root. ☐

Example 3 $\dfrac{2x+1}{x+3} + \dfrac{3x-7}{2-x} = \dfrac{2x^2+10x-13}{6-x-x^2}$

Solution *Step 1.* Find (by inspection, if possible) the values that make any denominator equal to 0.

$$\begin{array}{ccc}
x+3=0 & 2-x=0 & 6-x-x^2=0 \\
x=-3 & 2=x & (-1)(6-x-x^2)=0 \\
 & & x^2+x-6=0 \\
 & & (x-2)(x+3)=0 \\
 & & x=2, -3
\end{array}$$

Thus, the excluded values are -3 and 2 so we write $x \neq -3, 2$.

Step 2. $(x+3)(x-2)\dfrac{2x+1}{x+3} + (x+3)(x-2)\dfrac{3x-7}{2-x}$

$$= (x+3)(x-2)\frac{2x^2+10x-13}{6-x-x^2}$$

Step 3. $(x+3)(x-2)\dfrac{2x+1}{x+3} + (x+3)(x-2)\overset{(-1)}{\dfrac{3x-7}{2-x}}$

$$= (x+3)(x-2)\overset{(-1)}{\frac{2x^2+10x-13}{(3+x)(2-x)}}$$

$$(x-2)(2x+1) + (x+3)(-1)(3x-7) = (-1)(2x^2+10x-13)$$
$$2x^2 - 3x - 2 - 3x^2 - 2x + 21 = -2x^2 - 10x + 13$$
$$x^2 + 5x + 6 = 0$$
$$(x+2)(x+3) = 0$$
$$x = -2, -3$$

Step 4. From Step 1, $x = -3$ is extraneous, so the solution set is $\{-2\}$. □

Rational expressions are sometimes referred to as **ratios**. Ratios can be expressed three ways:

Words	*Symbols*	*Fractions*
20 to 1	20:1	$\dfrac{20}{1}$
5 to 4	5:4	$\dfrac{5}{4}$

A **proportion** is a statement of equality between two ratios. Proportions often give rise to rational equations.

Example 4 In a can of mixed nuts the ratio of cashews to peanuts is one to six. If a given machine releases 46 cashews into a can, how many peanuts should be released?

Solution $\dfrac{\text{NUMBER OF CASHEWS}}{\text{NUMBER OF PEANUTS}} = \dfrac{1}{6}$ This is the given ratio

Fill in the given quantities.

$$\dfrac{46}{\text{NUMBER OF PEANUTS}} = \dfrac{1}{6}$$

Let $p = $ NUMBER OF PEANUTS released:

$$\dfrac{46}{p} = \dfrac{1}{6}$$

Solve the resulting equation with $p \neq 0$.

$$\dfrac{46}{p}(6p) = \dfrac{1}{6}(6p)$$
$$276 = p$$

Thus, 276 peanuts should be released. □

We also use proportions and rational equations when dealing with **similar triangles**.

SIMILAR TRIANGLES

$\triangle ABC$ is similar to $\triangle A'B'C'$ if the corresponding angles are equal, and we write

$\triangle ABC \sim \triangle A'B'C'$

Essentially, this means that triangles are similar if they have the same shape (see Figure 5.1).

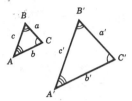

Figure 5.1 Similar Triangles

If two triangles are similar, then the corresponding sides are proportional:

$$\frac{a}{c} = \frac{a'}{c'} \qquad \frac{a}{b} = \frac{a'}{b'} \qquad \frac{b}{c} = \frac{b'}{c'} \qquad \text{and so forth}$$

This information has a wide variety of applications. Example 5 shows how to measure the width of a river by using similar triangles

Example 5 Find the distance across the river shown in Figure 5.2.

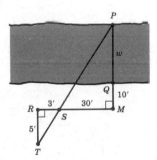

Figure 5.2 Finding the Distance Across a River

Solution Pick a reference point P on the other side of the river (see Figure 5.2). Measure a given distance, say 10 feet from the river bank (point M). Pace out another distance, say 30 feet (this is some convenient arbitrary distance), and place a stake at S. Now pace out another triangle so that there is a right angle at R, and TSP forms a straight line. If RS is 3 feet and RT is 5 feet, you can now find the width of the river, w (distance PQ). Since their corresponding angles are equal, $\triangle RST \sim \triangle PSM$. Now,

$$\frac{SM}{MP} = \frac{SR}{RT}$$

since corresponding sides are proportional. Fill in the missing values to obtain

$$\frac{30}{w+10}=\frac{3}{5}$$

Solve the proportion:

$$30(5)=3(w+10) \qquad \text{Multiply both sides by } 5(w+10), \text{ and simplify.}$$
$$150=3w+30$$
$$120=3w$$
$$40=w \qquad \text{Remember that the answer to a word problem should be in words, not in a math equation.}$$

The river is 40 feet wide. ☐

Problem Set 5.4

A *Solve the equations in Problems 1–18.*

See Examples 1 and 2.

1. $\dfrac{D}{3}+8=-\dfrac{D}{5}$

2. $\dfrac{3}{A}+8=-\dfrac{5}{A}$

3. $\dfrac{5P}{2}-\dfrac{21}{10}=\dfrac{2P}{5}$

4. $\dfrac{2}{5M}+\dfrac{1}{10}=\dfrac{5}{2M}$

5. $\dfrac{2}{5}N+\dfrac{1}{10}=\dfrac{5}{2}$

6. $\dfrac{5I}{I+1}-5=\dfrac{5}{I}$

7. $\dfrac{5}{V}+\dfrac{1}{2V}-\dfrac{15}{3V}=1$

8. $\dfrac{H}{H-1}=\dfrac{H+2}{H-2}$

9. $\dfrac{S-10}{6}+\dfrac{S}{3}=\dfrac{6(S+3)}{18}-3$

10. $\dfrac{5}{Q-3}+7=\dfrac{2-4Q}{6-2Q}$

11. $\dfrac{3}{L}-\dfrac{4}{L-1}=\dfrac{-4}{2L}$

12. $\dfrac{2G-4}{G+1}-\dfrac{6G}{3G+1}=0$

13. $\dfrac{3}{4J-8}-\dfrac{1}{24}=\dfrac{2}{3J-6}$

14. $\dfrac{3}{5W+5}-\dfrac{1}{40}=\dfrac{3}{4W+4}$

15. $\dfrac{6}{T-5}-\dfrac{3}{T+2}=\dfrac{6T}{T^2-3T-10}$

16. $\dfrac{3}{E}+\dfrac{2}{E-4}=\dfrac{4(E-4)}{E^2-4E}$

17. $\dfrac{2U-11}{U^2-9}=\dfrac{U}{U-3}-\dfrac{U-1}{U+3}$

18. $\dfrac{3}{C-4}+\dfrac{4}{C+4}=\dfrac{17}{C^2-16}$

B
Algebra Adage

19. Use Problems 1–18 to complete the algebra adage below. Replace each value within parentheses by the capital letters from the problems above. The letters O and R have been filled in for you.

$(O)(6)(-4)$ $\qquad (-7)(\tfrac{2}{3})(O)(-2)(-4)$ $\qquad (-15)(O)(21)(-\tfrac{1}{2})(3)(-\tfrac{1}{2})(5)(-4)$
$(-\tfrac{1}{2})(-2)$ $\qquad (9)(R)(-1)(6)(-2)(1)(-1)(R)(-4)(6)(9)$ $\qquad (21)(-\tfrac{8}{5})(-2)(9)$
$(6)(O)(9)$ $\qquad (9)(O)(-2)(-2)$ $\qquad (-\tfrac{1}{4})(R)(-1)(6)(-\tfrac{1}{2})(9)(-4)$
$(1)(R)(O)(4)(-4)(3)(9)(-\tfrac{1}{2})(5)(-4)(-2).$

20. Rephrase the algebra adage as a familiar proverb or saying.

Solve the equations in Problems 21–26.

See Example 3. **21.** $\dfrac{5-x}{x^2-x-6} - \dfrac{3}{x^2+2x} + \dfrac{1}{x} = 0$ **22.** $\dfrac{7-x}{x^2-x-12} - \dfrac{5}{x^2+3x} + \dfrac{1}{x} = 0$

23. $\dfrac{4x-1}{x^2-x-2} + \dfrac{5-3x}{x^2+4x+3} = \dfrac{x+11}{x^2+x-6}$

24. $\dfrac{3x+2}{x^2-9x+20} - \dfrac{2x+5}{x^2-8x+15} = \dfrac{x-18}{x^2-7x+12}$

25. $\dfrac{3}{x+2} + \dfrac{x-1}{x+5} = \dfrac{5x+20}{6x+24}$ **26.** $\dfrac{x-3}{x-2} + \dfrac{x-1}{x} = \dfrac{22x-110}{3x^2-15x}$

See Example 4. **27.** *Baking.* In a recipe for bread, flour and water are to be mixed in a ratio of 3 parts water to 5 parts flour. If 2.4 liters of water are called for, how much flour is needed?

28. The formula for a certain shade of green paint calls for mixing 8 parts blue with 3 parts yellow. If 7.5 liters of yellow are on hand, how much blue should be purchased to make up the proper mixture?

29. You've probably seen advertisements for posters that can be made from any photograph. If the finished poster will be 2 ft by 3 ft, it's likely that part of your original snapshot will be lost. Suppose you sent in a photo that measures 3″ × 5 ″. If the shorter side of the enlargement will be 2 ft, what size should the longer side be enlarged to for the entire snapshot to be represented?

30. Suppose you wish to make a scale drawing of your family room, which measures 18 ft by 25 ft. If the shorter side of the scale drawing is 6 inches, how long is the longer side of the scale drawing?

See Example 5. **31.** *Surveying.* Suppose you wish to measure the distance across the river shown in the figure. You find that distance *SM* is 35 ft, *RS* is 8 ft, and *RT* is 16 ft. How far is it across the river?

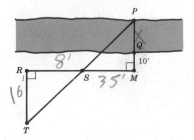

32. *Surveying.* Suppose *SM* of the figure in Problem 31 is 105 ft and *RS* is 12 ft, while *RT* is 36 ft. How far is it across the river?

Mind Bogglers

THINK
METRIC

33. Eight property owners are sharing expenses to have the road they live on improved. Each person's property is assessed according to the amount of land fronting the road. Three property owners have 25 meter fronts, two have 35 meter fronts, two have 40 meter fronts, and one has a 50 meter front. The total assessment is $85,000. How much should each owner pay?

34. At a certain hamburger stand the proprietor dispensed soft drinks out of two 16 gallon barrels, always making sure the barrels had equal amounts. At the end of the first day he wished to increase his profits, so he filled the soft-drink barrels with water, thus diluting the drink served. He repeated the procedure at the end of the second and third days. At the end of the fourth day he had 10 gallons left that contained 1 pint of pure soft drink remaining in both barrels. If the same amount was served each day, how much pure soft drink was served in the four days?

35. Show that the sum of any positive fraction and its multiplicative inverse is always greater than or equal to 2.

5.5 ~~messy~~ Complex Fractions

Whenever we've considered the expression $\frac{a}{b}$, we've limited a and b to polynomials. But suppose that a and b are themselves rational expressions.

COMPLEX
FRACTION

> If a or b in $\frac{a}{b}$ has fractional form, then $\frac{a}{b}$ is called a **complex fraction.**

To simplify complex fractions you only need to remember that $\frac{a}{b}$ means a divided by b. For example,

$$\frac{\dfrac{9x^2-1}{x^2-2x-8}}{\dfrac{3x+1}{x^2-16}}=\frac{9x^2-1}{x^2-2x-8}\div\frac{3x+1}{x^2-16}$$

$$\frac{\dfrac{x^2-4}{x^3-8}}{\dfrac{3x^2+5x-2}{x^2+2x+4}}=\frac{x^2-4}{x^3-8}\div\frac{3x^2+5x-2}{x^2+2x+4}$$

As you can see, division problems look terribly complicated, or *complex,* when written this way. But they are not difficult at all if you remember that they are just division problems. First, write the numerator as a simplified rational expression and then write the denominator as a simplified rational expression. Finally, divide the numerator by the denominator. Remember the following rule for division of fractions:

$$\frac{\dfrac{a}{b}}{\dfrac{c}{d}} = \frac{a}{b} \div \frac{c}{d}$$

$$= \frac{a}{b} \cdot \frac{d}{c} \qquad b, c, d \neq 0$$

This rule says that to simplify complex fractions, you **invert the denominator and multiply the result by the numerator.** To do this, the numerator and denominator should each first be written as a single fraction.

Example 1 Simplify the following expressions.

a. $\dfrac{2 + x^{-1}}{2^{-1} + 3^{-1}} = \dfrac{2 + \dfrac{1}{x}}{\dfrac{1}{2} + \dfrac{1}{3}}$

$= \dfrac{\dfrac{2x + 1}{x}}{\dfrac{5}{6}}$

$= \dfrac{2x + 1}{x} \cdot \dfrac{6}{5}$

$= \dfrac{12x + 6}{5x}$

b. $\dfrac{1 + \dfrac{2}{x}}{3 - \dfrac{4}{x}} = \dfrac{\dfrac{x + 2}{x}}{\dfrac{3x - 4}{x}}$

$= \dfrac{x + 2}{x} \cdot \dfrac{x}{3x - 4}$

$= \dfrac{x + 2}{3x - 4}$

□

A second method for simplifying complex fractions is to **multiply the numerator and denominator of the complex fraction by the LCD of the fractions appearing in the numerator and denominator.**

In Examples 2 and 3 simplify each expression.

Example 2   Rework Example 1a using the LCD method.

Solution $\dfrac{2+x^{-1}}{2^{-1}+3^{-1}}=\dfrac{2+\dfrac{1}{x}}{\dfrac{1}{2}+\dfrac{1}{3}}=\dfrac{\dfrac{2x+1}{x}}{\dfrac{5}{6}}$

The LCD of the fractions is $6x$, so multiply the numerator and denominator of the complex fraction by $6x$:

$$=\dfrac{\dfrac{2x+1}{x}}{\dfrac{5}{6}}\cdot\dfrac{6x}{6x}$$

$$=\dfrac{\dfrac{2x+1}{x}\cdot\dfrac{6x}{1}}{\dfrac{5}{6}\cdot\dfrac{6x}{1}}$$

$$=\dfrac{(2x+1)(6)}{5x}$$

$$=\dfrac{12x+6}{5x}\qquad\square$$

Example 3 $\dfrac{\dfrac{x^2-16}{x-2}}{\dfrac{x+4}{7x-14}}$

Solution   The LCD of the fractions is $7(x-2)$, so we have

$$\dfrac{\dfrac{x^2-16}{x-2}}{\dfrac{x+4}{7(x-2)}}\cdot\dfrac{7(x-2)}{7(x-2)}=\dfrac{(x^2-16)(7)}{x+4}$$

$$=\dfrac{7(x-4)(x+4)}{x+4}$$

$$=7x-28\qquad\square$$

Problem Set 5.5

Simplify the expressions in Problems 1–30. All values for the variables that could cause division by 0 are excluded.

A

See Examples 1–3.
You can use either method.

1. $\dfrac{\dfrac{2}{3}}{1+\dfrac{2}{3}}$ **2.** $\dfrac{2}{4-\dfrac{5}{6}}$ **3.** $\dfrac{9-\dfrac{2}{3}}{\dfrac{3}{4}}$ **4.** $\dfrac{2^{-1}+3^{-1}}{2+3}$

5. $\dfrac{5+6}{5^{-1}+6^{-1}}$ **6.** $\dfrac{8+4}{8^{-1}+4^{-1}}$ **7.** $\dfrac{\dfrac{5}{x}+\dfrac{1}{2x}}{1+\dfrac{1}{x}}$ **8.** $\dfrac{3-\dfrac{1}{x}}{\dfrac{2}{x^2}+\dfrac{3}{x}}$

9. $\dfrac{\dfrac{a+1}{a}}{\dfrac{a-1}{a^2}}$ **10.** $\dfrac{\dfrac{s}{4}}{1+\dfrac{1}{s}}$ **11.** $\dfrac{t+\dfrac{1}{3}}{\dfrac{t}{5}}$ **12.** $\dfrac{m+\dfrac{1}{2}}{\dfrac{1}{m}}$

13. $\dfrac{\dfrac{(n+1)(n-1)}{n+2}}{\dfrac{(n-4)(n+4)}{n+2}}$ **14.** $\dfrac{\dfrac{(m-2)(m+2)}{m+3}}{\dfrac{(m-1)(m+2)}{m+3}}$

B **15.** $\dfrac{\dfrac{m^2-16}{m-1}}{\dfrac{m-4}{5m-5}}$ **16.** $\dfrac{\dfrac{n^2+5n+6}{8n-4}}{\dfrac{n^2+n-6}{2n-1}}$ **17.** $\dfrac{\dfrac{y^2-4}{2y+1}}{\dfrac{y^2+y-2}{2y+1}}$

18. $\dfrac{\dfrac{x-1}{x+1}-\dfrac{x}{x-1}}{\dfrac{x+1}{x-1}-\dfrac{x-1}{x+1}}$ **19.** $\dfrac{\dfrac{s+t}{s-t}-\dfrac{s-t}{s+t}}{\dfrac{2}{s-t}+\dfrac{2}{s+t}}$ **20.** $\dfrac{\dfrac{1}{(x+h)^3}-\dfrac{1}{x^3}}{h}$

21. $\dfrac{\dfrac{1}{(x+h)^2}-\dfrac{1}{x^2}}{h}$ **22.** $\dfrac{\left(1+\dfrac{1}{x+h}\right)-\left(1+\dfrac{1}{x}\right)}{h}$

23. $\dfrac{\dfrac{1}{3(x+h)^2+1}-\dfrac{1}{3x^2+1}}{h}$ **24.** $\dfrac{\dfrac{1}{xy}+\dfrac{2}{yz}-\dfrac{3}{xz}}{2x^{-1}+3y^{-2}-4z^{-1}}$

25. $\dfrac{1+\dfrac{1}{1+\dfrac{x}{y}}}{1-\dfrac{2}{1+\dfrac{x}{y}}}$

26. $\dfrac{(x+4)^{-1}+3(x+2)^{-1}}{(x+5)^{-1}-2(x+1)^{-1}}$

27. $\dfrac{x+2-\dfrac{5}{x-3}}{x-1+\dfrac{3}{x-5}}$

28. $\dfrac{1}{1+\dfrac{1}{1+\dfrac{1}{1+1}}}$

29. $\dfrac{2}{2+\dfrac{2}{2+\dfrac{2}{2+2}}}$

30. $\dfrac{3}{3+\dfrac{3}{3+\dfrac{3}{3+3}}}$

Mind Bogglers

31. After working Problems 28–30, look for a pattern and then find the following *without* doing a lot of arithmetic.

a. $\dfrac{4}{4+\dfrac{4}{4+\dfrac{4}{4+4}}}$

b. $\dfrac{5}{5+\dfrac{5}{5+\dfrac{5}{5+5}}}$

c. $\dfrac{60}{60+\dfrac{60}{60+\dfrac{60}{60+60}}}$

d. $\dfrac{1{,}987}{1{,}987+\dfrac{1{,}987}{1{,}987+\dfrac{1{,}987}{1{,}987+1{,}987}}}$

e. $\dfrac{x}{x+\dfrac{x}{x+\dfrac{x}{x+x}}}$

Historical Note

Problem 32 is adapted from Sam Lloyd's *Covent Garden Problem*, which appeared in London half a century ago. It was also purported to have mystified the leading mathematicians of England (which is surely quite unlikely). However, the solution is surprisingly easy. See if you can solve the problem.

32. Mr. Smith and Mr. Boyle were selling handpainted mustache cups. For some unexplained reason, Mr. Boyle was called away and asked Mr. Smith to dispose of his stock. Now it appears that each had an equal number of cups, but Mr. Boyle's were more elaborate and were selling for two for $1 while Mr. Smith sold his for three for $1. However, to save some extra accounting problems, Mr. Smith sold the cups off at the rate of five cups for $2. Mr. Boyle returned to find that Mr. Smith was sold out but was also $7 short because of the new selling price. If they divided the money equally, how much did Mr. Boyle lose by this unfortunate partnership?

5.6 Review Problems

Complete the statements in Problems 1–5 with the word or words that make them complete and correct.

(5.1) **1.** A number is called a _rational_ number if it belongs to the set Q.

(5.1) **2.** If p and q are positive integers, then _____ and _____ are the standard forms for rational numbers.

(5.1) **3.** A _____ is a polynomial divided by a _____ polynomial.

(5.4) **4.** A _____ is a statement of equality between two ratios.

(5.4) **5.** Two triangles are _similar_ if their corresponding angles are equal.

(5.1) **6.** Replace the question mark by $=$ or $\neq$ to make a true statement.

   a. $\dfrac{14}{15} \; ? \; \dfrac{42}{45}$ **b.** $\dfrac{14}{71} \; ? \; \dfrac{98}{497}$

   c. $\dfrac{9}{15} \; ? \; \dfrac{55.8}{93}$ **d.** $\dfrac{x^2 + x - 2}{x^2 + 3x - 4} \; ? \; \dfrac{x^2 + 2x}{x^2 + 4x}$

Simplify each expression in Problems 7–11.

(5.2) **7.** $\dfrac{28x^2y}{245z^3} \div \dfrac{18xy^3}{35z^2}$

(5.2) **8.** $\dfrac{5m}{m-1} + 1$

(5.3) **9.** $\dfrac{(8x^2y)(2x^{-1}y^{-3})}{32x^{-2}y^{-5}}$

(5.2) **10.** $3 + \dfrac{3s+1}{4-2s} - \dfrac{4s-1}{3s-6}$

(5.5) **11.** $\dfrac{\dfrac{a-3}{a+3} - \dfrac{a}{a-3}}{\dfrac{a+3}{a-3} + \dfrac{3}{a+3}}$

(5.4) *Solve the equations given in Problems 12–18.*

   12. $\dfrac{t}{5t} + \dfrac{7}{15} = \dfrac{4}{3t}$ **13.** $\dfrac{4}{m-5} + 3 = \dfrac{5m}{10-2m}$

   14. $\dfrac{5}{3-y} + 4 = \dfrac{4}{y-3}$ **15.** $\dfrac{2x}{x+5} + 1 = \dfrac{3x}{x-5}$

   16. $\dfrac{(18 \times 10^4)(3 \times 10^{-6})^3}{36 \times 10^{12}} = x$ **17.** $\dfrac{2}{6x^2 + 14x - 12} - \dfrac{5}{3x-2} = \dfrac{1}{2x+6}$

18. $\dfrac{15}{x^2 - x - 2} - \dfrac{5}{x - 2} = \dfrac{4}{x + 1}$

$\dfrac{3}{8} + \dfrac{5}{8}$ (5.4) **19.** *Business.* Two people share a profit of $8,500. If the money is to be divided in a ratio of 3 to 5, how much will each receive?

(5.4) **20.** *Surveying.* Suppose you wish to measure the distance across a canyon, so you make the measurements shown in the figure. How far is it across the canyon (distance *PQ*)?

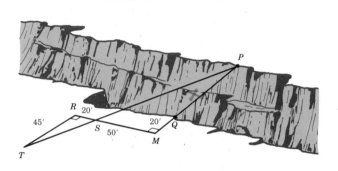

CHAPTER

6

Roots, Radicals, and Complex Numbers

Contents

6.1 Rational Exponents

In your previous work you have used square roots and perhaps cube roots. We now wish to generalize this idea to include other roots.

nTH ROOT

SQUARE ROOT

CUBE ROOT

> An **nth root** (where n is a natural number) of a number b is a if and only if $a^n = b$.
> If $n = 2$, it is called a **square root.**
> If $n = 3$, it is called a **cube root.**

Example 1   3 is a square root of 9 since $3^2 = 9$.   □

Example 2   −3 is a square root of 9 since $(-3)^2 = 9$.   □

Example 3   3 is a fourth root of 81 since $3^4 = 81$.   □

Example 4   −3 is a fourth root of 81 since $(-3)^4 = 81$.   □

Example 5   3 is a cube root of 27 since $3^3 = 27$.   □

Example 6   −3 is a cube root of −27 since $(-3)^3 = -27$.   □

Example 7   −4 is a cube root of −64 since $(-4)^3 = -64$.   □

Example 8   0 is a fifth root of 0 since $0^5 = 0$.   □

Example 9   1 is a ninth root of 1 since $1^9 = 1$.   □

Example 10   −2 is a tenth root of 1,024 since $(-2)^{10} = 1,024$.   □

If you carefully consider these examples you can make two observations:

1. A number may have more than one root (Examples 1 and 2; Examples 3 and 4).

2. Roots may be positive (Examples 1, 3, 5, and 9), negative (Examples 2, 4, 6, 7, and 10), or 0 (Example 8).

Also, notice that we have not used any symbol for roots in the above examples, though you have probably used $\sqrt{}$ or $\sqrt[3]{}$ before. We will delay using this *radical notation* until the next section, because the traditional notation requires a development of some new rules of algebra to tell us how to manipulate and simplify this notation. Instead, in this section we'll use a new notation that is consistent with exponential notation; that is, the positive square root of 2 is denoted by an exponent.

Find x so that:

The positive square root of 2 is equal to 2^x.

From the definition of square root, this means

$$2 = (2^x)^2$$

Historical Note

The use of negatives and fractions for exponents was introduced long after the radical symbol. John Wallis (1616–1703) appears to have been the first to use them, but their general acceptance followed a letter by Sir Isaac Newton to the Royal Society of London in which he explained them. The letter was dated June 13, 1676.

Or, if the properties of exponents are to hold,

$2^1 = 2^{2x}$

which seems to say (look at the exponents):

$1 = 2x$

$\dfrac{1}{2} = x$

Hence, the use of a fraction as an exponent will preserve the previous laws of exponents and give an alternative choice of notation for roots.

NOTATION FOR nTH ROOT
if n is an even natural number

If n is even, the positive nth root of b is denoted by

$b^{1/n}$

and the negative nth root of b is denoted by

$-b^{1/n}$

PRINCIPAL ROOT

The positive nth root, $b^{1/n}$, is called the **principal root.**

This notation follows naturally if the properties of exponents developed in Chapter 4 are to hold. For example,

Recall, $(b^m)^n = b^{mn}$

$(3^{1/2})^2 = 3^{2/2} = 3 \qquad (5^{1/4})^4 = 5^{4/4} = 5$

which means that $3^{1/2}$ is a positive square root of 3 and $5^{1/4}$ is a positive fourth root of 5. Or, looking at the problem a different way, if you want the positive square root of 9, you can write

$9^{1/2}$

and this can be simplified since $9 = 3^2$ and

$9^{1/2} = (3^2)^{1/2} = 3^1 = 3$

Thus, the principal square root of 9 is 3. To denote the negative square root of 9, write

$-9^{1/2} = -(3^2)^{1/2} = -(3^1) = -3$

A fourth root of 625 is found by

$(625)^{1/4} = (5^4)^{1/4} = 5^1 = 5$

For cube roots, fifth roots, or any odd roots, b is allowed to be any real number. In this case, there will be exactly one real root (possibly negative).

NOTATION FOR nTH
ROOT
if n is an odd natural
number

In n is odd, we denote the nth real root by

$b^{1/n}$

Thus, to find the real cube root of 64, write

$64^{1/3} = (4^3)^{1/3} = 4^1 = 4$

Also,

$(-32)^{1/5} = [(-2)^5]^{1/5} = (-2)^1 = -2$

Keeping this in mind, we can define a real nth root of a number b.

DEFINITION OF nTH
ROOT

If n is a natural number and b is a real number, then we define $b^{1/n}$ for each of the following cases:

n	$b > 0$	$b < 0$	$b = 0$
Even	$b^{1/n}$ is the positive nth real root of b $-b^{1/n}$ is the negative nth real root of b	Not defined	
Odd	$b^{1/n}$ is the nth real root of b		0

Example 11   Relate each of the following numbers to the given definition and simplify, if possible.

	Number	n	b	*Relate to Definition*
a.	$16^{1/2}$	2	16	$16^{1/2} = 4$ since $4^2 = 16$
b.	$-16^{1/2}$	2	16	$-16^{1/2} = -4$ since $(4)^2 = 16$
c.	$(-16)^{1/2}$	2	-16	Not defined since n is even and b is negative
d.	$64^{1/3}$	3	64	$64^{1/3} = 4$ since $4^3 = 64$
e.	$-64^{1/3}$	3	64	$-64^{1/3} = -4$ since $(4)^3 = 64$
f.	$(-64)^{1/3}$	3	-64	$(-64)^{1/3} = -4$ since $(-4)^3 = -64$
g.	$0^{1/4}$	4	0	$0^{1/4} = 0$ since $0^4 = 0$

We've used the properties of exponents stated in Chapter 4 to state the definition of nth root. From this definition, we know that $27^{1/3} = 3$, but how do you suppose we should define $27^{2/3}$? If those same laws of exponents are to hold, we should have

$$27^{2/3} = (27^{1/3})^2$$
$$= (3)^2$$
$$= 9$$

For this property to hold, we make the following definition.

DEFINITION OF
$b^{m/n}$

> Let m and n be any natural numbers without any common factors and let b be any real number for which $b^{1/n}$ is defined. Then
>
> $$b^{m/n} = (b^{1/n})^m \qquad \text{and} \qquad b^{-m/n} = \frac{1}{b^{m/n}}$$

If we now extend the laws of exponents first stated in Chapter 4 to include rational exponents, we have the laws for exponents given in the box. To avoid some difficulties that occur in more advanced work (see Problem 65), we'll limit variables used as bases of powers with rational exponents to positive numbers.

LAWS OF
EXPONENTS

> Let p and q represent any rational numbers, and let a and b represent any positive real numbers.
>
> **First Law** $\qquad b^p b^q = b^{p+q}$
> **Second Law** $\qquad (b^p)^q = b^{pq}$
> **Third Law** $\qquad (ab)^p = a^p b^p$
>
> **Fourth Law** $\qquad \left(\dfrac{a}{b}\right)^p = \dfrac{a^p}{b^p}$
>
> **Fifth Law** $\qquad \dfrac{b^p}{b^q} = b^{p-q}$

In Examples 12–20 simplify by using the laws of exponents.

Example 12

$$4^{1/2} = (2^2)^{1/2} \qquad \text{The first step is to factor the base.}$$
$$= 2^{2(1/2)} \qquad \text{Second law, multiply exponents.}$$
$$= 2^1 \qquad \text{Simplify.}$$
$$= 2 \qquad \qquad \square$$

Example 13

$$-(4^{1/2}) = -(2^2)^{1/2} \qquad \text{Notice that the base is 4 and not } -4.$$
$$= -2 \qquad \qquad \square$$

Example 14 $(-4)^{1/2}$ is not defined because the base of an even root is given as negative. Notice the use of the parentheses and the difference between this example and Example 13. The exponent doesn't apply to an opposite symbol "$-$" unless it is enclosed within parentheses. In $-4^{1/2}$ the negative isn't part of the square root, while in $(-4)^{1/2}$ it is.   □

Example 15 $(343)^{2/3} = (7^3)^{2/3}$
$$= 7^2$$
$$= 49$$ □

Example 16 $25^{-3/2} = (5^2)^{-3/2}$
$$= 5^{-3}$$
$$= \frac{1}{5^3}$$
$$= \frac{1}{125}$$ □

Example 17 $(-32)^{-3/2}$ is not defined since it can be written as $1/[(-32)^{1/2}]^3$ and we can't have the square root of a negative number in the set of real numbers.   □

Example 18 $2^{1/2} \cdot 2^{1/3} = 2^{1/2+1/3}$ Add exponents.
$$= 2^{3/6+2/6}$$ Exponents *are fractions*, so they need common denominators
$$= 2^{5/6}$$ before adding.   □

Example 19 $(2^{1/2} \cdot 2^{1/3})^6 = 2^{6/2} \cdot 2^{6/3}$
$$= 2^3 \cdot 2^2$$
$$= 2^5 \text{ or } 32$$ □

Example 20 $\dfrac{5^{1/3}}{5^2} = 5^{(1/3)-2}$
$$= 5^{(1/3)-(6/3)}$$
$$= 5^{-5/3} \text{ or } \frac{1}{5^{5/3}}$$ □

Even though the laws of exponents apply to expressions in the usual way, you must exercise special care when the exponents are fractions.

In Examples 21–24 simplify each expression. Assume the variables are all positive.

Example 21

$$\left[\frac{8x^{-3}y^6}{27x^3y^{-2/3}}\right]^{1/3} = \left[\frac{8}{27} \cdot \frac{x^{-3}}{x^3} \cdot \frac{y^6}{y^{-2/3}}\right]^{1/3}$$

Simplify the expression in brackets first.

$$= \left[\frac{8}{27} \cdot x^{-3-3} \cdot y^{6-(-2/3)}\right]^{1/3}$$

$$= \left[\frac{8}{27} x^{-6}y^{20/3}\right]^{1/3}$$

$$= \left(\frac{2^3}{3^3}\right)^{1/3}(x^{-6})^{1/3}(y^{20/3})^{1/3}$$

$$= \frac{2}{3} x^{-2}y^{20/9} \text{ or } \frac{2y^{20/9}}{3x^2}$$

☐

Example 22

$$x(x^{2/3} + x^{1/2}) = x^1x^{2/3} + x^1x^{1/2}$$
$$= x^{1+2/3} + x^{1+1/2}$$
$$= x^{5/3} + x^{3/2}$$

☐

Example 23

$$(x^{1/2} + y^{1/2})(x^{1/2} - y^{1/2}) = x^{1/2}x^{1/2} - x^{1/2}y^{1/2} + x^{1/2}y^{1/2} - y^{1/2}y^{1/2}$$
$$= x - y$$

☐

Example 24

$$(x^{1/2} + y^{1/2})^2 = x + 2x^{1/2}y^{1/2} + y$$ *Beware:* Notice that $(x^{1/2} + y^{1/2})^2 \neq x + y$. ☐

Problem Set 6.1

A *In Problems 1–8 compare the given numbers to the definition of $b^{1/n}$ and give the value of b and the value of n. Also, use the definition of $b^{1/n}$ to simplify each expression, or state that the expression is not defined (if that is the case).*

See Examples 11–14.

1. $25^{1/2}$ 2. $-25^{1/2}$ 3. $(-25)^{1/2}$ 4. $125^{1/3}$ 5. $-125^{1/3}$

6. $(-125)^{1/3}$ 7. $729^{1/6}$ 8. $(-729)^{1/6}$

If defined, simplify each expression in Problems 9–36.

See Examples 15–24.

9. $64^{2/3}$ 10. $-64^{2/3}$ 11. $(-64)^{2/3}$

12. $64^{3/2}$ 13. $-64^{3/2}$ 14. $(-64)^{3/2}$

15. $4^{1/3} \cdot 4^{2/3}$ 16. $5^{-2/3} \cdot 5^{-1/3}$ 17. $\dfrac{8^{2/3}}{8^{1/3}}$

18. $(2^{1/3} \cdot 3^{1/2})^6$ 19. $(2^6 \cdot 3^{12})^{1/6}$ 20. $(1,000)^{-2/3}$

21. $2^{1/2} \cdot 8^{1/2}$ 22. $3^{1/2} \cdot 27^{1/2}$ 23. $3^{1/3} \cdot 3^{3/4}$

see if perfect square or cube $(2^2)^{1/4} = 2^{2/4} = 2^{1/2})$ $= 2^{1/2}$

24. $5^{1/2} \cdot 5^{1/3} \cdot 5^{1/4}$

25. $\dfrac{3^{5/2}}{3^{1/2}}$

26. $\dfrac{4^{1/4}}{2^{1/2}}$

27. $\dfrac{5^{1/2}}{5^{1/3}}$

28. $\dfrac{4^{2/3}}{8^{1/6}}$

29. $(-3)^{1/2} \cdot 27^{1/2}$

30. $-3^{1/2} \cdot 27^{1/2}$

31. $[(-4)(-16)]^{-1/6}$

32. $[(-9)(-81)]^{-1/6}$

33. $(9^{1/2} + 4^{1/2})^2$

34. $(16^{1/2} + 9^{1/2})^2$

35. $(4^{1/2} + 16^{1/2})^2$

36. $(25^{1/2} + 4^{1/2})^2$

B   *If defined, simplify each expression in Problems 37–62, leaving only positive exponents in your answers. Assume that the domain for all variables is the set of positive real numbers.*

37. $\left(\frac{1}{8}\right)^{-2/3}$

38. $\left(-\frac{1}{8}\right)^{2/3}$

39. $\left(\frac{4}{25}\right)^{3/2}$

40. $\left(\frac{4}{25}\right)^{-3/2}$

41. $x^{5/7}x^{3/7}$

42. $x^{1/2}x^{1/3}$

43. $(x^{2/3}y^{-1/3})^3$

44. $(x^{1/2}y^{1/3})^6$

45. $(x^{1/4}y^{3/4})^{-2}$

46. $(a^{2^2+1})^{1/5}$

47. $(b^{2^2+1}b^5)^{1/10}$

48. $\left(\dfrac{x^{-2}y}{x^3y^2}\right)^{-1}$

See Example 20.

49. $\left(\dfrac{x^{-1}y^{-2}}{x^{-2}y^5}\right)^{1/3}$

50. $\left(\dfrac{m^{-3}}{m^{-1/2}}\right)^{-1}$

51. $\left(\dfrac{x^3y^3}{x^{-3}y^{-5}}\right)^{1/2}$

52. $\left(\dfrac{25s^{-2}t^3}{36s^4t^{-2}}\right)^{1/2}$

See Examples 22–24.

53. $x^{1/2}(x^{3/2} + x^{1/2})$

54. $x^{2/3}(x^{1/2} + x^{1/3})$

55. $(x^{1/2} - y^{1/2})^2$

56. $(a^{1/2} + b^{1/2})^2$

57. $(s^{1/2} + 3^{1/2})^2$

58. $(m^{1/2} - 5^{1/2})^2$

59. $(x^{1/3} + y^{1/3})(x^{2/3} - x^{1/3}y^{1/3} + y^{2/3})$

60. $(x^{1/3} - y^{1/3})(x^{2/3} + x^{1/3}y^{1/3} + y^{2/3})$

61. $(x+1)^{2/3}[(x+1)^{1/3} + (x+1)]$

62. $(x-y)^{-2/3}[(x-y)^{5/3} + (x-y)]$

Mind Bogglers

63. Find the error in the following "proof":

$$2 = 2$$
$$ = 4^{1/2} \qquad \text{Definition of square root}$$
$$ = [(-2)^2]^{1/2} \qquad \text{Substitute } (-2)^2 = 4$$
$$ = (-2)^{2(1/2)} \qquad \text{Second law: } (b^p)^q = b^{pq}$$
$$ = (-2)^1 \qquad \text{Since } 2 \cdot \frac{1}{2} = 1$$
$$ = -2$$

Therefore, $2 = -2$.

Problem 64 shows that the laws of exponents on page 179, as well as the definition of $b^{m/n}$, will hold if we allow a and b to be any nonzero real numbers. And b can't be negative when the exponent is even. (Also, see Problem 65.)

64. Notice from Problem 63 that $(b^p)^q = b^{pq}$ does not hold if b is negative and p is even. However, if p is odd, then b may be negative. Construct an example similar to Problem 63, choosing a negative value for b and an odd value for p. Show that there is no inconsistency for this example.

65. We have a law of exponents that states

$$(ab)^p = a^p b^p$$

Here's an example:

$8 = 64^{1/2}$
$= (4 \cdot 16)^{1/2}$
$= 4^{1/2} \cdot 16^{1/2}$
$= 2 \cdot 4$
$= 8$

But look at the following example.

$8 = 64^{1/2}$
$= [(-4)(-16)]^{1/2}$
$= (-4)^{1/2}(-16)^{1/2}$ which is not defined

Where is the error?

66. If we let x be any real number, is the following equation true?

$(x^2)^{1/2} = x$

Notice that $(x^2)^{1/2}$ is defined for *both* $x = 2$ and $x = -2$. Do both these values satisfy the above equation? Why or why not?

6.2　Radicals as Rational Exponents

The familiar radical notation, using the symbol $\sqrt{}$, is defined in the box.

Definition of Radicals

For a natural number $n \geq 2$ and b a positive number,

$\sqrt[n]{b} = b^{1/n}$

RADICAL
INDEX
BASE
RADICAND

The symbol $\sqrt{}$ is called a **radical,** n is called the **index,** and b is called the **base** or **radicand.** (For $n = 2$, $\sqrt[2]{b}$ is written $\sqrt{b}$ with the index 2 understood.)

The requirement that b is a positive number was made for simplicity and is more restrictive than necessary. Actually, b could be any real number except when n is even, in which case b must not be negative. However, for purposes of this section, variables under radicals are positive.

From this definition of radicals, it follows that if m is also a natural number, then

$b^{m/n} = (b^{1/n})^m = (\sqrt[n]{b})^m$

and

$b^{m/n} = (b^m)^{1/n} = \sqrt[n]{b^m}$

Many of the problems we do are worked using rational exponents. However, because of the widespread use of radical notation, it is also convenient to work without changing to rational exponents. For ease of computation, you should be able to work with both forms as well as change from one form to the other.

In Examples 1–4 write each expression using radical notation. (The replacement set of the variables is the set of positive real numbers.)

Example 1 $9^{2/3} = (9^2)^{1/3}$
$$= \sqrt[3]{9^2}$$ □

Example 2 $x^{4/5} = (x^4)^{1/5}$
$$= \sqrt[5]{x^4}$$ □

Example 3 $y^{-3/4} = (y^{-3})^{1/4}$ *Note:* If a fractional exponent is negative, write it in standard
$$= \sqrt[4]{y^{-3}}$$ form so that the denominator (the index of the radical) is positive.

$$= \sqrt[4]{\dfrac{1}{y^3}}$$ □

Example 4 $(x^2 + y^2)^{1/2} = \sqrt{x^2 + y^2}$ *Beware:* Don't be tempted to write $x + y$. Replace x by
2 and y by 3 to see that $(x^2 + y^2)^{1/2} \neq x + y$.   □

Examples 1–4 show how to write fractional exponents as radicals. Now, reverse the process and write radicals as fractional exponents in Example 5.

Example 5   Write each expression using rational exponents. (The replacement set of the variables is the set of positive real numbers.)

a. $\sqrt[5]{-2x^3} = (-2x^3)^{1/5}$ b. $3\sqrt[4]{5x^3} = 3(5x^3)^{1/4}$

c. $-2y\sqrt[6]{x^6 + y^6} = -2y(x^6 + y^6)^{1/6}$ d. $\dfrac{4}{\sqrt{x}} - \dfrac{3}{4\sqrt{y}} = 4x^{-1/2} - \dfrac{3}{4}y^{-1/2}$ □

Irrational Numbers

Remember that when working in the set of integers, we can add, subtract, and multiply without difficulty (the integers are *closed* for these operations). Then, we attempt division:

$$\frac{10}{2} = 5 \qquad \frac{35}{-5} = -7 \qquad \frac{-4{,}821}{3} = -1{,}607$$

Some divisions give integers. However, other divisions are *impossible in the set of integers:*

$$\frac{1}{2} \qquad \frac{11}{7} \qquad \frac{-11}{5}$$

In order to be able to carry out these operations, we *define* a new kind of number (called a *fraction*), so we can say

$$1 \div 2 \quad \text{is the } \textit{number} \quad \frac{1}{2}$$

Thus, in mathematics we have two meanings for $\frac{1}{2}$:

1. **An operation,** as in $1 \div 2$
2. **A number,** one-half

The same idea is used with radicals. We begin by thinking of square root as an operation:

$$\sqrt{4} = 2 \qquad \sqrt{81} = 9 \qquad \sqrt{2.25} = 1.5 \qquad \sqrt{15{,}129} = 123$$

Recall that a number is *rational* if it has a decimal representation that either terminates or repeats.

Some square roots can be represented in the set of rationals. However, other square roots are *impossible to find in the set of rationals:*

$$\sqrt{2} \qquad \sqrt{3} \qquad \sqrt{5}$$

So far in this chapter, we've used *roots as an operation.* Now, we wish to *define* new kinds of numbers (called *irrationals*) so we can say that

the square root of 2 is the *number* $\sqrt{2}$

There are two meanings for $\sqrt{2}$:

1. **An operation,** square root of 2
2. **The number,** $\sqrt{2}$. This is the positive number that can be multiplied by itself to give 2. There is no repeating or terminating decimal representation for this number.

It is just as hopeless to try to write $\sqrt{2}$ as a rational number as it is to try to write $\frac{1}{2}$ as an integer.

In Examples 6–9 classify each number as an integer or noninteger.

Example 6 $\frac{85}{5}$ *Integer* because $\frac{85}{5} = 17$ □

Example 7 $\frac{92}{5}$ *Noninteger* because there is no integer that can be multiplied by 5 to give 92   □

Example 8 $-\frac{481}{3}$ *Noninteger*   □

Example 9 $-\frac{483}{7}$ *Integer*   □

In Examples 10–13 classify each number as rational or irrational.

Example 10 $\sqrt{144}$ *Rational* because $12 \cdot 12 = 144$ □

Example 11 $\sqrt{14}$ *Irrational* because $3(3) = 9$ and $4(4) = 16$ and there are no perfect squares between 9 and 16   □

Example 12 $\sqrt[5]{240}$ *Irrational* because $2^5 = 32$ and $3^5 = 243$ and there are no perfect fifth powers between 32 and 243   □

Example 13 $\sqrt[4]{81}$ *Rational* because $3^4 = 81$ □

In the next section, we'll discuss the simplification of radicals. But for now it is important to recognize expressions such as $\sqrt{2}$, $\sqrt[3]{9}$, $\sqrt[3]{18}$, $\sqrt[4]{32}$ as numbers that can't be written as terminating or repeating decimals (that is, they are not rational). Some radical expressions are rational numbers and some radical expressions are not. Notice from Examples 10–13 that if the radical expression $\sqrt[n]{b}$ is a rational number, then b can be written as the nth power of a rational number. Thus,

$$\sqrt[3]{8} = \sqrt[3]{2^3} = 2 \quad \text{and} \quad \sqrt[5]{32} = \sqrt[5]{2^5} = 2$$

are rational numbers. On the other hand, numbers such as

$$\sqrt{2} \qquad \sqrt[3]{2} \qquad \sqrt[3]{4} \qquad \sqrt[4]{10}$$

are not rational numbers.

Even though a number may be irrational, you can determine its size by comparison with rational numbers. For example, to find a decimal approximation of the number $\sqrt{2}$, you can place it between two counting numbers.

Since $1^2 < 2$ and $2^2 > 2$, you see that

$$1 < \sqrt{2} < 2$$

If you wish a more accurate approximation of $\sqrt{2}$, you can place it between two rational numbers that are closer than one unit apart:

$$1.4 < \sqrt{2} < 1.5$$

since

$$1.96 = 1.4^2 < 2 < 1.5^2 = 2.25$$

When you press $\boxed{\checkmark}$ $\boxed{2}$ on a calculator and the display shows 1.414213562 it *does not* mean that

$$\sqrt{2} = 1.414213562$$

since $1.414213562^2 = 1.999999998944727844 \neq 2$. It *does* mean that

$$1.41421356 < \sqrt{2} < 1.41421357$$

You can write rational *approximations* for irrational numbers to any desired degree of accuracy.

Historical Note

Students often say that work with radicals is difficult. However, in the 16th century there were four symbols for indicating roots: the letters R and *l* (both lowercase and capital), √, and the fractional exponent. To complicate matters, these symbols were used not only for roots but for unknown quantities. Also, the radical signs for cube root and fourth root had different shapes and by the close of the 16th century there were 25 or more symbols for radicals.

In Examples 14–19 plot the numbers on a real number line.

Example 14 $\sqrt{2}$ From the discussion above, $1.4 < \sqrt{2} < 1.5$. See Figure 6.1 below. ☐

Example 15 $-\sqrt{9}$ $-\sqrt{9} = -3$ since $3^2 = 9$; see Figure 6.1 below. ☐

Example 16 $\sqrt{\dfrac{1}{4}}$ $\sqrt{\dfrac{1}{4}} = \dfrac{1}{2}$ since $\left(\dfrac{1}{2}\right)^2 = \dfrac{1}{4}$; see Figure 6.1. ☐

Example 17 $8^{1/3}$ $8^{1/3} = (2^3)^{1/3} = 2^1$; see Figure 6.1. ☐

Example 18 $-4^{1/2}$ $-4^{1/2} = -(2^2)^{1/2}$ Notice that the negative sign is not included within the
                              $= -2^1$ parentheses; if it were, this number would be undefined.
                              $= -2$ ☐

Example 19 $\sqrt[5]{150}$ Notice that $2^5 < 150 < 3^5$ so that $2 < \sqrt[5]{150} < 3$.
                 On a calculator, $\sqrt[5]{150} \approx 2.724069928$ ☐

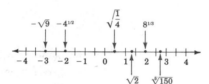

Figure 6.1

Problem Set 6.2

A   *Write each expression in Problems 1–20 using radical notation. Assume that the replacement set for the variables is the set of positive real numbers.*

See Examples 1–4.

1. $25^{2/3}$ 2. $49^{3/2}$ 3. $2x^{1/2}$ 4. $(2x)^{1/2}$
5. $4x^{2/3}$ 6. $-3x^{4/5}$ 7. $(-2x)^{2/3}$ 8. $2x^{1/2}y^{1/3}$
9. $(3x^2y^3)^{1/6}$ 10. $(x+y)^{1/2}$ 11. $(x^2+y^2)^{1/2}$ 12. $3(x^3+y^3)^{1/3}$
13. $3x^{-1/3}$ 14. $-4x^{-3/5}$ 15. $2x^{-1/2}+3y^{-1/2}$
16. $\frac{1}{3}(x^2+y^{1/2})^{-1/2}$ 17. $\frac{1}{4}(3x+2)^{-1/2}$ 18. $\frac{1}{9}(2x-1)^{-2/3}$
19. $(x^2+2xy+y^2)^{-2/3}$ 20. $(x-y)^{2/3}(x^2-xy+y^2)^{-2/3}$

Write each expression in Problems 21–40 using positive fractional exponents. Assume the replacement set for the variables is chosen so each radicand is positive.

See Example 5.

21. $\sqrt{5}$ 22. $\sqrt{8}$ 23. $\sqrt[4]{2^3}$ 24. $\sqrt[5]{x^2}$

25. $\sqrt[3]{x+y}$ 26. $\sqrt[3]{x}+\sqrt[3]{y}$ 27. $\sqrt[3]{x^3+y^3}$ 28. $\sqrt[3]{(x+y)^2}$

29. $\sqrt[5]{-2x^3}$ 30. $3\sqrt{xy}$ 31. $4\sqrt[4]{x^2y^3}$ 32. $\dfrac{3}{\sqrt[3]{xy}}$

33. $\dfrac{-2}{x\sqrt[3]{y}}$ **34.** $\dfrac{2}{\sqrt{x}}+\dfrac{4}{\sqrt{y}}$ **35.** $\dfrac{2+3x}{\sqrt{x}+\sqrt{y}}$ **36.** $\dfrac{2+3x}{\sqrt{x+y}}$

37. $\dfrac{-5x^2}{\sqrt[3]{x^2-y^2}}$ **38.** $\dfrac{-5x^2}{\sqrt[3]{x^2}-\sqrt[3]{y^2}}$ **39.** $\dfrac{-5x^2}{\sqrt[3]{(x-y)^2}}$ **40.** $\sqrt[8]{\dfrac{2^2}{5^3}x^7y^5}$

Classify the numbers in Problems 41–48 as integers or nonintegers.

See Examples 6–9.   **41.** $\dfrac{18}{5}$ **42.** $\dfrac{125}{-5}$ **43.** $\dfrac{-63}{9}$ **44.** $\dfrac{123}{-9}$ **45.** $\dfrac{-617}{-5}$

46. $\dfrac{-979}{11}$ **47.** $\dfrac{-19}{\frac13}$ **48.** $\dfrac{\frac12}{\frac14}$

Classify the numbers in Problems 49–64 as rational or irrational.

See Examples 10–13.   **49.** $\sqrt{169}$ **50.** $\sqrt{170}$ **51.** $\sqrt8$ **52.** $\sqrt{16}$
53. $\sqrt[3]{4}$ **54.** $\sqrt[3]{25}$ **55.** $\sqrt[3]{16}$ **56.** $\sqrt[3]{100}$
57. $\sqrt[4]{100}$ **58.** $\sqrt[4]{10,000}$ **59.** $\sqrt{3,600}$ **60.** $\sqrt{3,800}$
61. $\sqrt{1,849}$ **62.** $\sqrt{2,164}$ **63.** $\sqrt{2,401}$ **64.** $\sqrt[4]{2,401}$

B   *Without using tables or a calculator, find the approximate location of each of the sets of numbers in Problems 65–68 on a real number line.*

See Examples 14–19.   **65.** $\sqrt3,\ \sqrt[3]{18},\ -\sqrt[4]{7}$ **66.** $\sqrt[3]{-12},\ -\sqrt{(1/2)},\ -\sqrt[4]{150}$
67. $-11^{1/2},\ 15^{1/3},\ 15^{2/3}$ **68.** $20^{1/2},\ 30^{1/3},\ 40^{1/4}$

69. On a calculator, the display for $\sqrt3$ is `1.732050808`. Show that
$$1.732050808^2 \neq 3$$
by finding the exact value of 1.732050808^2.

70. On a calculator, the display for $\sqrt5$ is `2.236067977`. Show that
$$2.236067977^2 \neq 5$$
by finding the exact value of 2.236067977^2.

71. Perhaps you have a calculator with an nth root function and can find decimal approximations for the numbers in Problems 65–68. However, even if your calculator has only the four fundamental operations, you can find a good approximation for the nth root of a number. For example, suppose you wish to find $\sqrt[5]{2,000}$.

Step 1. Let $N =$ BASE; for this example, $N = 2,000$. Since $(\sqrt[5]{N})^5 = N$, we focus our attention on N and fifth powers of numbers.

Step 2. Find integers n and $n + 1$ so that
$$n^5 \leq N \leq (n+1)^5$$

We know $2^5 = 32$ and $10^5 = 100,000$, so

$$2^5 < N < 10^5$$

Now we turn to a calculator to refine this estimate to

$$4^5 < N < 5^5$$

since $4^5 = 1,024$ and $5^5 = 3,125$. This tells us that

$$4 < \sqrt[5]{N} < 5$$

Step 3. Repeat the process of Step 2 for the next decimal place. On a calculator you can find

$$4.5^5 = 1845.28125 \qquad \text{and} \qquad 4.6^5 = 2059.62976$$

This information tells you that

$$4.5^5 < N < 4.6^5 \qquad \text{or} \qquad 4.5 < \sqrt[5]{N} < 4.6$$

Step 4. Repeat the process of Step 2 to obtain the next decimal place. Step 2 can be repeated as often as necessary to obtain the desired accuracy.

$$4.57^5 = 1993.338249 \qquad \text{and} \qquad 4.58^5 = 2015.242855$$

Thus,

$$4.57 < \sqrt[5]{2,000} < 4.58$$

You also can see by inspection that it is closer to 4.57 than to 4.58. Thus, to the nearest hundredth,

$$\sqrt[5]{2,000} \approx 4.57$$

Now, use a calculator to find the following to the nearest hundredth:
a. $\sqrt[3]{3,000}$ b. $\sqrt[4]{4,000}$

72. Use a calculator to find the following numbers to the nearest hundredth:
a. $\sqrt[5]{5,000}$ b. $\sqrt[6]{6,000}$

73. Use a calculator to find the following numbers to the nearest hundredth:
a. $\sqrt[7]{7,000}$ b. $\sqrt[8]{8,000}$

Mind Boggler 74. By looking at your answers for Problems 71–73, try to make a conjecture about $\sqrt[T]{1,000T}$ when T is very large.

6.3 Square Roots

Recall that the square root of 2 is a *number* that, when squared, gives the product 2. It is not a rational number, so its decimal representation doesn't terminate or repeat. We represent the positive square root of 2 by the symbol $\sqrt{2}$. Similarly, $\sqrt{3}$, $\sqrt{5}$, $\sqrt{6}$, $\sqrt{7}$, and $\sqrt{8}$ all do not have terminating or repeating decimal representations and are therefore irrational numbers. On the other hand, some radicals, such as $\sqrt{1}$, $\sqrt{4}$, $\sqrt{9}$, and $\sqrt{16}$ *do* have rational representations, so we don't consider these forms simplified. Therefore, we need to formalize some procedures for simplifying square roots.

LAWS OF SQUARE
ROOTS

Laws of Square Roots

Let a and b be positive numbers. Then:

1. $\sqrt{0} = 0$
2. $\sqrt{a^2} = a$
3. $\sqrt{ab} = \sqrt{a}\,\sqrt{b}$
4. $\sqrt{\dfrac{a}{b}} = \dfrac{\sqrt{a}}{\sqrt{b}}$

These laws allow us to formulate a definition for the simplest form of a square root.

SIMPLEST FORM OF
A SQUARE ROOT

A square root is in **simplest form** if:
1. The radicand has no exponent larger than 1 when it is written in factored form.
2. The radicand is not written as a fraction or by using negative exponents.
3. There are no square root symbols used in the denominators of fractions.

If an expression involving a square root symbol is in simplest form, then it is irrational. On the other hand, if it is not in simplest form, then you may or may not know whether the number is rational or irrational.

Example 1 Simplify: $\sqrt{8}$

Solution *Step 1.* Factor the radicand:

$$\sqrt{8} = \sqrt{2^3}$$

Step 2. Since this is a square root, write the radicand as a product of as many factors with exponents of 2 as possible and write the remaining factors with exponents of 1:

$$\sqrt{2^3} = \sqrt{2^2 \cdot 2^1}$$

Step 3. Use Law 3 for square roots:

$$\sqrt{2^2 \cdot 2^1} = \sqrt{2^2} \cdot \sqrt{2^1}$$

Step 4. Use Law 2 for square roots:

$$\sqrt{2^2} \cdot \sqrt{2^1} = 2 \cdot \sqrt{2} \quad \text{or simply} \quad 2\sqrt{2}$$

Notice that the simplified form still contains a radical, so $\sqrt{8}$ is an irrational number. ☐

This whole process is usually condensed as shown in the examples below.

In Examples 2–12 simplify the given radical expression.

Example 2 $\sqrt{196} = \sqrt{14^2}$
$= 14$

Factor the radicand. A factor tree can be used when you don't see any factors that are square numbers: 196

$$\begin{array}{c} 2 \cdot 98 \\ 2 \cdot 2 \cdot 49 \\ 2 \cdot 2 \cdot 7 \cdot 7 \end{array}$$

This simplified form doesn't contain a radical, so $\sqrt{196}$ is a rational number. ☐

Example 3 $\sqrt{32} = \sqrt{16 \cdot 2}$
$= \sqrt{16}\,\sqrt{2}$
$= 4\sqrt{2}$

Or 32

$$\begin{array}{c} 2 \cdot 16 \\ 2 \cdot 4 \cdot 4 \\ 2 \cdot 2 \cdot 2 \cdot 2 \cdot 2 = 2^5 \end{array}$$

Now write this using square factors: $2^2 \cdot 2^2 \cdot 2$ ☐

Example 4 $\sqrt{1,260} = \sqrt{2^2 \cdot 3^2 \cdot 5 \cdot 7}$
$= \sqrt{2^2} \cdot \sqrt{3^2} \cdot \sqrt{5 \cdot 7}$
$= 2 \cdot 3\sqrt{35}$
$= 6\sqrt{35}$

1,260

$$\begin{array}{c} 10 \cdot 126 \\ 2 \cdot 5 \cdot 2 \cdot 63 \\ 2 \cdot 5 \cdot 2 \cdot 9 \cdot 7 \\ 2 \cdot 5 \cdot 2 \cdot 3 \cdot 3 \cdot 7 = 2^2 \cdot 3^2 \cdot 5 \cdot 7 \end{array}$$

From now on this step will not be shown, but should be done mentally. ☐

Example 5 $\sqrt{(x+y)^2} = x+y$ ☐

Example 6 $\sqrt{x^2+y^2}$ is simplified; there are no square factors. □

Example 7
$$6\sqrt{9x+18}\cdot 5\sqrt{5x+10}=6\cdot 5\sqrt{(9x+18)(5x+10)}$$
$$=30\sqrt{9(x+2)(5)(x+2)}$$
$$=30\sqrt{3^2(x+2)^2(5)}$$
$$=30\cdot 3(x+2)\sqrt{5}$$
$$=90(x+2)\sqrt{5}$$ □

Example 8
$$\frac{3}{\sqrt{7}}=\frac{3}{\sqrt{7}}\cdot\frac{\sqrt{7}}{\sqrt{7}}$$
$$=\frac{3\sqrt{7}}{7}\quad\text{or}\quad\frac{3}{7}\sqrt{7}$$

Multiply by 1, written so the number that appears in the denominator will be free of radicals when multiplied. Remember, the radical is not simplified if there is a square root as a denominator. □

Example 9
$$\sqrt{.1}=\sqrt{\frac{1}{10}}$$
$$=\sqrt{\frac{1}{10}\cdot\frac{10}{10}}$$
$$=\frac{\sqrt{10}}{\sqrt{100}}$$
$$=\frac{\sqrt{10}}{10}$$ □

Example 10
$$\frac{x+y}{\sqrt{x}}=\frac{x+y}{\sqrt{x}}\cdot\frac{\sqrt{x}}{\sqrt{x}}$$ Multiply by 1.
$$=\frac{(x+y)\sqrt{x}}{x}$$ Since $\sqrt{x}\cdot\sqrt{x}=x$. □

Example 11
$$\sqrt{48x^{-2}y^3}=\sqrt{\frac{16\cdot 3y^3}{x^2}}$$
$$=\frac{\sqrt{4^2\cdot y^2\cdot 3\cdot y}}{\sqrt{x^2}}$$
$$=\frac{4y}{x}\sqrt{3y}$$

Or 48
 $4\cdot 12$
 $2\cdot 2\cdot 2\cdot 2\cdot 3=2^4\cdot 3$ □

Example 12
$$\sqrt{\frac{3y^2}{25x}}=\frac{\sqrt{3y^2}}{\sqrt{5^2x}}$$
$$=\frac{\sqrt{3y^2}}{\sqrt{5^2x}}\cdot\frac{\sqrt{x}}{\sqrt{x}}$$
$$=\frac{\sqrt{3xy^2}}{\sqrt{5^2x^2}}$$
$$=\frac{y\sqrt{3x}}{5x}$$

Multiply by 1, written as $\sqrt{x}/\sqrt{x}$, to eliminate the radical in the denominator. □

Sometimes it is necessary to combine certain operations when simplifying square roots. These are illustrated in the following **examples**.

Example 13   Simplify the given expressions.

a. $\sqrt{5^2 - 4(1)(-3)} = \sqrt{25 + 12}$ **b.** $\sqrt{2^2 - 4(1)(-15)} = \sqrt{4 + 60}$

$\qquad\qquad\qquad\quad = \sqrt{37}$ $\qquad\qquad\qquad\quad = \sqrt{64}$

$\qquad\qquad\qquad\qquad\qquad\qquad\qquad\qquad\qquad\qquad\qquad\quad = 8$

c. $\sqrt{4^2 - 4(9)(-4)} = \sqrt{16 + 144}$

$\qquad\qquad\qquad\quad = \sqrt{160}$

$\qquad\qquad\qquad\quad = \sqrt{16 \cdot 10}$

$\qquad\qquad\qquad\quad = 4\sqrt{10}$

Alternate simplification: Instead of multiplying, adding, and then factoring, it is often easier to factor first:

$\sqrt{4^2 - 4(9)(-4)} = \sqrt{4^2(1 + 9)}$

$\qquad\qquad\qquad\quad = 4\sqrt{10}$

d. $\sqrt{10^2 - 4(5)(-15)} = \sqrt{2^2 \cdot 5^2 + 2^2 \cdot 5 \cdot 3 \cdot 5}$

$\qquad\qquad\qquad\qquad = \sqrt{2^2 \cdot 5^2(1 + 3)}$

$\qquad\qquad\qquad\qquad = \sqrt{2^2 \cdot 5^2 \cdot 2^2}$

$\qquad\qquad\qquad\qquad = 2 \cdot 5 \cdot 2$

$\qquad\qquad\qquad\qquad = 20$ ☐

Certain expressions involve operations combined with radicals. In Section 6.5 we'll discuss these operations completely, but here we'll simply remind you that the usual algebraic procedures still apply.

Example 14 $2 + \sqrt{5}$ is in simplest form.   ☐

Example 15 $6 + 3\sqrt{5}$ can be factored as $3(2 + \sqrt{5})$.   ☐

Example 16 $\dfrac{6 + 3\sqrt{5}}{3}$ can be simplified by factoring and reducing:

$\dfrac{6 + 3\sqrt{5}}{3} = \dfrac{3(2 + \sqrt{5})}{3}$

$\qquad\qquad = 2 + \sqrt{5}$ ☐

Example 17 $\dfrac{\sqrt{5}}{3}$ can be written as $\dfrac{1}{3}\sqrt{5}$.   ☐

Example 18 $\dfrac{2 + \sqrt{5}}{3}$ can be written as $\dfrac{1}{3}(2 + \sqrt{5})$.   ☐

Example 19
$$\frac{-(-2)+\sqrt{(-2)^2-4(2)(-1)}}{2(2)}=\frac{2+\sqrt{4+4\cdot 2}}{4}$$

$$=\frac{2+\sqrt{4(1+2)}}{4}$$

$$=\frac{2+2\sqrt{1+2}}{4}$$

$$=\frac{2(1+\sqrt{3})}{4}$$

$$=\frac{1+\sqrt{3}}{2}$$ □

One of the most common applications using square roots involves a result known as the **Pythagorean theorem.**

PYTHAGOREAN
THEOREM

Pythagorean Theorem

If a triangle with legs a and b and hypotenuse c is a right triangle, then

$$c^2 = a^2 + b^2$$

Example 20   Find the lengths of the missing sides of the given right triangles.
a. Legs 1 in. and 2 in.   **b.** Hypotenuse 6 cm and leg 4 cm

Solution **a.** $c^2 = a^2 + b^2$ **b.** Let a be the unknown leg. Then,
               $= 1^2 + 2^2$
               $= 5$ $c^2 = a^2 + b^2$
               $c = \pm\sqrt{5}$ By the square $36 = a^2 + 16$
                              root property $a^2 = 20$
Since c represents a dis- $a = \pm\sqrt{20}$
tance, it must be positive, so $= \pm 2\sqrt{5}$
reject the negative root. The
hypotenuse is $\sqrt{5}$ in.   The unknown leg is $2\sqrt{5}$ cm.
                                                                        □

Problem Set 6.3

A   *Simplify the expressions in Problems 1–44.*

See Examples 1–4.   **1.** $-\sqrt{9}$ **2.** $-\sqrt{121}$ **3.** $\sqrt{125}$ **4.** $\sqrt{96}$
                    5. $\sqrt{1,000}$ **6.** $\sqrt{2,100}$ **7.** $-\sqrt{4,410}$ **8.** $-\sqrt{2,240}$

9. $4\sqrt{75}$ 10. $-3\sqrt{90}$ 11. $-2\sqrt{48}$ 12. $6\sqrt{96}$

See Examples 8–9. 13. $\sqrt{\dfrac{1}{2}}$ 14. $\sqrt{\dfrac{3}{5}}$ 15. $-\sqrt{\dfrac{1}{3}}$ 16. $-\sqrt{\dfrac{3}{7}}$

17. $-\sqrt{0.4}$ 18. $-\sqrt{0.1}$ 19. $\sqrt{\dfrac{144}{3}}$ 20. $\sqrt{0.75}$

21. $\dfrac{1}{\sqrt{2}}$ 22. $\dfrac{-2}{\sqrt{3}}$ 23. $\dfrac{-1}{\sqrt{5}}$ 24. $\dfrac{-5}{\sqrt{10}}$

See Example 13. 25. $\sqrt{7^2-4(3)(2)}$ 26. $\sqrt{8^2-4(5)(2)}$
27. $\sqrt{3^2-4(5)(-3)}$ 28. $\sqrt{1^2-4(1)(-1)}$
29. $\sqrt{4^2-4(5)(-3)}$ 30. $\sqrt{10^2-4(5)(-5)}$
31. $\sqrt{12^2-4(3)(12)}$ 32. $\sqrt{18^2-4(9)(-7)}$

See Examples 14–18. 33. $\dfrac{6+2\sqrt{3}}{2}$ 34. $\dfrac{8-4\sqrt{5}}{4}$ 35. $\dfrac{12-3\sqrt{2}}{6}$ 36. $\dfrac{18-6\sqrt{5}}{12}$

37. $\dfrac{4+6\sqrt{2}}{-2}$ 38. $\dfrac{6-8\sqrt{3}}{2}$ 39. $\dfrac{3-9\sqrt{x}}{3}$ 40. $\dfrac{9+3\sqrt{x}}{-3}$

41. $\dfrac{-2+8\sqrt{6}}{-2}$ 42. $\dfrac{-9+6\sqrt{13}}{-12}$ 43. $\dfrac{10+5\sqrt{3}}{25}$ 44. $\dfrac{20-4\sqrt{5}}{10}$

Let a right triangle have legs a and b and let the hypotenuse be c. Fill in the blanks in Problems 45–50.

See Example 20. 45. $a=2$, $b=3$, $c=$ _____   46. $a=2$, $b=2$, $c=$ _____
47. $a=$ _____, $b=3$, $c=7$ 48. $a=$ _____, $b=4$, $c=8$
49. $a=2$, $b=$ _____, $c=6$ 50. $a=3$, $b=$ _____, $c=12$

B *Simplify the expressions in Problems 51–76. Assume that the replacement set for the variables is such that all radicands are positive.*

See Examples 5–7. 51. $\sqrt{(x-y)^2}$ 52. $\sqrt{x^2-y^2}$
53. $\sqrt{x^2+2xy+y^2}$ 54. $\sqrt{a^2+2ab+b^2}$
55. $\sqrt{4x^2-4xy+y^2}$ 56. $\sqrt{x^2-6xy+9y^2}$
57. $3\sqrt{x+2}\cdot6\sqrt{x}$ 58. $10\sqrt{y+6}\cdot5\sqrt{y}$
59. $7\sqrt{x(x+3)}\cdot3\sqrt{x+3}$ 60. $-9\sqrt{x(x+9)}\cdot3\sqrt{x^2+5x}$
61. $5\sqrt{3x+15}\cdot(-6)\sqrt{2x+10}$ 62. $-2\sqrt{x^2+3x+2}\cdot5\sqrt{x+1}$

See Examples 10–12. 63. $\dfrac{3}{\sqrt{x}}$ 64. $\dfrac{-5}{\sqrt{y}}$ 65. $\dfrac{x+2}{\sqrt{x+2}}$ 66. $\dfrac{y+3}{\sqrt{y+3}}$

67. $\sqrt{\dfrac{4x^2}{25y}}$ 68. $\sqrt{\dfrac{5y}{16x}}$ 69. $\sqrt{512x^{-1}y^6}$ 70. $\sqrt{64x^{-2}y^3}$

71. $\dfrac{5x+5y}{\sqrt{8(x+y)^2}}$ 72. $\dfrac{4x-4y}{\sqrt{27(x-y)^2}}$

See Example 19. **73.** $\dfrac{-5+\sqrt{5^2-4(2)(3)}}{2(2)}$ **74.** $\dfrac{-(-3)-\sqrt{(-3)^2-4(6)(-5)}}{2(6)}$

75. $\dfrac{-10-\sqrt{10^2-4(3)(5)}}{2(3)}$ **76.** $\dfrac{-(-12)+\sqrt{(-12)^2-4(6)(-1)}}{2(6)}$

Mind Bogglers   **77.** The number 3 can be written

$$3 \times \frac{3}{3}$$

using exactly three threes. Find another way to write 3 using exactly three threes.

78. Cut the piece shown in Figure 6.2 into a square whose side measures $\sqrt{5}$ cm.

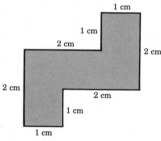

Figure 6.2

6.4 Simplifying Radicals

The laws of square roots introduced in the last section can be generalized and proved by using fractional exponents, as shown in the box on page 197.

These laws of radicals allow us to formulate the **criteria for a radical in simplest form.** All variables in this section satisfy the conditions set forth in the laws of radicals. An algebraic expression containing radicals is called a **radical expression.**

I. A simplified form of a radical expression contains no radical for which the radicand has a factor with a power greater than or equal to the index of the radical.

This first criterion says that you factor the expression under the radical symbol and eliminate any powers that are greater than or equal to the index. You should use Law 1 and Law 2 of radicals to do this. When using fractional exponents, this means that you should write the exponent as a mixed number.

LAWS OF RADICALS

Laws of Radicals

Let a and b be positive real numbers, and let m, n, and k be natural numbers greater than or equal to 2. Then:

	Square Root Form	*General Form*	*Proof*
1.	$\sqrt{a^2} = a$	$\sqrt[n]{a^n} = a$	$\sqrt[n]{a^n} = (a^n)^{1/n}$
			$= a^{n/n}$
			$= a$
2.	$\sqrt{ab} = \sqrt{a}\,\sqrt{b}$	$\sqrt[n]{ab} = \sqrt[n]{a}\,\sqrt[n]{b}$	$\sqrt[n]{ab} = (ab)^{1/n}$
			$= (a)^{1/n}(b)^{1/n}$
			$= \sqrt[n]{a}\,\sqrt[n]{b}$
3.	$\sqrt{\dfrac{a}{b}} = \dfrac{\sqrt{a}}{\sqrt{b}}$	$\sqrt[n]{\dfrac{a}{b}} = \dfrac{\sqrt[n]{a}}{\sqrt[n]{b}}$	$\sqrt[n]{\dfrac{a}{b}} = \left(\dfrac{a}{b}\right)^{1/n}$
			$= \dfrac{(a)^{1/n}}{(b)^{1/n}}$
			$= \dfrac{\sqrt[n]{a}}{\sqrt[n]{b}}$

For roots greater than 2, there is an additional law of radicals:

4.	$\sqrt[kn]{b^{km}} = \sqrt[n]{b^m}$	$\sqrt[kn]{b^{km}} = (b^{km})^{1/kn}$
		$= b^{km/kn}$
		$= b^{m/n}$
		$= \sqrt[n]{b^m}$

In Examples 1–7 simplify the given expressions and leave your answers in radical notation. Notice the pattern for working with mixed numbers as exponents. It is particularly useful when the radicals become complicated.

Example 1 $5^{1/3}$ and $5^{2/3}$ are simplified. In radical notation,

$$5^{1/3} = \sqrt[3]{5} \qquad 5^{2/3} = (5^2)^{1/3}$$
$$= \sqrt[3]{5^2}$$
$$= \sqrt[3]{25}$$

$\square$

Example 2 $5^{3/3} = 5^1 \qquad$ Since $\dfrac{3}{3} = 1$

$$= 5$$

$\square$

Example 3 $5^{4/3}$ First, use radical notation:

$$5^{4/3} = (5^4)^{1/3}$$
$$= \sqrt[3]{5^4}$$
$$= \sqrt[3]{5^3 \cdot 5}$$
$$= 5\sqrt[3]{5}$$

Next, work this problem using an alternate method (mixed numbers):

$$5^{4/3} = 5^{1+(1/3)}$$
$$= 5^1 \cdot 5^{1/3}$$
$$= 5\sqrt[3]{5}$$ □

Example 4 $5^{5/3} = 5^{1+(2/3)}$
$$= 5\sqrt[3]{5^2}$$ □

Example 5 $5^{6/3} = 5^2$ □

Example 6 $5^{7/3} = 5^{2+(1/3)}$
$$= 5^2 \sqrt[3]{5}$$
$$= 25 \sqrt[3]{5}$$ □

Example 7 $5^{8/3} = 5^{2+(2/3)}$
$$= 5^2 \sqrt[3]{5^2}$$
$$= 25 \sqrt[3]{25}$$ □

Example 8 $2^{5/2} = 2^{2+(1/2)}$ *Think:* $2^{2+(1/2)} = 2^2 \cdot 2^{1/2}$
$$= 4\sqrt{2}$$ $= 4\sqrt{2}$ □

Example 9 $3^{9/4} = 3^{2+(1/4)}$
$$= 9\sqrt[4]{3}$$ *Think:* $3^2 \cdot 3^{1/4} = 9\sqrt[4]{3}$ □

Example 10 $2^{14/3} = 2^{4+(2/3)}$
$$= 2^4 \sqrt[3]{2^2}$$ *Think:* $2^4 \cdot 2^{2/3}$
$$= 16\sqrt[3]{4}$$ □

Example 11 $\sqrt[3]{125} = (5^3)^{1/3}$ *Step 1.*   Factor radicand using exponents. You can use a factor tree:
$$= 5^1$$ 125
$$= 5$$ $\diagup\diagdown$
                                                  5 · 25
                                              $\diagup$ $\diagup\diagdown$
                                                5 · 5 · 5

Step 2.   Use the second law of exponents to simplify.   □

Example 12 $\sqrt[3]{135} = (3^3 \cdot 5)^{1/3}$ *Step 1.* Factor radicand.

$$135$$
$$5 \cdot 27$$
$$5 \cdot 3 \cdot 9 = 3^3 \cdot 5$$

$= 3 \cdot 5^{1/3}$ *Step 2.* Use properties of exponents to simplify.

$= 3\sqrt[3]{5}$ □

Example 13 $\sqrt[5]{256} = (2^8)^{1/5}$ *Step 1.* Factor 256. (Can you draw the factor tree?)

$= 2^{8/5}$ *Step 2.* Use properties of exponents. Write the exponent as a mixed

$= 2^{1+(3/5)}$ number, and then break it up as shown.

$= 2^1 \cdot 2^{3/5}$

$= 2\sqrt[5]{2^3}$

$= 2\sqrt[5]{8}$ □

Example 14 $\sqrt[4]{3^9} = (3^9)^{1/4}$ In radical form, this problem can be worked as follows:

$= 3^{9/4}$

$= 3^{2+(1/4)}$ $\sqrt[4]{3^9} = \sqrt[4]{3^4 \cdot 3^4 \cdot 3}$

$= 3^2 \cdot 3^{1/4}$ $= \sqrt[4]{3^4}\,\sqrt[4]{3^4}\,\sqrt[4]{3}$

$= 9\sqrt[4]{3}$ $= 3 \cdot 3\,\sqrt[4]{3}$

                    $= 9\sqrt[4]{3}$ □

Example 15 $\sqrt[3]{x^6} = x^{6/3}$

$= x^2$ □

Example 16 $2\sqrt[3]{9x - 27} \cdot 5\sqrt[3]{x^2 - 6x + 9} = (2 \cdot 5)[9(x - 3)]^{1/3}[(x - 3)^2]^{1/3}$

$= 10[3^2(x - 3)]^{1/3}[(x - 3)^2]^{1/3}$

$= 10 \cdot 3^{2/3}(x - 3)^{1/3}(x - 3)^{2/3}$

$= 10(x - 3)\sqrt[3]{9}$ □

II. A simplified form of a radical expression contains no radical in the denominator. This means that there should be no fractional exponents as denominators in the simplified form.

Example 17 Simplify: $\dfrac{3}{\sqrt{7}}$

Solution $\dfrac{3}{\sqrt{7}} = \dfrac{3}{7^{1/2}}$ We worked this example in the last section by using radical notation. The process when using fractional exponents is the same; multiply by 1 so that the exponents on the factors in the denominator are whole numbers.

$= \dfrac{3}{7^{1/2}} \cdot \dfrac{7^{1/2}}{7^{1/2}}$

$= \dfrac{3 \cdot 7^{1/2}}{7}$ For *exponents*, this means you want to *add* a fraction to $\frac{1}{2}$ to obtain the *next larger whole number.* In this example, $\frac{1}{2} + \frac{1}{2} = 1$

$= \dfrac{3\sqrt{7}}{7}$ □

The process of eliminating the radicals from the denominator, as illustrated by Example 17, is called **rationalizing the denominator.**

In Examples 18–21 simplify the given expressions.

Example 18

$$\frac{3}{\sqrt[3]{7}} = \frac{3}{7^{1/3}}$$

This fraction is 1

$$= \frac{3}{7^{1/3}} \cdot \frac{7^{2/3}}{7^{2/3}}$$

The *form* of the fraction is picked so that the exponents add up to a whole number. In this example, $\frac{2}{3}$ was used because $\frac{1}{3} + \frac{2}{3} = 1$.

$$= \frac{3 \cdot 7^{2/3}}{7^1}$$

$$= \frac{3\sqrt[3]{7^2}}{7}$$

$$= \frac{3}{7}\sqrt[3]{49}$$

□

Example 19

$$\frac{3}{\sqrt[3]{32}} = \frac{3}{2^{5/3}}$$

$$= \frac{3}{2^{5/3}} \cdot \frac{2^{1/3}}{2^{1/3}}$$

This is 1; we picked the exponent $\frac{1}{3}$ because $\frac{5}{3} + \frac{1}{3} = \frac{6}{3} = 2$, which is the *next larger whole number.*

$$= \frac{3 \cdot 2^{1/3}}{2^2}$$

$$= \frac{3}{4}\sqrt[3]{2}$$

□

Example 20

$$\frac{6x^2}{\sqrt[3]{2x}} = \frac{6x^2}{(2x)^{1/3}} \cdot \frac{(2x)^{2/3}}{(2x)^{2/3}}$$

$$= \frac{6x^2(2x)^{2/3}}{(2x)^1}$$

$$= 3x\sqrt[3]{4x^2}$$

□

Example 21

$$\frac{3x}{\sqrt[6]{32x^2}} = \frac{3x}{(2^5 x^2)^{1/6}}$$

$$= \frac{3x}{2^{5/6}x^{2/6}} \cdot \frac{2^{1/6}x^{4/6}}{2^{1/6}x^{4/6}}$$

$$= \frac{3x(2x^4)^{1/6}}{2x}$$

$$= \frac{3}{2}\sqrt[6]{2x^4}$$

□

III. *A simplified form of a radical expression contains no fraction within a radical.* Remember, negative exponents under radicals are considered to be fractions within radicals and consequently need to be simplified.

In Examples 22 and 23 simplify the given radical expressions.

Example 22

$$\sqrt{\frac{3y^2}{25x}} = \frac{(3y^2)^{1/2}}{(5^2x)^{1/2}}$$

This example was worked in the last section using radical notation.

$$= \frac{3^{1/2}y^{2/2}}{5^{2/2}x^{1/2}} \cdot \frac{x^{1/2}}{x^{1/2}}$$

$$= \frac{y(3x)^{1/2}}{5x}$$

$$= \frac{y\sqrt{3x}}{5x}$$

□

Example 23

$$\sqrt[5]{128x^{-6}y^{12}} = (2)^{7/5}x^{-6/5}y^{12/5}$$

$$= \frac{(2)^{1+(2/5)}y^{2+(2/5)}}{x^{1+(1/5)}}$$

$$= \frac{(2)(2)^{2/5}y^2y^{2/5}}{xx^{1/5}} \cdot \frac{x^{4/5}}{x^{4/5}}$$

$$= \frac{2y^2(2)^{2/5}y^{2/5}x^{4/5}}{x^2}$$

$$= \frac{2y^2}{x^2}\sqrt[5]{4x^4y^2}$$

□

IV. *A simplified form of a radical expression has no common factors (other than 1) between the exponent of the radicand and the index of the radical.*

Example 24

$$\sqrt[4]{4} = (2^2)^{1/4}$$

Notice that when working in fractional exponent form, this simplification is nothing more than reducing the fractional exponent.

$$= 2^{2/4}$$

$$= 2^{1/2}$$

$$= \sqrt{2}$$

□

Example 25

$$\frac{\sqrt[6]{4x^{14}}}{\sqrt[6]{32x^2}} = \frac{2^{2/6}x^{14/6}}{2^{5/6}x^{2/6}}$$

$$= 2^{-3/6}x^{12/6}$$

$$= \frac{x^2}{2^{1/2}} \cdot \frac{2^{1/2}}{2^{1/2}}$$

$$= \frac{x^2}{2}\sqrt{2}$$

Now let's summarize.

SIMPLIFIED
RADICAL
EXPRESSION

A **radical expression** is simplified if all four of the following conditions are satisfied:

I. When the radicand is written in completely factored form, there is no factor raised to a power greater than or equal to the index of the radical.
II. No radical appears in a denominator.
III. No fraction or negative exponent appears within a radical.
IV. There is no common factor (other than 1) between the exponent of the radicand and the index of the radical.

Problem Set 6.4

A *Simplify each expression in Problems 1–56. Assume that the replacement set for the variables is such that all radicands are positive.*

See Examples 1–16.

1. $\sqrt[3]{64}$	2. $\sqrt[3]{27}$	3. $\sqrt[3]{24}$	4. $\sqrt[3]{108}$
5. $\sqrt[3]{432}$	6. $\sqrt[4]{32}$	7. $\sqrt[4]{48}$	8. $\sqrt[5]{768}$
9. $\sqrt[3]{1,000,000}$	10. $\sqrt[8]{1,024}$	11. $\sqrt[6]{512}$	12. $\sqrt[6]{128}$
13. $\sqrt[5]{128}$	14. $\sqrt{1,250 \cdot 8^3}$	15. $\sqrt[3]{x^4y^5}$	16. $\sqrt[3]{w^6t^5}$
17. $\sqrt[3]{u^7t^8}$	18. $\sqrt[4]{x^5y^7z^3}$	19. $\sqrt[4]{x^3y^7}$	20. $\sqrt[3]{48y^4}$

See Examples 17–21.

21. $\dfrac{3}{\sqrt{2}}$	22. $\dfrac{5}{\sqrt{3}}$	23. $\dfrac{2}{\sqrt[3]{8}}$	24. $\dfrac{3}{\sqrt[3]{9}}$
25. $\dfrac{3}{\sqrt[3]{5}}$	26. $\dfrac{5}{\sqrt[3]{16}}$	27. $\dfrac{1}{\sqrt[3]{25}}$	28. $\dfrac{1}{\sqrt[4]{2}}$
29. $\dfrac{1}{\sqrt[4]{4}}$	30. $\dfrac{1}{\sqrt[4]{8}}$	31. $\dfrac{5}{\sqrt[3]{16}}$	32. $\dfrac{9}{\sqrt[3]{81}}$
33. $\dfrac{1}{\sqrt{x}}$	34. $\dfrac{1}{\sqrt[3]{x}}$	35. $\dfrac{1}{\sqrt[4]{x}}$	36. $\dfrac{1}{\sqrt[5]{x}}$

37. $\dfrac{x^4}{\sqrt{x}}$ $\qquad$ **38.** $\dfrac{x^3}{\sqrt[3]{x}}$ $\qquad$ **39.** $\dfrac{x^2}{\sqrt[4]{x}}$ $\qquad$ **40.** $\dfrac{x}{\sqrt[5]{x}}$

See Examples 22 and 23.

41. $\sqrt{\dfrac{3}{4}}$ $\qquad$ **42.** $\sqrt{\dfrac{3}{2}}$ $\qquad$ **43.** $\sqrt[3]{\dfrac{5}{8}}$ $\qquad$ **44.** $\sqrt[3]{\dfrac{5}{9}}$

45. $\sqrt[3]{\dfrac{3}{5}}$ $\qquad$ **46.** $\sqrt[3]{\dfrac{5}{16}}$ $\qquad$ **47.** $\sqrt[3]{\dfrac{1}{25}}$ $\qquad$ **48.** $\sqrt[4]{\dfrac{1}{2}}$

49. $\sqrt[4]{\dfrac{1}{4}}$ $\qquad$ **50.** $\sqrt[4]{\dfrac{1}{8}}$ $\qquad$ **51.** $\sqrt{\dfrac{5x^2}{36y}}$ $\qquad$ **52.** $\sqrt{\dfrac{9x}{49y^3}}$

See Examples 24 and 25.

53. $\sqrt[8]{4}$ $\qquad$ **54.** $\sqrt[6]{9}$ $\qquad$ **55.** $\sqrt[6]{8x^3}$ $\qquad$ **56.** $\sqrt[8]{9x^4}$

B *Simplify each expression in Problems 57–76. Assume that the replacement set for the variables is such that all radicands are positive.*

See Example 16.

57. $\sqrt{4x^2 - 4xy + y^2}$ $\qquad\qquad$ **58.** $\sqrt{x^2 - 6xy + 9y^2}$

59. $(4\sqrt[3]{5x + 5})(7\sqrt[3]{x^2 + 2x + 1})$ $\qquad$ **60.** $(3\sqrt{2x^2 - 2y^2})(5\sqrt{5x^2 - 5y^2})$

See Examples 18–21.

61. $\dfrac{6x^3}{\sqrt[3]{3x}}$ $\qquad\qquad$ **62.** $\dfrac{15y^2}{\sqrt[3]{9y}}$

63. $\dfrac{5x + 5y}{\sqrt[3]{8(x + y)^2}}$ $\qquad\qquad$ **64.** $\dfrac{4x - 4y}{\sqrt[5]{8(x - y)^3}}$

65. $\dfrac{\sqrt[6]{8x^{12}}}{\sqrt[6]{128x^2}}$ $\qquad\qquad$ **66.** $\dfrac{\sqrt[8]{9x^3}}{\sqrt[4]{1,024x^{15}}}$

67. $\dfrac{16x^2 + 16xy + 4y^2}{\sqrt[3]{16(2x + y)^2}}$ $\qquad\qquad$ **68.** $\dfrac{x^3 + y^3}{\sqrt{x^2 - xy + y^2}}$

See Examples 22 and 23.

69. $\sqrt[5]{\dfrac{x^8}{128}}$ $\qquad\qquad$ **70.** $\sqrt[5]{\dfrac{128}{x^8}}$

71. $\sqrt[5]{\dfrac{x^{-10}}{128}}$ $\qquad\qquad$ **72.** $\sqrt[5]{\left(\dfrac{x^{-10}}{128}\right)^{-1}}$

73. $\sqrt[5]{128x^{-6}y^{11}}$ $\qquad\qquad$ **74.** $\sqrt[3]{512x^{-5}y^8}$

75. $\sqrt[6]{512x^{-9}y^{12}}$ $\qquad\qquad$ **76.** $\sqrt[4]{512x^{-5}y^2}$

77. *Physics.* The initial velocity, v, of an object (in meters per second) reaching a height of h meters is given by (neglecting air resistance)

$$v = \sqrt{64h}$$

What is the necessary velocity to shoot a projectile 1,000 m?

78. *Physics.* What is the necessary velocity in Problem 77 to shoot a projectile 3,000 m?

Mind Boggler **79.** If we allow x to be any real number, then

$$\sqrt[n]{x^n} \neq x$$

under certain conditions. For example, if $x = -2$ and $n = 2$, then

$$\sqrt{(-2)^2} \neq -2$$

since $\sqrt{(-2)^2} = \sqrt{4} = \sqrt{2^2} = 2$. State a formula that simplifies $\sqrt[n]{x^n}$ for all values of x and n, where x is a real number and $n \geq 2$, n a natural number.

6.5 Operations with Radicals

You now have the necessary mechanics for adding, subtracting, multiplying, and dividing radicals. Assume that all variables are restricted so that all radical expressions are defined.

Addition and Subtraction

The procedure for adding and subtracting radical expressions is to find similar terms. Use the distributive property on those radicals that have the same index *and also* the same radicand. For example,

$$5\sqrt{2} + 7\sqrt{2} = (5+7)\sqrt{2}$$
$$= 12\sqrt{2}$$

Note that just as $5x + 7y$ can't be simplified further (there aren't any similar terms), $5\sqrt{2} + 7\sqrt[3]{2}$ can't be simplified since the indexes aren't the same, and $5\sqrt{2} + 7\sqrt{3}$ can't be simplified since the radicands aren't the same.

Example 1 Simplify the given expressions, if possible.

a. $6\sqrt{7} + 3\sqrt{7} = (6+3)\sqrt{7}$ **b.** $4\sqrt{x} - 7\sqrt{x} = -3\sqrt{x}$
$= 9\sqrt{7}$

c. $2\sqrt[3]{3} + 4\sqrt{2} - (5\sqrt{2} + 4\sqrt[3]{3})$ **d.** $\sqrt{8} + \sqrt[3]{2} = 2\sqrt{2} + \sqrt[3]{2}$
$= 2\sqrt[3]{3} + 4\sqrt{2} - 5\sqrt{2} - 4\sqrt[3]{3}$
$= -2\sqrt[3]{3} - \sqrt{2}$ □

Example 1d can't be simplified further since the indexes are not the same. However, we should first simplify each radical and then combine, if possible, as shown in Example 2.

Example 2 $\sqrt[3]{\dfrac{2}{3}} + \dfrac{2\sqrt[3]{18}}{3} + \sqrt[3]{486} = \dfrac{\sqrt[3]{18}}{3} + \dfrac{2\sqrt[3]{18}}{3} + \sqrt[3]{27 \cdot 18}$

$$= \dfrac{1}{3}\sqrt[3]{18} + \dfrac{2}{3}\sqrt[3]{18} + 3\sqrt[3]{18}$$

$$= 4\sqrt[3]{18}$$ □

Products

Since

$$\sqrt[n]{a}\ \sqrt[n]{b} = \sqrt[n]{ab}$$

you can multiply radicals *provided* they have the same index.

In Examples 3–9 simplify the given expression, if possible. The set of replacements for the variables is the set of positive real numbers.

Example 3 $\sqrt[3]{x^2} \cdot \sqrt[3]{x} = \sqrt[3]{x^3}$
$$= x \qquad\qquad \square$$

Example 4 $\sqrt{2}\sqrt{18} = \sqrt{36}$
$$= 6 \qquad\qquad \square$$

Example 5 $\sqrt[4]{3}\ \sqrt[4]{9} = \sqrt[4]{27} \qquad\qquad \square$

Example 6 $\sqrt{2}\ \sqrt[3]{3}$ You can't directly multiply these radicals because the indexes aren't the same. However, you can make the indexes the same by finding the least common denominator of the fractional exponents:

$$\begin{aligned}
\sqrt{2}\ \sqrt[3]{3} &= 2^{1/2} \cdot 3^{1/3} \\
&= 2^{3/6} \cdot 3^{2/6} \\
&= (2^3 \cdot 3^2)^{1/6} \\
&= \sqrt[6]{72}
\end{aligned} \qquad\qquad \square$$

Example 7 $\begin{aligned}[t]
(\sqrt{3} + 2)(\sqrt{3} - 2) &= (\sqrt{3} + 2)(\sqrt{3}) + (\sqrt{3} + 2)(-2) \\
&= 3 + 2\sqrt{3} + (-2)\sqrt{3} + (-4) \\
&= -1
\end{aligned} \qquad\qquad \square$

Example 8 $\begin{aligned}[t]
\sqrt{12y}\,(\sqrt{y} + \sqrt{3}) &= \sqrt{12y^2} + \sqrt{36y} \\
&= 2y\sqrt{3} + 6\sqrt{y}
\end{aligned} \qquad\qquad \square$

Example 9 $\begin{aligned}[t]
(\sqrt{x} + \sqrt{y})^2 &= (\sqrt{x})^2 + 2\sqrt{x}\sqrt{y} + (\sqrt{y})^2 \qquad \text{\small Don't forget that middle term!} \\
&= x + 2\sqrt{xy} + y
\end{aligned}$

This example illustrates a common mistake when working with radicals; remember that $(a + b)^2 = a^2 + 2ab + b^2$, *not* $a^2 + b^2$. When working this example remember that $(\sqrt{x} + \sqrt{y})$ is a binomial. $\square$

Quotients

The process of dividing radical expressions is a process of rationalizing the denominator.

Example 10   Simplify: $\dfrac{5x\sqrt{3}}{\sqrt{2x}}$

Solution $\dfrac{5x\sqrt{3}}{\sqrt{2x}} = \dfrac{5x\sqrt{3}}{\sqrt{2x}} \cdot \dfrac{\sqrt{2x}}{\sqrt{2x}}$

$= \dfrac{5x\sqrt{6x}}{2x}$

$= \dfrac{5}{2}\sqrt{6x}$ $\qquad\qquad\qquad\qquad\qquad$ $\square$

If there are two terms in the denominator such as

$$\dfrac{5x\sqrt{3}}{\sqrt{2x}+3}$$

Recall that $a+b$ and $a-b$ are *conjugates*. Also, notice that if we multiply conjugates, then

$(a+b)(a-b) = a^2 - b^2$

you must multiply by 1, where it is written in the form of the **conjugate** of the denominator, as shown in color in the following **examples**.

In Examples 11–13 simplify the given expressions, if possible.

This is 1.

Example 11 $\dfrac{5x\sqrt{3}}{\sqrt{2x}+3} = \dfrac{5x\sqrt{3}}{\sqrt{2x}+3} \cdot \dfrac{\sqrt{2x}-3}{\sqrt{2x}-3}$

$= \dfrac{5x\sqrt{6x} - 15x\sqrt{3}}{2x-9}$ $\qquad\qquad$ $\square$

Example 12 $\dfrac{xy}{\sqrt{5}-\sqrt{2}} = \dfrac{xy}{\sqrt{5}-\sqrt{2}} \cdot \dfrac{\sqrt{5}+\sqrt{2}}{\sqrt{5}+\sqrt{2}}$

$= \dfrac{xy(\sqrt{5}+\sqrt{2})}{5-2}$

$= \dfrac{xy(\sqrt{5}+\sqrt{2})}{3}$ or $\dfrac{xy}{3}(\sqrt{5}+\sqrt{2})$ $\qquad$ $\square$

Example 13 $\dfrac{1+\sqrt{3}}{1-\sqrt{3}} = \dfrac{1+\sqrt{3}}{1-\sqrt{3}} \cdot \dfrac{1+\sqrt{3}}{1+\sqrt{3}}$

$= \dfrac{1+2\sqrt{3}+3}{1-3}$

$= \dfrac{4+2\sqrt{3}}{-2}$

$= \dfrac{-2(-2-\sqrt{3})}{-2}$

$= -2-\sqrt{3}$

Beware! Be sure to *factor* the numerator before simplifying. (You can, however, often do this step in your head.) $\qquad$ $\square$

The next two examples are presented together so that you can see the differences between them. In Example 14 you are dividing by an expression with two terms, which requires using the conjugate. In Example 15 you are dividing by a single radical.

Example 14
$$\frac{x}{\sqrt{x}-3} = \frac{x}{\sqrt{x}-3} \cdot \frac{\sqrt{x}+3}{\sqrt{x}+3} \qquad \text{1, written as a quotient of conjugates}$$
$$= \frac{x(\sqrt{x}+3)}{x-9} \quad \text{or} \quad \frac{x\sqrt{x}+3x}{x-9}$$ ☐

Example 15
$$\frac{x}{\sqrt{x-3}} = \frac{x}{\sqrt{x-3}} \cdot \frac{\sqrt{x-3}}{\sqrt{x-3}} \qquad \text{1, found by looking at the denominator of the given fraction}$$
$$= \frac{x\sqrt{x-3}}{x-3}$$ ☐

Problem Set 6.5

For this problem set, assume that the replacement set for the variables is the set of positive real numbers.

A *Mentally simplify the expressions in Problems 1–18, if possible.*

See Example 1.
1. $2\sqrt{3}+5\sqrt{3}$
2. $\sqrt{7}-3\sqrt{7}$
3. $4\sqrt{5}+3\sqrt{2}$

See Examples 3–5.
4. $\sqrt[3]{3}\,\sqrt[3]{9}$
5. $\sqrt[4]{8}\,\sqrt[4]{2}$
6. $\sqrt[5]{x}\,\sqrt[5]{x^3}$
7. $(2\sqrt{3})^2$
8. $(4\sqrt{2})^2$
9. $(3\sqrt{5})^2$

See Examples 7–9.
10. $-3(1-2\sqrt[3]{4})$
11. $\sqrt{3}(3\sqrt{3}+2\sqrt{2})$
12. $\sqrt{2}(1-\sqrt{2})$
13. $(\sqrt{x}+1)^2$
14. $(\sqrt{y}-1)^2$
15. $(\sqrt{x}+y)^2$
16. $(\sqrt{5}+\sqrt{3})^2$
17. $(y+2\sqrt{x})^2$
18. $(\sqrt{2}-\sqrt{5})^2$

Simplify the expressions in Problems 19–36, if possible.

See Examples 1 and 2.
19. $3\sqrt{2}+5\sqrt{5}-(3\sqrt{5}+2\sqrt{2})$
20. $4\sqrt[3]{4}+3\sqrt[3]{9}-(3\sqrt[3]{4}+3\sqrt[3]{9})$
21. $\sqrt[3]{x}+\sqrt{y}+2\sqrt[3]{x}+\sqrt[3]{y}$
22. $4\sqrt{y}+3\sqrt{x}-2\sqrt{y}-4\sqrt{xy}$
23. $\sqrt{8}+4\sqrt{2}$
24. $5\sqrt{2x}-2\sqrt{8x}$
25. $5\sqrt{x}-(4\sqrt{y}+5\sqrt{x})$
26. $2\sqrt[3]{16}-\sqrt[3]{2}$

See Example 2.
27. $5\sqrt[3]{32}-(\sqrt[3]{2}+3\sqrt[3]{4})$
28. $\sqrt{75}+2\sqrt{18}-4\sqrt{12}$
29. $\sqrt{27}+3\sqrt{72}-3\sqrt{12}$
30. $4\sqrt{72}-2\sqrt{75}+3\sqrt{12}$

31. $5\sqrt{12}-3\sqrt{18}+2\sqrt{72}$
32. $\sqrt{5}+\dfrac{1}{\sqrt{5}}$

33. $\sqrt{3}-\dfrac{1}{\sqrt{3}}$
34. $\sqrt{\dfrac{3}{5}}+\sqrt{20}$

35. $\dfrac{1}{2}\sqrt{18}+\dfrac{3}{\sqrt{2}}-3\sqrt{50}$
36. $\sqrt{\dfrac{1}{3}}+\dfrac{2\sqrt{3}}{3}+\sqrt{75}$

Find calculator

B   *Simplify the expressions in Problems 37–61, if possible.*

See Example 6.   **37.** $\sqrt{2}\,\sqrt[4]{4}$ **38.** $\sqrt[3]{3}\,\sqrt[4]{4}$ **39.** $\sqrt{2}\,\sqrt[3]{5}$

40. $\sqrt[3]{3}\,\sqrt{5}$ **41.** $\dfrac{\sqrt[3]{3}}{\sqrt[4]{4}}$ **42.** $\dfrac{\sqrt{2}}{\sqrt[3]{3}}$

See Example 10.   **43.** $\dfrac{\sqrt{6}+\sqrt{8}}{\sqrt{2}}$ **44.** $\dfrac{\sqrt{3}+\sqrt{12}}{\sqrt{3}}$ **45.** $\dfrac{xy - y\sqrt{x^2 y}}{xy}$

See Example 2.   **46.** $\sqrt{18}+\dfrac{2}{\sqrt{2}}-4\sqrt{50}$ **47.** $\sqrt[3]{81}+\dfrac{3}{\sqrt[3]{3}}-2\sqrt[3]{24}$

See Examples 7–9.   **48.** $(\sqrt[3]{x}+1)(\sqrt[3]{x^2}-\sqrt[3]{x}+1)$ **49.** $(\sqrt[3]{y}-1)(\sqrt[3]{y^2}+\sqrt[3]{y}+1)$

See Examples 11–13.   **50.** $\dfrac{1}{\sqrt{2}+1}$ **51.** $\dfrac{2}{\sqrt{5}-1}$ **52.** $\dfrac{st}{\sqrt{3}+\sqrt{5}}$

53. $\dfrac{1+\sqrt{2}}{1-\sqrt{2}}$ **54.** $\dfrac{1+\sqrt{5}}{1-\sqrt{5}}$ **55.** $\dfrac{1-\sqrt{x}}{1+\sqrt{x}}$

See Examples 14 and 15.   **56.** $\dfrac{2\sqrt{x}-5}{\sqrt{x}+\sqrt{5}}$ **57.** $\dfrac{2\sqrt{x}-5}{\sqrt{x+5}}$ **58.** $\dfrac{y}{\sqrt{y+2}}$

59. $\dfrac{y}{\sqrt{y}+2}$ **60.** $\dfrac{mn}{\sqrt{m^2+n^2}}$ **61.** $\dfrac{mn}{\sqrt{m+n}}$

In Problems 62–79, find the value of the capital letter.

These problems combine operations with radicals.

62. $A=\dfrac{1}{6}(6-\sqrt{6})(3\sqrt{2}-2\sqrt{3})(4\sqrt{2}+3\sqrt{3})$

63. $B=\sqrt{3}(\sqrt{27}+\sqrt{48}-\sqrt{12})$

64. $C=\sqrt{2}\left(\sqrt{18}-\sqrt{72}+\dfrac{4}{\sqrt{2}}\right)$

65. $D=(\sqrt{6}+\sqrt{3})(\sqrt{6}-2\sqrt{3})(\sqrt{8})$

66. $E=\sqrt{8-2\sqrt{7}}\,\sqrt{8+2\sqrt{7}}$

67. $F=(4+\sqrt{3})(4-\sqrt{3})$

68. $G=(\sqrt{5}-\sqrt{3})^2+(\sqrt{5}+\sqrt{3})^2$

69. $H=(\sqrt{2}-\sqrt{3})^2+(\sqrt{2}+\sqrt{3})^2$

70. $I=(2-\sqrt{3})(\sqrt{3}+1)^2$

71. $L=(3-\sqrt{5})(\sqrt{5}+3)$

72. $M=(4)\left(\dfrac{1}{2}+\dfrac{\sqrt{2}}{2}\right)\left(\dfrac{1}{2}-\dfrac{\sqrt{2}}{2}\right)$

73. $N=(2+\sqrt{2})(3-\sqrt{2})(4-\sqrt{2})$

74. $P=(2+\sqrt{6})(3+\sqrt{2})(2-\sqrt{6})(3-\sqrt{2})$

75. $R=(2\sqrt{3}-3\sqrt{2})(3\sqrt{2}+2\sqrt{3})$

76. $S=\dfrac{(2\sqrt{3}-\sqrt{6})(3\sqrt{3}+3\sqrt{6})}{\sqrt{2}}$

77. $T = \dfrac{(2\sqrt{3} - 1)}{\sqrt{3} + 2}(5\sqrt{3} + 8)$

78. $U = \dfrac{\sqrt{20} - 2}{\sqrt{5} + 2}(7 + 3\sqrt{5})$

79. $W = \dfrac{2(3\sqrt{2} - 8\sqrt{3})(4\sqrt{2} + \sqrt{3})}{\sqrt{6}}$

Algebra Adage

80. Replace each number within parentheses with the capital letter from Problems 62–79 that has the value shown. Some letters have been supplied as further clues.

(5)(14)   (O)(V)(6)(−6)(5)(15)(8)(14)(−12)(5)(14)(−2)(6)
(O)(13)   (−2)(8)(4)(2)(14)(5)(−6)(Y)   (5)(−6)(11)(2)(9)(11)(9)
(10)(2)(4)(4)   (−12)(5)(−1)(5)(16)(6)   (11)(10)(6)
(−14)(O)(−6)(−6)(2)(−12)(16)(6).

81. Translate the algebra adage into the common proverb it paraphrases.

Mind Bogglers

82. Simplify: $\dfrac{-7}{\sqrt[3]{2} - \sqrt[3]{7}}$

83. Simplify: $\dfrac{\sqrt{2} - \sqrt{5}}{\sqrt{2} + \sqrt{3} + \sqrt{5}}$

6.6 Complex Numbers

Historical Note

Descartes classified numbers as *real* and *imaginary* in 1637, and Euler was the first to use the letter *i* and the name *complex number*.

Throughout this chapter, all the variables under radicals have been positive real numbers. There are several reasons for this. First, if the index is even, negative values of the radicand are not defined. For example, by definition,

$$\sqrt{-4} = a \qquad \text{means} \qquad -4 = a^2$$

but no real number squared can be negative. Also, if the radicand is negative with an even index, the laws of radicals don't hold (see Problem Set 6.1, Problems 63–66, and Problem Set 6.4, Problem 79). Nevertheless, problems that give rise to the square root of a negative number are still occasionally encountered, so we'll now investigate this possibility.

It is important to remember that *in the set of real numbers, the square roots of negative numbers do not exist.* We therefore define a number that is *not a real number.* This number is denoted by *i* and defined as follows.

IMAGINARY UNIT, *i*

The number *i,* called the **imaginary unit,** is defined as a number with the following properties:

$$i^2 = -1$$

and if $a > 0$, then $\sqrt{-a} = i\sqrt{a}$.

The number i is *not a real number,* but with this number, you can write the square root of any negative number as the product of a real number and the number i.

Example 1   **a.** $\sqrt{-1} = i\sqrt{1}$ **b.** $\sqrt{-4} = i\sqrt{4}$
                                 $= i$ $= 2i$
                 c. $\sqrt{-5} = i\sqrt{5}$ **d.** $\sqrt{-b} = i\sqrt{b}$ for $b > 0$ □

Now consider a new set of numbers that *includes the real numbers as a subset.*

The set of **complex numbers** is the set of numbers of the form

  $a + bi$

where a and b are real numbers and i is the imaginary unit. In symbols,

  $C = \{a + bi \,|\, a, b \in \mathcal{R}, \quad i^2 = -1\}$

Now if $b = 0$, then the subset of the set of complex numbers represented by

  $a + 0i = a$

is the set of real numbers. If $a = 0$ and $b = 1$, the expression is the imaginary unit:

  $0 + 1i = i$

If $a = 0$ and $b \neq 0$, then we have what is called a **pure imaginary number:**

  $0 + bi = bi$

A complex number is **simplified** when it is written in the form

  $a + bi$

where a and b are real numbers and $i = \sqrt{-1}$.

So that we can do arithmetic with complex numbers, we define equality, addition, subtraction, and distributivity of two complex numbers $a + bi$ and $c + di$.

COMPLEX
NUMBERS

Historical Note

The idea of the square root of a negative number has bothered mathematicians for years. The Hindus Mahavira (850) and Bhaskara (1150) were aware of the problem, but the first to seriously consider them was Girolamo Cardano (1501–1576), who referred to them as *sophistic* (which means clever or plausible but unsound and tending to mislead). Cardano was an illegitimate son of a jurist and was interested in astrology. He was imprisoned for a time on charges of heresy because of a horoscope of Christ he published. He also predicted the date of his death, and when the day came he found himself in good health, so he drank poison to fulfill his prophecy.

EQUALITY,
ADDITION,
SUBTRACTION, AND
DISTRIBUTIVITY OF
COMPLEX
NUMBERS

Definitions

Let $a + bi$ and $c + di$ be any complex numbers. Then

Equality	$a + bi = c + di$ if and only if $a = c$ and $b = d$
Addition	$(a + bi) + (c + di) = (a + c) + (b + d)i$
Subtraction	$(a + bi) - (c + di) = (a - c) + (b - d)i$
Distributivity	$c(a + bi) = ca + cbi$

In Examples 2–10 write each complex number in the form $a + bi$ and state whether each is real, pure imaginary, or neither.

Example 2

$$\sqrt{-9} = i\sqrt{9}$$
$$= 3i \text{ or } 0 + 3i$$

It is pure imaginary. □

Example 3

$$5 = 5 + 0i$$

Real □

Example 4

$$6 + 4i, \quad 3 - i, \quad \sqrt{2} - \sqrt{3}i$$

These are all in simplified form $a + bi$; neither. □

Example 5

$$4 + 6\sqrt{-5} = 4 + 6i\sqrt{5} \text{ or } 4 + 6\sqrt{5}i$$ If you write $\sqrt{5}\,i$ instead of $i\sqrt{5}$, be sure that you do *not* include i under the radical.

Neither □

Example 6

$$\frac{2 - \sqrt{-8}}{2} = \frac{1}{2}(2 - i\sqrt{8})$$

$$= \frac{1}{2}(2 - 2\sqrt{2}\,i)$$

$$= 1 - \sqrt{2}\,i$$

Neither □

Example 7

$$(3 + 4i) + (2 + 3i) = 5 + 7i$$

Neither □

Example 8

$$(2 - i) - (3 - 2i) = -1 + i$$

Neither □

Example 9 $(6 + 2i) + (2 - 2i) = 8$ or $8 + 0i$

Real   □

Example 10 $(4 + 3i) - (4 - 2i) = 5i$ or $0 + 5i$

Pure imaginary   □

Notice that, by definition, complex numbers are added and subtracted as if they were ordinary binomials where all the variables are real. Multiplication of complex numbers can also be treated as ordinary binomial multiplication, except that, since $i^2 = -1$, i^2 should be replaced by -1 whenever it occurs.

$$(a + bi)(c + di) = ac + adi + bci + \boldsymbol{bdi^2} \qquad \text{Notice:} \quad bdi^2 = bd(-1)$$
$$= ac + adi + bci - \boldsymbol{bd} \qquad\qquad\qquad = -bd$$
$$= (ac - bd) + (ad + bc)i$$

We take this as our definition of multiplication of complex numbers.

MULTIPLICATION
OF COMPLEX
NUMBERS

> If $a + bi$ and $c + di$ are any two complex numbers, then
>
> $$(a + bi)(c + di) = (ac - bd) + (ad + bc)i$$

It is not necessary to memorize this definition since you handle two complex numbers as you would any binomials, remembering that $i^2 = -1$.

Example 11   Notice the following pattern:

$i = i$	$i^5 = i^4 \cdot i = i$	$i^9 = (i^4)^2 \cdot i = i$
$i^2 = -1$	$i^6 = i^4 \cdot i^2 = -1$	$i^{10} = (i^4)^2 \cdot i^2 = -1$
$i^3 = i \cdot i^2 = -i$	$i^7 = i^4 \cdot i^3 = -i$	$i^{11} = (i^4)^2 \cdot i^3 = -i$
$i^4 = i^2 \cdot i^2 = (-1)(-1) = 1$	$i^8 = i^4 \cdot i^4 = 1$	$i^{12} = (i^4)^2 \cdot i^4 = 1$

Example 12   Simplify each of the given expressions.   □

a. $i^{2,001} = i^{2,000} \cdot i$
$$= (i^4)^{500} \cdot i$$
$$= (1)i$$
$$= i$$

b. $3(2 + i) = 6 + 3i$

c. $i(3 - 2i) = 3i - 2i^2$
$$= 3i - 2(-1)$$
$$= 2 + 3i$$

d. $(2 + i)(3 - i) = 6 - 2i + 3i - i^2$
$$= 6 + i + 1$$
$$= 7 + i$$

e. $(2 + 3i)(4 + 2i) = 8 + 16i + 6i^2$
$$= 8 + 16i - 6$$
$$= 2 + 16i$$

f. $(4 - 3i)(2 - i) = 8 - 10i + 3i^2$
$$= 5 - 10i$$

Complex = Imaginary + Reals

a + bi = def. of complex numbers

g. $(3 - 2i)(3 + 2i) = 9 - 4i^2$
$$= 13$$

h. $(2 - \sqrt{-4})(4 + \sqrt{-9}) = (2 - 2i)(4 + 3i)$
$$= 8 - 2i - 6i^2$$
$$= 14 - 2i \qquad \square$$

Notice that in Example 12h we changed to the form $a + bi$ *before* multiplying. The reason for doing this is because the property

$$\sqrt{a}\,\sqrt{b} = \sqrt{ab}$$

applies *only if a and b are both positive.* This means

$$\sqrt{-4}\,\sqrt{-9} \neq \sqrt{(-4)(-9)}$$
$$= \sqrt{36}$$
$$= 6$$

But instead,

$$\sqrt{-4}\,\sqrt{-9} = (i\sqrt{4})(i\sqrt{9}) \qquad \text{By definition.}$$
$$= i^2[\sqrt{(4)(9)}] \qquad \text{The property holds now because the numbers within}$$
$$= (-1)\sqrt{36} \qquad \text{the radicals are positive.}$$
$$= -6$$

Example 13
$$\sqrt{-8}\,\sqrt{-3} = (\sqrt{8}\ i)(\sqrt{3}\ i)$$
$$= 2\sqrt{2}\,\sqrt{3}\ i^2$$
$$= -2\sqrt{6} \qquad \square$$

For division, use the process of rationalizing the denominator that was developed earlier in this chapter. Notice in Example 12g that when multiplying a complex number by its conjugate, the result is a real number. In general,

$$(a + bi)(a - bi) = a^2 - b^2i^2$$
$$= a^2 + b^2$$

which is real since a and b are real.

In Examples 14 and 15 simplify each expression.

Example 14
$$\frac{7 + i}{2 + i} = \frac{7 + i}{2 + i} \cdot \frac{2 - i}{2 - i}$$
$$= \frac{14 - 5i - i^2}{4 - i^2}$$
$$= \frac{15 - 5i}{5}$$
$$= 3 - i$$

You can check this division in the same way you check any division problem. For example, $\frac{10}{5} = 2$ can be checked by multiplying: $5 \cdot 2 = 10$.

Check: $(2+i)(3-i) = 6+i-i^2$
$$= 7+i \qquad \square$$

Example 15 $\dfrac{15-\sqrt{-25}}{2-\sqrt{-1}} = \dfrac{15-5i}{2-i} \cdot \dfrac{2+i}{2+i}$

$$= \frac{30+5i-5i^2}{4-i^2}$$

$$= \frac{35+5i}{5}$$

$$= 7+i \qquad \square$$

Problem Set 6.6

A   *Write each of the complex numbers in Problems 1–18 in the form a + bi.*

See Example 1.

1. $\sqrt{-16}$ **2.** $\sqrt{-25}$ **3.** $\sqrt{-27}$ **4.** $\sqrt{-125}$

See Examples 2–6.

5. $\sqrt{-6}$ **6.** $\sqrt{-7}$ **7.** $4\sqrt{-36}$ **8.** $\dfrac{\sqrt{-8}}{2}$

9. $\dfrac{3\sqrt{-49}}{7}$ **10.** $\dfrac{6+\sqrt{-18}}{3}$ **11.** $\left(\dfrac{2+\sqrt{5}}{\sqrt{2}}\right)^2$ **12.** $6+\sqrt{7}$

13. $2+\sqrt{3}-4+\sqrt{-2}$ **14.** $(6-\sqrt{2})+(2-\sqrt{-4})$

15. $(3+\sqrt{-8})+\sqrt{-3}$ **16.** $\dfrac{2+\sqrt{-8}}{-2}$

17. $\dfrac{-5+\sqrt{-50}}{5}$ **18.** $\dfrac{3+\sqrt{-12}}{-3}$

Simplify each expression in Problems 19–42.

See Examples 7–10.

19. $(3+2i)+(5+4i)$ **20.** $(6-2i)+(4+3i)$
21. $(3+2i)-(4+3i)$ **22.** $5i-(2-3i)$
23. $6i-(3+4i)$ **24.** $(5-2i)-(5+2i)$
25. $5(2+3i)$ **26.** $-7(3-2i)$
27. $-3(4-3i)$ **28.** $4(2-i)-3(-1-i)$
29. $3(7-4i)+2(-3-i)$ **30.** $2(4+3i)-3(2-7i)$

See Examples 11 and 12.

31. $-i^2$ **32.** $-i^3$ **33.** i^{15} **34.** $(-i)^2$
35. $(-i)^3$ **36.** $-i^{16}$ **37.** $i(2+3i)$ **38.** $i(5-2i)$
39. $(3-i)(2+i)$ **40.** $(4-i)(2+i)$ **41.** $(6-2i)^2$ **42.** $(3+4i)^2$

B *Simplify each expression in Problems 43–60.*

See Examples 12 and   **43.** $(\sqrt{5}+\sqrt{2}\,i)(\sqrt{5}-\sqrt{2}\,i)$ **44.** $(\sqrt{3}-\sqrt{5}\,i)(\sqrt{3}+\sqrt{5}\,i)$
13.   **45.** $(2+\sqrt{-1})(3+\sqrt{-1})$ **46.** $(4-\sqrt{-4})(3-\sqrt{-4})$

See Examples 14 and   **47.** $(\sqrt{3}+4i)^2$ **48.** $(\sqrt{5}-2i)^2$ **49.** $\dfrac{-2}{1+i}$ **50.** $\dfrac{4}{5-2i}$
15.

51. $\dfrac{2+3i}{4-i}$ **52.** $\dfrac{1}{i}$ **53.** $\dfrac{3}{i}$ **54.** i^{-3}

55. $\dfrac{10-\sqrt{-25}}{2-\sqrt{-1}}$ **56.** $\dfrac{4-\sqrt{-4}}{1+\sqrt{-1}}$ **57.** $\dfrac{\sqrt{-1}+1}{\sqrt{-1}-1}$ **58.** $\dfrac{10-\sqrt{-25}}{3-\sqrt{-1}}$

59. $[(2+\sqrt{3})+(4-\sqrt{2})i][(2+\sqrt{3})-(4-\sqrt{2})i]$
60. $[(4-\sqrt{2})+(3-\sqrt{2})i][(1+\sqrt{2})+(2-\sqrt{2})i]$

Mind Bogglers   **61.** What is wrong with the following "proof"?

$\sqrt{-1}=\sqrt{-1}$ Property of equality

$\sqrt{\dfrac{1}{-1}}=\sqrt{\dfrac{-1}{1}}$ $-1=\dfrac{1}{-1}$ and $-1=\dfrac{-1}{1}$

$\dfrac{\sqrt{1}}{\sqrt{-1}}=\dfrac{\sqrt{-1}}{\sqrt{1}}$ Property of radicals

$\dfrac{1}{i}=\dfrac{i}{1}$ $\sqrt{1}=1$ and $\sqrt{-1}=i$

$\dfrac{i}{i^2}=i$ $\dfrac{1}{i}\cdot\dfrac{i}{i}=\dfrac{i}{i^2}$ and $\dfrac{i}{1}=i$

$\dfrac{i}{-1}=i$ $i^2=-1$

$-i=i$ Which is impossible!

62. Show that $x=4$ and $x=\sqrt[3]{2+\sqrt{-121}}+\sqrt[3]{2-\sqrt{-121}}$ are roots of $x^3=15x+4$.

6.7 Review Problems

1. Fill in the missing word or words to make each of the following statements complete and correct.

(6.2)   **a.** Given $\sqrt[n]{b}$, the symbol $\sqrt{}$ is called a _radicand_, and n is called the _root_.

(6.6)   **b.** The set of numbers of the form $a+bi$, where a and b are real numbers and $i=\sqrt{-1}$, is the set of _complex_ numbers.

(6.4)   **c.** The process by which we free the denominator of radical expressions is called _____.

(6.6)   **d.** The number i is defined so that $i^2 =$ ___-1___ and is called the _____.

(6.6)   **e.** The complex numbers $a + bi$ and $c + di$ are equal if and only if $a = c + b = d$.

(6.1)   *Simplify each expression in Problems 2–4, if they are defined. The variables are all positive.*

2. **a.** $(-8)^{1/3}$ **b.** $(-8)^{1/2}$

3. **a.** $(3^{1/3} \cdot 2^{1/2})^6$ **b.** $\dfrac{y^{1/2}}{y^{1/3}}$

4. **a.** $(4x^2 y^{-2})^{1/2}$ **b.** $(x^{1/2} x^{3/2})^{-1/2}$

(6.2)   **5.** Without using a table or a calculator, plot the numbers given in Problem 6 (below) on the given number line.

Simplify each expression in Problems 6–20, if possible. Assume that the replacement set for the variables is chosen so that the radicands are positive.

(6.3)   **6.** **a.** $\sqrt{27}$ **b.** $\dfrac{4}{\sqrt{5}}$

(6.3)   **7.** **a.** $6 + 2\sqrt{27}$ **b.** $2 - 3\sqrt{8}$

(6.3)   **8.** **a.** $\dfrac{4 + \sqrt{8}}{2}$ **b.** $\dfrac{-(-9) + \sqrt{(-9)^2 - 4(3)(6)}}{2(3)}$

(6.3)   **9.** **a.** $(3\sqrt{5})^2$ **b.** $(\sqrt{2} + 3)^2$

(6.3)   **10.** **a.** $\sqrt{x^2 + y^2}$ **b.** $\sqrt{x^2 + 2xy + y^2}$

(6.4)   **11.** **a.** $2\sqrt[3]{5} - 3\sqrt[3]{5}$ **b.** $\sqrt{2} + 3\sqrt[3]{2} - 7\sqrt{2}$

(6.4)   **12.** **a.** $\sqrt[3]{200}$ **b.** $\sqrt[3]{-8x^{-5}y^7}$

(6.5)   **13.** **a.** $(x^2 + y^2)^{1/2}$ **b.** $\sqrt[6]{8x^8}\,\sqrt[6]{16x^2}$

(6.5)   **14.** **a.** $\sqrt{(3 - y)^{-1}}$ **b.** $\sqrt{3^{-1} + y^{-1}}$

(6.5)   **15.** **a.** $\sqrt{2}(\sqrt{3} + \sqrt[3]{4})$ **b.** $\sqrt{2} + \dfrac{1}{\sqrt{2}}$

(6.5)   **16.** **a.** $\dfrac{x}{2 + \sqrt{x}}$ **b.** $\dfrac{x}{\sqrt{2 + x}}$

(6.5)   **17.** **a.** $\sqrt{2}(\sqrt{3} + x)^{-1}$ **b.** $\sqrt{2}(\sqrt{3 + x})^{-1}$

(6.6)   **18.** **a.** $4 - (3 + 3i)$ **b.** $5 + \sqrt{-4} + \sqrt{-9}$

(6.6)   **19.** **a.** i^{10} **b.** $\dfrac{2}{i}$

(6.6)   **20.** **a.** $(\sqrt{-2} + 3)^2$ **b.** $\dfrac{3i}{5 - 2i}$

CHAPTER

7

Quadratic Equations

Contents

$$\sqrt{4} -1(3+3i)$$
$$4-3-3i$$
$$1-3i$$

7.1   Completing the Square

The area, A, of a square is given by the formula $A = s^2$, where s is the length of a side of the square. Using this formula, determine the dimensions of a square if its area is 75 cm².

$$A = s^2$$
$$75 = s^2$$
$$0 = s^2 - 75$$
$$s^2 - 75 = 0$$

The binomial is not factorable with integers, and thus there is no rational solution. The roots must be irrational and the following property may be applied.

SQUARE ROOT PROPERTY

> If $x^2 = a$, then $x = \sqrt{a}$ or $x = -\sqrt{a}$ or both.

The expression "$x = \sqrt{a}$ or $x = -\sqrt{a}$ or both" is usually written as $x = \pm\sqrt{a}$. The symbol $\pm$ is commonly used to mean "plus or minus." The square root property may now be used to solve the equation from the problem above.

Example 1   Solve for s: $s^2 = 75$

Solution $$s^2 = 75$$
$$s = \pm\sqrt{75}$$
$$= \pm 5\sqrt{3} \qquad \square$$

However, in applying this solution to the original problem, $-5\sqrt{3}$ is excluded because s is a distance and therefore must be nonnegative. Finally, since this is a distance, you may want to give the answer as a decimal approximation. So, the distance is 8.7 cm, to the nearest tenth of a centimeter.

Example 2   Solve for x: $(x + 2)^2 = 5$

Solution $$(x + 2)^2 = 5$$
$$x + 2 = \pm\sqrt{5}$$
$$x = -2 \pm \sqrt{5} \qquad \square$$

Example 3   A number is 3 more than a second number whose square is 7. What is the first number?

Solution $$\left(\begin{smallmatrix}\text{SECOND}\\\text{NUMBER}\end{smallmatrix}\right)^2 = \left[\left(\begin{smallmatrix}\text{FIRST}\\\text{NUMBER}\end{smallmatrix}\right) - 3\right]^2 = 7$$

Historical Note

As early as 2000 B.C., the Babylonians had evolved a well-developed algebra. It did not have the symbolism we associate with modern-day algebra but was written out in words. However, they solved quadratic equations by using a general formula and by completing the square. The Greeks solved such equations geometrically.

Let $n = $ FIRST NUMBER. Then

$$(n-3)^2 = 7$$
$$n - 3 = \pm\sqrt{7}$$
$$n = 3 \pm \sqrt{7}$$
$$n = 3 + \sqrt{7} \quad \text{or} \quad n = 3 - \sqrt{7}$$

The number is either $3 + \sqrt{7}$ or $3 - \sqrt{7}$. □

The quadratic equations solved so far in this section have been in a special form. One member is a perfect square, so the square root property applies. But what about quadratics that do not appear as perfect squares? Well, the work of this section is to make them appear in that form so that they can be solved. First, then, how do you recognize a perfect square?

$$(x - a)^2 = x^2 - 2ax + a^2$$
$$(x + a)^2 = x^2 + 2ax + a^2$$

Notice that in both of the above equations, if you take half of the coefficient of x and square it, you obtain the last term. That is, $\frac{1}{2}(\pm 2a) = \pm a$ and $(\pm a)^2 = a^2$. Consider the following examples.

In Examples 4 and 5 supply the missing term.

Example 4
$$x^2 + 6x + ? = x^2 + 6x + \left(\frac{1}{2} \cdot 6\right)^2 \qquad \text{Take half and square.}$$

$$= x^2 + 6x + 3^2 \qquad \text{Write in factored form as a perfect square.}$$
$$= x^2 + 6x + 9$$
$$= (x + 3)^2 \qquad \qquad \qquad \square$$

Example 5
$$y^2 - 7y + ? = y^2 - 7y + \left(\frac{1}{2} \cdot 7\right)^2$$

$$= y^2 - 7y + \left(\frac{7}{2}\right)^2$$

$$= y^2 - 7y + \frac{49}{4}$$

$$= \left(y - \frac{7}{2}\right)^2 \qquad \qquad \square$$

In this process, the constant necessary to make a perfect square is added to the original expression. The process is called **completing the square,** and it may be applied to the solution of quadratics. But you'll see later that it has other useful applications, especially in graphing various curves. However, now let's apply this process to solve equations. The only caution is that when you add a constant to complete the square, you must add it to *both* members of the equation. The method is illustrated by the following examples.

In Examples 6–12 solve by first completing the square.

Example 6

Solution

$$x^2 - 10x - 2 = 0$$
$$x^2 - 10x + ? = 2 + ?$$ Isolate variable terms.

$$x^2 - 10x + \left(\frac{1}{2} \cdot 10\right)^2 = 2 + \left(\frac{1}{2} \cdot 10\right)^2$$ Complete the square.

$$x^2 - 10x + \mathbf{25} = 2 + \mathbf{25}$$ Simplify.
$$(x - 5)^2 = 27$$ Factor.
$$x - 5 = \pm\sqrt{27}$$ Use the square root property.
$$x - 5 = \pm 3\sqrt{3}$$ Remember $\pm$.
$$x = 5 \pm 3\sqrt{3}$$ Solve for x.
$$x = 5 + 3\sqrt{3} \quad \text{or} \quad x = 5 - 3\sqrt{3}$$ ☐

Example 7

Solution

$$x^2 + 2x - 15 = 0$$
$$x^2 + 2x + ? = 15 + ?$$

Here we take an example that is factorable. Solve by factoring to check the results.

$$x^2 + 2x + \left(\frac{1}{2} \cdot 2\right)^2 = 15 + \left(\frac{1}{2} \cdot 2\right)^2$$

$$x^2 + 2x + 1 = 15 + 1$$
$$(x + 1)^2 = 16$$
$$x + 1 = \pm\sqrt{16}$$
$$x + 1 = \pm 4$$
$$x = -1 \pm 4$$
$$x = -1 + 4 \quad \text{or} \quad x = -1 - 4$$
$$x = 3 \qquad\qquad\quad x = -5$$ ☐

Example 8

Solution

$$x^2 - 3x = 1$$
$$x^2 - 3x + ? = 1 + ?$$

$$x^2 - 3x + \left(\frac{1}{2} \cdot 3\right)^2 = 1 + \left(\frac{1}{2} \cdot 3\right)^2$$

$$x^2 - 3x + \frac{9}{4} = \frac{4}{4} + \frac{9}{4}$$

$$\left(x - \frac{3}{2}\right)^2 = \frac{13}{4}$$

$$x - \frac{3}{2} = \pm\sqrt{\frac{13}{4}}$$

$$x - \frac{3}{2} = \pm\frac{\sqrt{13}}{2}$$

$$x = \frac{3 \pm \sqrt{13}}{2}$$

$$x = \frac{3 + \sqrt{13}}{2} \quad \text{or} \quad x = \frac{3 - \sqrt{13}}{2}$$ ☐

Example 9
Solution

$$x^2 - 4x = 2$$
$$x^2 - 4x + 4 = 2 + 4$$
$$(x - 2)^2 = 6$$
$$x - 2 = \pm\sqrt{6}$$
$$x = 2 \pm \sqrt{6}$$
$$x = 2 + \sqrt{6} \quad \text{or} \quad x = 2 - \sqrt{6}$$

In this example, we're omitting several steps. This should look more like your actual work.

□

Example 10

$$2x^2 + 4x + 1 = 0$$

Solution

$$x^2 + 2x + \frac{1}{2} = 0$$

$$x^2 + 2x = -\frac{1}{2}$$

$$x^2 + 2x + 1 = -\frac{1}{2} + 1$$

$$(x + 1)^2 = \frac{1}{2}$$

$$x + 1 = \pm\sqrt{\frac{1}{2}}$$

$$x + 1 = \pm\frac{1}{2}\sqrt{2}$$

$$x = -1 \pm \frac{1}{2}\sqrt{2}$$

$$x = -1 + \frac{1}{2}\sqrt{2} \quad \text{or} \quad x = -1 - \frac{1}{2}\sqrt{2}$$

The coefficient of x^2 must be 1, so we divide through by the leading coefficient if it is other than 1.

□

Example 11
Solution

$$x^2 - 6x + 13 = 0$$
$$x^2 - 6x = -13$$
$$x^2 - 6x + 9 = -13 + 9$$
$$(x - 3)^2 = -4$$
$$x - 3 = \pm\sqrt{-4}$$
$$x - 3 = \pm 2i$$
$$x = 3 \pm 2i$$
$$x = 3 + 2i \quad \text{or} \quad x = 3 - 2i$$

The constant on the right side of the equation may be negative, so the method provides complex solutions as well as real ones.

□

Example 12 Solve for x and approximate the irrational roots to the nearest tenth.

$$3x^2 + 10x + 6 = 0$$

Solution

$$x^2 + \frac{10}{3}x + 2 = 0$$

$$x^2 + \frac{10}{3}x = -2$$

$$x^2 + \frac{10}{3}x + \left(\frac{5}{3}\right)^2 = -2 + \left(\frac{5}{3}\right)^2$$

$$\left(x + \frac{5}{3}\right)^2 = -2 + \frac{25}{9}$$

$$\left(x + \frac{5}{3}\right)^2 = \frac{7}{9}$$

$$x + \frac{5}{3} = \pm \frac{\sqrt{7}}{3}$$

$$x = \frac{-5 \pm \sqrt{7}}{3}$$

$$x \approx \frac{-5 \pm 2.65}{3}$$

Recall that the symbol "$\approx$" is used to mean "approximately equal to." It is, interestingly enough, approximately an equal sign.

$$x \approx \frac{-5 + 2.65}{3} \quad \text{or} \quad x \approx \frac{-5 - 2.65}{3}$$

$$x \approx \frac{-2.35}{3} \qquad\qquad x \approx \frac{-7.65}{3}$$

$$x \approx -.8 \qquad\qquad\quad x \approx -2.6 \qquad\qquad\qquad \square$$

Historical Note

The early Greeks had little algebraic symbolism but are famous for their geometry. Numbers were represented by lengths, and algebraic operations were carried out geometrically. Many of the propositions in Euclid's *Elements* (ca. 300 B.C.) are actually algebraic identities in geometric form. For example, one proposition establishes the identity $(a + b)^2 = a^2 + 2ab + b^2$ much as the geometric interpretation is shown on this page. It isn't surprising that x^2 and x^3 are now called *square* and *cube* after their geometric counterparts.

Geometric Interpretation

We began this section with a discussion of the area of a square. Now, notice that $x^2 + 6x$ can be interpreted as the area of a rectangle with sides x and $x + 6$ (see Figure 7.1a).

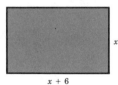

Figure 7.1a

The side with length $x + 6$ can be divided into two parts, x and 6 (Figure 7.1b), and the 6 can be further divided into equal lengths of 3 each (Figure 7.1c).

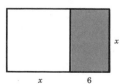

Figure 7.1b

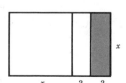

Figure 7.1c

One of the long narrow rectangles on the length 3 can be moved (Figure 7.1d) so that there are two lengths of $x + 3$. But this leaves a small square missing from a complete square (Figure 7.1e).

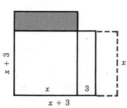

Figure 7.1d   Figure 7.1e

If you add this little square of side 3, you add 3^2 or 9 to $x^2 + 6x$ and obtain a square with area of $(x + 3)^2$ or $x^2 + 6x + 9$. This is a graphic, step-by-step illustration of just what you do when you complete the square to solve a quadratic.

Problem Set 7.1

A   *Solve each equation in Problems 1–10 by the square root method.*

See Examples 1–3.

1. $4u^2 = 3$
2. $9u^2 = 2$
3. $(v - 3)^2 = 25$
4. $(v + 5)^2 = 16$
5. $(3w + 1)^2 = 49$
6. $(2w - 3)^2 = 81$
7. $(x - 3)^2 = 3$
8. $(x + 2)^2 = 2$
9. $(5y - 4)^2 = 48$
10. $(4y + 3)^2 = 98$

Supply the missing term to complete the square in Problems 11–20, and factor as a perfect square.

See Examples 4 and 5.

11. $a^2 + 12a$
12. $a^2 - 22a$
13. $b^2 - 3b$
14. $b^2 + 5b$
15. $11c + c^2$
16. $13c + c^2$
17. $d^2 + \dfrac{5}{3} d$
18. $d^2 + \dfrac{7}{4} d$
19. $e^2 - 2\sqrt{3}\, e$
20. $e^2 + 4\sqrt{5}\, e$

$c^2 + 11c\left(\dfrac{11}{2}\right)^2 =$

$c^2 + 11c + \dfrac{22}{4}$

$\left(c + \dfrac{11}{2}\right)^{2.4}$

In Problems 21–40 solve each equation by completing the square.

See Examples 6–11.

21. $x^2 + 4x - 5 = 0$
22. $y^2 - 6y + 7 = 0$
23. $x^2 - 4x + 5 = 0$
24. $y^2 + 6y + 7 = 0$
25. $x^2 - 4x + 2 = 0$
26. $y^2 - 6y + 5 = 0$
27. $x^2 + 3x - 4 = 0$
28. $y^2 - 5y + 6 = 0$

29. $x^2 - 2x = 1$ 30. $y^2 - 4y = 1$
31. $x^2 = 6x - 2$ 32. $y^2 = 2 - 6y$
33. $x^2 + 6x - 7 = 0$ 34. $y^2 - 4y - 3 = 0$
35. $6x^2 = x + 2$ 36. $8y^2 + 2y = 3$

37. $x^2 + x = \dfrac{3}{4}$ 38. $y^2 - y = \dfrac{2}{9}$

39. $x^2 + 2x = \dfrac{1}{4}$ 40. $y^2 - \dfrac{2}{3}y = \dfrac{1}{9}$

B   *In Problems 41–50 solve by completing the square, and estimate the roots to the nearest tenth.*

See Example 12.   41. $4h^2 - 21 = 5h$ 42. $7k^2 - 10 = k^2$
43. $3m^2 - 10m + 7 = 0$ 44. $9n^2 - 42n + 40 = 0$
45. $49v^2 + 42v = 4$ 46. $25w^2 = 20w + 7$
47. $9x^2 + 6x = 4$ 48. $9y^2 = 12y + 1$
49. $p^2 + 2\sqrt{5}\,p + 5 = 0$ 50. $q^2 - 2\sqrt{7}\,q + 7 = 0$

Problems 51–55 use the following relationship: The intensity of illumination I, in lumens per square foot, at a distance s, in feet, from a source of light of c candlepower can be expressed as $I = c/s^2$.

51. *Physics.* How far from a 45 candlepower light is the illumination .2 lumen per square foot?
52. *Physics.* A 75 candlepower source is how far away from a point of illumination of 3 lumens per square foot?
53. *Physics.* How far, to the nearest tenth of a foot, is a point with illumination 2 lumens per square foot from a 35 candlepower light source?
54. *Physics.* A 55 candlepower light gives an illumination of 3 lumens per square foot how far away from the light, to the nearest foot?
55. *Physics.* Lights of 90 and 40 candlepower are 100 feet apart. At what distance from the stronger light should an object be placed to receive the same illumination from both lights?

See Example 3.   56. A number is two less than a second number whose square is five. What is the number?
57. A number is two more than a second number whose square is three. What is the number?

Problems 58–60 relate to the following formula: If P dollars are invested for two years at an interest rate of x compounded annually, the investment will grow to $A = P(1 + x)^2$.

58. *Finance.* At what rate of interest will $100 grow to $121 in two years?
59. *Finance.* At what rate of interest will $100 grow to $144 in two years?
60. *Finance.* At what rate of interest will $100 grow to $132 in two years? Approximate to the nearest tenth of a percent.

Mind Bogglers   **61.** You have a 144 square foot floor that you want to cover, and you have 144 square feet of carpet with which to cover the floor. Unfortunately, the floor is 12 ft by 12 ft and the piece of carpeting is 9 ft by 16 ft (see the figure). What is the minimum number of pieces into which you must cut the rectangle in order to be able to reassemble it into a square? Show how to complete this square.

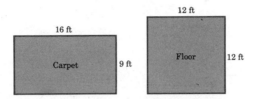

62. Complete the square again! The piece of linoleum shown in the figure was a real buy at a remnant sale. You have now found a use for it, but you must use the entire piece to cover a square region. With a minimum number of cuts and so that the pattern is not spoiled, show how this can be done.

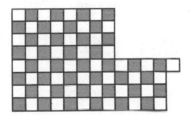

7.2   The Quadratic Formula

People used to say that if you knew the formula, you could plug it in and turn the crank. A formula can certainly simplify procedures. Today, when we talk about plugging it in, we think of pushing buttons of an electronic calculator. But neither a formula nor a calculator is any good unless you know what the formula is for and how to use the calculator. The last section led us toward solving *any* quadratic, factorable or not. Completing the square gives us that ability, so let's consider *any* quadratic with real coefficients a, b, and c.

$$ax^2 + bx + c = 0 \qquad a \neq 0$$

If you solve for x, you will have a formula that can be used to solve any quadratic with real coefficients, since you will have solved for x in terms of a, b, and c. Solve by completing the square:

$$ax^2 + bx + c = 0 \qquad a \neq 0$$

$$x^2 + \frac{b}{a}x + \frac{c}{a} = 0 \qquad \text{Divide by } a.$$

$$x^2 + \frac{b}{a}x = -\frac{c}{a} \qquad \text{Subtract } \frac{c}{a}.$$

$$x^2 + \frac{b}{a}x + \left(\frac{1}{2}\cdot\frac{b}{a}\right)^2 = \left(\frac{1}{2}\cdot\frac{b}{a}\right)^2 - \frac{c}{a} \qquad \text{Complete the square.}$$

$$\left(x + \frac{b}{2a}\right)^2 = \frac{b^2}{4a^2} - \frac{c}{a} \qquad \text{Simplify.}$$

$$\left(x + \frac{b}{2a}\right)^2 = \frac{b^2}{4a^2} - \frac{4ac}{4aa}$$

$$\left(x + \frac{b}{2a}\right)^2 = \frac{b^2 - 4ac}{4a^2}$$

$$x + \frac{b}{2a} = \pm\sqrt{\frac{b^2 - 4ac}{4a^2}} \qquad \text{Square root property.}$$

$$x + \frac{b}{2a} = \frac{\pm\sqrt{b^2 - 4ac}}{2a} \qquad \text{Simplify.}$$

$$x = -\frac{b}{2a} \pm \frac{\sqrt{b^2 - 4ac}}{2a} \qquad \text{Solve for } x.$$

$$x = \frac{-b \pm \sqrt{b^2 - 4ac}}{2a} \qquad \text{Combine fractions.}$$

This result is called the **quadratic formula** and will prove to be very useful. To use it, you have only to know the coefficients *a*, *b*, and *c*, and substitute their values into the formula.

The Quadratic Formula
If $ax^2 + bx + c = 0$, $a \neq 0$, then
$$x = \frac{-b \pm \sqrt{b^2 - 4ac}}{2a}$$

It's important to remember that the $\pm$ notation may give two values. It will be sufficient to leave the solution in this form until you determine the form the answer should take. That is, you may need an exact root or an approximation.

In Examples 1–4 solve for x.

Example 1 $6x^2 - x - 15 = 0$

  Solution $(6)x^2 + (-1)x + (-15) = 0$

          $a = 6$ $b = -1$ $c = -15$ Identify a, b, and c. Watch your signs.

$$x = \frac{-b \pm \sqrt{b^2 - 4ac}}{2a}$$

$$x = \frac{-(-1) \pm \sqrt{(-1)^2 - 4(6)(-15)}}{2(6)}$$ Substitute.

$$x = \frac{1 \pm \sqrt{1 + 360}}{12}$$

$$x = \frac{1 \pm \sqrt{361}}{12}$$ Simplify.

$$x = \frac{1 \pm 19}{12}$$

$$x = \frac{1 + 19}{12} \quad \text{or} \quad x = \frac{1 - 19}{12}$$

$$= \frac{20}{12} \qquad\qquad = -\frac{18}{12}$$

$$x = \frac{5}{3} \qquad\qquad x = -\frac{3}{2}$$

Example 2 $2x^2 + 4x + 1 = 0$

  Solution $a = 2$ $b = 4$ $c = 1$

$$x = \frac{-(4) \pm \sqrt{(4)^2 - 4(2)(1)}}{2(2)}$$

$$x = \frac{-4 \pm \sqrt{8}}{4}$$

$$x = \frac{-4 \pm 2\sqrt{2}}{4}$$

$$x = \frac{-2 \pm \sqrt{2}}{2} \quad \text{or} \quad x = -1 \pm \frac{1}{2}\sqrt{2}$$

Example 3 $x^2 - 6x + 13 = 0$

Solution $a = 1$ $b = -6$ $c = 13$

$$x = \frac{-(-6) \pm \sqrt{(-6)^2 - 4(1)(13)}}{2(1)}$$

$$x = \frac{6 \pm \sqrt{-16}}{2}$$

$$x = \frac{6 \pm 4i}{2}$$

$$x = 3 \pm 2i$$ □

Example 4   Solve and approximate to the nearest hundredth.

$$3x^2 + 10x + 6 = 0$$

Solution $a = 3$ $b = 10$ $c = 6$

$$x = \frac{-10 \pm \sqrt{10^2 - 4(3)(6)}}{2(3)}$$

$$x = \frac{-10 \pm \sqrt{28}}{6}$$

$$x = \frac{-10 \pm 2\sqrt{7}}{6}$$

$$x = \frac{-5 \pm \sqrt{7}}{3}$$

$$x \approx \frac{-5 \pm 2.646}{3}$$

$$x \approx \frac{-2.354}{3} \quad \text{or} \quad x \approx \frac{-7.646}{3}$$

$$x \approx -.78 \qquad\qquad x \approx -2.55$$ □

You may have noticed that the last three examples are identical to Examples 10–12 in the previous section, where they were solved by completing the square. You certainly can appreciate the use of the quadratic formula by comparing these solutions to those found by completing the square. But if you notice that the quadratic is factorable, finding the solution by factoring is simpler than either using the formula or completing the square.

Restrictions

While the quadratic formula gives you a tremendous advantage, it does have certain limitations. It involves both a fraction and a radical, so implicit restrictions must be considered. The denominator of the fraction must be nonzero. It is zero if $a = 0$; but if $a = 0$, there is no second-degree term and the formula does not apply.

The radicand must be nonnegative if the value of the radical is to be real. Thus, $b^2 - 4ac < 0$ means $\sqrt{b^2 - 4ac}$ is not a real number, thus yielding complex solutions. In fact, there will be two complex solutions and they are conjugates. (Why?)

Notice further that if $b^2 - 4ac = 0$, then $\sqrt{b^2 - 4ac} = 0$, and $(-b \pm 0)/2a$ has only one value, $-b/2a$. The number $b^2 - 4ac$ determines both the number *and* the kind of solutions for the quadratic. For this reason, $b^2 - 4ac$ is called the **discriminant** of the quadratic $ax^2 + bx + c$.

Tells you what kind of answer you'll have

The Discriminant of the Quadratic Equation

If $ax^2 + bx + c = 0$ for real numbers a, b, and c, $a \neq 0$, then $d = b^2 - 4ac$ is called the **discriminant,** and:

If $d < 0$,   there are no real roots.
If $d = 0$,   there is one real root.
If $d > 0$,   there are two real roots.

Additionally, for rational numbers a, b, and c:

If d is a perfect square,* the roots are rational.
If d is not a perfect square,* the roots are irrational.

---

* Perfect square here means that d is the square of a rational number.

In Examples 5–8 determine the number and kind of roots from the value of the discriminant.

Example 5 $2x^2 - 3x + 2 = 0$

Solution $d = b^2 - 4ac$
$d = (-3)^2 - 4(2)(2)$
$d = 9 - 16$
$d = -7$

$d < 0$, so there are no real roots.   □

Example 6 $12x^2 - 5x - 2 = 0$

Solution $d = (-5)^2 - 4(12)(-2)$
$d = 25 + 96$
$d = 121$
$d = 11^2$

$d > 0$, so there are two real roots.   □

Example 7 $4x^2 - 4\sqrt{3}\,x + 3 = 0$ Recall that a, b, and c are real numbers. Here, $b = -4\sqrt{3}$,

Solution $d = (-4\sqrt{3})^2 - 4(4)(3)$ an irrational number.
$d = 48 - 48$

$d = 0$; there is one real solution.   □

Example 8 $13x^2 + 10x - 7 = 0$

Solution $d = 10^2 - 4(13)(-7)$
$d = 100 + 364$
$d = 464$

$d > 0$; there are two real roots.   □

More About Coefficients

The quadratic formula and the discriminant both depend on the coefficients of the quadratic. Another useful property of the coefficients can be established by looking at the roots, r_1 and r_2.

$$x = r_1 \qquad \text{or} \qquad x = r_2$$
$$x - r_1 = 0 \qquad\qquad x - r_2 = 0$$
$$(x - r_1)(x - r_2) = 0$$
$$x^2 - (r_1 + r_2)x + r_1 r_2 = 0$$
$$x^2 - \left(\begin{array}{c}\text{SUM OF}\\\text{ROOTS}\end{array}\right)x + \left(\begin{array}{c}\text{PRODUCT}\\\text{OF ROOTS}\end{array}\right) = 0$$

Comparing this result to $ax^2 + bx + c = 0$ or to $x^2 + (b/a)x + c/a = 0$, we can summarize the property.

SUM AND PRODUCT
PROPERTY

If $ax^2 + bx + c = 0$, and has roots r_1 and r_2, then

$$r_1 + r_2 = -\frac{b}{a} \qquad \text{and} \qquad r_1 r_2 = \frac{c}{a}$$

In Examples 9–11 solve by the quadratic formula and check by the sum and product property.

Example 9 $x^2 - 4x + 29 = 0$

Solution $x = \dfrac{4 \pm \sqrt{16 - 116}}{2}$

$x = \dfrac{4 \pm \sqrt{-100}}{2}$

$$x = \frac{4 \pm 10i}{2}$$

$$x = 2 \pm 5i$$

And now check:

$$\text{SUM} = (2 + 5i) + (2 - 5i) = 4$$
$$\text{PRODUCT} = (2 + 5i)(2 - 5i) = 4 + 25 = 29$$
$$x^2 - (4)x + (29) = 0 \checkmark$$

Example 10 $4x^2 - 12x + 7 = 0$

Solution
$$x = \frac{12 \pm \sqrt{144 - 112}}{8}$$

$$x = \frac{12 \pm \sqrt{32}}{8}$$

$$x = \frac{12 \pm 4\sqrt{2}}{8}$$

$$x = \frac{3 \pm \sqrt{2}}{2}$$

Check:

$$\text{SUM} = \left(\frac{3 + \sqrt{2}}{2}\right) + \left(\frac{3 - \sqrt{2}}{2}\right) = \frac{6}{2} = 3$$

$$\text{PRODUCT} = \left(\frac{3 + \sqrt{2}}{2}\right)\left(\frac{3 - \sqrt{2}}{2}\right) = \frac{9 - 2}{4} = \frac{7}{4}$$

$$x^2 - (3)x + \left(\frac{7}{4}\right) = 0$$

$$4x^2 - 12x + 7 = 0 \checkmark$$

Example 11   The area of a right triangle is one square unit. One side is two units longer than the other. Find the lengths of the sides of the triangle.

Solution $\text{AREA} = \frac{1}{2}(\text{BASE})(\text{HEIGHT})$
$1 = \frac{1}{2}(\text{BASE})(\text{BASE} + 2)$

Let $b = \text{BASE}$. Then

$$1 = \frac{1}{2}(b)(b + 2)$$

$$2 = b(b + 2)$$

$$2 = b^2 + 2b$$

$$0 = b^2 + 2b - 2$$

$$b = \frac{-2 \pm \sqrt{12}}{2}$$

$$b = -1 \pm \sqrt{3}$$

$$\text{BASE} = -1 + \sqrt{3} \qquad \text{Sides must be positive.}$$

$$\text{BASE} + 2 = 1 + \sqrt{3}$$

However, the Pythagorean theorem is necessary to find the third side.

$$(\text{HYPOTENUSE})^2 = (-1 + \sqrt{3})^2 + (1 + \sqrt{3})^2$$
$$= 4 - 2\sqrt{3} + 4 + 2\sqrt{3}$$
$$= 8$$
$$\text{HYPOTENUSE} = 2\sqrt{2}$$

The sides are $-1 + \sqrt{3}$, $1 + \sqrt{3}$, and $2\sqrt{2}$ (or approximately .732, 2.732, and 2.828). $\qquad\square$

Problem Set 7.2

A *In Problems 1–10 specify the constants a, b, and c for each equation when written in the form $ax^2 + bx + c = 0$, and find the discriminant.*

See Examples 1–8.

1. $x^2 + 7x + 2 = 0$ **2.** $x^2 + 11x + 5 = 0$ **3.** $x^2 = 3 - 8x$

4. $x^2 = 2x - 5$ **5.** $2x^2 - 3 = 4x$ **6.** $3x^2 = 2x - 1$

7. $3x^2 = 5x$ **8.** $5x^2 = 3$ **9.** $\frac{1}{2}x = \sqrt{2} - 2x^2$

10. $\sqrt{3} - 3x^2 = \frac{1}{3}x$

In Problems 11–20 use the sum and product property to determine the quadratic equation with integer coefficients, given the roots specified. Use the discriminant to check that the number and kind of roots are correct.

See Examples 9 and 10.

11. $17, -6$ **12.** $-13, 8$ **13.** $\frac{1}{2}, -\frac{1}{3}$

14. $\frac{1}{4}, -\frac{1}{2}$ **15.** $5 + \sqrt{6}, 5 - \sqrt{6}$ **16.** $7 - \sqrt{10}, 7 + \sqrt{10}$

17. $4 \pm i$ **18.** $1 \pm 3i$ **19.** $2 \pm i\sqrt{3}$

20. $3 \pm i\sqrt{5}$

In Problems 21–30 solve each equation using the quadratic formula.

See Examples 1–4.

21. $12A^2 - 5A - 3 = 0$ **22.** $30B^2 + 13B - 10 = 0$

23. $C^2 - 4C + 1 = 0$ **24.** $E^2 - 4E - 1 = 0$

25. $G^2 + 10G + 21 = 0$ **26.** $H^2 - 6H - 43 = 0$

27. $2I^2 - 6I + 3 = 0$ **28.** $3J^2 - 4J + 2 = 0$

29. $25L^2 + 10L - 12 = 0$ **30.** $16M^2 + 24M - 2 = 0$

B *In Problems 31–38 solve each equation using the quadratic formula.*

See Examples 1–4.
31. $(N-4)(N+4)=4N$ **32.** $(Y-3)(Y+3)=6(Y+1)$

33. $\dfrac{2}{P}-1=\dfrac{2}{P^2}$ **34.** $\dfrac{5}{Q^2}+\dfrac{4}{Q}+1=0$

35. $R^2+4=3\sqrt{2}\,R$ **36.** $S^2-4\sqrt{3}\,S+9=0$

37. $\dfrac{1}{T-1}+\dfrac{1}{T^2-2T+1}=3$ **38.** $\dfrac{8}{U-1}+\dfrac{9(U+1)}{U^2+6U-7}=1$

Algebra Adage   **39.** Use Problems 21–38 to complete the algebra adage below. Replace the numbers in parentheses with the letters from Problems 21–38 that have the best approximations to the values shown. Remember that quadratics may have two solutions.

(.57)(*O*)   (.40)(4.2)
(2.4)(−1.6)(.08)(.75)(.27)(15.6)(−.92)(−.33)(1.8)(−.24)
(2.4)(1.7)   (1.8)(*O*)   (−.83)(−.24)
(6.5)(4.2)(.75)(1.4)(.52)(7.9)
(2.8)(.63)(−3)(10.2)(.57)(−.24)(*O*)(−4.6)(5.2).

40. Translate the algebra adage above into the common proverb it paraphrases.

Use a calculator to obtain solutions correct to the nearest hundredth in Problems 41–44.

41. $x^2-11.001x+24.098=0$ **42.** $x^2+4.09x=0.078$

43. $\sqrt{2}\,x^2-x\sqrt{5}-\pi=0$ **44.** $\pi x^2+\sqrt{3}+x\sqrt{7}=0$

In Problems 45–57 give each answer as a decimal correct to the nearest tenth, if irrational.

See Examples 5–8.
45. Show that there is *no* real number such that its square increased by nine is equal to five times the number.
46. Show that there is *exactly one* real number such that its square decreased by $2\sqrt{3}$ times the number is equal to negative three.

See Example 11.
47. The area of a right triangle is 17 cm². One leg is 2 cm longer than the other. What is the length of the shortest side?
48. The hypotenuse of a right triangle is 13, and one leg is 6 units shorter than the other. Find the dimensions of the figure.

THINK METRIC
49. The volume of one cube is 10 cm³ greater than another cube whose side is 1 cm shorter. Find the length of a side of the smaller cube.
50. One cubic box is packed inside another whose side is 2 ft longer. If it takes 56 ft³ of packing material to fill the space around the smaller box, what is the size of the larger box?

The Greeks held that there was one most pleasing ratio of height to width in a rectangle. If the height is h and width is w, this ratio is given by:

$$\frac{w}{h} = \frac{h}{h+w} \qquad (or \quad h^2 - wh - w^2 = 0)$$

This relationship is called the **divine proportion** *or* **golden section** *or* **golden ratio** *and can be observed in ancient Greek architecture. Problems 51–54 deal with the golden ratio.*

51. If the height is one unit, what must the width be?

52. If a window is to be 5 feet wide, how high should it be, to the nearest tenth of a foot, to be a golden rectangle?

53. If a canvas for a painting is 18 inches wide, how high should it be, to the nearest inch, to be in the divine proportion?

54. A photograph is to be printed on a rectangle in the divine proportion. If it is 9 cm high, how wide is it, to the nearest centimeter?

55. *Navigation.* A boat that travels 15 mph in still water goes upriver in an hour more than it takes to return. If the trip is 54 miles each way, what is the rate of the current of the river?

56. *Navigation.* A small plane has a cruising speed of 165 mph. The pilot is able to make a 600 mile flight with the wind in 40 minutes less than the return flight against the wind. What is the speed of the wind?

57. *Navigation.* Two ships pass at sea, one headed north and the other moving east 5 mph slower than the first. An hour later, they are 14 miles apart. How fast is each ship moving?

58. The longest rod that will just fit inside a rectangular box, if placed diagonally top to bottom, is 17 inches. The box is 1 inch shorter and 3 inches longer than it is wide. How much must you cut off the rod so that it will lie flat in the bottom of the container? What are the dimensions of the box?

59. Use a calculator with RPN (Hewlett-Packard, Novus, and so on). The button diagram in the margin indicates a sequence of operations on certain numbers. Answer the following questions about the calculation.

    a. What is being calculated?

    b. Can the calculation be shortened? If so, specify a more efficient scheme.

    c. Make an equivalent diagram for a calculator with algebraic logic (Texas Instruments, Rockwell, Commodore, and many others) instead of RPN.

27
ENTER ↑
ENTER ↑
×
4
ENTER ↑
12
×
7
×
−
$\sqrt{x}$
STO
+
24
÷
Answer

27
RCL
−
24
÷
Answer

7.3 Quadratic Forms

Historical Note

Sonja Kovalevsky (1850–1891) was a gifted, Russian-born mathematician. She left Russia in 1868 because Russian universities were closed to women. She went first to the University of Heidelberg in Germany, but she wished to study with the famous mathematician Karl Weierstrass in Berlin. The University in Berlin also did not accept women and would make no exceptions, so she studied privately with Weierstrass and was awarded a degree of Doctor of Philosophy, *in absentia*, from Göttingen, which excused her from an oral examination due to the quality of her thesis. It is said that her early interest in mathematics was due in part to an odd wallpaper that covered a room in the family's country estate. It turned out to be lecture notes on higher mathematics purchased by her father during his student days. She was fascinated by the wallpaper and spent hours trying to make sense of it.

Now that you have a formula for solving quadratics, you can apply it to many equations in other forms. Recall from Chapter 4 that certain polynomial equations are quadratic-like in form and can be solved by quadratic methods. An equation with radicals may be equivalent to a quadratic equation. A system of equations may have quadratic members, or quadratic inequalities may not be factorable. These concerns will occupy us for the remainder of this chapter, and the geometry of the quadratic function will be one topic of the next chapter.

Equations with Radicals

If you're solving an equation such as

$$x - 3 = 2\sqrt{x}$$

you might be tempted to simply square both sides of the equation to eliminate the radical. This, however, creates an unexpected difficulty:

$$
\begin{aligned}
(x - 3)^2 &= (2\sqrt{x})^2 \\
x^2 - 6x + 9 &= 4x \\
x^2 - 10x + 9 &= 0 \\
(x - 9)(x - 1) &= 0 \\
x = 9 \quad &\text{or} \quad x = 1
\end{aligned}
$$

But when you check these solutions,

$$
\begin{array}{ll}
x = 9 & x = 1 \\
9 - 3 \overset{?}{=} 2\sqrt{9} & 1 - 3 \overset{?}{=} 2\sqrt{1} \\
6 = 2 \cdot 3 \text{ checks} & -2 = 2 \text{ doesn't check}
\end{array}
$$

If you square both sides of an equation, the solutions of the resulting equation may not satisfy the original equation. However, the following property may be stated.

Property of Squaring

If both sides of an equation are squared, the solution set of the resulting equation will contain all of the solutions of the original equation.

This means that the equation obtained by squaring will definitely give all solutions of the original equation, but it *also* may have solutions that are not solutions of the original equation. The values that do not check are called **extraneous solutions.** So, for $x - 3 = 2\sqrt{x}$, the only solution is $x = 9$. Each solution obtained by the property of squaring *must* be checked in the original equation.

Example 1 $\sqrt{x} = 3$

Solution $(\sqrt{x})^2 = (3)^2$
$$x = 9$$

The solution checks in the original equation, and there are no extraneous solutions.   □

Example 2 $\sqrt{x-2} = 2 - x$

Solution $(\sqrt{x-2})^2 = (2-x)^2$
$$x - 2 = 4 - 4x + x^2$$
$$0 = x^2 - 5x + 6$$
$$0 = (x-3)(x-2)$$
$$x = 3 \quad \text{or} \quad x = 2$$

Now check the solutions in the original equation.

$x = 3$: $\sqrt{3-2} \overset{?}{=} 2 - 3$ $x = 2$: $\sqrt{2-2} \overset{?}{=} 2 - 2$
$\sqrt{1} \overset{?}{=} -1$ $\sqrt{0} \overset{?}{=} 0$
$1 \neq -1$ $0 = 0$

3 is extraneous and the solution is $x = 2$.   □

Example 3 $\sqrt{x+5} + \sqrt{x} = 2$

Solution   First isolate one radical.
$$\sqrt{x+5} = 2 - \sqrt{x}$$
$$(\sqrt{x+5})^2 = (2 - \sqrt{x})^2$$
$$x + 5 = 4 - 4\sqrt{x} + x$$
$$1 = -4\sqrt{x}$$
$$1^2 = (-4\sqrt{x})^2$$
$$1 = 16x$$
$$\frac{1}{16} = x$$

Check the solution in the original equation.

$$\sqrt{\frac{1}{16} + 5} + \sqrt{\frac{1}{16}} = \sqrt{\frac{81}{16}} + \sqrt{\frac{1}{16}}$$
$$= \frac{9}{4} + \frac{1}{4} = \frac{10}{4} = \frac{5}{2}$$

$$\frac{5}{2} \neq 2$$

$\frac{1}{16}$ is an extraneous root, so the solution set is empty. □

Example 4 $\sqrt{2x+4} - \sqrt{x+3} - 1 = 0$

Solution

$$\sqrt{2x+4} = \sqrt{x+3} + 1 \qquad \text{Isolate one radical.}$$

$$2x+4 = x+3+2\sqrt{x+3}+1 \qquad \text{Square both sides.}$$

$$x = 2\sqrt{x+3} \qquad \text{Isolate the remaining radical.}$$

$$x^2 = 4(x+3) \qquad \text{Square again, and solve the}$$

$$x^2 = 4x+12 \qquad \qquad \text{resulting quadratic.}$$

$$x^2 - 4x - 12 = 0$$

$$(x-6)(x+2) = 0$$

$$x = 6 \quad \text{or} \quad x = -2$$

$$x = 6: \quad \sqrt{12+4} - \sqrt{6+3} - 1 \overset{?}{=} 0 \qquad \text{Check the roots.}$$

$$4 - 3 - 1 \overset{?}{=} 0$$

$$0 = 0 \text{ checks} \qquad x = 6 \text{ checks}$$

$$x = -2: \quad \sqrt{-4+4} - \sqrt{-2+3} - 1 \overset{?}{=} 0$$

$$0 - 1 - 1 \overset{?}{=} 0$$

$$-2 \neq 0 \text{ doesn't check} \qquad x = -2 \text{ doesn't check}$$

-2 is extraneous, and the solution is $x = 6$. □

Quadratic-Like Equations

Some equations have a quadratic form although they are of higher degree. This fourth-degree equation,

Also recall Example 1 in Section 4.7.

$$x^4 - 5x^2 + 4 = 0$$

is actually "quadratic in x^2,"

$$(x^2)^2 - 5(x^2) - 4 = 0$$

which factors to

$$(x^2 - 1)(x^2 - 4) = 0$$

Thus,

$$x^2 - 1 = 0 \qquad\qquad \text{or} \quad x^2 - 4 = 0$$
$$(x - 1)(x + 1) = 0 \qquad\qquad (x - 2)(x + 2) = 0$$
$$x = 1 \quad \text{or} \quad x = -1 \qquad x = 2 \quad \text{or} \quad x = -2$$

Solution: 1, −1, 2, −2

The fourth-degree polynomial equation was factored using quadratic methods and gave four distinct solutions. Not all higher-degree polynomials will factor in this way; in fact, very few will. However, higher-order expressions will result from raising both sides of an equation to a power. Consequently, the examples that follow and the problems in the problem set were very carefully chosen for you.

In Examples 5–7 solve for x.

Example 5 $\qquad\quad x^{2/3} - 2x^{1/3} - 3 = 0$ $\qquad\qquad$ This is a quadratic in $x^{1/3}$.

Solution $\qquad (x^{1/3})^2 - 2(x^{1/3}) - 3 = 0$
$$(x^{1/3} - 3)(x^{1/3} + 1) = 0$$
$$x^{1/3} = 3 \quad \text{or} \quad x^{1/3} = -1 \qquad \text{Cube each member.}$$
$$x = 27 \qquad\qquad x = -1$$

Check, since cubing may introduce an extraneous root:
$$27^{2/3} - 2(27^{1/3}) - 3 \overset{?}{=} 0 \qquad\qquad (-1)^{2/3} - 2(-1)^{1/3} - 3 \overset{?}{=} 0$$
$$9 - 6 - 3 = 0 \qquad\qquad\qquad 1 + 2 - 3 = 0$$

Solution: 27, − 1 $\qquad\qquad\qquad\qquad\qquad\qquad\qquad\qquad\qquad$ □

Example 6 $\qquad\qquad\qquad 4x^4 + 3 = 13x^2$

Solution $\qquad 4(x^2)^2 - 13(x^2) + 3 = 0$
$$(4x^2 - 1)(x^2 - 3) = 0$$
$$4x^2 - 1 = 0 \quad \text{or} \quad x^2 - 3 = 0$$
$$4x^2 = 1 \qquad\qquad x^2 = 3$$
$$x^2 = \frac{1}{4} \qquad\qquad x = \pm\sqrt{3}$$
$$x = \pm\frac{1}{2}$$

Solution: $\dfrac{1}{2}, -\dfrac{1}{2}, \sqrt{3}, -\sqrt{3}$ $\qquad\qquad\qquad\qquad\qquad\qquad\qquad$ □

Example 7 $\qquad \left(\dfrac{x^2 + 1}{x}\right)^2 - 6\left(\dfrac{x^2 + 1}{x}\right) + 8 = 0$

Solution Let $u = \dfrac{x^2 + 1}{x}$ and substitute, to obtain

$$u^2 - 6u + 8 = 0$$
$$(u - 2)(u - 4) = 0$$
$$u = 2 \quad \text{or} \quad u = 4$$

It is helpful to substitute when the expression is complicated

Thus,

$$\frac{x^2 + 1}{x} = 2 \quad \text{or} \quad \frac{x^2 + 1}{x} = 4$$

$$x^2 - 2x + 1 = 0 \qquad x^2 - 4x + 1 = 0$$

$$(x - 1)^2 = 0 \qquad\qquad x = \frac{4 \pm \sqrt{12}}{2}$$

$$x = 1 \qquad\qquad x = 2 \pm \sqrt{3}$$

Solution: $1, 2 + \sqrt{3}, 2 - \sqrt{3}$ ☐

Problem Set 7.3

Solve the equations in Problems 1–30 for all real roots. Don't forget to check for extraneous roots when necessary.

A

See Examples 1 and 2.

1. $\sqrt{5x - 9} = 4$
2. $\sqrt{7x - 2} = 3$
3. $(3x + 7)^{1/2} - x = 1$
4. $(9x + 28)^{1/2} - x = 4$
5. $5 = \sqrt{3x + 13} - x$
6. $x - (3x - 2)^{1/2} = 0$
7. $\sqrt{x + 7} = 7 - \sqrt{x}$
8. $(5x + 1)^{1/2} - 3 = 0$

See Examples 5 and 6.

9. $x^4 + 6x^2 = 27$
10. $x^4 = 4x^3 + x^2$
11. $4 = \sqrt{7 - 2x}$
12. $\sqrt{9 - 5x} = 3$
13. $\sqrt{x + 3} = 2\sqrt{x}$
14. $3\sqrt{x} = \sqrt{11 - 2x}$
15. $x\sqrt{5 - x^2} = 2$
16. $x\sqrt{10 - x^2} = 4$

B

See Examples 3 and 4.

17. $\sqrt{7}\,x = 7\sqrt{x + 2} - 2\sqrt{7}$
18. $4\sqrt{2}\,x = 2\sqrt{5x + 2} - \sqrt{2}$
19. $\sqrt{x^2 - 4x - 12} = x - 6$
20. $\sqrt{x + 5} + \sqrt{x} = 5$
21. $\sqrt{x + 12} + \sqrt{x} = 2$
22. $\sqrt{2x + 11} - \sqrt{2x - 1} = 2$
23. $\sqrt{x - 5} + \sqrt{x + 10} = 3$
24. $\sqrt{x + 31} - \sqrt{x + 14} = 1$
25. $\sqrt{x + 12} - \sqrt{x - 12} = 2$
26. $\sqrt{3 - 2x} - \sqrt{2x + 2} = 3$

See Example 7.

27. $\left(\dfrac{x - 2}{x}\right)^2 - 2\left(\dfrac{x - 2}{x}\right) - 15 = 0$
28. $\left(\dfrac{x - 3}{x^2}\right)^2 + 6\left(\dfrac{x - 3}{x^2}\right) + 8 = 0$
29. $\left(\dfrac{x^2 - 6}{x}\right)^2 - 12\left(\dfrac{x^2 - 6}{x}\right) + 35 = 0$
30. $\left(\dfrac{x^2 + 5}{2x}\right)^2 - 5\left(\dfrac{x^2 + 5}{2x}\right) + 6 = 0$

Mind Bogglers   *Solve the equations in Problems 31–34 for all real roots.*

31. $\sqrt{\sqrt{x+3}-\sqrt{2-x}}=1$ 32. $\sqrt{\sqrt{2x+1}-\sqrt{x}}=1$

33. $(3x^2+4x+5)-9\sqrt{3x^2+4x+5}=10$

34. $2x^2+3x-\sqrt{2x^2+3x+7}=5$

35. Show <u>how</u> to find the simplified numerical value of
$\sqrt{7+\sqrt{48}}+\sqrt{7-\sqrt{48}}$
without the use of a calculator.

7.4   Variation

Sometimes quadratic relationships are indicated by using some special terminology taken from the sciences. For example, the formula

$$d=16t^2$$

is used to represent the distance, d, that an object will fall in a given time, t. A scientist might describe this relationship by saying "The distance a body falls from rest *varies directly as* (or *is directly proportional to*) the square of the time it falls (disregarding air resistance)."

This same terminology is also used with linear or higher-power expressions, as outlined in the following definition.

VARIATION

If variables x and y are related so that

1. $y=kx$,   we say that *y* **varies directly as** *x* or that *y* **is directly proportional to** *x.*

2. $y=kx^2$,   we say that *y* **varies directly as the square of** *x* or that *y* **is directly proportional to the square of** *x.*

3. $y=\dfrac{k}{x}$,   we say that *y* **varies inversely as** *x* or that *y* **is inversely proportional to** *x.*

4. $y=\dfrac{k}{x^2}$,   we say that *y* **varies inversely as the square of** *x* or that *y* **is inversely proportional to the square of** *x.*

Example 1   The surface area of a sphere varies directly as the square of the radius. If the surface area is 16π cm² when the radius is 2 cm, what is the surface area when the radius is 10 cm?

Solution   *Step 1.*   Use the definition of variation (definition 2 in the box):

If S is the surface area and r is the radius, then

$$S = kr^2$$

Step 2. Use the given ordered pair to determine the value of k:
The given ordered pair is $(2, 16\pi)$.

$$16\pi = k(2)^2$$
$$4\pi = k$$

Step 3. The formula is $S = 4\pi r^2$. Now we can find S for any given value
of r; in particular, if $r = 10$ cm, we see that

$$S = 4\pi(10 \text{ cm})^2$$
$$= 400\pi \text{ cm}^2 \qquad \square$$

Example 2 The intensity of light is inversely proportional to the square of the distance
from its source. If a certain light source projects 7.5 ft-candles at 10 ft,
what is the intensity of this lamp at 5 ft?

Solution A Proceed as in the first example.

Step 1. $I = \dfrac{k}{d^2}$

Step 2. $7.5 = \dfrac{k}{10^2}$

$750 = k$

Step 3. $I = \dfrac{750}{d^2}$; if $d = 5$, then

$$I = \frac{750}{5^2}$$
$$= 30$$

The intensity at 5 ft is 30 ft-candles. $\qquad \square$

Solution B It is not necessary to first find k if you solve the equation $I = k/d^2$ for
the unknown k: $k = Id^2$. Write an equation involving the variables for
the two different sets of conditions:

(1) $\quad I_1 = 7.5 \qquad$ (2) $\quad I_2 = $ Unknown
$\quad\quad d_1 = 10 \qquad\qquad\quad d_2 = 5$

Now, $I_1 d_1^2 = I_2 d_2^2$, so

$$7.5(10)^2 = I_2(5)^2$$
$$\frac{7.5(100)}{25} = I_2$$
$$30 = I_2 \qquad \square$$

Other types of variation involve more than one variable.

If the variables x, y, and z are related so that

1. $z = kxy$,   we say that **z varies jointly as x and y.**
2. z is a **combination** of x and y, then you can write these variations.

For example, "z varies directly as the square of x and inversely as the cube of y" is written as

$$z = k \frac{x^2}{y^3}$$

In Examples 3 and 4 write each statement as an equation, using k as the constant of variation.

Example 3   The stiffness of a rectangular beam varies jointly as the breadth and the cube of its depth.

Solution $S = kwd^3$, where $S =$ STIFFNESS OF BEAM, $w =$ BREADTH, $d =$ DEPTH   □

Example 4   The *f*-stop of a camera varies directly as the focal length of the lens and inversely as the diameter of the lens opening.

Solution $N = k \dfrac{l}{d}$, where $N = f$-STOP, $l =$ FOCAL LENGTH, $d =$ DIAMETER   □

Problem Set 7.4

A   *Write each statement in Problems 1–24 as an equation, using k as the constant of variation. Be sure to identify your variables if they are not given.*

See Examples 1–4.

1. x varies directly as y.
2. m varies inversely as n.
3. s is directly proportional to the square of t.
4. v is directly proportional to the square of t.
5. A varies jointly as l and w.
6. V varies jointly as l, w, and h.
7. V is directly proportional to the cube of r.
8. S varies jointly as θ and the square of r.
9. C varies directly as t and inversely as r.
10. x varies directly as the cube of y and inversely as the square of z.
11. The volume of a sphere varies directly as the cube of its radius.

12. *Physics.* The distance that a spring stretches is directly proportional to the force applied.

13. *Physics.* The current in an electrical circuit is inversely proportional to the resistance.

14. *Physics.* The current in a wire varies directly as the electromotive force and inversely as the resistance.

15. *Finance.* The simple interest earned in a given time varies jointly as the principal and the interest rate.

16. *Chemistry.* The pressure exerted by a liquid at a given point is directly proportional to the depth of that point below the surface of the liquid.

17. *Physics.* The force with which the earth attracts an object above the earth's surface varies inversely with the square of the distance from the center of the earth.

18. *Physics.* The frequency of vibration of air in an open pipe organ is inversely proportional to the length of the pipe.

19. *Chemistry.* The volume of a gas varies directly as the temperature and inversely as the pressure.

20. *Engineering.* The strength of a rectangular beam varies directly as its width and the square of its depth.

21. *Chemistry.* The kinetic energy varies jointly as the mass and the square of the velocity.

22. *Engineering.* The stiffness of a beam varies jointly as the breadth and depth and inversely as the square of the length.

23. *Physics.* The amount of heat put out by an electrical appliance varies jointly as time and resistance and the square of the current.

24. *Physics.* The centripetal force of a body moving in a circular path at a constant speed varies inversely as the radius of the path.

B 25. If w varies directly as t, find w when $t = 15$ if it is known that $w = 7$ when $t = 5$.

See Examples 1 and 2. 26. If t varies inversely as s, find t when $s = 13$ if it is known that $t = 2$ when $s = 5$.

27. If p is directly proportional to the square of q, find p when $q = 2$ if it is known that $p = 5$ when $q = 4$.

28. If x is directly proportional to the square of z, find x when $z = 5$ if it is known that $x = 10$ when $z = 2$.

29. If A varies jointly as l and w, find A when $l = 10$ and $w = 6$ if it is known that $A = 28$ when $l = 7$ and $w = 4$.

30. If V varies jointly as l, w, and h, find V when $l = 7$, $w = 2$, and $h = 2$ if it is known that $V = 30$ when $l = 5$, $w = 3$, and $h = 2$.

31. If the volume of a sphere varies directly as the cube of its radius, find its volume when the radius is 6 cm if it is known that the volume of the sphere is 36π cm³ when the radius is 3 cm.

32. *Physics.* If the distance a spring stretches is directly proportional

to the force applied, determine how far a force of 15 kilograms will stretch the spring. A preliminary experiment shows that a force of 20 kilograms will stretch the spring 12 cm.

33. *Physics.* If the current in an electrical circuit is inversely proportional to the resistance, what is the current when the resistance is 5 ohms if it is known that the resistance is 4 ohms when the current is 25 amp?

34. *Finance.* If the simple interest earned in a given time varies jointly as the principal and the interest rate, how much will $1,500 at 8% earn in the same period that $1,000 earns $350 at 7%?

35. *Chemistry.* If the pressure exerted by a liquid at a given point is directly proportional to the depth of that point below the surface of the liquid, what is the pressure on a submarine at 300 ft if the water pressure on that submarine at a depth of 100 ft is 400 pounds per square foot?

36. *Physics.* If the frequency of vibration of air in an open pipe organ is inversely proportional to the length of the pipe, how long should the pipe be to cause the air to vibrate 16 times per second? Suppose that it is known that air in an 8 ft pipe vibrates at 64 times per second.

37. *Chemistry.* If the volume of a gas varies directly as the temperature and inversely as the pressure, find the volume at 360 degrees Kelvin and a pressure of 30 pounds per square centimeter. A preliminary experiment shows that this gas occupies a volume of 5 liters at 320 degrees Kelvin and a pressure of 16 pounds per square centimeter.

THINK
METRIC

7.5 Review Problems

Fill in the word or words that make the statements in Problems 1–10 complete and correct.

(7.1) **1.** If _____, then $x = \sqrt{a}$ or $x = -\sqrt{a}$ or both.

In Problems 2–8 a, b, c, and d refer to the quadratic equation $ax^2 + bx + c = 0$, $a \neq 0$, and $d = b^2 - 4ac$.

(7.2) **2.** The quadratic formula is derived by the technique known as

_____.

(7.2) **3.** The quadratic formula is $x = $ _____.

(7.2) **4.** The quantity $b^2 - 4ac$ is called the _____ of the quadratic.

(7.2) **5.** If $d > 0$, there are _____ roots.

(7.2) **6.** If r_1 and r_2 are the roots of $ax^2 + bx + c = 0$, then
$r_1 + r_2 = $ _____.

(7.2) **7.** The product of the roots of $ax^2 + bx + c = 0$ is _____.

(7.3)   **8.** Values found in the solution of a radical equation that do not check in the original equation are called _____ roots.

(7.4)   **9.** If a varies _____ as b, then $a = kb$.

(7.4)   **10.** If x varies directly as y^2 and inversely as z^3, then $x =$ _____ .

(7.1)   **11.** Solve $(x - 2)^2 = 8$ by the square root method.

(7.1)   **12.** Solve $y^2 - 4 = 4y$ by completing the square, and estimate the roots to the nearest tenth.

(7.1)   **13.** *Finance.* If P dollars are invested for two years at rate r compounded annually, the investment will grow to $A = P(1 + r)^2$. What rate of interest will allow the money to double?

(7.2)   **14.** Write a quadratic equation with the following roots:
    a. -3 and 5
    b. $1 + \sqrt{2}$ and $1 - \sqrt{2}$
    c. $4 \pm i$

(7.2)   **15.** Specify the number and nature of the roots of $5x^2 - 16x + 13 = 0$ without solving.

(7.2)   **16.** Use the quadratic formula to solve: $4x^2 - 2x - 1 = 0$.

(7.2)   **17.** The hypotenuse of a right triangle is 17 m. The longer leg is 1 m less than twice the shorter. What is the perimeter of the triangle?

(7.3)   **18.** Solve for z.
    a. $\sqrt{1 - 2z} = 3$
    b. $\sqrt{z - 2} - \sqrt{2z + 3} = 2$

(7.4)   **19.** *Engineering.* The strength S of a rectangular beam varies jointly as its width w and the square of its depth d. Write this statement as an equation, using k as the constant of proportionality.

(7.4)   **20.** *Business.* The most economical right circular cylindrical tin cans contain the greatest volume for a given amount of material. For such a container the height varies directly as the diameter. The height is 16 cm for a diameter of 4π cm. Find the height if the diameter is 8 cm.

CHAPTER

8

Systems of Equations and Inequalities

Contents

8.1 Systems of Linear Equations in Two Variables

In Chapter 3 we considered the solution of a first-degree equation in two variables. Now, consider two such equations *simultaneously* (at the same time). For example,

$$\begin{cases} 3x - 2y = 15 \\ x + y = 20 \end{cases}$$

The brace symbol means that the solution is the set of all ordered pairs (x, y) that satisfy *both* equations at the same time. Graphically, the solution is the *intersection* of the solution sets of the two equations. These equations are called a *simultaneous system of linear equations*, or simply, a **system of equations.**

SOLUTION TO A
SYSTEM OF LINEAR
EQUATIONS

> **The solution to a system of linear equations**
>
> $$\begin{cases} a_1 x + b_1 y = c_1 \\ a_2 x + b_2 y = c_2 \end{cases}$$
>
> is the set of all ordered pairs (x, y) that satisfy both equations *simultaneously*. There are three possibilities:
> 1. There is a *single* ordered pair satisfying both equations.
> 2. There are *no* ordered pairs satisfying both equations. This system is called an **inconsistent system.**
> 3. There are *infinitely many* ordered pairs satisfying both equations. Any ordered pair satisfying one equation also satisfies the other. This system is called a **dependent system.**

Solution by Graphing

Since each of the equations is linear, the graphical solution of the system is the intersection of the graphs of the two equations. In two dimensions, two lines may be related in one of three ways: (1) they intersect at a single point, (2) there is no intersection (the lines are parallel), or (3) the lines coincide. These possibilities are illustrated by the examples below.

In Examples 1–3 solve each system.

Example 1 $$\begin{cases} 3x - 2y = 15 \\ x + y = 20 \end{cases}$$

Solution   Graph each line separately on the same coordinate axes, as shown in Figure 8.1.

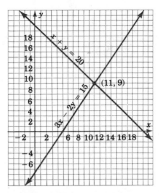

Figure 8.1

Next, find the point of intersection by inspection. For this example, the solution is (11, 9). You can leave your answer in ordered-pair notation, but remember that this means $x = 11$ when $y = 9$. $\square$

Example 2

$$\begin{cases} 2x + 2y = 10 \\ x + y = 20 \end{cases}$$

Solution Graph the lines, as shown in Figure 8.2. Solve each equation for y:

$$\begin{cases} y = -x + 5 \\ y = -x + 20 \end{cases}$$

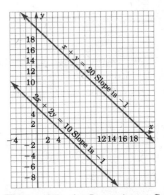

Figure 8.2 An Inconsistent System

Since these lines have the same slope and different y-intercepts, they are parallel, so there is no point of intersection and the solution set is empty. This system is *inconsistent*. $\square$

Example 3
$$\begin{cases} x - \frac{2}{3}y = 5 \\ -3x + 2y = -15 \end{cases}$$

Solution Graph the lines, as shown in Figure 8.3.

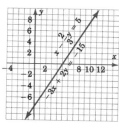

Figure 8.3 A Dependent System

The equations represent the same line, and there are an unlimited number of solutions. Any ordered pair satisfying one equation also satisfies the other. This system is *dependent*. □

Solution by the Addition Method

The graphical method for solving a system of equations is an approximation, since reading the point of intersection depends on the accuracy with which the lines are drawn and on an ability to interpret the coordinates of the point. Therefore, other methods of solution are needed. One of these, called the **addition method**—also sometimes called **linear combination**—requires the equations to be manipulated so that the coefficients of one of the variables are opposites. Then the equations are added to eliminate that variable.

ADDITION METHOD FOR SOLVING A SYSTEM OF EQUATIONS

Addition Method

1. *Multiply* one or both of the equations by constants so that the coefficients of one of the variables are opposites.
2. *Add* corresponding members of the equations to obtain a new equation in a single variable.
3. *Solve* the derived equation for that variable.
4. *Substitute* the value of the one variable into either of the original equations, and solve for the second variable.
5. *State the solution.*

If you want to check your work, you can substitute your solution into *both* equations to make sure they are satisfied.

In Examples 4 and 5 solve each system by the addition method.

Example 4
$$\begin{cases} 3x - 2y = 15 \\ x + y = 20 \end{cases}$$

Solution   *Step 1, Multiply.*   Multiply the second equation by 2. (Indicate this by writing a 2 outside the braces.)

$$2 \begin{cases} 3x - 2y = 15 \\ x + y = 20 \end{cases}$$

Step 2, Add.   After multiplying the second equation by 2, add to eliminate y. (Indicate this by writing a + outside the braces.)

$$+ \begin{cases} 3x - 2y = 15 \\ 2x + 2y = 40 \end{cases}$$

$$5x \qquad = 55$$

Step 3, Solve

$$x = 11 \qquad \text{Divide both sides by 5.}$$

Step 4, Substitute

$$(11) + y = 20 \qquad \text{Replace } x \text{ by 11 in either of the given equations.}$$
$$y = 9 \qquad \text{Solve for } y.$$

Check in the first equation:

$$3(11) - 2(9) = 33 - 18$$
$$= 15 \checkmark$$

Check in the second equation:

$$11 + 9 = 20 \checkmark$$

Step 5, State Solution.   The solution is (11, 9).   □

Example 5 $\begin{cases} 3x + 2y = 1 \\ 5x + 2y = 7 \end{cases}$

You can subtract corresponding members of equations to eliminate one variable, but errors are often less likely if you follow the addition procedure. Thus, in this example, multiply the first equation by (-1) and then add.

Multiply $-1 \begin{cases} 3x + 2y = 1 \\ 5x + 2y = 7 \end{cases}$

Add $+ \begin{cases} -3x - 2y = -1 \\ 5x + 2y = 7 \end{cases}$

Solve $\begin{aligned} 2x &= 6 \\ x &= 3 \end{aligned}$

Substitute $\begin{aligned} 3(3) + 2y &= 1 \\ 2y &= -8 \\ y &= -4 \end{aligned}$

State Solution: The solution is (3, −4).   □

Remember that an equation may or may not have a variable. When you add equations, the result will generally have a single variable that can be solved as shown in Examples 4 and 5. Examples 6 and 7 show what happens when you add equations and obtain no variables.

Example 6 $\begin{cases} 2x + 2y = 10 \\ x + y = 20 \end{cases}$

Solution   *Multiply* $-2 \begin{cases} 2x + 2y = 10 \\ x + y = 20 \end{cases}$

Add $+ \begin{cases} 2x + 2y = 10 \\ -2x - 2y = -40 \end{cases}$
$$0 = -30$$

There are no (x, y) values that make this solution true! Thus, the solution set is empty, and we say the system is *inconsistent*. Graphically this means that the lines represented by the equations are parallel. This is true whenever you add to obtain an equation that is false (as with $0 = -30$, $5 = 1$, $-3 = 3$, etc.).   □

Example 7 $\begin{cases} x - \frac{2}{3}y = 5 \\ -3x + 2y = -15 \end{cases}$

Solution $3 \begin{cases} x - \frac{2}{3}y = 5 \\ -3x + 2y = -15 \end{cases}$

$+ \begin{cases} 3x - 2y = 15 \\ -3x + 2y = -15 \end{cases}$
$$0 = 0$$

This is always true, so the equations are *dependent*. Graphically this means that the equations are represented by the same line. This is true whenever you add to obtain an equation that is true (as with $0 = 0$, $2 = 2$, $5 = 5$, etc.).   □

Solution by Substitution

Sometimes it's convenient to use a third method called **substitution.** This method requires you to solve one of the equations for *either* variable and then substitute this expression into the other equation.

SUBSTITUTION
METHOD FOR
SOLVING SYSTEMS
OF EQUATIONS

Substitution Method

1. *Solve* one of the equations for one of the variables. Usually you will want to solve for the variable with the simplest coefficient (hopefully, 1).
2. *Substitute* the expression that you obtain into the other equation.
3. *Solve* the resulting single equation for the value of that variable.
4. *Substitute* that value into either of the original equations to determine the value of the other variable.
5. *State the solution.*

In Examples 8–10 solve each system by the substitution method.

Example 8

$$\begin{cases} 3x - 2y = 15 \\ x + y = 20 \end{cases}$$

Solution

Step 1, Solve. Before you begin, *look* at the equations and *decide* which variable would be easier to solve for. In this example, either x or y in the second equation looks like a good choice, so we'll solve it for y:

$$y = -x + 20$$

Step 2, Substitute

$$3x - 2(-x + 20) = 15$$

Step 3, Solve

$$3x + 2x - 40 = 15$$
$$5x - 40 = 15$$
$$5x = 55$$
$$x = 11$$

Step 4, Substitute

$$y + 11 = 20$$
$$y = 9$$

If you wish, you can check these values in the other equation:

$$3(11) - 2(9) = 33 - 18$$
$$= 15$$

Step 5, State Solution. The solution is (11, 9). □

Example 9
$$\begin{cases} 2x - y = 5 \\ x = 3 \end{cases}$$

Solution   *Step 1, Solve.*   When one equation is already solved for one of the variables, the substitution method is especially easy. The second equation is given solved for x.

Step 2, Substitute

$$2(3) - y = 5$$

Step 3, Solve

$$-y = -1$$

$$y = 1$$

Step 4, Substitute.   This step is not necessary in this problem since you now know *both* values.

Step 5, State Solution.   The solution is (3, 1).   ☐

Example 10
$$\begin{cases} a = 200 + .10s \\ a = .12s \end{cases}$$

Solution

Solve	$a = 200 + .10s$
Substitute	$200 + .10s = .12s$
Solve	$200 = .02s$
	$10,000 = s$
Substitute	$a = .12(10,000)$
	$= 1,200$

State Solution: The solution is $a = 1,200$ and $s = 10,000$.   ☐

Remember not to use ordered pair notation for the answer unless you are given which variable represents the first component. We've agreed that when the variables x and y are used, the form is (x, y), but we've made no such agreement for other variables. So, if you just wrote the answer as (1,200, 10,000), you would not know whether $a = 1,200$ or $a = 10,000$.

Word Problems

In this section we continue our procedure of giving you *continued* practice with word problems. You won't learn how to solve word problems if you only do them once or twice a semester. Remember to make the change from words to algebra by small steps. Don't try to solve the problem all at once with a flash of insight. Don't be too eager to use a variable. First digest the facts of the problem using several unknowns. Rewrite the relationships several ways. The point at which you introduce a variable should be natural and unforced. In fact, it should amount to nothing more than assigning a letter to a clearly isolated quantity. As you practice this technique you will find yourself able to solve more and more word problems.

Steps in Solving Word Problems
(Review Section 2.2, If Necessary)

1. *Read the problem.* Note what the problem is all about. Don't focus on numbers but rather on processes. You can't work a problem you don't understand.
2. *Restate the problem.* Restate it many times and in as many ways as necessary to classify the facts and relationships of the problem. Look for equality. If you can't find equal quantities, you will never find an equation.
3. *Write the equation or equations that evolve from the facts of the problem.* Don't rush this step. *Evolve* is the key word. The discovery of the equation should be the result of your understanding of the problem and not your algebraic skill.
4. *Choose a variable or variables.* Don't rush or force this step.
5. *Solve the equation or equations.* Check the results in the original problem. Solutions should make sense.
6. *State an answer to the problem.* This is not necessarily the answer to the equation or system of equations you solved.

Example 11 Suppose the ground speed of a bird flying with the wind is 21 kph, but against this same wind the bird would have a ground speed of only 5 kph. What is the bird's rate in still air? What is the rate of the wind?

Solution
$$\begin{cases} \text{RATE AGAINST THE WIND IS } 5 \\ \text{RATE WITH THE WIND IS } 21 \end{cases}$$

$$\begin{cases} \left(\begin{array}{c}\text{RATE OF}\\ \text{BIRD}\end{array}\right) - \left(\begin{array}{c}\text{RATE OF}\\ \text{WIND}\end{array}\right) = 5 \\ \left(\begin{array}{c}\text{RATE OF}\\ \text{BIRD}\end{array}\right) + \left(\begin{array}{c}\text{RATE OF}\\ \text{WIND}\end{array}\right) = 21 \end{cases}$$

$b - w = 5$
$b + w = 21$

Let $b =$ RATE OF BIRD and $w =$ RATE OF WIND. Notice the difference between this solution and the method of solution outlined in Section 2.2. In both sections, you begin solving a word problem without any limitation on the number of variables used. The equation (or equations) then *evolve* to other equations using fewer variables. In Section 2.2 the equations evolved to the point where there was a single unknown. You could do the same thing for this example. However, *now* you know how to handle systems of equations, so you can choose *two* variables, use *two* equations, and *solve the system.* This latter procedure is the one illustrated on the next page.

$$+\begin{cases} b - w = 5 \\ b + w = 21 \end{cases}$$
$$\begin{array}{rl} 2b & = 26 \\ b & = 13 \end{array}$$

$$(13) + w = 21 \qquad Check: \quad 13 - 8 = 5$$
$$\qquad\qquad w = 8 \qquad\qquad\qquad 13 + 8 = 21$$

The rate of the bird in still air is 13 kph, and the rate of the wind is 8 kph.

□

Problem Set 8.1

A *Solve Problems 1–6 by graphing.*

See Examples 1–3.

1. $\begin{cases} x - y = 2 \\ 2x + 3y = 9 \end{cases}$
  2. $\begin{cases} 3x - 4y = 16 \\ -x + 2y = -6 \end{cases}$

3. $\begin{cases} y = 3x + 1 \\ x - 2y = 8 \end{cases}$
  4. $\begin{cases} 2x - 3y = 12 \\ -4x + 6y = 18 \end{cases}$

5. $\begin{cases} y = \frac{2}{3}x - 5 \\ 2x - 3y = 15 \end{cases}$
  6. $\begin{cases} 200x - y = 0 \\ 50x + 2y = 450 \end{cases}$

Solve Problems 7–12 by adding.

See Examples 4–7.

7. $\begin{cases} x + y = 16 \\ x - y = 10 \end{cases}$
  8. $\begin{cases} x + y = 560 \\ x - y = 490 \end{cases}$

9. $\begin{cases} 3x - 2y = -17 \\ x + 2y = 5 \end{cases}$
  10. $\begin{cases} 3x - 2y = 18 \\ 3x + 5y = -24 \end{cases}$

11. $\begin{cases} 6x - 4y = 10 \\ -3x + 2y = -5 \end{cases}$
  12. $\begin{cases} 5s_1 + 2s_2 = 23 \\ 2s_1 + 7s_2 = 34 \end{cases}$

Solve Problems 13–18 by substitution.

See Examples 8–10.

13. $\begin{cases} y = -2x + 3 \\ 3x + 2y = -17 \end{cases}$
  14. $\begin{cases} 5x - 2y = -19 \\ x = 3y + 4 \end{cases}$

15. $\begin{cases} 2x - 3y = 15 \\ y = \frac{2}{3}x - 5 \end{cases}$
  16. $\begin{cases} x + y = 12 \\ .6y = .5(12) \end{cases}$

17. $\begin{cases} x + y = 16 \\ x - y = 10 \end{cases}$
  18. $\begin{cases} 3x - 2y = -17 \\ x + 2y = 5 \end{cases}$

B *Solve Problems 19–42 using any method you wish.*

See Examples 1–10.

19. $\begin{cases} x + 3y = 0 \\ x - 3y = -12 \end{cases}$
  20. $\begin{cases} x = y + 2 \\ y = 3x - 13 \end{cases}$

21. $\begin{cases} x + y = 14 \\ x - y = 6 \end{cases}$
  22. $\begin{cases} x - 2y = 5 \\ x + 2y = 7 \end{cases}$

23. $\begin{cases} 2x + 3y = 5 \\ 3x - 2y = 1 \end{cases}$
  24. $\begin{cases} 3x - 2y = 1 \\ 4x + 3y = 7 \end{cases}$

25. $\begin{cases} y = 9 - 2x \\ x + 4y = 8 \end{cases}$

26. $\begin{cases} 2x + 3y = 5 \\ x = 2y + 6 \end{cases}$

27. $\begin{cases} y = x + 1 \\ y = 2x - 6 \end{cases}$

28. $\begin{cases} a = 100 + .05s \\ a = .10s \end{cases}$

29. $\begin{cases} x = -5y \\ 2y - 3x = 17 \end{cases}$

30. $\begin{cases} y = 2x + 1 \\ 2y - 5x = 2 \end{cases}$

31. $\begin{cases} 2x + 3y = 6 \\ 2x + 5y = -2 \end{cases}$

32. $\begin{cases} 5x + 4y = 4 \\ 3x + 2y = 0 \end{cases}$

33. The intersection of the following lines: passing through (1, 1) and (4, 2), and passing through (3, 1) and (0, −2).

34. The intersection of the following lines: passing through (−1, 2) and (2, −1), and passing through (0, −4) and (6, 0).

35. $\begin{cases} 100x - y = 0 \\ 50x + y = 300 \end{cases}$

36. $\begin{cases} x = \frac{3}{4}y - 2 \\ 3y - 4x = 5 \end{cases}$

37. $\begin{cases} q + d = 147 \\ .25q + .10d = 24.15 \end{cases}$

38. $\begin{cases} x + y = 10 \\ .4x + .9y = .5(10) \end{cases}$

39. $\begin{cases} 7x - 3y = 6 \\ y = \frac{7}{3}x - 2 \end{cases}$

40. $\begin{cases} 5x + 35 = 6y \\ 5x + 6y = 145 \end{cases}$

41. $\begin{cases} 400x + 3y - 2{,}800 = 0 \text{ passes through } (1, 800) \text{ and } (7, 0) \\ 200x - 3y + 400 = 0 \text{ passes through } (1, 200) \text{ and } (7, 600) \end{cases}$

42. $\begin{cases} y - 75 = 3(x - 9) \text{ passes through } (6, 66) \text{ and } (9, 75) \\ y - 74 = -5(x - 6) \text{ passes through } (6, 74) \text{ and } (8, 64) \end{cases}$

See Example 11. 43. If a bird flies 40 mph with the wind, but only 10 mph against the wind, what is the rate of the bird in still air? What is the rate of the wind?

Solution: Fill in the blanks.

$\begin{cases} \text{RATE WITH THE WIND is } \underline{\quad\textbf{a.}\quad} \\ \underline{\qquad\textbf{b.}\qquad} \text{ is 10 mph.} \end{cases}$

$\begin{cases} \begin{pmatrix} \text{RATE OF} \\ \text{BIRD} \end{pmatrix} \underline{\quad\textbf{c.}\quad} \begin{pmatrix} \text{RATE OF} \\ \text{WIND} \end{pmatrix} = 40 \\ \underline{\qquad\textbf{d.}\qquad} = 10 \end{cases}$

Let $b =$ RATE OF BIRD and $w =$ RATE OF WIND.

$\begin{cases} \underline{\qquad\textbf{e.}\qquad} = 40 \\ \underline{\qquad\textbf{f.}\qquad} = 10 \end{cases}$

$\begin{aligned} 2b &= 50 & 25 + w &= 40 \\ b &= \underline{\quad\textbf{g.}\quad} & w &= \underline{\quad\textbf{h.}\quad} \end{aligned}$

The rate of the bird in still air is 25 mph and the rate of the wind is 15 mph.

See Example 11 and
Problem 43.
44. *Aviation.* Show the steps in solving the following problem:

If a plane flies 400 mph with the wind, but only 100 mph against the wind, what is the rate of the plane in still air? What is the rate of the wind?

Note: The question is asking you to show the steps in the solution (similar to Problem 43), and not just find the answer. However, so that you can check your solution, the answer is: The plane's rate in still air is 250 mph, and the rate of the wind is 150 mph.

See Problems 43
and 44.
45. *Sports.* Show the steps in solving the following problem:

If a swimmer is able to swim 2 mph when swimming with the current, but only $\frac{1}{2}$ mph when swimming against the current, what is the current's rate?

Answer (see note for Problem 44): The current is $\frac{3}{4}$ mph.

Show your work, as well as the answers, for Problems 46–49.

46. *Navigation.* A boat is able to make 16 knots with the current but only 10 knots against the current. What is the rate of the current?

47. *Flight.* An airplane is able to travel 560 mph with the wind but only 490 mph when flying into the wind. What would be the speed of the plane in still air?

48. *Business.* In counting change, you find you have $24.15 in quarters and dimes. If there are 147 coins, how many are quarters? [*Hint:* This is not exactly the same as Problems 43–47, but the procedure is the same.]

49. *Business.* Suppose you want to sell T-shirts to students on your campus. You need to decide on a price that's between $1 and $7, so you conduct an intensive market-research survey and find that 800 students will buy a T-shirt for $1, but none will buy a T-shirt for $7. You also find a supplier who can supply 200 shirts if they are sold for $1, and will supply 600 if they are sold for $7. What is the price for which the supply equals the demand? How many T-shirts could you expect to sell if both the supply and the demand are linear? [*Hint:* Try a graphical solution.]

8.2 Cramer's Rule

A very useful method for solving a system of linear equations is called **Cramer's rule.** It solves a linear system *by formula.* Consider a general linear system with two variables:

$$\begin{cases} a_1x + b_1y = c_1 \\ a_2x + b_2y = c_2 \end{cases}$$

Solve this system by adding:

$$\begin{array}{r} b_2 \\ -b_1 \end{array} \begin{cases} a_1x + \quad b_1y = c_1 \\ a_2x + \quad b_2y = c_2 \end{cases}$$

$$+ \begin{cases} a_1b_2x + b_1b_2y = b_2c_1 \\ -a_2b_1x - b_1b_2y = -b_1c_2 \end{cases}$$

$$\overline{(a_1b_2 - a_2b_1)x = b_2c_1 - b_1c_2}$$

$$x = \frac{b_2c_1 - b_1c_2}{a_1b_2 - a_2b_1} \qquad \text{provided } a_1b_2 - a_2b_1 \neq 0$$

Similarly, solve for y (the steps are left for you):

$$y = \frac{a_1c_2 - a_2c_1}{a_1b_2 - a_2b_1}$$

The difficulty with using this result for finding x and y is that it is next to impossible to remember it! To help with this problem, the following notation is used.

Historical Note

Determinants were invented in 1750 by Gabriel Cramer. It is curious that Cramer was a French-speaking Swiss and would have pronounced his name "cra-mare," while generations of students have called it "kramer's rule" with the German sound.

The Determinant of the Coefficients of a System of Two Linear Equations with Two Unknowns

The **determinant** of the coefficients of the system

$$\begin{cases} a_1x + b_1y = c_1 \\ a_2x + b_2y = c_2 \end{cases}$$

is a real number denoted by D and defined by

$$D = \begin{vmatrix} a_1 & b_1 \\ a_2 & b_2 \end{vmatrix}$$

$$= a_1b_2 - a_2b_1$$

Example 1 Evaluate the given determinants.

a. $\begin{vmatrix} 1 & 2 \\ 3 & 4 \end{vmatrix} = (1)(4) - (3)(2)$

$\qquad = 4 - 6$

$\qquad = -2$

b. $\begin{vmatrix} -3 & -2 \\ 4 & 1 \end{vmatrix} = (-3)(1) - (4)(-2)$

$\qquad = -3 + 8$

$\qquad = 5$

c. $\begin{vmatrix} 0 & -3 \\ 2 & 5 \end{vmatrix} = 0 - (-6)$

$\qquad = 6$

d. $\begin{vmatrix} s & -t \\ u & v \end{vmatrix} = sv - (-tu)$

$\qquad = sv + tu$

e. $\begin{vmatrix} c_1 & b_1 \\ c_2 & b_2 \end{vmatrix} = b_2c_1 - b_1c_2$ **f.** $\begin{vmatrix} a_1 & c_1 \\ a_2 & c_2 \end{vmatrix} = a_1c_2 - a_2c_1$

Notice that the solution of the system

$$\begin{cases} a_1x + b_1y = c_1 \\ a_2x + b_2y = c_2 \end{cases}$$

can now be rewritten using determinant notation:

$$x = \frac{b_2c_1 - b_1c_2}{a_1b_2 - a_2b_1} \qquad y = \frac{a_1c_2 - a_2c_1}{a_1b_2 - a_2b_1}$$

$$= \frac{\begin{vmatrix} c_1 & b_1 \\ c_2 & b_2 \end{vmatrix}}{\begin{vmatrix} a_1 & b_1 \\ a_2 & b_2 \end{vmatrix}} \qquad = \frac{\begin{vmatrix} a_1 & c_1 \\ a_2 & c_2 \end{vmatrix}}{\begin{vmatrix} a_1 & b_1 \\ a_2 & b_2 \end{vmatrix}}$$

Notice that the denominator of both x and y is D. The numerators are also found by looking at the original system (see Examples 1e and 1f).

Let D_x be the determinant in which the coefficients of x in the system are replaced by the constant numbers c_1 and c_2, respectively, and let D_y be the determinant in which the coefficients of y in the original system are replaced by the constant numbers c_1 and c_2, respectively. With this notation, we can state a formula for the solution of a system of linear equations, and in this form it is easy to remember.

CRAMER'S RULE

Cramer's Rule
The solution to the system

$$\begin{cases} a_1x + b_1y = c_1 \\ a_2x + b_2y = c_2 \end{cases}$$

is

$$x = \frac{D_x}{D} \quad \text{and} \quad y = \frac{D_y}{D} \qquad \text{where } D \neq 0$$

In Examples 2 and 3 solve each system using Cramer's rule.

Example 2 $\begin{cases} 3x - 2y = 15 \\ x + y = 20 \end{cases}$

Solution $x = \dfrac{\begin{vmatrix} 15 & -2 \\ 20 & 1 \end{vmatrix}}{\begin{vmatrix} 3 & -2 \\ 1 & 1 \end{vmatrix}} \qquad y = \dfrac{\begin{vmatrix} 3 & 15 \\ 1 & 20 \end{vmatrix}}{5}$

$$x = \frac{15+40}{3+2} \qquad\qquad y = \frac{60-15}{5}$$

$$= \frac{55}{5} \qquad\qquad\qquad = \frac{45}{5}$$

$$= 11 \qquad\qquad\qquad\quad = 9$$

The solution is (11, 9). Notice that since the denominator is the same for both x and y, it did not need to be evaluated a second time when finding y. □

Example 3 $\begin{cases} 3x - 2y = 5 \\ 5x + 3y = -3 \end{cases}$

Solution $x = \dfrac{\begin{vmatrix} 5 & -2 \\ -3 & 3 \end{vmatrix}}{\begin{vmatrix} 3 & -2 \\ 5 & 3 \end{vmatrix}} \qquad\qquad y = \dfrac{\begin{vmatrix} 3 & 5 \\ 5 & -3 \end{vmatrix}}{19}$

$$= \frac{15-6}{9+10} \qquad\qquad = \frac{-9-25}{19}$$

$$= \frac{9}{19} \qquad\qquad\qquad = \frac{-34}{19}$$

The solution is $(\frac{9}{19}, -\frac{34}{19})$. □

If the system is dependent or inconsistent, then $D = 0$ and Cramer's rule fails. If *both* $D_x = 0$ *and* $D = 0$, then the system is *dependent*, whereas if $D_x \neq 0$ and $D = 0$, then the system is *inconsistent*.

In Examples 4 and 5 solve each system.

Example 4 $\begin{cases} 2x + 2y = 10 \\ x + y = 20 \end{cases}$

Solution $x = \dfrac{\begin{vmatrix} 10 & 2 \\ 20 & 1 \end{vmatrix}}{\begin{vmatrix} 2 & 2 \\ 1 & 1 \end{vmatrix}}$

$$= \frac{10-40}{2-2}$$

$$= \frac{-30}{0} \longleftarrow \text{—— Impossible, so Cramer's rule fails.}$$

Since $D_x \neq 0$ and $D = 0$, the system is inconsistent (parallel lines). □

Example 5
$$\begin{cases} x - \frac{2}{3}y = 5 \\ -3x + 2y = -15 \end{cases}$$

inconsistent lines are parallel

Solution
$$x = \frac{\begin{vmatrix} 5 & -\frac{2}{3} \\ -15 & 2 \end{vmatrix}}{\begin{vmatrix} 1 & -\frac{2}{3} \\ -3 & 2 \end{vmatrix}}$$

$$= \frac{10 - (-15)(-\frac{2}{3})}{2 - (-3)(-\frac{2}{3})}$$

$$= \frac{10 - 10}{2 - 2}$$

$$= \frac{0}{0} \longleftarrow \text{Impossible, so Cramer's rule fails.}$$

Since $D_x = D = 0$, the system is dependent (same line). $\square$

Problem Set 8.2

A   *Evaluate the determinants in Problems 1–9.*

See Example 1.

1. $\begin{vmatrix} 2 & 3 \\ 1 & 4 \end{vmatrix}$ 2. $\begin{vmatrix} 5 & 1 \\ 6 & 2 \end{vmatrix}$ 3. $\begin{vmatrix} 4 & 2 \\ 1 & 3 \end{vmatrix}$

4. $\begin{vmatrix} 3 & -2 \\ 6 & 1 \end{vmatrix}$ 5. $\begin{vmatrix} -6 & 1 \\ -2 & 3 \end{vmatrix}$ 6. $\begin{vmatrix} -8 & 2 \\ -6 & 3 \end{vmatrix}$

7. $\begin{vmatrix} 3 & 0 \\ 2 & 1 \end{vmatrix}$ 8. $\begin{vmatrix} 2 & -1 \\ 3 & 0 \end{vmatrix}$ 9. $\begin{vmatrix} -8 & -4 \\ -6 & -3 \end{vmatrix}$

Solve the systems given in Problems 10–24 by using Cramer's rule.

See Examples 2 and 3.

10. $\begin{cases} x + y = 2 \\ 2x - 3y = -1 \end{cases}$ 11. $\begin{cases} 2x - y = 0 \\ 3x - 4y = -2 \end{cases}$ 12. $\begin{cases} x + 2y = 2 \\ x - 2y = 4 \end{cases}$

13. $\begin{cases} 4x - 3y = 8 \\ 7x - 4y = 9 \end{cases}$ 14. $\begin{cases} x - y = 2 \\ 2x + 3y = 9 \end{cases}$ 15. $\begin{cases} 3x - 2y = 0 \\ 2x + 3y = 13 \end{cases}$

16. $\begin{cases} 2x + y = 8 \\ 3x - 2y = 5 \end{cases}$ 17. $\begin{cases} 2x - 5y = 1 \\ 3x - 8y = 2 \end{cases}$ 18. $\begin{cases} 3x + 5y = 8 \\ 4x - 3y = 1 \end{cases}$

19. $\begin{cases} 7x - 9y = 3 \\ 5x - 6y = 3 \end{cases}$ 20. $\begin{cases} x + 2y = 10 \\ 5x + 3y = 1 \end{cases}$ 21. $\begin{cases} x + 3y = -2 \\ 2x + 5y = 11 \end{cases}$

22. $\begin{cases} x + 3y = 3 \\ 4x - 6y = -6 \end{cases}$ 23. $\begin{cases} x + 2y = 3 \\ 3x + 4y = 3 \end{cases}$ 24. $\begin{cases} 7x + 5y = 1 \\ -3x + 4y = 18 \end{cases}$

B   *Solve the systems given in Problems 25–36 by using Cramer's rule.*

See Examples 2–5.

25. $\begin{cases} 3x + 4y = 7 \\ 2y + x = 2 \end{cases}$ 26. $\begin{cases} 2x - y = 14 \\ 3y + 4x = 8 \end{cases}$ 27. $\begin{cases} x + 3y = -2 \\ 5y + 2x = 3 \end{cases}$

with fractions multiply by common denominator

28. $\begin{cases} 5x - 6y + 2 = 0 \\ 6y - 5x - 18 = 0 \end{cases}$

29. $\begin{cases} 4y + 5x = 2 \\ y = -\frac{5}{4}x + 1 \end{cases}$

30. $\begin{cases} y = \frac{3}{7}x + 2 \\ 3x - 7y + 14 = 0 \end{cases}$

31. $\begin{cases} x = -\frac{5}{8}y + 3 \\ 8x + 5y - 24 = 0 \end{cases}$

32. $\begin{cases} 2x - 3y = 5 \\ y = \frac{2}{3}x + 1 \end{cases}$

33. $\begin{cases} x - 2y = 6 \\ y = \frac{1}{2}x - 3 \end{cases}$ $\frac{0}{0}$ *Dependent system*

34. $\begin{cases} x + y = a \\ x - y = b \end{cases}$

35. $\begin{cases} ax + by = 1 \\ bx + ay = 0 \end{cases}$

36. $\begin{cases} ax + by = 0 \\ bx + ay = 1 \end{cases}$

37. *Navigation.* If you can row downstream at 12 mph and upstream at 2 mph, what is the rate of the current?

38. *Aviation.* If an airplane can travel 370 mph with the wind, but only 320 mph against the wind, what is the plane's speed in still air?

39. *Aviation.* A charter flight has signed up 100 travelers. They are told that if they can sign up an additional 25 persons, they can save $78 each. What is the cost per person if 100 persons make the trip?

40. *Business.* An old computer terminal can process 20 orders per minute while a new terminal can process 50 orders per minute. What is the total time required to process 20,100 orders if the new terminal works 8 hours less than the old terminal?

Mind Bogglers   *Solve the systems in Problems 41–43 using Cramer's rule.*

41. $\begin{cases} \dfrac{3}{x} - \dfrac{2}{y} = -1 \\[2mm] \dfrac{7}{x} - \dfrac{6}{y} = -2 \end{cases}$

42. $\begin{cases} \dfrac{3}{x} + \dfrac{4}{y} = 6 \\[2mm] \dfrac{5}{x} + \dfrac{3}{y} = -1 \end{cases}$

43. $\begin{cases} \dfrac{5}{x} + \dfrac{1}{y} = 3 \\[2mm] \dfrac{1}{2x} - \dfrac{2}{y} = 1 \end{cases}$

44. Show that if two rows of a determinant are the same, then its value is 0.

45. Show that $\begin{vmatrix} a_1 & b_1 \\ a_2 & b_2 \end{vmatrix} = \begin{vmatrix} a_1 + a_2 & b_1 + b_2 \\ a_2 & b_2 \end{vmatrix}$

46. Show that the following is true for any constant k:

$$\begin{vmatrix} a_1 & b_1 \\ a_2 & b_2 \end{vmatrix} = \begin{vmatrix} a_1 & b_1 + ka_1 \\ a_2 & b_2 + ka_2 \end{vmatrix}$$

8.3 Systems of Linear Equations in Three Variables

Systems of equations with more than two variables are encountered frequently and have important applications. Consider a system of three linear equations in three variables:

$$\begin{cases} x + y + 2z = 0 \\ 2x - y - z = 1 \\ x + 2y + 3z = 1 \end{cases}$$

The **solution** to such a system is the **set of all ordered triplets (x, y, z) that satisfy all three equations simultaneously.** The set of all such ordered triplets of numbers is called the **solution set** of the system. The triple $(0, -2, 1)$ satisfies the first two equations but not the third. Thus, $(0, -2, 1)$ is not a solution of the system.

The addition method developed for systems of two equations can be extended to solve a system of three equations.

EXTENDED
ADDITION
METHOD

Extended Addition Method

1. *Choose* two equations from the system.
    a. *Multiply* one or both of the equations by constants so that the coefficients of one of the variables are opposites.
    b. *Add* corresponding members of the equations to obtain a new equation in two variables.
2. *Choose* a different pair of equations, one of which is the equation that was *not* used in Step 1. *Multiply* and *add* as in Step 1 to obtain a second equation in the *same* two variables.
3. *Solve* the system formed by the two equations obtained in Steps 1 and 2.
4. *Substitute* the solution to the system of two equations in two unknowns into any one of the original equations to find the value of the third variable.

In Examples 1–3 solve each system.

Example 1

$$\begin{cases} x + y + 2z = 0 \\ 2x - y - z = 1 \\ x + 2y + 3z = 1 \end{cases}$$

Solution   *Step 1.* Choosing the first two equations, you may simply add to eliminate the variable y:

$$+\begin{cases} x + y + 2z = 0 \\ 2x - y - z = 1 \end{cases}$$
$$\overline{3x + z = 1}$$

Step 2. Using the second two equations, twice the second added to the third eliminates the same variable y:

$$+\begin{cases} 4x - 2y - 2z = 2 \\ x + 2y + 3z = 1 \end{cases}$$
$$\overline{5x + z = 3}$$

Step 3. Now, form a system with the resulting equations and solve for x and z:

$$-1 \begin{cases} 3x + z = 1 \\ 5x + z = 3 \end{cases}$$

$$+ \begin{cases} -3x - z = -1 \\ \underline{5x + z = 3} \\ \quad 2x \quad\;\; = 2 \\ \qquad\; x = 1 \end{cases}$$

$$5(1) + z = 3$$
$$z = -2$$

Step 4. Finally, substitute into one of the original equations to find the value of y:

$$1 + y + 2(-2) = 0$$
$$y - 3 = 0$$
$$y = 3$$

The solution is $(1, 3, -2)$. ☐

Example 2
$$\begin{cases} 2x + 3y + 2z = 3 \\ 3x - 4y - 5z = -2 \\ 4x - 2y - 3z = 2 \end{cases}$$

Solution Select any pair to eliminate one of the variables (first and second for this example):

$$\begin{matrix} 3 \\ -2 \end{matrix} \begin{cases} 2x + 3y + 2z = 3 \\ 3x - 4y - 5z = -2 \end{cases}$$

$$+ \begin{cases} 6x + 9y + 6z = 9 \\ \underline{-6x + 8y + 10z = 4} \\ \quad 17y + 16z = 13 \end{cases}$$

Select another pair (first and third for this example):

$$\begin{matrix} 2 \\ -1 \end{matrix} \begin{cases} 2x + 3y + 2z = 3 \\ 4x - 2y - 3z = 2 \end{cases}$$

$$+ \begin{cases} 4x + 6y + 4z = 6 \\ \underline{-4x + 2y + 3z = -2} \\ \quad 8y + 7z = 4 \end{cases}$$

Next, consider the system consisting of these two equations:

$$\begin{matrix} -7 \\ 16 \end{matrix} \begin{cases} 17y + 16z = 13 \\ 8y + 7z = 4 \end{cases}$$

$$+ \begin{cases} -119y - 112z = -91 \\ \underline{128y + 112z = 64} \\ \quad 9y \qquad\;\; = -27 \\ \qquad\;\; y = -3 \end{cases}$$

$$8(-3) + 7z = 4$$
$$7z = 28$$
$$z = 4$$

$$\begin{aligned} 2x + 3(-3) + 2(4) &= 3 \\ 2x - 9 + 8 &= 3 \\ 2x &= 4 \\ x &= 2 \end{aligned}$$

1 point
no points
1 plane
inconsistent = parallel

The solution is (2, −3, 4). □

Example 3 $\begin{cases} x + 2y = 2 \\ x + y + z = 1 \\ x - 2z = 1 \end{cases}$

Solution Combine the first two equations, eliminating y to obtain an equation in x and z. The third equation can then be used as a second equation in x and z.

(Equation I) + (−2)(Equation II), Equation III: $\begin{cases} -x - 2z = 0 \\ x - 2z = 1 \end{cases}$

$$+\begin{cases} -x - 2z = 0 \\ x - 2z = 1 \end{cases}$$

$$\begin{aligned} -4z &= 1 \\ z &= -\tfrac{1}{4} \end{aligned}$$

$$\begin{aligned} x - 2(-\tfrac{1}{4}) &= 1 \\ x + \tfrac{1}{2} &= 1 \\ x &= \tfrac{1}{2} \end{aligned}$$

$$\begin{aligned} \tfrac{1}{2} + 2y &= 2 \\ 2y &= \tfrac{3}{2} \\ y &= \tfrac{3}{4} \end{aligned}$$

The solution is $(\frac{1}{2}, \frac{3}{4}, -\frac{1}{4})$. □

The examples illustrate consistent systems. If the process produces an equation that is a false equation, such as $0 = 3$, then the system is inconsistent and has no solution. If one of the equations produced is a true equation, such as $0 = 0$, then the system either has infinitely many solutions or has none. This last case is different from the system with two equations in two variables. In that case, if $0 = 0$ was obtained, the system was dependent and had infinitely many solutions.

Problem Set 8.3

Solve the systems in Problems 1–20.

A
See Examples 1–3.

1. $\begin{cases} x + 2y + z = 9 \\ x + y - z = 5 \\ 3x - y + 2z = 12 \end{cases}$

2. $\begin{cases} x + 3y - z = 1 \\ x - y + 2z = -4 \\ 2x + y + 3z = 2 \end{cases}$

3. $\begin{cases} x+\ y+\ z=1 \\ x+3y-\ z=11 \\ 2x+\ y+2z=1 \end{cases}$ 4. $\begin{cases} x+\ y+\ z=2 \\ x+4y+\ z=5 \\ 2x+\ y+3z=1 \end{cases}$

5. $\begin{cases} x-2y+z=-1 \\ 3x-\ y+z=8 \\ x-2y-z=-15 \end{cases}$ 6. $\begin{cases} x-2y-\ z=-5 \\ x-\ y+\ z=-4 \\ 2x+\ y+4z=3 \end{cases}$

7. $\begin{cases} x+y-\ z=0 \\ x+y+\ z=2 \\ 3x-y-4z=3 \end{cases}$ 8. $\begin{cases} x+\ y+3z=2 \\ x+\ z=3 \\ 3x+\ y=-2 \end{cases}$

9. $\begin{cases} x+2y+z=1 \\ x-y=2 \\ 2x+z=2 \end{cases}$ 10. $\begin{cases} x+\ y-\ z=0 \\ 3x+\ y-2z=1 \\ x-3y+\ z=2 \end{cases}$

B 11. $\begin{cases} x+y+z=1 \\ x+y+z=3 \\ x-y-z=0 \end{cases}$ 12. $\begin{cases} x-y-z=3 \\ -x+y+z=2 \\ x-y+z=1 \end{cases}$

13. $\begin{cases} x-z=1 \\ y+z=1 \\ z-x=2 \end{cases}$ 14. $\begin{cases} x-3z=-1 \\ y+3x=1 \\ 3z-\ x=1 \end{cases}$

15. $\begin{cases} x+z=1 \\ 3x-y=1 \\ 2y+z=2 \end{cases}$ 16. $\begin{cases} x+\ y+\ z=1 \\ x-3z=0 \\ 4y-2z=1 \end{cases}$

17. $\begin{cases} x+\ y+z=2 \\ 2z-y=1 \\ 3z-x=2 \end{cases}$ 18. $\begin{cases} x-2y-\ z=2 \\ x-\ y+\ z=1 \\ 2x+\ y+4z=0 \end{cases}$

19. $\begin{cases} x+2y+\ z=14 \\ 3x+3y-\ z=-5 \\ 2x-4y-5z=9 \end{cases}$ 20. $\begin{cases} x-4y-\ z=-4 \\ 2x-2y+\ z=1 \\ 3x-8y+3z=0 \end{cases}$

Mind Bogglers *Solve the systems in Problems 21–24.*

21. $\begin{cases} \dfrac{1}{x}+\dfrac{1}{y}+\dfrac{2}{z}=1 \\ \dfrac{2}{x}+\dfrac{1}{y}-\dfrac{2}{z}=1 \\ \dfrac{3}{x}+\dfrac{4}{y}+\dfrac{4}{z}=2 \end{cases}$ 22. $\begin{cases} \dfrac{4}{x}-\dfrac{1}{y}-\dfrac{1}{z}=1 \\ \dfrac{3}{x}+\dfrac{1}{y}+\dfrac{3}{z}=1 \\ \dfrac{2}{x}+\dfrac{1}{y}+\dfrac{1}{z}=1 \end{cases}$

23. $\begin{cases} \dfrac{3}{x}+\dfrac{1}{y}+\dfrac{2}{z}=1 \\ \dfrac{2}{x}-\dfrac{1}{y}+\dfrac{3}{z}=-6 \\ \dfrac{1}{x}+\dfrac{1}{y}+\dfrac{2}{z}=-3 \end{cases}$ 24. $\begin{cases} \dfrac{1}{x}+\dfrac{1}{y}+\dfrac{2}{z}=3 \\ \dfrac{1}{x}+\dfrac{2}{y}+\dfrac{4}{z}=3 \\ \dfrac{1}{x}-\dfrac{3}{y}-\dfrac{5}{z}=5 \end{cases}$

8.4   Determinants

Just as determinants helped solve a system with two equations and two unknowns, they can also help solve larger systems. In this section, we'll focus upon three linear equations with three unknowns, but in later courses you'll generalize these same results to larger systems.

Consider the determinant

$$\begin{vmatrix} a_1 & b_1 & c_1 \\ a_2 & b_2 & c_2 \\ a_3 & b_3 & c_3 \end{vmatrix}$$

The **minor** of an element of a determinant is the (smaller) determinant that remains after deleting all entries in its row and column.

Example 1   The minor of a_1 is found by deleting the shaded portion.

$$\begin{vmatrix} a_1 & b_1 & c_1 \\ a_2 & b_2 & c_2 \\ a_3 & b_3 & c_3 \end{vmatrix} \qquad \text{Minor:} \quad \begin{vmatrix} b_2 & c_2 \\ b_3 & c_3 \end{vmatrix}$$

□

Example 2   The minor of b_3 in the determinant of Example 1 is: $\begin{vmatrix} a_1 & c_1 \\ a_2 & c_2 \end{vmatrix}$ □

Example 3   The minor of -3 in

$$\begin{vmatrix} 6 & 2 & -4 \\ -3 & 4 & 0 \\ 5 & 3 & -2 \end{vmatrix} \quad \text{is} \quad \begin{vmatrix} 2 & -4 \\ 3 & -2 \end{vmatrix} \begin{aligned} &= -4 + 12 \\ &= 8 \end{aligned}$$

□

Example 4   The minor of 4 in the determinant of Example 3 is

$$\begin{vmatrix} 6 & -4 \\ 5 & -2 \end{vmatrix} \begin{aligned} &= -12 + 20 \\ &= 8 \end{aligned}$$

□

Example 5   The minor of 0 in the determinant of Example 3 is

$$\begin{vmatrix} 6 & 2 \\ 5 & 3 \end{vmatrix} \begin{aligned} &= 18 - 10 \\ &= 8 \end{aligned}$$

□

The **cofactor** of an element in a determinant is $(+1)$ or (-1) times its minor, as determined by the following pattern:

$$\begin{matrix} + & - & + \\ - & + & - \\ + & - & + \end{matrix}$$

Look at the pattern. Each *position* is designated by $+$ or $-$; it doesn't matter what the entry in that position is—it can be positive, negative, or

0—the *cofactor* of that entry is $(+1)$ times the minor of that entry if the *position* is shown as $+$ in the pattern. If the *position* is shown as $-$ in the pattern, then the cofactor of that entry is (-1) times the minor of that entry. Study Examples 6–8.

In Examples 6–8 find the cofactor of the requested entry in the determinant below.

$$\begin{vmatrix} 6 & 2 & -4 \\ -3 & 4 & 0 \\ 5 & 3 & -2 \end{vmatrix}$$

[handwritten: Determinant]

[handwritten marginalia: Cover up term using and its row and the row ⊥ to it (for a + c terms) For middle term cover up its row and the row doubly + change sign to its opposite of b term ↓ middle term]

Example 6 6; $+\begin{vmatrix} 4 & 0 \\ 3 & -2 \end{vmatrix} = +(-8-0)$
$$= -8$$

Example 7 2; $-\begin{vmatrix} -3 & 0 \\ 5 & -2 \end{vmatrix} = -(6-0)$
$$= -6$$

Example 8 -4; $+\begin{vmatrix} -3 & 4 \\ 5 & 3 \end{vmatrix} = +(-9-20)$
$$= -29$$

VALUE OF A
DETERMINANT
WITH 3 ROWS AND
3 COLUMNS

The Value of a Determinant Expanded About the First Row:

$$\begin{vmatrix} a_1 & b_1 & c_1 \\ a_2 & b_2 & c_2 \\ a_3 & b_3 & c_3 \end{vmatrix} = a_1(\text{Cofactor of } a_1) + b_1(\text{Cofactor of } b_1) + c_1(\text{Cofactor of } c_1)$$

$$= a_1\begin{vmatrix} b_2 & c_2 \\ b_3 & c_3 \end{vmatrix} - b_1\begin{vmatrix} a_2 & c_2 \\ a_3 & c_3 \end{vmatrix} + c_1\begin{vmatrix} a_2 & b_2 \\ a_3 & b_3 \end{vmatrix}$$

$$= a_1(b_2c_3 - b_3c_2) - b_1(a_2c_3 - a_3c_2) + c_1(a_2b_3 - a_3b_2)$$

In Examples 9 and 10 evaluate each determinant by expanding about the first row.

Example 9 $\begin{vmatrix} 6 & 2 & -4 \\ -3 & 4 & 0 \\ 5 & 3 & -2 \end{vmatrix} = 6(\text{Cofactor of } 6) + 2(\text{Cofactor of } 2) + (-4)(\text{Cofactor of } -4)$

From Example 6
From Example 7
From Example 8

$$= 6(-8) + 2(-6) + (-4)(-29)$$
$$= -48 - 12 + 116$$
$$= 56$$

Example 10
$$\begin{vmatrix} -2 & 3 & 5 \\ 1 & -1 & 3 \\ 6 & 0 & 1 \end{vmatrix} = (-2)(\text{Cofactor of } -2) + 3(\text{Cofactor of } 3) + 5(\text{Cofactor of } 5)$$

Note: This is from the position sign of cofactor.

$$= -2\begin{vmatrix} -1 & 3 \\ 0 & 1 \end{vmatrix} - 3\begin{vmatrix} 1 & 3 \\ 6 & 1 \end{vmatrix} + 5\begin{vmatrix} 1 & -1 \\ 6 & 0 \end{vmatrix}$$

$$= -2(-1 - 0) - 3(1 - 18) + 5(0 + 6)$$
$$= 2 + 51 + 30$$
$$= 83 \qquad\qquad \square$$

It is possible to expand a determinant about other rows (or columns). For Example 9, **expanding about the second row** gives:

$$-3(\text{Cofactor of } -3) + 4(\text{Cofactor of } 4) + 0(\text{Cofactor of } 0)$$

$$= -3\left[-\begin{vmatrix} 2 & -4 \\ 3 & -2 \end{vmatrix}\right] + 4\left[+\begin{vmatrix} 6 & -4 \\ 5 & -2 \end{vmatrix}\right] + 0\left[-\begin{vmatrix} 6 & 2 \\ 5 & 3 \end{vmatrix}\right]$$

$$= 3(-4 + 12) + 4(-12 + 20) - 0(18 - 10)$$
$$= 24 + 32 - 0$$
$$= 56$$

Notice that this result is the same as when it was **expanded about the first row**. This is a general result.

> **Evaluating a Determinant**
> The value of a determinant is the same regardless of the row (or column) about which it is expanded.

In Examples 11 and 12 expand the determinant below as indicated.

$$\begin{vmatrix} -1 & 3 & 4 \\ 1 & -1 & 2 \\ 3 & -2 & 1 \end{vmatrix}$$

Positive position

Negative position

Example 11 *Third row:*
$$\begin{vmatrix} -1 & 3 & 4 \\ 1 & -1 & 2 \\ 3 & -2 & 1 \end{vmatrix} = (3)\begin{vmatrix} 3 & 4 \\ -1 & 2 \end{vmatrix} - (-2)\begin{vmatrix} -1 & 4 \\ 1 & 2 \end{vmatrix} + (1)\begin{vmatrix} -1 & 3 \\ 1 & -1 \end{vmatrix}$$

Positive position

$$= 3(6 + 4) + 2(-2 - 4) + (1 - 3)$$
$$= 30 - 12 - 2$$
$$= 16 \qquad\qquad \square$$

Example 12   *Second column:*

Negative position

Positive position

$$\begin{vmatrix} -1 & 3 & 4 \\ 1 & -1 & 2 \\ 3 & -2 & 1 \end{vmatrix} = -(3)\begin{vmatrix} 1 & 2 \\ 3 & 1 \end{vmatrix} + (-1)\begin{vmatrix} -1 & 4 \\ 3 & 1 \end{vmatrix} - (-2)\begin{vmatrix} -1 & 4 \\ 1 & 2 \end{vmatrix}$$

Negative position

$$= -3(1-6) - (-1-12) + 2(-2-4)$$
$$= -3(-5) + 13 + 2(-6)$$
$$= 15 + 13 - 12$$
$$= 16 \qquad \square$$

If the determinant has some zero entries it is advisable to choose a row or column containing those zeros in order to simplify the arithmetic.

In Examples 13 and 14 expand each determinant.

Example 13

Expand about second column.   You don't need to calculate these cofactors because the product is 0.

$$\begin{vmatrix} 1 & 0 & -1 \\ 0 & 1 & 2 \\ -1 & 0 & 2 \end{vmatrix} = -0\begin{vmatrix} 0 & 2 \\ -1 & 2 \end{vmatrix} + (1)\begin{vmatrix} 1 & -1 \\ -1 & 2 \end{vmatrix} - 0\begin{vmatrix} 1 & -1 \\ 0 & 2 \end{vmatrix}$$
$$= (2-1)$$
$$= 1 \qquad \square$$

Example 14

Expand about third column.

$$\begin{vmatrix} 3 & 2 & 0 \\ 6 & -3 & 0 \\ -1 & -4 & 1 \end{vmatrix} = (1)\begin{vmatrix} 3 & 2 \\ 6 & -3 \end{vmatrix}$$

You don't even need to write down the other terms because with 0 entries the products are 0.

$$= (-9 - 12)$$
$$= -21 \qquad \square$$

Cramer's rule extends to three linear equations with three unknowns.

CRAMER'S RULE

Cramer's Rule for a Linear System of Three Equations with Three Unknowns

The solution to the system

$$\begin{cases} a_1 x + b_1 y + c_1 z = d_1 \\ a_2 x + b_2 y + c_2 z = d_2 \\ a_3 x + b_3 y + c_3 z = d_3 \end{cases}$$

is

$$x = \frac{D_x}{D} \qquad y = \frac{D_y}{D} \qquad z = \frac{D_z}{D} \qquad \text{where } D \neq 0$$

D is the determinant of the coefficients; and D_x, D_y, and D_z are the determinants found by substituting d_1, d_2, and d_3 into the determinant D as follows:

For D_x substitute for a_1, a_2, and a_3
For D_y substitute for b_1, b_2, and b_3
For D_z substitute for c_1, c_2, and c_3

Notice that these are substitutions for the *coefficients* of x for D_x, of y for D_y, and of z for D_z.

In Examples 15 and 16 solve each system using Cramer's rule.

Example 15

$$\begin{cases} x - 2y - 3z = 3 \\ x + y - z = 2 \\ 2x - 3y - 5z = 5 \end{cases}$$

Solution

$$D = \begin{vmatrix} 1 & -2 & -3 \\ 1 & 1 & -1 \\ 2 & -3 & -5 \end{vmatrix}$$

$$= 2\begin{vmatrix} -2 & -3 \\ 1 & -1 \end{vmatrix} - (-3)\begin{vmatrix} 1 & -3 \\ 1 & -1 \end{vmatrix} + (-5)\begin{vmatrix} 1 & -2 \\ 1 & 1 \end{vmatrix}$$

$$= \quad 2(2+3) + 3(-1+3) + (-5)(1+2)$$

$$= \quad 10 + 6 - 15$$

$$= \quad 1$$

$$D_x = \begin{vmatrix} 3 & -2 & -3 \\ 2 & 1 & -1 \\ 5 & -3 & -5 \end{vmatrix} \qquad D_y = \begin{vmatrix} 1 & 3 & -3 \\ 1 & 2 & -1 \\ 2 & 5 & -5 \end{vmatrix} \qquad D_z = \begin{vmatrix} 1 & -2 & 3 \\ 1 & 1 & 2 \\ 2 & -3 & 5 \end{vmatrix}$$

$$= \quad -1 \qquad\qquad\qquad = \quad 1 \qquad\qquad\qquad = \quad -2$$

The details of these expansions are left for you to verify. Thus, by Cramer's rule,

$$x = \frac{D_x}{D} \qquad y = \frac{D_y}{D} \qquad z = \frac{D_z}{D}$$

$$= \frac{-1}{1} \qquad = \frac{1}{1} \qquad = \frac{-2}{1}$$

$$= -1 \qquad = 1 \qquad = -2$$

The solution $(x, y, z) = (-1, 1, -2)$.   □

Example 16 $\begin{cases} y + z = -1 \\ x + z = -1 \\ y + z = -5 - 2x \end{cases}$

Solution   Rewrite in the usual form, noting the coefficients (you can usually do this mentally):

$$\begin{cases} 0x + 1y + 1z = -1 \\ 1x + 0y + 1z = -1 \\ 2x + 1y + 1z = -5 \end{cases}$$

$$D = \begin{vmatrix} 0 & 1 & 1 \\ 1 & 0 & 1 \\ 2 & 1 & 1 \end{vmatrix} = -\begin{vmatrix} 1 & 1 \\ 1 & 1 \end{vmatrix} - \begin{vmatrix} 0 & 1 \\ 2 & 1 \end{vmatrix}$$

$$= -(1 - 1) - (0 - 2)$$
$$= 2$$

Coefficients of x replaced

$$D_x = \begin{vmatrix} -1 & 1 & 1 \\ -1 & 0 & 1 \\ -5 & 1 & 1 \end{vmatrix} = -(-1)\begin{vmatrix} 1 & 1 \\ 1 & 1 \end{vmatrix} - \begin{vmatrix} -1 & 1 \\ -5 & 1 \end{vmatrix}$$

$$= 0 - (-1 + 5)$$
$$= -4$$

$$x = \frac{D_x}{D} = \frac{-4}{2}$$
$$= -2$$

Find the other solutions by substitution.

Use second equation to find z: Use first equation to find y:

$x + z = -1$ $y + z = -1$
$-2 + z = -1$ $y + 1 = -1$
$z = 1$ $y = -2$

To check, substitute these values into all three equations:

$$y + z = -2 + 1 = -1 \checkmark$$
$$x + z = -2 + 1 = -1 \checkmark$$
$$2x + y + z = 2(-2) + (-2) + 1$$
$$= -4 - 2 + 1$$
$$= -5 \checkmark$$

Solution: $(-2, -2, 1)$ □

Problem Set 8.4

A *Evaluate the determinants in Problems 1–15. If you wish to check, evaluate the determinant using a different row or column.*

See Examples 9–14.

1. $\begin{vmatrix} 2 & 0 & 0 \\ 0 & 3 & -1 \\ 2 & 1 & 0 \end{vmatrix}$ **2.** $\begin{vmatrix} 0 & 0 & 2 \\ 3 & 2 & -1 \\ 1 & -2 & 0 \end{vmatrix}$ **3.** $\begin{vmatrix} 0 & 2 & 0 \\ 2 & 0 & 1 \\ 2 & -1 & 3 \end{vmatrix}$

4. $\begin{vmatrix} 1 & 1 & 1 \\ 1 & 3 & 2 \\ 1 & -2 & 1 \end{vmatrix}$ **5.** $\begin{vmatrix} -2 & 1 & 3 \\ 1 & 1 & 1 \\ 2 & 1 & 1 \end{vmatrix}$ **6.** $\begin{vmatrix} 2 & 1 & 2 \\ -1 & 3 & 1 \\ 1 & 1 & 1 \end{vmatrix}$

7. $\begin{vmatrix} 2 & -1 & 2 \\ 4 & 1 & 3 \\ 8 & -1 & 1 \end{vmatrix}$ **8.** $\begin{vmatrix} 5 & -1 & 2 \\ 1 & 1 & 3 \\ 5 & -1 & 1 \end{vmatrix}$ **9.** $\begin{vmatrix} 2 & 5 & 2 \\ 4 & 1 & 3 \\ 8 & 5 & 1 \end{vmatrix}$

10. $\begin{vmatrix} 2 & -1 & 5 \\ 4 & 1 & 1 \\ 8 & -1 & 5 \end{vmatrix}$ **11.** $\begin{vmatrix} 2 & 3 & 1 \\ 1 & -1 & 2 \\ 3 & 2 & -1 \end{vmatrix}$ **12.** $\begin{vmatrix} 2 & 5 & 2 \\ 6 & -1 & 2 \\ 1 & 2 & -1 \end{vmatrix}$

13. $\begin{vmatrix} 2 & 0 & 1 \\ 1 & 6 & 2 \\ 3 & 1 & -1 \end{vmatrix}$ **14.** $\begin{vmatrix} 2 & 3 & 0 \\ 1 & -1 & 6 \\ 3 & 2 & 1 \end{vmatrix}$ **15.** $\begin{vmatrix} 1 & -3 & 3 \\ 3 & 2 & -5 \\ 4 & 1 & -6 \end{vmatrix}$

B *Use Cramer's rule to solve the systems in Problems 16–31.*

See Examples 15 and 16.

16. $\begin{cases} x + y + z = 3 \\ x + 3y + 2z = 6 \\ x - 2y + z = 0 \end{cases}$ **17.** $\begin{cases} -2x + y + 3z = -11 \\ x + y + z = -1 \\ 2x + y + z = 1 \end{cases}$

18. $\begin{cases} 2x + y + 2z = -4 \\ -x + 3y + z = 20 \\ x + y + z = 0 \end{cases}$ **19.** $\begin{cases} 2x - y + 2z = 5 \\ 4x + y + 3z = 1 \\ 8x - y + z = 5 \end{cases}$

20. $\begin{cases} 2x + y = 7 \\ 3y - z = 4 \\ x = 2 \end{cases}$ **21.** $\begin{cases} 2x - y + 3z = 20 \\ 2x + y = 11 \\ y = 3 \end{cases}$

22. $\begin{cases} 3x + 2y - z = -1 \\ x - 2y = -13 \\ z = 2 \end{cases}$ **23.** $\begin{cases} 4x + y = -2 \\ 2x - y + 4z = -16 \\ -3x + 2y + z = 4 \end{cases}$

24. $\begin{cases} x + 2z = 13 \\ 2x + y = 8 \\ -2y = 40 \end{cases}$ **25.** $\begin{cases} 4x + y = -2 \\ 3x + 2z = -9 \\ 2y + 3z = -5 \end{cases}$

26. $\begin{cases} x + 2y + z = 9 \\ x + y - z = 5 \\ 3x - y + 2z = 12 \end{cases}$ **27.** $\begin{cases} x + 3y - z = -2 \\ x - y + 2z = -4 \\ 2x + y - 3z = 3 \end{cases}$

28. $\begin{cases} 2x + 3y + 3 = 0 \\ 3x + 2y + 2 = 5z \\ 4z - 3y = 8 \end{cases}$ **29.** $\begin{cases} 2x + y = z + 1 \\ 3x + 2 = y + z \\ z - 3 + 4x = 2y \end{cases}$

30. $\begin{cases} x - 2z = 1 \\ 2x + 3y + 3 = 0 \\ 4x - 3y - 4z = 3 \end{cases}$ **31.** $\begin{cases} x - 3y + 3z = 1 \\ 3x + 2y - 5z = 4 \\ 4x + y - 6z = 5 \end{cases}$

Mind Bogglers *Use the determinant below for Problems 32–34. Verify that you obtain the same result for each of Problems 32–34.*

$$\begin{vmatrix} a_1 & b_1 & c_1 \\ a_2 & b_2 & c_2 \\ a_3 & b_3 & c_3 \end{vmatrix}$$

32. Expand along the second row.
33. Expand along the third row.
34. Expand along the first column.

8.5 Systems of Linear Inequalities

The **solution** of a system of inequalities is the set of all replacements for the variables that make all the inequalities true simultaneously (at the same time). In this book, we'll limit the number of unknowns to two, so the solution of a system is the set of all ordered pairs (x, y) that satisfy *each* of the inequalities in the system. Graphically, this is the intersection of the solution sets of the individual inequalities.

In Examples 1 and 2 graph the solution set of the given system of linear inequalities.

Example 1 $\begin{cases} x + 2y \leq 18 \\ x + y \geq 4 \end{cases}$

Solution Graph both inequalities on the same set of axes.

Part I. Graph $x + 2y \leq 18$.
 Boundary: $x + 2y = 18$
$$y = -\tfrac{1}{2}x + 9$$
 Intercept is $(0, 9)$ and the slope is $-\tfrac{1}{2}$; since it is $\leq$, draw the boundary as a solid line.
 After drawing the boundary, select a test point not on the boundary. Choose $(0, 0)$.
 Test: $x + 2y \leq 18$
$0 + 2(0) \leq 18$ True; shade this portion, as shown in Figure 8.4.

Part II. Graph $x + y \geq 4$.
 Boundary: $x + y = 4$
 Draw this line on the same coordinate axes.
 Test point: $(0, 0)$
 Test: $0 + 0 \geq 4$
$0 \geq 4$ False; shade the other portion, as shown in Figure 8.4.

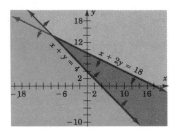

Figure 8.4

The solution of the system is the intersection of the half-planes from Parts I and II. This is indicated by the darkest shading in Figure 8.4.   □

Example 2

$$\begin{cases} 2 < x \\ x \le 8 \\ y \ge -1 \\ y < 3 \end{cases}$$

Solution   *Part I.*   Graph $2 < x$.
Boundary: $2 = x$ (dotted because it is $<$); shade portion to the right of the line.

Part II.   Graph $x \le 8$.
Boundary: $x = 8$ (solid because it is $\le$); shade portion to the left of the line.

Part III. Graph $y \ge -1$.
Boundary: $y = -1$ (solid); shade above.

Part IV.   Graph $y < 3$.
Boundary: $y = 3$ (dotted); shade below.

Figure 8.5a shows the results of Parts I–IV. Notice that, even in a fairly simple example, dealing with several shaded portions can become confusing. For this reason, you can indicate the half-planes by arrows, as shown in Figure 8.5b. Now, look at this figure and try to visualize the intersection. The result is shown in Figure 8.5c.

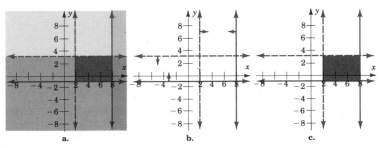

a.   b.   c.

Figure 8.5   □

Sometimes a *between* relationship is used. Notice in Example 2 that x is between 2 and 8, and y is between -1 and 3. These relationships can be written as

$$\begin{cases} 2 < x \le 8 \\ -1 \le y < 3 \end{cases}$$

Example 3 Graph the solution set of

$$\begin{cases} -3 \le x < 5 \\ 2 < y \le 6 \end{cases}$$

Solution x is between -3 and 5, as shown in Figure 8.6a.
y is between 2 and 6, as shown in Figure 8.6b.
The simultaneous solution is the intersection of the two shaded regions, as shown in Figure 8.6c.

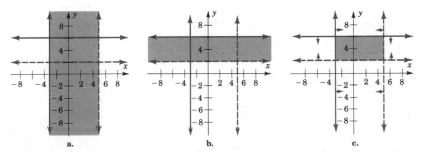

Figure 8.6

Linear inequalities can be included with linear equalities in the same system. Remember, a system is the intersection of the individual solution sets.

Example 4 Graph the solution of

$$\begin{cases} 2x + 3y = 6 \\ 2 \le x < 8 \end{cases}$$

Solution *Part I.* Graph $2x + 3y = 6$
$$y = -\tfrac{2}{3}x + 2$$

Intercept is 2 and slope is $-\tfrac{2}{3}$ (see Figure 8.7a).
Part II. Graph $2 \le x < 8$ (see Figure 8.7a).
The solution is the intersection of the two parts, as shown in Figure 8.7b. Notice that the solution is a line segment and it includes an end point at $x = 2$ but excludes the end point at $x = 8$.

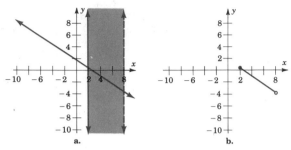

Figure 8.7   □

The next example includes a large number of individual parts, but consider each one in its turn and you'll find it is not too difficult. Be sure to be very neat and keep track of the half-planes by the use of arrows as shown in Example 3. Example 5 is a prelude to a topic called *linear programming,* which is considered in later mathematics courses.

Example 5   Graph the solution set of

$$\begin{cases} x + 2y \le 18 \\ x + y \ge 4 \\ x - y > -2 \\ x - 10 < 0 \\ x \ge 0 \\ y \ge 0 \end{cases}$$

Solution   This system adds additional restrictions to the system graphed in Example 1 (see Figure 8.4). Notice that

$$\begin{cases} x \ge 0 \\ y \ge 0 \end{cases}$$

represents the first quadrant along with the positive axes and the origin. Thus, this is the intersection of the solution set from Example 1 and the first quadrant, as shown in Figure 8.8a. Next, add the last two restrictions to the system:

$$\begin{cases} x - y > -2 \\ x - 10 < 0 \end{cases}$$

Graph: $x - y > -2$		*Graph:* $x - 10 < 0$	
Boundary: $x - y = -2$	Dotted	*Boundary:* $x - 10 = 0$	Dotted
Test point: $(0, 0)$		*Test point:* $(0, 0)$	
$0 - 0 > -2$	True	$0 - 10 < 0$	True

The graph is the shaded portion shown in Figure 8.8b.

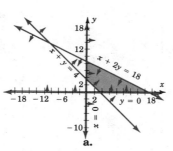

Figure 8.8

Problem Set 8.5

A *Graph the solution set of each system of inequalities in Problems 1–22.*

See Example 1. **1.** $\begin{cases} x + 3y \le 15 \\ x + y \ge 2 \end{cases}$ **2.** $\begin{cases} x - 2y < 10 \\ 2x + y \ge 1 \end{cases}$ **3.** $\begin{cases} 4x - 3y < 2 \\ x + 2y < 4 \end{cases}$

4. $\begin{cases} 3x - 2y > 4 \\ x + y \le 10 \end{cases}$ **5.** $\begin{cases} x \le y \\ 3x + 2y > 6 \end{cases}$ **6.** $\begin{cases} x \ge y \\ 2x + 3y < 6 \end{cases}$

See Example 2. **7.** $\begin{cases} x < 0 \\ y < 0 \end{cases}$ **8.** $\begin{cases} x \ge 0 \\ y < 0 \end{cases}$ **9.** $\begin{cases} x \ge 0 \\ y \ge 0 \end{cases}$

See Example 3. **10.** $\begin{cases} 1 \le x \le 4 \\ -2 \le y \le 3 \end{cases}$ **11.** $\begin{cases} -5 \le x \le 2 \\ -4 \le y \le -2 \end{cases}$ **12.** $\begin{cases} -6 \le x \le 0 \\ -3 \le y \le 4 \end{cases}$

13. $\begin{cases} 2x - 3y > 15 \\ -5 \le y \le -2 \end{cases}$ **14.** $\begin{cases} 4x + y \le 5 \\ -2 < y < 2 \end{cases}$ **15.** $\begin{cases} 2x + 3y < 15 \\ -3 \le y \le 4 \end{cases}$

16. $\begin{cases} 3x + 2y < 12 \\ -2 \le x \le 7 \end{cases}$ **17.** $\begin{cases} y \le x - 6 \\ -5 \le x \le -\frac{7}{2} \end{cases}$ **18.** $\begin{cases} y \le -x - 16 \\ -\frac{13}{2} \le x \le -5 \end{cases}$

See Example 4. **19.** $\begin{cases} y = x + 12 \\ -14 \le x \le -5 \end{cases}$ **20.** $\begin{cases} y = x - 6 \\ -5 \le x \le 4 \end{cases}$ **21.** $\begin{cases} y = -x - 16 \\ -11 \le y \le -2 \end{cases}$

22. $\begin{cases} y = 2 - x \\ -2 < y \le 7 \end{cases}$

B *Graph the solution set of each system in Problems 23–34.*

See Example 5. **23.** $\begin{cases} x \ge 0 \\ y \ge 0 \\ 4x - 3y < 2 \\ x + 2y < 4 \end{cases}$ **24.** $\begin{cases} x > 0 \\ y > 0 \\ x \le y \\ 2x + 3y > 6 \end{cases}$ **25.** $\begin{cases} y < -x - 6 \\ -7 \le x \le -5 \\ y \ge -7 \end{cases}$

26. $\begin{cases} y \ge \frac{2}{3}x \\ y \le -\frac{2}{3}x \\ x \ge -3 \end{cases}$ **27.** $\begin{cases} y \ge -x - 6 \\ -1 \le y \le 1 \\ x \le -3 \end{cases}$ **28.** $\begin{cases} x + 2y \le 18 \\ x + y \ge 4 \\ x - y \ge -2 \end{cases}$

29. $\begin{cases} x + 3y \le 18 \\ x + y \ge 2 \\ x - 8 \le 0 \end{cases}$ **30.** $\begin{cases} 2x + 3y \le 9 \\ x + y > 4 \\ y + 5 > 0 \end{cases}$ **31.** $\begin{cases} x \ge 0 \\ y \ge 0 \\ x + y \le 8 \\ y \le 4 \\ x \le 6 \end{cases}$

32. $\begin{cases} x \ge 0 \\ y \ge 0 \\ x + y \le 9 \\ 2x - 3y \ge -6 \\ x - y \le 3 \end{cases}$ **33.** $\begin{cases} x \ge 0 \\ y \ge 0 \\ 2x + y \ge 8 \\ y \le 5 \\ x - y \le 2 \\ 3x - y \ge 5 \end{cases}$ **34.** $\begin{cases} x \ge 0 \\ y \ge 0 \\ 2x + y \ge 8 \\ x - 2y \le 7 \\ x - y \ge -3 \\ x \le 9 \end{cases}$

**Mind Boggler
Palatable
Plotting**

35. Graph the solution sets for Problems 17–22 and 25–27 on the same coordinate axes so that $-15 \le x \le 10$ and $-15 \le y \le 10$.

8.6 Review Problems

Fill in the word or words that make the statements in Problems 1–5 complete and correct.

(8.1)   **1.** If there is no solution to a linear system, it is called a(an) _____ system. If there are infinitely many solutions, the system is called a(an) _____ system.

(8.2)   **2.** If $D = \begin{vmatrix} a & b \\ c & d \end{vmatrix}$

then D is called a _____ and its value is

_____.

(8.3)   **3.** The method of solving a system of linear equations by determinants is called _____.

(8.4)   **4.** If $\begin{cases} a_1 x + b_1 y + c_1 z = d_1 \\ a_2 x + b_2 y + c_2 z = d_2 \\ a_3 x + b_3 y + c_3 z = d_3 \end{cases}$

then (in determinant form):

$D = $ _____   and $D_z = $ _____

(8.4)   **5.** If $\begin{vmatrix} 3 & 4 & -2 \\ -3 & -1 & 1 \\ -4 & 0 & 5 \end{vmatrix}$

then the minor of 4 (simplified) is _____ and the co-factor of -3 (in simplified form) is _____.

Solve the systems in Problems 6–12 by the indicated method.

(8.1) **6.** By graphing   **7.** By adding   **8.** By substitution

$$\begin{cases} 3x - 2y = 10 \\ y = -2x + 2 \end{cases} \qquad \begin{cases} 2x + 5y = 27 \\ 3x - 15y = -117 \end{cases} \qquad \begin{cases} 5x - 7y = 4 \\ y = 8x - 37 \end{cases}$$

(8.2) **9.** By Cramer's rule

$$\begin{cases} 3x + 2y = 5 \\ 5x - 3y = -2 \end{cases}$$

(8.3) **10.** By the extended addition method

$$\begin{cases} x + y + z = 2 \\ x + 2y - 2z = 1 \\ x + y + 3z = 4 \end{cases}$$

(8.4) **11.** By Cramer's rule

$$\begin{cases} 3x - 2y + 17 = 0 \\ 5x + 4y + z = 8 \\ 3x + z + 2 = 0 \end{cases}$$

(8.5) **12.** By graphing

$$\begin{cases} x \geq 0 \\ y \geq 0 \\ x + 3y < 6 \\ 3x + y \leq 6 \end{cases}$$

Solve the systems in Problems 13–19 by any appropriate method, but solve at least one by each of the following methods: graphing (Sections 8.1, 8.5); adding (Sections 8.1, 8.3); substitution (Section 8.1); or Cramer's rule (Sections 8.2, 8.4).

13. $\begin{cases} 3x - 4y = 31 \\ x + 2y = -3 \end{cases}$ **14.** $\begin{cases} y = 2x - 15 \\ 3x + 2y = 40 \end{cases}$ **15.** $\begin{cases} 2x - 5y = 3 \\ y = \frac{2}{3}x - 3 \end{cases}$

16. $\begin{cases} 8x - 3y = 2 \\ 5x + 2y = 3 \end{cases}$ **17.** $\begin{cases} x + 2y + z = 1 \\ 2x - y + z = 4 \\ x + y - 2z = 7 \end{cases}$ **18.** $\begin{cases} -4 \leq x < 2 \\ 1 \leq y < 3 \end{cases}$

19. $\begin{cases} 2x - 3y < 9 \\ 5x - y \geq 5 \end{cases}$

(8.1, 8.2) **20.** *Navigation.* A boat travels 30 mph (relative to the shore) on the downstream run. However, on the upstream run the boat is slowed to 20 mph because of the current. What is the rate of the boat in still water?

CHAPTER

9

Functions, Relations, and Conic Sections

Contents

9.1 Functions

Ordered pairs were introduced in Chapter 3 so that linear equations and inequalities in two variables could be discussed. However, ordered pairs are not restricted to the linear case. In this chapter we'll study certain types of quadratic (or second-degree) equations and inequalities.

RELATION

> A **relation** is a set of ordered pairs.

A relation is a set of ordered pairs, and each ordered pair has a first component and a second component. The **domain** (denoted by D) of a relation is the set of all replacements for the first component, and must always be stated or implied. **If the domain is not explicitly stated, we will assume that the domain is the set of all real numbers for which the given relationship makes sense.** The **range** (denoted by R) of a relation is the set of all replacements for the second component. Recall from Chapter 3 that the variable associated with the first component is called the **independent variable** and the variable associated with the second component is called the **dependent variable.**

There are several ways a relation can be specified.

Example 1   A relation can be specified by a set.

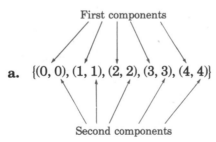

First components

a. {(0, 0), (1, 1), (2, 2), (3, 3), (4, 4)}

Second components

$D = \{0, 1, 2, 3, 4\}; \quad R = \{0, 1, 2, 3, 4\}$

b. {(0, 0), (1, 1), (2, 4), (3, 9), (4, 16)}
$D = \{0, 1, 2, 3, 4\}; \quad R = \{0, 1, 4, 9, 16\}$

c. {(0, 0), (1, 1), (−1, 1), (2, 4), (−2, 4)}
$D = \{0, 1, -1, 2, -2\}; \quad R = \{0, 1, 4\}$

d. {(0, 0), (1, 1), (1, −1), (4, 2), (4, −2)}
$D = \{0, 1, 4\}; \quad R = \{0, 1, -1, 2, -2\}$

Notice that {0, 1, 4} = {0, 1, 1, 4, 4}; if a number appears more than once in a set, list it only once when writing the set. □

Example 2   A relation can be specified by a table.

r	V
0	0
1	π
2	4π
3	9π
4	16π

$D = \{0, 1, 2, 3, 4\}$
$R = \{0, \pi, 4\pi, 9\pi, 16\pi\}$

□

Example 3   A relation can be specified by an equation or inequality.

a. $y \leq 2x + 1$

To be precise we should probably write this as $\{(x, y) | y \leq 2x + 1\}$, but it is understood that x is the first component and y is the second component. It is also understood that x and y are real numbers.

This represents the set of all ordered pairs satisfying this relationship. The domain and range are the set of all real numbers. It is *not correct* to say *x is the domain.* Remember that *x is a member of the domain.* The domain and range are *sets.* Even though the domain and range are both the set of real numbers and the relation is an infinite set, don't make the mistake of assuming that all ordered pairs of real numbers are included. For example,

(4, 1) belongs to the relation since it satisfies $y \leq 2x + 1$:

$1 \leq 2(4) + 1$ True

(1, 4) doesn't belong to the relation since it doesn't satisfy $y \leq 2x + 1$:

$4 \leq 2(1) + 1$ False

Can you name three additional ordered pairs that belong to this relation? Also, can you name three additional ordered pairs that do not belong to this relation?

The answers to these questions vary, but some possibilities are:

Belong to the relation
$\{(1, 1), (1, 2), (7, 2), \ldots\}$

Don't belong to the relation
$\{(4, 0), (4, -1), (3, -8), \ldots\}$

b. $y = (5x + 1)/(x - 1)$

The domain is all real numbers for which the equation determines a real y value; thus, $x \neq 1$. (If $x = 1$, then there would be division by 0.)

c.   If a projectile is propelled upward with an initial velocity of 160 ft/sec, the distance d above the ground at the end of t seconds is given by

$d = 160t - 16t^2$ $0 \leq t \leq 10$ It is implied that d is a real number.

$D = \{t | 0 \leq t \leq 10\}$

□

Example 4   A relation can be specified by a graph.

Historical Note

The terminology we're using in this book is primarily due to Lejeune Dirichlet (1805–1859), whose formulation is worth repeating: "A *variable* is a symbol which represents any one of a set of numbers; if two variables x and y are so related that whenever a value is assigned to x there is automatically assigned, by some rule or correspondence, a value to y, then we say y is a (single-valued) *function* of x. The variable x, to which values are assigned at will, is called the *independent variable,* and the variable y, whose values depend upon those of x, is called the *dependent variable*. The permissible values that x may assume constitute the *domain of definition* of the function, and the values taken on by y constitute the *range of values* of the function."* Did you note the date this was written? Who called this new math?

* From *An Introduction to the History of Mathematics,* Third Edition, by Howard Eves (New York: Holt, Rinehart & Winston, 1969), pp. 371–372.

a. $D = \{0, 1, 2, 3, 4\}$
$R = \{0, 1, 2, 3, 4\}$

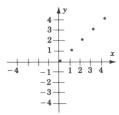

b. $D = \{0, 1, 4\}$
$R = \{0, 1, -1, 2, -2\}$

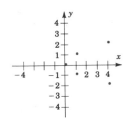

c. $D = \{r \mid r \geq 0\}$
$R = \{V \mid V \geq 0\}$

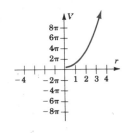

d. $D = \{\text{Reals}\}$
$R = \{\text{Reals}\}$

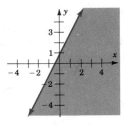

e. $D = \{x \mid x \leq 0\}$
$R = \{\text{Reals}\}$

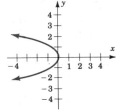

f. $D = \{\text{Reals}\}$
$R = \{y \mid y \leq 0\}$

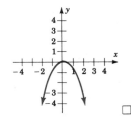

The examples above illustrate two possibilities:

1.   The first component of an ordered pair may be associated with **exactly one second component**, as in Examples 1a–1c.

Example 1a

0 ——→ 0
1 ——→ 1
2 ——→ 2
3 ——→ 3
4 ——→ 4

Example 1b

0 ——→ 0
1 ——→ 1
2 ——→ 4
3 ——→ 9
4 ——→ 16

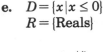

Notice that the value of the second component *depends on* the value of the first component.

2.   Or, the first component may be associated with **more than one second component**, as in Example 1d.

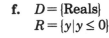

The first type of relation is given a special name:

FUNCTION

> A **function** is a set of ordered pairs in which each first component is associated with exactly one second component.

Examples 1a–1c are functions, while Example 1d is not. Example 3a is not a function since we can find ordered pairs with the same first component and different second components, for example,

(2, 1)   and   (2, 3)

that satisfy the relation

$y \le 2x + 1$ *Check:*   (2, 1); $1 \le 2(2) + 1$
                              (2, 3); $3 \le 2(2) + 1$

Both are true, so they belong to the relation. Thus, a single first component, 2, is associated with more than one second component, and so the relation is not a function.

The graphs of Example 4 make it easy to determine whether the given relation is a function. Imagine a vertical line being moved from left to right across the graph. If at any one place the vertical line crosses the graph in more than one point, then the relation is not a function, because each crossing point associates a single x value with more than one y value. This vertical-line sweep is sometimes called the **vertical-line test.** It is used when you're given a graph and must determine whether the relation is a function. Thus, Examples 4a, 4c, and 4f are functions, while Examples 4b, 4d, and 4e are not functions.

If the domain is finite, you can find the range and specify the relation as a set of ordered pairs, as shown in Examples 5–8.

In Examples 5–8 let $D = \{-1, 0, 3\}$. Write the relation as a set of ordered pairs and tell whether or not it is a function.

Example 5 $y = |x + 1|$

Solution   *If $x = -1$:* $y = |-1 + 1|$
                          $= 0$
        Ordered pair: $(-1, 0)$
     If $x = 0$: $y = |0 + 1|$
                  $= 1$
        Ordered pair: $(0, 1)$
     If $x = 3$: $y = |3 + 1|$
                  $= 4$
        Ordered pair: $(3, 4)$
Relation: $\{(-1, 0), (0, 1), (3, 4)\}$. It is a function.   □

Example 6 $x = y^2 - 1$

Solution   *If* $x = -1$: $-1 = y^2 - 1$
$$0 = y^2$$
$$y = 0$$
Ordered pair: $(-1, 0)$

If $x = 0$: $0 = y^2 - 1$
$$0 = (y - 1)(y + 1)$$
$$y = 1, -1$$
Ordered pairs: $(0, 1), (0, -1)$

If $x = 3$: $3 = y^2 - 1$
$$0 = y^2 - 4$$
$$0 = (y - 2)(y + 2)$$
$$y = 2, -2$$
Ordered pairs: $(3, 2), (3, -2)$

Relation: $\{(-1, 0), (0, 1), (0, -1), (3, 2), (3, -2)\}$. It is not a function.   □

Example 7

x	y
-1	1
0	1
3	1

Solution   Relation is $\{(-1, 1), (0, 1), (3, 1)\}$. It is a function.   □

Example 8

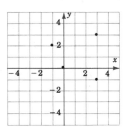

Solution   Relation is $\{(-1, 2), (0, 0), (3, -1), (3, 3)\}$. It is not a function.   □

Problem Set 9.1

A   *In Problems 1–16 classify the sets as relations, functions, both, or neither.*

See Examples 1–4.

1. $\{(4, 1), (5, 2), (6, 5), (4, 2)\}$ **2.** $\{(6, 3), (4, 2), (5, -1), (6, 3)\}$
3. $\{(7, 9), (5, -1), (5, 2), (6, -10)\}$ **4.** $\{1, 2, 3, 4\}$

Vertical-line Test with pencil

5. {(Δ, *), (†, ‡), (‡, †), (*, ¶)}   **6.** $x = 2y + 3$

7. $y = 2x + 3$ **8.** {(s, t)| s ≤ t}

9. $x = y^2$ **10.** $y = x^2$

11. 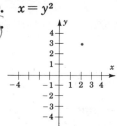   **12.** 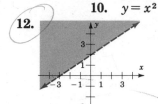   **13.**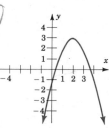

14. 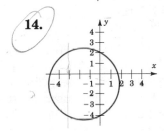   **15.** 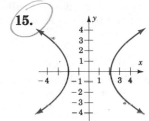   **16.**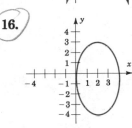

B *In Problems 17–26 let D={0, 4, 10}. Find the range, and tell whether the given relation is a function.*

See Examples 5–8.   **17.** $x = y^2$ **18.** $y = x^2$ **19.** $y = |x|$

                               20. $x = |y|$ **21.** $y = 2x^2 + x - 2$ **22.** $x = y^2 - y - 2$

23.

x	y
0	3
4	8
10	-1

24.

x	y
0	0
4	0
10	0

25. 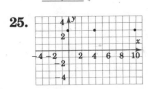   **26.**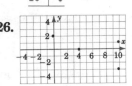

27. *Physics.*   The distance (in feet) that an object falls (neglecting air resistance) is a function of time and is given by the formula

$$d = 16t^2$$

If you drop a rock into a well, how far has the rock fallen after 1 sec? 4 sec? 10 sec? 16 sec? Write your answers as a set of ordered pairs *(t, d)*.

28. *Physics.*   The velocity *v* (in feet per second) of a rock dropped into a well is given by the formula

$$v = 32t$$

(neglecting air resistance). Find the velocity of the rock after 1 sec; 4 sec; 10 sec; and 16 sec. Write your answers as a set of ordered pairs (t, v).

29. The following story appeared in the February 26, 1974 issue of the *New York Times:*

> Dale Robinson made a swan dive off the roof of a seven-story building yesterday and falling 80 feet a second, made a graceful landing into a 20-by-25 foot air cushion. He made one full flip during his one-and-a-half second descent.

Using the formula given in Problem 27, find an error in this quotation.

30. Use the formula given in Problem 28 and refer to the news article in Problem 29. How long after Dale Robinson jumped was he falling at 80 feet per second? Was he always falling at 80 feet per second?

31. *Physics.* If an object is projected vertically from the ground at 108.36 ft/sec, then (ignoring air resistance) the distance (in feet) of the object above the ground at time t is given by the equation

$$d = 108.36t - 16t^2$$

What is the height (in feet) at $t = 1.2$ sec? At $t = 2.3$ sec? If the relation is specified by (t, d), what is the domain (the distance is nonnegative)?

32. *Physics.* The projectile in Problem 31 has velocity v at time t given by

$$v = 108.36 - 32t$$

What are the velocities for $t = 1.2$ sec? $t = 2.3$ sec? If the relation is specified by (t, v), what is the domain (the velocity is positive)?

Mind Bogglers

33. In this section we used relations, or sets of ordered pairs, in the context of numbers. But the notion of relation is more general. Let x and y represent people. Then

$A = \{(x, y) | x \text{ is an ancestor of } y\}$

$B = \{(x, y) | x \text{ is a brother of } y\}$

$C = \{(x, y) | x \text{ is a cousin of } y\}$

$F = \{(x, y) | x \text{ is the father of } y\}$

$M = \{(x, y) | x \text{ is married to } y\}$

$W = \{(x, y) | x \text{ weighs within 5 pounds of } y\}$

Notice that A, B, C, F, M, and W are relations, since they are sets of ordered pairs. A relation R is said to be:

(1) *Reflexive* if $(x, x) \in R$ for all x in the domain
(2) *Symmetric* if whenever $(x, y) \in R$, then $(y, x) \in R$
(3) *Transitive* if whenever $(x, y) \in R$ and $(y, z) \in R$, then $(x, z) \in R$
Which of these properties are satisfied by each of the relations A, B, C, F, M, and W?

34. Let x and y be any real numbers. Also let

$$D = \{(x, y)\,|\,x \le y\}$$
$$E = \{(x, y)\,|\,x = y\}$$
$$G = \{(x, y)\,|\,x \approx y\}$$

Which of the properties (reflexive, symmetric, and transitive) described in Problem 33 are satisfied by each of the relations D, E, and G?

35. Let

$$H = \{(x, y)\,|\,x \sim y, \text{ where } x \text{ and } y \text{ are triangles}\}$$
$$I = \{(x, y)\,|\,x \subseteq y, \text{ where } x \text{ and } y \text{ are sets}\}$$
$$J = \{(x, y)\,|\,x \perp y, \text{ where } x \text{ and } y \text{ are lines}\}$$
$$K = \{(x, y)\,|\,x \parallel y, \text{ where } x \text{ and } y \text{ are lines}\}$$

$\sim$ means "is similar to"
$\subseteq$ means "is a subset of"
$\perp$ means "is perpendicular to"
$\parallel$ means "is parallel to"

Which of the reflexive, symmetric, and transitive properties (see Problem 33) are satisfied by each of the relations H, I, J, and K?

36. A relation is called an *equivalence relation* if it satisfies the reflexive, symmetric, and transitive properties. Which of the relations in Problems 33–35 are equivalence relations?

9.2 Evaluation of Functions

When a relation is a function, a shorthand notation is used to designate the function. This notation uses some letter of the alphabet; for example, if

$$f = \{(x, y)\,|\,y = 2x + 3\} \qquad \text{and} \qquad g = \{(x, y)\,|\,y = x^2 - 4\}$$

then these functions can be distinguished from one another by calling one f and the other g. Suppose you are given some number on the domain of each of these functions, say 3, and you want to find the second component associated with 3.

Function f: If $x = 3$, then the second component is $y = 2(3) + 3$
$$= 9$$

The ordered pair is $(3, 9)$.

Function g: If $x = 3$, then the second component is $y = 3^2 - 4$
$$= 5$$

The ordered pair is $(3, 5)$.

To condense this information, we go one step further and use the symbol

$$f(x)$$

to denote the second component associated with x for the function f. The symbol "$f(x)$" is read "f of x." Thus, for the above examples, write

$$f(3) = 2(3) + 3 \qquad \text{and} \qquad g(3) = 3^2 - 4$$
$$ = 9 \qquad\qquad\qquad\qquad\quad = 5$$

FUNCTIONAL
NOTATION

Functional Notation

If f represents a function, then x denotes a first component of an ordered pair in the set f, and $f(x)$ denotes the second component associated with x for an ordered pair in the set f.

Beware! "$f(x)$" does not mean "f times x." Up to now, when you saw two variables separated only by parentheses, it always meant multiplication. However, in this context, f does not represent a variable, but a set of ordered pairs.

Since you have been writing (x, y), notice that

$$f(x) = y$$

which means that you can use $f(x)$ instead of y. That is, the shorter form

$$f(x) = 2x + 3$$

can be used in place of the form

$$f = \{(x, y) \mid y = 2x + 3\}$$

Example 1 Let

$$f_1 = \{(0, 0), (1, 1), (2, 4), (-2, 4), (3, 9), (-3, 9)\}$$
$$f_2 = \{(5, 1), (4, 3), (3, 17), (2, 0)\}$$
$$f_3 = \{(1, 1), (2, 1), (3, 2), (4, 3), (5, 5), (6, 8), (7, 13)\}$$

Find the following:

    a. $f_1(2)$ **b.** $f_3(2)$ **c.** $f_2(2)$ **d.** $f_2(5)$ **e.** $f_3(7)$

Solution **a.** To find $f_1(2)$, you want the second component of the ordered pair associated with 2 for the function named by f_1:

$$f_1(2) = 4$$

  b. $f_3(2) = 1$ **c.** $f_2(2) = 0$ **d.** $f_2(5) = 1$ **e.** $f_3(7) = 13$ ☐

This new notation is used extensively in mathematics. Remember

$$f(\underbrace{x})$$

⌐x is a member of the domain

└$f(x)$ is a member of the range

and $f(x)$ is the member of the range that is associated with x. This number $f(x)$ can be added, subtracted, multiplied, and divided by other numbers.

Example 2 Let

$$F(x) = 5x \qquad G(x) = x^2 \qquad H(x) = 3x^2 + 2$$

Find each functional value:

a. $F(3) = 15$ since $5 \cdot 3 = 15$

Replace x by 3

b. $F(4) = 20$ since $5 \cdot 4 = 20$

Replace x by 4

c. $F(10) = 5 \cdot 10$
$= 50$

d. $G(4) = 4^2$
$= 16$

e. $H(5) = 3 \cdot 5^2 + 2$
$= 77$

f. $H(0) = 3 \cdot 0^2 + 2$
$= 2$

g. Since $F(x) = 5x$

$$F(w) = 5w$$

Replace x by w

h. Since $H(x) = 3x^2 + 2$

$$H(t) = 3t^2 + 2$$

Replace x by t

i. $F(2x + 3) = 5(2x + 3)$ since $5 \cdot (2x + 3) = 10x + 15$
$= 10x + 15$

Replace x by $(2x + 3)$

j. $H(t + h) = 3(t + h)^2 + 2$
$= 3t^2 + 6th + 3h^2 + 2$

k. $\dfrac{G(x + h) - G(x)}{h}$

First find $G(x + h)$:

$$G(x + h) = (x + h)^2$$
$$= x^2 + 2xh + h^2$$

Next, subtract $G(x) = x^2$:

$$G(x + h) - G(x) = x^2 + 2xh + h^2 - x^2$$
$$= 2xh + h^2$$

Finally, divide by h:

$$\frac{G(x + h) - G(x)}{h} = \frac{2xh + h^2}{h}$$

$$= \frac{(2x + h)h}{h}$$

$$= 2x + h \qquad \qquad \square$$

Problem Set 9.2

A   *Let* $f = \{(0, 0), (1, 3), (2, 6), (3, 11), (4, 18)\}$
$g = \{(6, 3), (5, 3), (4, 3), (3, 2), (2, 1)\}$
$h = \{(1, -3), (2, -5), (3, 5), (4, 0), (8, 15)\}$

Find the functional value for each of the expressions in Problems 1–3.

See Example 1.

1. a. $f(1)$ **b.** $g(2)$ **c.** $h(3)$ **d.** $f(4)$ **e.** $g(5)$
2. a. $h(4)$ **b.** $g(4)$ **c.** $f(0)$ **d.** $f(3)$ **e.** $g(6)$
3. a. $g(3)$ **b.** $f(2)$ **c.** $h(1)$ **d.** $h(2)$ **e.** $h(8)$

See Examples 2a–2f.

4. If $A(x) = x^2$, find $A(5)$.   **5.** If $B(x) = 5 - 3x$, find $B(4)$
6. If $C(x) = 2 - 5x$, find $C(-3)$.   **7.** If $D(s) = 4s^3$, find $D(0)$.
8. If $E(m) = 5m^3 - 4$, find $E(2)$.
9. If $F(u) = 2u^2 + u + 4$, find $F(-4)$.
10. If $G(w) = 3w^2 - 7w - 4$, find $G(4)$.
11. If $H(x) = 2x^2 + 5x - 4$, find $H(-4)$.

12. If $I(x) = \dfrac{x + 8}{x - 1}$, find $I(0)$.   **13.** If $J(k) = \dfrac{k + 4}{k - 1}$, find $J(6)$.

14. If $K(q) = \dfrac{q + 8}{q - 2}$, find $K(7)$.   **15.** If $L(a) = \dfrac{a + 14}{a}$, find $L(-7)$.

16. If $M(b) = (b - 1)(b + 3)$, find $M(-5)$.
17. If $N(p) = (2p + 3)(3p - 2)$, find $N(1)$.
18. If $P(x) = 5x^2 + 3x - 10$, find $P(-3)$.

19. If $R(t) = \dfrac{6t^2 + t - 1}{3t - 1}$, find $R(3)$.

20. If $S(n) = \dfrac{6n^2 - n - 5}{n - 1}$, find $S(11)$.

21. If $T(x) = \dfrac{8x^2 - 5x - 3}{x - 1}$, find $T(-1)$.

22. If $U(b) = \dfrac{b^3 - 1}{b^2 + b + 1}$, find $U(19)$.

23. If $Y(u) = \dfrac{u^3 + 1}{u^2 - u + 1}$, find $Y(-13)$.

B
Algebra Adage

24. Complete the algebra adage by replacing the numbers within parentheses by the functional names from Problems 4–23. For example, since $A(5) = 25$ in Problem 4, you should replace each 25 by the functional name A.

(2)(O)(8)(5)   (25)(5)(0)   (25)

(17)(O)(12)(26)(25)(5)(−8)(O)(5)

(−5)(7)(25)(V)(36)(−1)(36)(0)   (18)(26)

(25)   (3)(5)(O)(−1)(−1)   (−8)(5)

(O)(7)(0)(36)(7)   (−5)(O)

(26)(7)(O)(17)(18)(7)(36)   (25)

(−7)(7)(25)(Z)(−8)(36)(7)   (32)(−8)(−1)(−1)(36)(0)

(W)(−8)(−5)(8)   (7)(25)(−8)(5)(W)(25)(−5)(36)(7).

25. Paraphrase the adage from Problem 24 into a familiar proverb or phrase.

See Examples 2g–2k.

26. If $f(x) = 4x + 3$, find:
    a. $f(2)$
    b. $f(2 + h)$
    c. $f(2 + h) - f(2)$
    d. $\dfrac{f(2 + h) - f(2)}{h}$

27. If $g(t) = t^2 - 3$, find:
    a. $g(x)$
    b. $g(x + h)$
    c. $g(x + h) - g(x)$
    d. $\dfrac{g(x + h) - g(x)}{h}$

28. If $f(x) = x^2 + x + 2$, find:
    a. $f(x + h)$
    b. $f(x + h) - f(x)$
    c. $\dfrac{f(x + h) - f(x)}{h}$

In Problems 29–34 find $\dfrac{f(x + h) - f(x)}{h}$ *for the given function f.*

See Example 2k.

29. $f(x) = 5x$
30. $f(x) = 2x - 1$
31. $f(x) = x^2$

32. $f(x) = x^2 + 5$
33. $f(x) = \dfrac{1}{x^2 + 2}$
34. $f(x) = \dfrac{x + 1}{x - 1}$

Mind Bogglers   **35.** A man has four sons, and each son has four sons.
                 a. How many fathers and sons are there?
                 b. How many father/son pairs are there?
                 c. How many pairs of brothers are there?
                 d. How many uncle/nephew pairs are there?
                 e. How many pairs of cousins are there?

36. *Physics.* Let d be a function that represents the distance (in feet) that an object falls in t seconds (ignoring air resistance). Then

$$d(t) = 16t^2$$

      a. Find the distance an object falls from $t = 2$ to $t = 5$ seconds.
      b. Find the distance an object falls from $t = x$ to $t = x + h$ seconds.
      c. Give a physical interpretation for

$$\frac{d(x + h) - d(x)}{h}$$

9.3 Parabolas

Standard Parabolas

Consider the following quadratic relations:

    (1) $y = x^2$ (2) $x = y^2$

Are either or both of these functions? We begin by plotting points to draw the graphs of each.

In Examples 1 and 2 graph the given equations by plotting points.

Example 1 $y = x^2$

x	y
0	0
1	1
-1	1
2	4
-2	4
3	9
-3	9

Example 2 $x = y^2$

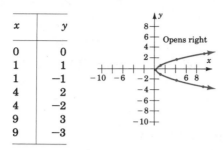

x	y
0	0
1	1
1	−1
4	2
4	−2
9	3
9	−3

Examples 1 and 2 illustrate a curve called a **parabola.** This curve is a common, and important, curve in mathematics. Notice that the parabola in Example 1 is a function and opens upward. Any parabola that opens up will have a **minimum point;** this is the point on the curve with the smallest second component. For Example 1, the minimum point is (0, 0). This minimum point is called the **vertex.**

The parabola of Example 2 is *not* a function; it opens to the right, and has a leftmost point at (0, 0). This leftmost point is called its **vertex.** Also, notice that the points on one side of the vertex form a mirror image of the points on the other side. If you were to hold a rectangular mirror on the paper to illustrate this idea, where would you place it? For Example 1, on the *y*-axis, and for Example 2, on the *x*-axis. This line, called the **axis of symmetry,** varies from parabola to parabola. See Figure 9.1.

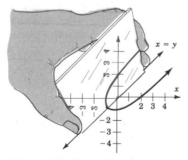

Figure 9.1 Symmetry

The reason we've focused on Examples 1 and 2 is because we graph all other parabolas by comparing them to one of these. For this reason, we'll call these the **standard parabolas.**

STANDARD
PARABOLA

An equation of the form

$$y = x^2 \quad \text{(up)} \qquad \text{or} \qquad x = y^2 \quad \text{(right)}$$

has a graph which is called a **standard parabola.**

Variations of Standard Parabolas

Next, consider the parabolas:

(1) $y = ax^2$ (2) $x = ay^2$

In Examples 3 and 4 graph the given equations by plotting points.

Example 3 $y = 2x^2$

x	y
0	0
1	2
−1	2
2	8
−2	8
3	18
−3	18

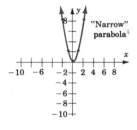

Example 4 $x = \frac{1}{4}y^2$

x	y
0	0
$\frac{1}{4}$	1
$\frac{1}{4}$	−1
1	2
1	−2
4	4
4	−4

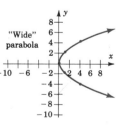

If $a > 1$, then the parabola will appear narrower ("skinny") than the standard parabola. If $0 < a < 1$, then the parabola will appear wider ("fat") than the standard parabola. Now, suppose a is negative.

In Examples 5 and 6 graph the given equations by plotting points.

Example 5 $y = -\frac{1}{3}x^2$

x	y
0	0
1	$-\frac{1}{3}$
-1	$-\frac{1}{3}$
3	-3
-3	-3
6	-12
-6	-12

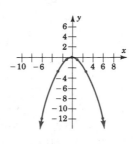

Example 6 $x = -3y^2$

x	y
0	0
-3	1
-3	-1
-12	2
-12	-2
-27	3
-27	-3

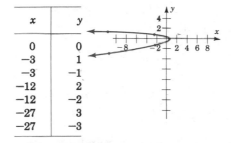

PARABOLAS WITH
VARIED SIZE

Summary

$y = ax^2$ opens up if $a > 0$ $x = ay^2$ opens right if $a > 0$
          opens down if $a < 0$ opens left if $u < 0$

If $|a| > 1$,   parabola is narrow
    $|a| = 1$,   parabola is standard
$0 < |a| < 1$,   parabola is wide

Translated Parabolas

So far, the examples in this section have all been parabolas with vertices at the origin. Other parabolas may have vertices at other points. Let (h, k) denote the vertex of a parabola.

VERTEX FORM
EQUATIONS OF
PARABOLAS

A parabola with vertex at (h, k) has an equation in one of the following forms:

$y - k = a(x - h)^2$ Opens up or down
$x - h = a(y - k)^2$ Opens right or left

Example 7   Name the vertex of each parabola.

a. $y - 3 = 2(x - 4)^2$ b. $y + 2 = 4(x - 5)^2$
     Vertex: $(4, 3)$ *Vertex:* $(5, -2)$

c. $y + 7 = -\frac{2}{3}(x + 1)^2$ d. $x - 5 = -3(y + 3)^2$
     Vertex: $(-1, -7)$ *Vertex:* $(5, -3)$

e. $x + 4 = \frac{1}{2}(y + 2)^2$
     Vertex: $(-4, -2)$ ☐

Be careful! Notice that the first component of the vertex is h (the quantity subtracted from x), and the second component is k.

Unfortunately, you are not usually given this form of the equation, but instead the equations of parabolas in standard form.

> STANDARD FORM
> EQUATIONS OF
> PARABOLAS
>
> The graphs of the equations
>
> $$y = ax^2 + bx + c \quad \text{and} \quad x = ay^2 + by + c$$
>
> are parabolas if $a \neq 0$. (If $a = 0$, they are lines.) These are called the **standard form equations of parabolas.**

The problem now is to change the standard form into the vertex form. To do this, you complete the square, as discussed in Section 7.1.

In Examples 8–10 complete the square and find the vertex for each parabola.

Example 8 $y = x^2 - 4x + 7$

Solution   *Step 1.* Subtract (or add) as necessary to obtain a form for which the constant term is on the same side of the equation as the first-degree term.

$$y - 7 = x^2 - 4x$$

Step 2. Divide both sides by the coefficient of the squared term (so that it is 1). It is already 1 for this example.

Step 3. Complete the square in x (if x is the squared term) or in y (if y is the squared term). Do this by adding the appropriate constant to both sides:

Remember that to complete the square you look here; add $\frac{1}{2}$ the square of this coefficient to both sides.

$$y - 7 + 4 = x^2 - 4x + 4$$

Add 4 to both sides.

Step 4. Simplify and factor:

$$y - 3 = (x - 2)^2$$

Step 5. Multiply both sides by an appropriate constant so that the coefficient of the first-degree term is 1. It is 1 in this example.

The vertex is (2, 3). □

Example 9 $y = 2x^2 - 4x + 6$

Solution   *Step 1.* $y - 6 = 2x^2 - 4x$
Step 2. $\frac{1}{2}y - 3 = x^2 - 2x$
Step 3. $\frac{1}{2}y - 3 + 1 = x^2 - 2x + 1$
Step 4. $\frac{1}{2}y - 2 = (x - 1)^2$
Step 5. $y - 4 = 2(x - 1)^2$

The vertex is (1, 4). □

Example 10 $y^2 - 4y + 8x - 2 = 0$

Solution   *Step 1.* $-8x + 2 = y^2 - 4y$
Step 2. Coefficient of y^2 is 1.
Step 3. $-8x + 2 + 4 = y^2 - 4y + 4$
Step 4. $-8x + 6 = (y - 2)^2$
Step 5. $x - \frac{3}{4} = -\frac{1}{8}(y - 2)^2$

The vertex is $(\frac{3}{4}, 2)$. □

Intercepts

Remember, for $y = ax^2 + bx + c$, if $a > 0$, the parabola opens up; if $a < 0$, it opens down.

You can now determine whether the parabola opens up or down, and by completing the square, you can determine the vertex *(h, k)*. Next, you need to plot a few points to finish the job of graphing the parabola. Some points of special significance are the intercepts.

y-Intercept

For parabolas that open up or down, first find the **y-intercept.** This is the point at which the parabola passes through the y-axis. We find this point by letting $x = 0$, and substituting into the equation:

$$y = ax^2 + bx + c$$
$$y = a(0^2) + b(0) + c$$
$$y = c$$

which is the point (0, *c*). This is the y-intercept. Since the axis of symmetry is the vertical line through the vertex, you can now find a second point and sketch the parabola.

In Examples 11 and 12 graph each parabola.

Example 11 $y = x^2 - 4x + 7$

Solution   Since $a > 0$, the parabola opens up. From Example 8, the equation can be written as $y - 3 = (x - 2)^2$, so the vertex is (2, 3). By inspection, the y-intercept is (0, 7). The line of symmetry is drawn through the vertex, as shown in Figure 9.2a. This line of symmetry is usually drawn mentally, and does not become part of the graph.

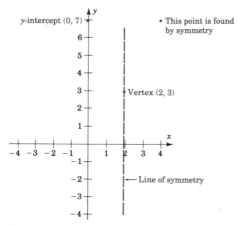

Figure 9.2a

The parabola can now be drawn using the three known points, as shown in Figure 9.2b.

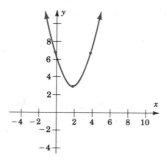

Figure 9.2b   Graph of $y = x^2 - 4x + 7$ □

Example 12 $y = 2x^2 - 4x + 6$

Solution   Since $a > 0$, the parabola opens up. The vertex is known to be (1, 4) from Example 9, and the intercept is (0, 6) by inspection. The graph is shown in Figure 9.3.

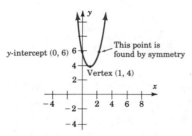

Figure 9.3 Graph of $y = 2x^2 - 4x + 6$

x-Intercept

For parabolas that open right or left, first find the **x-intercept.** This is the point at which the parabola passes through the x-axis. For $y = 0$,

Remember, for $x = ay^2 + by + c$, if $a > 0$, the parabola opens to the right; if $a < 0$, it opens left.

$$x = ay^2 + by + c$$
$$x = a(0^2) + b(0) + c$$
$$x = c$$

which is the point $(c, 0)$. This is the x-intercept.

In Examples 13 and 14 graph each parabola.

Example 13 $x = 2y^2 - 12y + 10$

Solution   The x-intercept is $(10, 0)$. Complete the square to find the vertex:

$$x - 10 = 2y^2 - 12y$$
$$\tfrac{1}{2}x - 5 = y^2 - 6y$$
$$\tfrac{1}{2}x - 5 + 9 = y^2 - 6y + 9$$
$$\tfrac{1}{2}x + 4 = (y - 3)^2$$
$$x + 8 = 2(y - 3)^2$$

The vertex is $(-8, 3)$. Sketch the parabola, as shown in Figure 9.4.

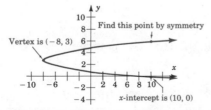

Figure 9.4 Graph of $x = 2y^2 - 12y + 10$

Example 14 $y^2 - 4y + 8x - 2 = 0$

Solution $8x = -y^2 + 4y + 2$

$x = -\frac{1}{8}y^2 + \frac{1}{2}y + \frac{1}{4}$

The x-intercept is $(\frac{1}{4}, 0)$, and the parabola opens to the left. From Example 10, the vertex is $(\frac{3}{4}, 2)$. Don't let the fractions bother you too much, since you can vary the scale to suit the points you must plot, as shown in Figure 9.5. Choose a scale that doesn't put the vertex and intercepts too close together.

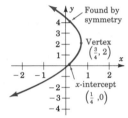

Figure 9.5   Graph of $y^2 - 4y + 8x - 2 = 0$

Additional Intercepts

Now we wish to find the x-intercepts for parabolas that open up or down, and the y-intercepts for parabolas that open right or left.

	Equation	Opens	x-Intercepts	y-Intercepts
Table 9.1 Intercepts for Parabolas	$y = ax^2 + bx + c$ $a \neq 0$	Up if $a > 0$ Down if $a < 0$	$\left(\dfrac{-b + \sqrt{b^2 - 4ac}}{2a}, 0\right)$ $\left(\dfrac{-b - \sqrt{b^2 - 4ac}}{2a}, 0\right)$	$(0, c)$
	$x = ay^2 + by + c$ $a \neq 0$	Up if $a > 0$ Down if $a < 0$	$(c, 0)$	$\left(0, \dfrac{-b + \sqrt{b^2 - 4ac}}{2a}\right)$ $\left(0, \dfrac{-b - \sqrt{b^2 - 4ac}}{2a}\right)$

You can see in Table 9.1 that the solutions of the quadratic equation

$$ax^2 + bx + c = 0$$

are the x-intercepts of the quadratic function

$$y = ax^2 + bx + c$$

Sometimes we call the x-intercepts the **zeros** of the equation. The relationship between the zeros of the equation and a parabola is shown below in Figure 9.6.

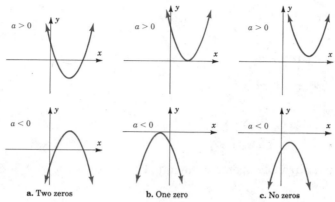

a. Two zeros   **b.** One zero   **c.** No zeros

Figure 9.6   Zeros of a Quadratic Function

In Examples 15–17 find all the intercepts for the given equation.

Example 15 $2x^2 + 3x - y + 4 = 0$

Solution   Solve for the variable that is not the second-degree variable; in this example, solve for y:

$$y = 2x^2 + 3x + 4$$

From Table 9.1, this parabola opens up. The y-intercept is (0, 4). For the x-intercepts, solve

$$2x^2 + 3x + 4 = 0$$

$$x = \frac{-3 \pm \sqrt{3^2 - 4(2)(4)}}{2(2)}$$

$$= \frac{-3 \pm \sqrt{9 - 32}}{4}$$

$$= \frac{-3 \pm \sqrt{-23}}{4}$$

This is not a real number, so there are *no* x-intercepts.   □

Example 16 $2x + 3y + 4 = y^2$

Solution   Solve for x:

$$2x = y^2 - 3y - 4$$

$$x = \tfrac{1}{2}y^2 - \tfrac{3}{2}y - 2$$

From Table 9.1, this parabola opens to the right. The x-intercept is $(-2, 0)$. For the y-intercepts, solve

$$\tfrac{1}{2}y^2 - \tfrac{3}{2}y - 2 = 0$$
$$y^2 - 3y - 4 = 0$$
$$(y - 4)(y + 1) = 0 \qquad \text{You can factor instead of using the quadratic formula.}$$
$$y = 4, -1$$

The y-intercepts are $(0, 4)$ and $(0, -1)$. $\square$

Example 17 $3y^2 + y + 2x - 5 = 0$

Solution Solve for x:

$$2x = -3y^2 - y + 5$$
$$x = -\tfrac{3}{2}y^2 - \tfrac{1}{2}y + \tfrac{5}{2}$$

This parabola opens to the left. The x-intercept is $(0, \tfrac{5}{2})$. For the y-intercepts, solve

$$-\tfrac{3}{2}y^2 - \tfrac{1}{2}y + \tfrac{5}{2} = 0$$
$$3y^2 + y - 5 = 0$$
$$y = \frac{-1 \pm \sqrt{1 - 4(3)(-5)}}{2(3)}$$
$$= \frac{-1 \pm \sqrt{61}}{6}$$

The y-intercepts are $\left(0, \dfrac{-1 + \sqrt{61}}{6}\right)$ and $\left(0, \dfrac{-1 - \sqrt{61}}{6}\right)$. $\square$

Calculator Comment

In Example 17 the y-intercepts were written in exact form. However, if you are going to plot these intercepts when graphing, you need to approximate the coordinates of these points. You can use your calculator to help you do this. The sequence shown below uses algebraic logic.

	Press	Display
	$\boxed{1}$	1
	$\boxed{+/-}$	-1
*	$\boxed{+}$	-1.
	$\boxed{61}$	61.
	$\boxed{\checkmark}$	7.8102497
	$\boxed{=}$	6.8102497
	$\boxed{\div}$	6.8102497
	$\boxed{6}$	6.
	$\boxed{=}$	1.1350416

Repeat the above sequence with the step marked * changed to a subtraction to find the other value: -1.4683749 Thus, to the nearest hundredth, the y-intercepts in Example 17 are $(0, 1.14)$ and $(0, -1.47)$.

Problem Set 9.3

A   1.   *By inspection*, state which of the equations given below in Problems 3–17 are functions.

     2.   In Problems 3–17 state whether you would choose x values or y values when making up a table of values.

Graph the equations in Problems 3–17.

See Examples 1–6.

3. $y=x^2$	**4.** $x=y^2$	**5.** $y=-x^2$	**6.** $x=-y^2$
7. $y=-2x^2$	**8.** $y=3x^2$	**9.** $x=6y^2$	**10.** $x=-8y^2$
11. $y=10x^2$	**12.** $y=\frac{1}{2}x^2$	**13.** $y=-\frac{1}{2}x^2$	**14.** $y=-\frac{1}{3}x^2$
15. $x=\frac{1}{4}y^2$	**16.** $x=-\frac{1}{2}y^2$	**17.** $x=\frac{1}{10}y^2$	

Name the vertex of each parabola given in Problems 18–27. Tell which way it opens and classify it as narrow, standard, or wide.

See Example 7.

18. $y-4=5(x-3)^2$	**19.** $y+3=-6(x-5)^2$
20. $y+1=-\frac{1}{3}(x+2)^2$	**21.** $x-5=-2(y+3)^2$
22. $x+3=\frac{3}{7}(y-1)^2$	**23.** $x+1=-10(y+2)^2$
24. $y-1=(x+4)^2$	**25.** $y=(x-5)^2$
26. $y=-2(x-3)^2$	**27.** $y=-\frac{1}{5}x^2$

Sketch the parabolas in Problems 28–35 using the given information.

See Examples 11–14.

   28. Opens up; vertex $(2, 3)$; y-intercept 7

   29. Opens right; vertex $(-2, 1)$; x-intercept 5

   30. Opens up; vertex $(-4, -6)$; y-intercept 10

   31. Opens right; vertex $(0, 5)$; x-intercept 25

   32. Opens down; vertex $(2, 3)$; y-intercept -1

   33. Opens left; vertex $(-2, 3)$; x-intercept -11

   34. Opens down; vertex $(-3, 4)$; y-intercept -5

   35. Opens left; vertex $(5, 1)$; x-intercept -4

B   *Complete the square and find the vertex for the parabolas given in Problems 36–43.*

See Examples 8–10.

36. $y=x^2-6x+9$	**37.** $y=x^2-8x+16$
38. $y=\frac{1}{2}x^2-4x+8$	**39.** $y=\frac{1}{3}x^2-2x+3$
40. $x=3y^2-12y+12$	**41.** $x=2y^2-4y+2$
42. $x=\frac{1}{5}y^2-2y+5$	**43.** $x=\frac{1}{5}y^2+2y+5$

Sketch each parabola in Problems 44–51 by first completing the square to find the vertex.

See Examples 11–14.

44. $y = x^2 - 4x + 8$
45. $x = y^2 - 10y + 25$
46. $x = y^2 - 2y + 4$
47. $x = y^2 + 8y + 17$
48. $y = x^2 + 4x + 8$
49. $2x - 6y - 9 = y^2$
50. $x^2 + 6x + 3y = 0$
51. $x^2 - 4x + 4y + 20 = 0$

Find all the intercepts for the equations given in Problems 52–61.

Calculator Application: If you have a calculator, write the irrational coordinates approximated to the nearest hundredth.

See Examples 15–17.

52. $y = x^2 - x - 6$
53. $x = y^2 + 2y - 8$
54. $x = 6y^2 - y - 15$
55. $y = 6x^2 - x - 2$
56. $y = x^2 - 4x + 1$
57. $x = y^2 - 6y + 7$
58. $x = 4y^2 - 12y + 7$
59. $y = 2x^2 - 6x + 3$
60. $y = x^2 + 4x + 5$
61. $x = y^2 - 2y + 10$

Mind Boggler

62. Sometimes a parabola is defined geometrically, and the equation is derived from the geometric conditions. For example, we might define a parabola as the set of all points in the plane that are equidistant from a given point (called the *focus*) and a given line (called the *directrix*).

a. Use the special graph paper shown in the figure (where F is the focus and L is the directrix) to plot all points that are equidistant from F and L. Let L be the x-axis and the line through the vertex, and let F be the origin.

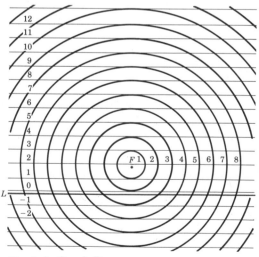

Parabola Graph Paper

   b. What are the coordinates of the vertex?
   c. Which way does the parabola open?
   d. Given what we've done in this section, state the equation of this parabola.

In the next Mind Boggler (see Problem Set 9.4), we'll use the definition of a parabola given in this problem to *derive* its equation.

9.4 Distance Formula and Circles

Suppose you want to find the distance between any two points on a plane. To do this, you need to remember the Pythagorean theorem from Chapter 6.

DISTANCE
FORMULA

> If $P_1(x_1, y_1)$ and $P_2(x_2, y_2)$ are any two points, then the distance, d, from P_1 to P_2 is
>
> $$d = \sqrt{(x_2 - x_1)^2 + (y_2 - y_1)^2}$$

The derivation of this distance formula is straightforward. Let $A = (x_1, y_1)$ and $B = (x_2, y_2)$. Draw a line through A parallel to the x-axis and a line through B parallel to the y-axis, as shown in Figure 9.7. These lines intersect at a point C with coordinates (x_2, y_1).

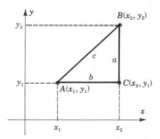

Figure 9.7 Distance between (x_1, y_1) and (x_2, y_2)

According to the Pythagorean theorem,

$$c = \sqrt{a^2 + b^2}$$

The lengths of the sides a and b can be measured as distances on the y-axis and the x-axis, respectively. These are

$$a = |y_2 - y_1| \qquad \text{and} \qquad b = |x_2 - x_1|$$

Substitute these into the Pythagorean theorem:

$$c = \sqrt{|x_2 - x_1|^2 + |y_2 - y_1|^2}$$

Notice that if you take the absolute value of a number and then square it, the result is the same as simply squaring the number in the first place. This means that you can write

$$c = \sqrt{(x_2 - x_1)^2 + (y_2 - y_1)^2}$$

If we denote the hypotenuse, c, by the letter d for distance, the result is the distance formula.

Example 1   Find the distance between the given points.

a. $A(5, 2)$ and $B(8, 6)$

$$d = \sqrt{(8-5)^2 + (6-2)^2}$$
$$= \sqrt{3^2 + 4^2}$$
$$= \sqrt{9 + 16}$$
$$= \sqrt{25}$$
$$= 5$$

b. $A(3, -1)$ and $B(5, -4)$

$$d = \sqrt{(5-3)^2 + [(-4)-(-1)]^2}$$
$$= \sqrt{2^2 + (-3)^2}$$
$$= \sqrt{4 + 9}$$
$$= \sqrt{13}$$

c. $(4, 9)$ and $(6, 5)$

$$d = \sqrt{(6-4)^2 + (5-9)^2}$$
$$= \sqrt{2^2 + (-4)^2}$$
$$= \sqrt{4 + 16}$$
$$= \sqrt{20}$$
$$= 2\sqrt{5}$$

d. (x, y) and $(0, 0)$

$$d = \sqrt{(x-0)^2 + (y-0)^2}$$
$$= \sqrt{x^2 + y^2}$$

e. (x, y) and (h, k)

$$d = \sqrt{(x-h)^2 + (y-k)^2}$$

These last two examples lead us to the equation of a circle. Do you recall the definition from geometry?

CIRCLE   A **circle** is the set of all points in a plane that are a given distance (called the **radius**) from a given point (called the **center**).

Consider a circle with center (h, k) and radius r. Then from the definition of a circle, the distance from (h, k) to *any point* (x, y) on the circle is equal to r. Thus,

$$r = \sqrt{(x-h)^2 + (y-k)^2} \quad \text{or} \quad r^2 = (x-h)^2 + (y-k)^2$$

> **Equation of a Circle**
> The graph of the equation
>
> $$(x - h)^2 + (y - k)^2 = r^2$$
>
> is a circle with center at (h, k) and radius $r > 0$.

In Examples 2–8 graph each equation.

Example 2 $(x + 3)^2 + (y + 1)^2 = 9$

Solution   By inspection, the center is $(-3, -1)$ and the radius is 3. The graph is shown in Figure 9.8.

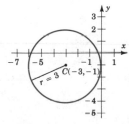

Figure 9.8   Graph of $(x + 3)^2 + (y + 1)^2 = 9$

Example 3 $(x - 2)^2 + (y - 3)^2 = 5$

Solution   By inspection, the center is $(2, 3)$ and the radius is $\sqrt{5}$. The graph is shown in Figure 9.9.

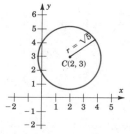

Figure 9.9   Graph of $(x - 2)^2 + (y - 3)^2 = 5$

Example 4 $x^2 + y^2 = 1$

Solution You can think of this as the form

$$(x - 0)^2 + (y - 0)^2 = 1$$

so by inspection, the center is (0, 0) and the radius is 1. This is sometimes called the **unit circle,** and the graph is shown in Figure 9.10.

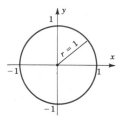

Figure 9.10   Graph of the Unit Circle   □

Example 5 $(x - 4)^2 + (y - 1)^2 = 0$

Solution This looks like the equation of a circle with center (4, 1) where $r = 0$. Since circles must have $r > 0$, this is not a circle. It is sometimes called a *degenerate circle,* and is a single point. In this example, the single point is (4, 1), as shown in Figure 9.11.

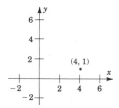

Figure 9.11   Graph of $(x - 4)^2 + (y - 1)^2 = 0$ ⊡

Example 6 $x^2 + y^2 + 2 = 0$

Solution The solution set for $x^2 + y^2 = -2$ is empty since $x^2 + y^2$ is always nonnegative.   □

Example 7 $(x + 2)^2 + (y + 4) = 3$

Solution $y + 1 = (-1)(x + 2)^2$

This is a parabola that opens down, with the vertex at (−2, −1) and the y-intercept at $y = -5$. The graph is shown in Figure 9.12.

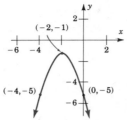

Notice: What is a parabola doing in a section on circles? Don't assume that all the graphs are circles without carefully looking at the equation!

Figure 9.12 Graph of $(x+2)^2 + (y+4) = 3$

Example 8 $x^2 + y^2 - 2x + 8y + 4 = 0$

Solution If the equation isn't in standard form, you need to complete the square. If there are *both* x^2 and y^2 terms, separate the x and y variables and complete the square in each.

$$(x^2 - 2x) + (y^2 + 8y) = -4$$
$$(x^2 - 2x + 1) + (y^2 + 8y + 16) = -4 + 1 + 16$$

Add 1 to both sides to complete the square in x

Add 16 to both sides to complete the square in y

$$(x-1)^2 + (y+4)^2 = 13$$

We recognize this as a circle with center $(1, -4)$ and radius $\sqrt{13}$, as shown in Figure 9.13.

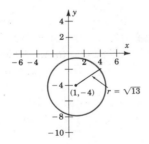

Figure 9.13 Graph of $x^2 + y^2 - 2x + 8y + 4 = 0$

Problem Set 9.4

A *Find the distance between the points given in Problems 1–9.*

See Example 1.

1. (5, 1) and (8, 5)
3. (−2, 4) and (0, 0)

2. (1, 4) and (13, 9)
4. (0, 0) and (5, −2)

5. (4, 5) and (3, −1)   6. (−2, 1) and (−1, −5)
7. (−4, 3) and (h, k) 8. (a, b) and (c, d)
9. $(4x, 5x)$ and $(−3x, 2x)$; $x > 0$

Graph the equations in Problems 10–35.

See Examples 2 and 3.   10. $(x − 4)^2 + (y − 1)^2 = 49$ 11. $(x − 5)^2 + (y − 3)^2 = 64$
                         12. $(x − 1)^2 + (y − 2)^2 = \frac{1}{4}$ 13. $(x − 2)^2 + (y − 1)^2 = \frac{1}{9}$
See Examples 4–7.   14. $x^2 + y^2 = 4$ 15. $x^2 + y^2 = 9$
                         16. $x^2 + y^2 = 25$ 17. $y^2 = 100 − x^2$
                         18. $x^2 = 16 − y^2$ 19. $y^2 = 36 − x^2$
                         20. $x^2 + y^2 + 3 = 0$ 21. $x^2 + y^2 − 3 = 0$
                         22. $x^2 + y^2 − 4 = 0$ 23. $x + y = −4$
                         24. $y^2 − x + 1 = 0$ 25. $x^2 + y + 2 = 0$
                         26. $(y − 2)^2 + (x + 4)^2 = 10$ 27. $(y + 4)^2 + (x − 7)^2 = 8$
                         28. $(x + 4)^2 + (y − 2) = 7$ 29. $(x − 3)^2 + (y + 1) − 9 = 0$
                         30. $(x − 1)^2 + (y + 5)^2 + 10 = 0$ 31. $(x − 1)^2 + (y + 5)^2 − 10 = 0$
                         32. $(x + 4) + (y − 3) = 7$ 33. $(x + 2) + (y + 7) = 4$
                         34. $(x + 1)^2 + (y + 2) = 0$ 35. $(x − 3)^2 + (y + 1) = −9$

B   *Graph the equations in Problems 36–45.*

See Example 8.   36. $x^2 + y^2 − 4x − 6y − 3 = 0$ 37. $x^2 + y^2 + 8x − 14y + 56 = 0$
                    38. $x^2 + y^2 − 10x + 8y + 33 = 0$ 39. $x^2 + y^2 + 2x − 10y − 23 = 0$
                    40. $x^2 + 4x + y + 3 = 0$ 41. $x^2 − 10x − y + 4 = 0$
                    42. $y^2 − x − 2y − 1 = 0$ 43. $y^2 − 2x + 6y + 11 = 0$
                    44. $4x^2 + 4y^2 + 24x − 16y + 27 = 0$
                    45. $9x^2 + 9y^2 − 18x − 54y + 74 = 0$

Mind Bogglers   46. In Problem 62 of Problem Set 9.3, we gave a geometric definition of
                        a parabola: a parabola is the set of all points in the plane that are
                        equidistant from a given point (called the *focus*) and a given line (called
                        the *directrix*). Let the point (0, 2) be the focus and let the directrix
                        be the line $y = −2$. Let (x, y) be any point on the parabola. Then,
                        using the distance formula for the distance between (x, y) and (0, 2)
                        and $y + 2$ as the distance between (x, y) and the directrix, derive the
                        equation of this parabola.
                    47. Repeat Problem 46 for the point $(0, c)$ and the line $y = −c$ for a positive
                        number c.

9.5 Conic Sections

So far, we've considered two curves that have second-degree equations.
The graphs of the parabola and circle are also called **conic sections,** or
conics, since they can be found by intersecting a plane and a cone. For
example, consider the cone and plane shown in Figure 9.14.

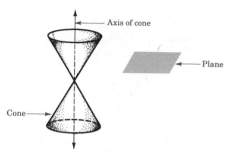

Figure 9.14   A Cone and a Plane

Suppose we pass the plane through the cone so that the cone's axis is perpendicular to the plane, as shown in Figure 9.15. The intersection of the plane and the cone is a **circle.**

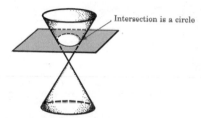

Figure 9.15   A Circle Found by the Intersection of a Cone and a Plane

We can also intersect a plane and a cone in other ways. For example, if the intersection is the one shown in Figure 9.16, the curve is a **parabola.**

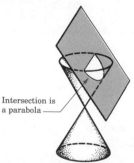

Figure 9.16   A Parabola Found by the Intersection of a Cone and a Plane

Other curves can be found by considering the intersection of a cone and a plane. They are shown in Figure 9.17. The curve in Figure 9.17a is called an **ellipse,** and the one in Figure 9.17b is called a **hyperbola.** Notice that a hyperbola is in two pieces. These two pieces *together* are called a hyperbola.

Historical Note

The Greek Apollonius (267–190 B.C.) was the first to use the words *ellipse, parabola,* and *hyperbola* in his work *Conic Sections,* consisting of eight books containing about 400 propositions. All his work was geometric, and the algebraic equation of the conics came much later.

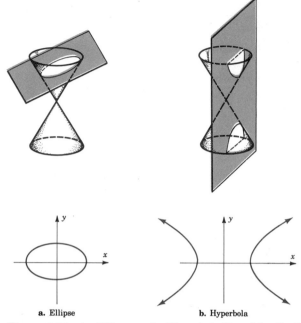

a. Ellipse   b. Hyperbola

Figure 9.17 An Ellipse and a Hyperbola Found by the Intersection of a Cone and a Plane

STANDARD FORM
EQUATION FOR AN
ELLIPSE AND A
HYPERBOLA

The graph of the equation

$$Ax^2 + By^2 = C \qquad A,\ B,\ C \neq 0$$

is an **ellipse** if A, B, and C have the same sign (all positive or all negative) and is a **hyperbola** if A and B have opposite signs.

Graphing the Ellipse

Consider an equation of the form

$$Ax^2 + By^2 = C$$

If A, B, and C are all negative, multiply both sides of the equation by (-1). Thus, without any loss of generality, assume that A, B, and C are all positive. Also, notice that if $A = B$, the equation is

$$Ax^2 + Ay^2 = C$$

or

$$x^2 + y^2 = \frac{C}{A}$$

which is a circle. Thus, the circle is a special case of the ellipse.

Consider the ellipse

$$9x^2 + 4y^2 = 36$$

As before, you can begin by plotting points. Choose x values and find corresponding y values, or choose y values and find corresponding x values, to arrive at the graph shown in Figure 9.18.

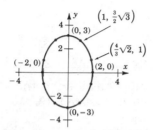

Figure 9.18 Graphing an Ellipse by Plotting Points

This curve is *centered at the origin* and is *symmetric* with respect to both the x- and y-axes. Once you know the general shape of an ellipse, it is not necessary to plot a lot of points. By plotting the x- and y-intercepts, you can generally sketch the curve. Also, if you rewrite the equation

$$Ax^2 + By^2 = C$$

by dividing both sides by C, you obtain the form

$$\frac{x^2}{a^2} + \frac{y^2}{b^2} = 1 \qquad \text{where} \quad a^2 = \frac{C}{A} \text{ and } b^2 = \frac{C}{B}$$

This is more convenient to work with, as shown by the following example.

Example 1   Graph $9x^2 + 4y^2 = 36$.

Solution   This is the ellipse shown in Figure 9.18, but now you can graph it by doing less arithmetic. Divide both sides of the equation by 36:

$$\frac{x^2}{4} + \frac{y^2}{9} = 1$$

Next, find four points—the points where the ellipse passes through the x- and y-axes. The y-intercepts are found when $x = 0$:

$$\frac{0^2}{4} + \frac{y^2}{9} = 1$$

$$\frac{y^2}{9} = 1$$

$$y^2 = 9$$

$$y = \pm 3$$

Thus, the ellipse passes through $(0, 3)$ and $(0, -3)$.

The x-intercepts are found when $y = 0$:

$$\frac{x^2}{4} + \frac{0^2}{9} = 1$$

$$\frac{x^2}{4} = 1$$

$$x^2 = 4$$

$$x = \pm 2$$

So the ellipse also passes through $(2, 0)$ and $(-2, 0)$.

By plotting these four points and remembering the shape of the ellipse, we can graph the curve, as shown in Figure 9.19.

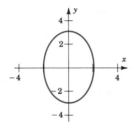

Figure 9.19 Graphing an Ellipse by Plotting Intercepts   □

Following the steps of Example 1, you can see that the x-intercepts are $(a, 0)$ and $(-a, 0)$, and the y-intercepts are $(0, b)$ and $(0, -b)$. These values can now be found by inspection rather than calculation.

INTERCEPT FORM
OF THE EQUATION
OF AN ELLIPSE

The graph of the equation

$$\frac{x^2}{a^2} + \frac{y^2}{b^2} = 1$$

is an ellipse centered at the origin with x-intercepts $\pm a$ and y-intercepts $\pm b$.

Example 2   Graph $25x^2 + 4y^2 = 100$.

Solution   Rewrite in intercept form:

$$\frac{25x^2}{100} + \frac{4y^2}{100} = 1$$

$$\frac{x^2}{4} + \frac{y^2}{25} = 1$$

By inspection, we see that the curve is an ellipse centered at the origin with x-intercepts ± 2 and y-intercepts ± 5. The graph is shown in Figure 9.20.

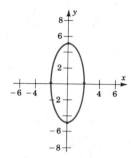

Figure 9.20   Graph of $25x^2 + 4y^2 = 100$

Example 3   Graph $3x^2 + 4y^2 = 12$.

Solution $\dfrac{x^2}{4} + \dfrac{y^2}{3} = 1$

The curve is an ellipse centered at the origin with x-intercepts ± 2 and y-intercepts $\pm\sqrt{3}$. The graph is shown in Figure 9.21.

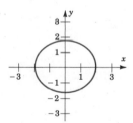

Figure 9.21   Graph of $3x^2 + 4y^2 = 12$

Graphing the Hyperbola

If you are given an equation of the form

$$Ax^2 + By^2 = C$$

where A and B have opposite signs, the graph is a hyperbola. By dividing by C, this equation can also be written in intercept form. Since the signs of A and B are opposites, there will be a subtraction of an x term or of a y term.

INTERCEPT FORM
OF THE EQUATION
OF A HYPERBOLA

The graph of the equation

$$\frac{x^2}{a^2} - \frac{y^2}{b^2} = 1 \quad \text{or} \quad \frac{y^2}{a^2} - \frac{x^2}{b^2} = 1$$

is a hyperbola centered at the origin with intercepts $\pm a$.

Notice that we didn't specify whether the intercepts are x-intercepts or y-intercepts. This is because the intercepts depend on which term is being subtracted, as shown by the following examples.

Example 4   Graph $\dfrac{x^2}{4} - \dfrac{y^2}{9} = 1$.

Solution   *x-intercepts:*   Let $y = 0$: $\dfrac{x^2}{4} = 1$

$$x^2 = 4$$
$$x = \pm 2$$

y-intercepts: Let $x = 0$: $-\dfrac{y^2}{9} = 1$

$$y^2 = -9$$

Squared term ⌢   ⌢ Negative

No y-intercepts, because a squared real number can't be negative.

x	y
0	Doesn't exist
± 2	0
± 4	$\sqrt{27} \approx 5.19$
± 6	$\sqrt{72} \approx 8.49$

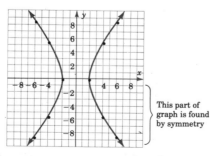

This part of
graph is found
by symmetry

Figure 9.22   Graph of $\dfrac{x^2}{4} - \dfrac{y^2}{9} = 1$

Example 5 Graph $\dfrac{y^2}{9} - \dfrac{x^2}{4} = 1$.

Solution *x-intercepts:* Let $y = 0$; no solution, so there are no x-intercepts.

y-intercepts: Let $x = 0$; then $y = \pm 3$.

Complete the graph by plotting points.

x	y
± 1	$\frac{3}{2}\sqrt{5} \approx 3.35$
± 2	$\sqrt{18} \approx 4.24$
± 4	$\sqrt{45} \approx 6.71$

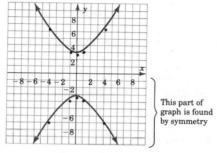

This part of graph is found by symmetry

Figure 9.23 Graph of $\dfrac{y^2}{9} - \dfrac{x^2}{4} = 1$

Summary

In more advanced courses, you'll consider other methods for graphing hyperbolas. Our use of hyperbolas in this course is very limited. Also, we've only considered ellipses and hyperbolas centered at the origin. In future work, you'll consider these curves located at places other than about the origin.

It is important that you be able to recognize types of curves *by looking only at the equation,* so study the summary in Table 9.2.

Table 9.2
Conic Sections

Curve	Equation	Instant Recognition
Line	$Ax + By + C = 0$	First-degree in both x and y
Parabola	$y = ax^2 + bx + c$ $x = ay^2 + by + c$	First-degree in one variable, second-degree in the other
Ellipse	$Ax^2 + By^2 = C$	Second-degree in both x and y; A and B have the same signs
Circle	$x^2 + y^2 = r^2$	Special case of ellipse where $A = B$
Hyperbola	$Ax^2 + By^2 = C$	Second-degree in both x and y; A and B have opposite signs

In Examples 6–12 identify each equation.

Example 6 $(y-2)^2+(x+1)^2=25$

Solution Circle; x and y are both second-degree with the same coefficients.   □

Example 7 $(y-2)^2+(x+1)=25$

Solution Parabola; y is second-degree and x is first-degree.   □

Example 8 $(y-2)+(x+1)=25$

Solution Line; both variables are first-degree.   □

Example 9 $(y-2)(y+1)=x$

Solution Parabola; second-degree in y and first-degree in x.   □

Example 10 $4x^2-3y^2=12$

Solution Hyperbola; second-degree coefficients have opposite signs.   □

Example 11 $4x^2+3y^2=12$

Solution Ellipse; second-degree coefficients have same signs.   □

Example 12 $6-5x^2=2y^2$

Solution Rewrite in standard form: $5x^2+2y^2=6$. It is an ellipse.   □

Problem Set 9.5

A *By inspection, classify each equation given in Problems 1–20 as a line, parabola, ellipse, or hyperbola. If an ellipse is also a circle, so state.*

See Examples 6–12.

1. $2x+3y=4$	**2.** $y=-2x+4$
3. $y=4x^2$	**4.** $x=2y^2$
5. $x^2+y^2=16$	**6.** $2x^2+y^2=16$
7. $2x^2-y^2=16$	**8.** $4x^2=4-3y^2$
9. $(x-2)^2+(y+3)^2=5$	**10.** $(x+4)^2+(y-2)=6$
11. $5x^2=9-5y^2$	**12.** $(x+4)+(y-2)=5$
13. $x^2+y-3=0$	**14.** $x^2+y^2-3=0$
15. $x^2-y^2+3=0$	**16.** $x^2-y^2-3=0$
17. $x^2+y^2+3x-4=0$	**18.** $(x+1)(x-4)=y$
19. $2x^2+y^2+5x=x^2+y^2+2y+3$	
20. $5x^2+2y^2+3x-4y=7+2y^2+5x^2$	

B *Graph each equation in Problems 21–30.*

See Examples 2 and 3.

21. $x^2+4y^2=4$	**22.** $9x^2+y^2=9$
23. $9x^2+4y^2=36$	**24.** $25x^2+4y^2=100$
25. $9x^2+25y^2=225$	**26.** $25x^2+9y^2=225$

27. $36x^2 + 4y^2 = 144$ **28.** $4x^2 = 144 - 36y^2$

29. $y = x^2 + 6x - 2$ **30.** $5x^2 + 25 = 16 - 5x^2$

Graph each equation in Problems 31–38 by plotting points.

See Examples 4 and 5.

31. $x^2 - y^2 = 1$ **32.** $y^2 - x^2 = 1$ **33.** $x^2 - 9y^2 = 9$

34. $y^2 - 9x^2 = 9$ **35.** $xy = 1$ **36.** $xy = -1$

37. $2x^2 - 3y^2 = 6$ **38.** $5x^2 - 3y^2 = -15$

Graph each pair of equations in Problems 39–42 on the same set of coordinate axes.

39. $x^2 + y^2 = 9$ **40.** $y = x^2$ **41.** $x^2 + y^2 = 16$

$4x^2 + y^2 = 36$ $x - y = -2$ $x - 2y = -4$

42. $4x^2 + y^2 = 12$

$y = 4x^2$

Mind Bogglers   **43.** Sometimes ellipses are defined geometrically and the equation is derived from the geometric conditions. For example, we might define an ellipse as the set of all points in the plane such that, for each point on the curve, the sum of its distances from two fixed points (called the *foci*) is a constant. Use the special graph paper shown in the figure, where F_1 and F_2 are the foci, to plot all points for which the sum of the distances from the foci is 12.

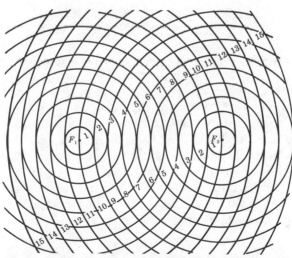

Ellipse and Hyperbola Graph Paper

44. Sometimes hyperbolas are defined geometrically and the equation is derived from the geometric conditions. For example, we might define a hyperbola as the set of all points in the plane such that, for each point on the curve, the difference of its distances from two fixed points (the *foci*) is a constant. Use the special graph paper given in Problem 43 to plot all points for which the difference of the distances from F_1 and F_2 is 8.

9.6   Quadratic Inequalities

We have considered all the curves that are shown in Figure 9.24. As you can see, each curve divides the plane into three regions:

1. Region I
2. Region II
3. The set of points on the curve

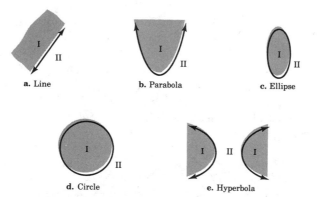

Figure 9.24   Regions of a Plane Determined by Different Curves

Since each curve is characterized by an equation, regions I and II can be described by an inequality.

The procedure for graphing a quadratic inequality is the same as the one used for lines. First, graph the boundary equation with a solid line if the inequality is $\geq$ or $\leq$ and a dotted line if the inequality is $>$ or $<$. A solid-line boundary indicates that the boundary is included in the solution set, and a dotted-line boundary indicates that it is not. Next, choose a test point that is not on the boundary and substitute it into the inequality. Then shade the appropriate region.

Example 1   Graph the relation $x^2 + 2x + y^2 + 6y \leq 6$.

Solution   Graph $x^2 + 2x + y^2 + 6y = 6$ by completing the square:

$$(x^2 + 2x + 1) + (y^2 + 6y + 9) = 6 + 1 + 9$$
$$(x + 1)^2 + (y + 3)^2 = 16$$

This is a circle with center $(-1, -3)$ and radius 4. Draw this boundary with a solid line and choose the test point $(0, 0)$:

$0^2 + 2 \cdot 0 + 0^2 + 6 \cdot 0 \leq 6$ True

Since $(0, 0)$ is in region I and makes the inequality true, shade region I as shown in Figure 9.25.

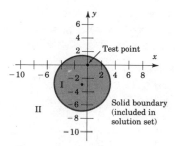

Figure 9.25   Graph of $x^2 + 2x + y^2 + 6y \leq 6$ □

Example 2   Graph the relation $y > x^2 - 4x + 3$.

Solution   Graph $y = x^2 - 4x + 3$:

$y + 1 = x^2 - 4x + 4$
$y + 1 = (x - 2)^2$

This is a parabola with vertex $(2, -1)$. Draw this boundary with a dotted line and choose the test point $(0, 0)$:

$0 > 0^2 - 4 \cdot 0 + 3$ False

Since $(0, 0)$ is in region II and makes the inequality false, shade region I as shown in Figure 9.26.

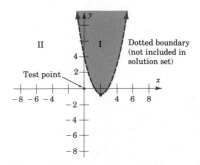

Figure 9.26   Graph of $y > x^2 - 4x + 3$ □

Example 3   Graph the relation $\dfrac{x^2}{25} + \dfrac{y^2}{9} \leq 1$, where $x < 3$.

Solution   First graph the ellipse; we've chosen the test point $(0, 0)$:

$$\frac{0^2}{25} + \frac{0^2}{9} \leq 1 \qquad \text{True}$$

This tells us that the solution set is inside the ellipse, including the boundary. Next, note the restriction $x < 3$ and shade only the portion of the solution set that satisfies the condition $x < 3$. The graph is shown below in Figure 9.27.

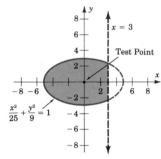

Figure 9.27   Graph of a Quadratic Inequality with a Restriction

Example 4   Graph $\begin{cases} x^2 + y^2 < 36 \\ x + 4 \geq y^2 \\ x > 0 \end{cases}$

Solution   Recall that the large brace symbol at the left means a simultaneous solution, which is the same as asking for the intersection of the individual solution sets. The desired graph is shown in Figure 9.28.

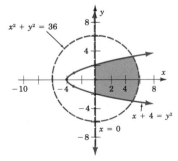

Figure 9.28   Graph of a System of Quadratic Inequalities

Problem Set 9.6

A *Graph each inequality given in Problems 1–16.*

See Examples 1 and 2.

1. $y \geq x^2$
2. $y \leq x^2$
3. $y - 1 > x^2$
4. $y > (x - 1)^2$
5. $x^2 + y^2 \leq 1$
6. $x^2 + y^2 \geq 1$
7. $x^2 + y^2 < 25$
8. $x^2 + y^2 \leq \frac{1}{4}$
9. $(x + 1)^2 + (y - 1)^2 < 9$

10. $(x - 1)^2 + (y + 3)^2 < 16$

11. $(y - 3) > (x + 4)^2$

12. $(x - 4) \leq (y - 3)^2$

13. $\frac{x^2}{4} + \frac{y^2}{25} \leq 1$

14. $\frac{x^2}{9} + \frac{y^2}{16} > 1$

15. $x^2 + 9y^2 \leq 36$

16. $4x^2 + y^2 < 36$

B *Graph each inequality given in Problems 17–26.*

See Examples 1 and 2.

17. $y \geq x^2 + 2x$
18. $x \geq y^2 + 6y$
19. $y \geq x^2 + 6x + 4$
20. $y^2 \leq x^2 + 6x$
21. $y \leq x^2 + 12x - 3$
22. $x^2 + y^2 \leq 2x - 4y - 5$
23. $x^2 - 2x + y^2 - 8y < 10$
24. $x^2 \geq 14 - 6x - y$
25. $x^2 - 4x + y^2 + 12y \geq 4$
26. $9x^2 + 16y^2 - 144 \leq 0$

Palatable Plotting *On the same set of coordinate axes graph Problems 27–37.*

27. $(x - 10)^2 + (y - 15)^2 \leq 49$
28. $x^2 + y^2 + 20x - 30y \leq -276$
29. $x^2 + y^2 = 121$
30. $(x - 4)^2 + (y - 3)^2 = 9$

See Example 3.

31. $(x + 4)^2 + (y - 3)^2 = 9$
32. $x^2 + y + 1 = 0$, where $y \geq -2$

See Example 4.

33. $\frac{x^2}{64} + \frac{y^2}{81} = 1$, where $y < -4$

34. $\begin{cases} (x - 4)^2 + (y - 3)^2 \leq 9 \\ (x - 8)^2 + y^2 \leq 25 \end{cases}$

35. $\begin{cases} x^2 + y^2 \leq 25 \\ (x + 4)^2 + (y - 3)^2 \leq 9 \end{cases}$

36. $\begin{cases} x \geq 0 \\ x^2 - 6x + 9y \geq 63 \\ x^2 + y^2 < 121 \end{cases}$

37. $\begin{cases} x < 0 \\ y - 8 \geq -\frac{1}{9}(x + 3)^2 \\ x^2 + y^2 < 121 \end{cases}$

Mind Boggler 38. In previous parts of the text, we've given a series of equations and asked you to sketch the curves on the same set of axes to form a picture (see Problems 27–37 above). Let's turn the tables now. Can you give a set of equations or inequalities that form a picture? Make it as simple or as complicated as you wish.

9.7 Review Problems

Fill in the word or words to make the statements in Problems 1–5 complete and correct.

(9.1) **1.** A function is a relation in which the first component is _____.

(9.2) **2.** If $y = f(x)$, then x is a member of the _____

(9.5) **3.** Fill in the names of the given equations:

    a. $y = ax^2 + bx + c$, $a \neq 0$, is a _____

    b. $x^2 + y^2 = r^2$, $r > 0$, is a _____

    c. $x = ay^2 + by + c$, $a \neq 0$, is a _____

    d. $\dfrac{x^2}{a^2} + \dfrac{y^2}{b^2} = 1$, $a, b \neq 0$, is a _____

    e. $y - k = a(x - h)^2$, $a \neq 0$, is a _____

    f. $\dfrac{x^2}{a^2} - \dfrac{y^2}{b^2} = 1$, $a, b \neq 0$, is a _____

    g. $(x - h)^2 + (y - k)^2 = r^2$, $r > 0$, is a _____

(9.3) **4.** The highest (or lowest) point of the parabola $y = ax^2 + bx + c$ is called the _____.

(9.4) **5.** The _____ formula says that if $P_1 = (x_1, y_1)$ and $P_2 = (x_2, y_2)$ are any two points, then the distance, d, from P_1 to P_2 is $d =$ _____.

(9.1) **6.** Classify each of the following sets as relations, functions, both, or neither.

    a. {(7,628, 4,175), (7,682, 4,157), (7,862, 4,175), (7,286, 4,751)}

    b. {(1,346, 8,214), (1,364, 8,142), (1,643, 8,241), (1,364, 8,124)}

    c. {68, 44, 17, 12}

    d. 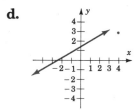   **e.** 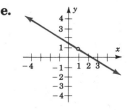   **f.**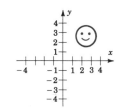

(9.2) **7.** Let $f(x) = 1 - x^2$ and $g(x)3 = 3x - 1$. Find:

    a. $f(1)$ **b.** $g(1)$ **c.** $f(t)$ **d.** $g(t)$

(9.2) **8.** For the function f defined in Problem 7, find

$$\frac{f(x + h) - f(x)}{h}$$

(9.4)   **9.** Find the distance between the given points.
       a. $(4, 5)$ and $(-1, 17)$ **b.** $(-3, -2)$ and the origin
       c. $(5, -3)$ and (h, k) **d.** $(4, -1)$ and $(-3, 2)$
       e. (s, t) and (u, v)

Graph the equations and inequalities in Problems 10–18.

(9.3)   **10.** $x = 5y^2 - 10y$
(9.5)   **11.** $y^2 = 10 - x^2$
(9.6)   **12.** $y < 5x^2 - 10x + 1$
(9.6)   **13.** $x^2 + y^2 \le 10$

(9.6)   **14.** $\dfrac{x^2}{49} + \dfrac{y^2}{64} > 1$

(9.4)   **15.** $x^2 + 10x + y^2 + 2y = 10$

(9.5)   **16.** $\dfrac{x^2}{9} + y^2 = 1$

(9.6)   **17.** $4x^2 + 49y^2 < 196$
(9.3)   **18.** $(y - 3) = 4(x + 4)^2$

(9.5)   *By inspection, classify each equation in Problems 19 and 20 as a line, parabola, circle, ellipse, or hyperbola.*

   19. **a.** $(y - 1) = 3(x + 1)$ **b.** $(y - 1) = 3(x + 1)^2$

       c. $y = 5x^2 - 3$ **d.** $\dfrac{x^2}{9} + \dfrac{y^2}{9} = 1$

       e. $\dfrac{x^2}{4} + \dfrac{y^2}{9} = 1$ **f.** $y = 3x^2 + 4x + 6$
       g. $x^2 + 2y^2 = 10$ **h.** $x^2 - 2y^2 = 10$
       i. $x^2 + y^2 = 10$ **j.** $y = 5x - 3$
   20. **a.** $x^2 + y^2 = 9$ **b.** $x^2 - y^2 = 9$
       c. $x^2 - y^2 = -9$ **d.** $(x - 2)^2 + (y - 1)^2 = 16$
       e. $y = 5x^2 - 15x + 25$ **f.** $x = 5y^2 - 15y + 25$
       g. $5y^2 - 4 = x^2$ **h.** $5y - 4 = x^2$
       i. $5y^2 - 4 = x$ **j.** $4x^2 + 3 = 2y^2$

CHAPTER
10

Exponential and Logarithmic Functions

Contents

10.1 Exponential Functions

In polynomials and rational expressions, the base is a variable and the exponent is a constant. The polynomial $x^3 + 7x + 5$ and the rational expression $\dfrac{x^2+1}{x}$ are examples. If the exponent is a variable, as in 10^x or 3^{1-2x}, the resulting expressions have vastly different properties from those of the polynomials and rational functions. Moreover, the applications of these functions are also different. Population growth, radioactive decay, money growing at interest, and profit falling in the face of rising overhead are all described by these functions.

Let's first recall the basic properties of exponents developed in Chapter 6, as listed below.

Laws of Exponents

If p and q are rational, and a and b are positive real numbers, then:

First Law	$b^p b^q = b^{p+q}$
Second Law	$(b^q)^p = b^{pq}$
Third Law	$(ab)^p = a^p b^p$
Fourth Law	$\left(\dfrac{a}{b}\right)^p = \dfrac{a^p}{b^p}$
Fifth Law	$\dfrac{b^p}{b^q} = b^{p-q}$

where $\quad b^0 = 1, \quad b^{-1} = \dfrac{1}{b}, \quad$ and $\quad b^{1/n} = \sqrt[n]{b}, \quad n$ a natural number.

Exponential Functions

If $y = b^x$, b is called the **base** and x is the **exponent**. The function defined by $f(x) = b^x$ is called an **exponential function**, where b is a positive constant other than 1. However, we have an unusual function since the domain is only defined for rational x. If you attempt to graph the function, it will consist of a series of distinct points. Admittedly, these points would be very close together, but it would be better if you could fill in the gaps in the real numbers by making some sense out of numbers like $2^{\sqrt{3}}$. The behavior of the function for the irrationals should be consistent with its behavior for the rationals. Look at the graph of $y = 2^x$ (Figure 10.1). As with polynomial functions, you can construct a table of values, plot these points, and then sketch a smooth curve through these points, as in Example 1.

Example 1   Sketch the graph of $y = 2^x$.

Solution

x	2^x
−3	.125
−2	.25
−1	.5
0	1
1	2
2	4
3	8

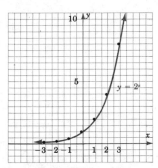

Figure 10.1

To ensure that Figure 10.1 is an accurate graph for all real values of x, the irrational values must have the following property.

SQUEEZE THEOREM

For any real number x and positive real number $b \neq 1$:

1. b^x is a unique real number.
2. If $h < x < k$ for rational numbers h and k, then $b^h < b^x < b^k$.

This will ensure that an irrational power has a real value and that its value is what you expect it to be. The graphs will be smooth—with no gaps or jumps. Now you can proceed to sketch graphs using rational values of x with the assurance that a smooth curve through those points will accurately graph all the real values.

Sketch the graphs of several exponential functions, as outlined in the examples below, and observe their behavior.

Example 2   Sketch the graph of $y = 3^x$. Make a table of values, and then sketch a smooth curve through the points.

Solution

x	3^x
−3	.037
−2	.111
−1	.333
0	1
1	3
2	9
3	27

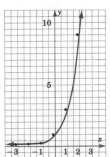

Figure 10.2

Example 3   Sketch the graph of $y = 2^{-x}$.

Solution

x	2^{-x}
-3	8
-2	4
-1	2
0	1
1	$\frac{1}{2}$
2	$\frac{1}{4}$
3	$\frac{1}{8}$

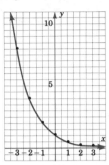

Figure 10.3   □

Notice the similarity of the graphs of $y = 2^x$ and $y = 2^{-x}$ (Figures 10.1 and 10.3). They are symmetric with respect to the y-axis (see Figure 10.4). This behavior is true in general for $y = b^x$ and $y = b^{-x}$. Additionally, $y = b^x$ is an increasing function for $b > 1$ and decreasing for $0 < b < 1$.

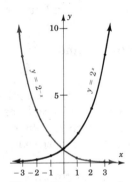

Figure 10.4

Example 4   Sketch the graph of $y = (\frac{1}{2})^x$.

Solution   Notice that $2^{-x} = (2^{-1})^x = (\frac{1}{2})^x$. Thus, the graphs of $y = 2^{-x}$ and $y = (\frac{1}{2})^x$ are identical. See Example 3.   □

Example 5   Sketch the graph of $y = 2^{|x|}$.

Solution

x	$|x|$	$2^{|x|}$
-3	3	8
-2	2	4
-1	1	2
0	0	1
1	1	2
2	2	4
3	3	8

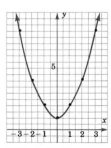

Figure 10.5   □

Example 6   Sketch the graph of $y = 2^{-x^2}$.

Solution   After compiling a table of values, you can see that no value exceeds 1. Thus, a different scale is used in Figure 10.6. Some additional values for $0 < x < 1$ can be obtained with the help of *a calculator* or *tables*.

x	$-x^2$	y
-3	-9	.002
-2	-4	.06
-1	-1	.5
0	0	1.0
1	-1	.5
2	-4	.06
3	-9	.002
.25		.96
.5		.84
.75		.68
1.5		.21

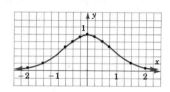

Key	Display
2	2
y^x	2
.25	.25
x^2	.625
+/−	−.625
=	.95760328

Figure 10.6

Example 7   Sketch the graph of $y = 2^{-1/2|x|}$. Before selecting values for the table, note that it would be better if x is even. Why?

Solution

x	$-\frac{1}{2}|x|$	y
-6	-3	.125
-4	-2	.25
-2	-1	.5
0	0	1.0
2	-1	.5
4	-2	.25
6	-3	.125

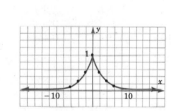

Figure 10.7

Exponential Equations

Many equations involving exponentials can be solved by using a property based on the fact that, if the bases and the exponents are equal, the numbers are equal.

PROPERTY OF
EXPONENTIALS

For nonzero real x and y and positive real $a \neq 1$, $b \neq 1$:

If $a^x = a^y$,   then $x = y$.
If $a^x = b^x$,   then $a = b$.

Example 8   Solve for x.

a.
$$5^x = 125$$
$$5^x = 5^3$$
Thus, $x = 3$

b.
$$x^3 = 64$$
$$x^3 = 4^3$$
Thus, $x = 4$

c.
$$36^x = 216$$
$$(6^2)^x = 6^3$$
$$6^{2x} = 6^3$$
Thus, $2x = 3$
$$x = \tfrac{3}{2}$$

d.
$$8^x = \tfrac{1}{4}$$
$$(2^3)^x = 2^{-2}$$
$$2^{3x} = 2^{-2}$$
Thus, $3x = -2$
$$x = -\tfrac{2}{3}$$

e.
$$4^{x-1} = 32^{2-3x}$$
$$(2^2)^{x-1} = (2^5)^{2-3x}$$
$$2^{2x-2} = 2^{10-15x}$$
Thus, $2x - 2 = 10 - 15x$
$$17x = 12$$
$$x = \tfrac{12}{17}$$

f.
$$(8x^3)^2 = (x^2 + 2x + 1)^3$$
$$[(2x)^3]^2 = [(x+1)^2]^3$$
$$(2x)^6 = (x+1)^6$$
Thus, $2x = x + 1$
$$x = 1$$

□

Table 10.1
Powers of 2 and 3

n	2^n	2^{-n}	$2^{1/n}$	3^n	3^{-n}	$3^{1/n}$
1	2	.5000	2.0000	3	.3333	3.0000
2	4	.2500	1.4143	9	.1111	1.7321
3	8	.1250	1.2599	27	.0370	1.4422
4	16	.0625	1.1892	81	.0123	1.3161
5	32	.0312	1.1487	243	.0041	1.2457
6	64	.0156	1.1225	729	.00137	1.2009
7	128	.0078	1.1041	2,187	.00045	1.1699
8	256	.0039	1.0905	6,561	.00015	1.1472
9	512	.00195	1.0801	19,683	.00005	1.1298
10	1,024	.00098	1.0718	59,049	.000017	1.1161

Problem Set 10.1

A   *Sketch the graphs of each set of functions given in Problems 1–6 on a single set of axes. Table 10.1 may be used to obtain points.*

See Examples 1–4.

1. $y = 2^x$, $y = 3^x$, $y = 4^x$
2. $y = 2^{-x}$, $y = 3^{-x}$, $y = 4^{-x}$
3. $y = (\tfrac{1}{2})^x$, $y = (\tfrac{1}{3})^x$, $y = (\tfrac{1}{4})^x$
4. $y = (\tfrac{1}{2})^{-x}$, $y = (\tfrac{1}{3})^{-x}$, $y = (\tfrac{1}{4})^{-x}$
5. $y = 2^x$, $x = 2^y$, $y = 2^{-x}$
6. $y = 3^x$, $x = 3^y$, $y = 3^{-x}$

Solve the exponential equations in Problems 7–20.

See Example 8.

7. $5^x = 625$
8. $3^x = 243$
9. $27^x = 9$
10. $125^x = 25$
11. $b^3 = 343$
12. $b^5 = 32$
13. $(\tfrac{2}{3})^x = \tfrac{27}{8}$
14. $(\tfrac{10}{7})^x = .49$

15. $8^{2x-2} = \frac{1}{16}$

16. $9^{3x-2} = \frac{1}{27}$

17. $(x^2 - 4x + 4)^3 = (27x^3)^2$

18. $64x^6 = (x^2 + 6x + 9)^3$

19. $9^{x+1} = 243^{1-2x}$

20. $125^{2-3x} = 625^{x-3}$

B *In Problems 21–28 sketch the graphs of each set of functions on a single set of coordinate axes. Table 10.1 or a calculator may be used to obtain points.*

See Examples 1–7.

21. $y = 2^{x^2}$, $y = 2^{|x|}$

22. $x = 2^y$, $x = 4^y$

23. $y = 2^x$, $y = 2^{-x^2}$

24. $y = 3^x$, $y = 3^{x/2}$

25. $y = 3^x$, $y = 3^{x+2}$, $y = 3^{x+4}$

26. $y = 2^{-x}$, $y = 2^{3-x}$, $y = 2^{6-x}$

27. $y = 2^x$, $y = 2^{x+3}$, $y = 2^{x-3}$

28. $y = 3^x$, $y = 3^{x-2}$, $y = 3^{x-4}$

Archaeology. *Problems 29 and 30 refer to the following:*

In archaeology, carbon-14 dating is a standard method of determining the age of certain artifacts. Radioactive substances slowly (or quickly) decompose or decay. We can measure decay rate by its half-life, which is the time required for one-half of a substance to decompose. A constant percentage of the total carbon present in all living matter is the radioactive form of carbon, ^{14}C. Carbon-14 has a half-life of approximately, 5,600 years. When an organic substance dies, the ^{14}C begins to decay, and the amount, A, remaining after t years is a measure of the substance's age. If A_0 is the original amount of carbon present, then

$$A = A_0 \left(\tfrac{1}{2}\right)^{t/h}$$

where h is the half-life.

29. Let $A_0 = 100$ and $h = 5,600$; sketch the graph of the decay of carbon-14 by plotting $A = f(t)$. (Take $t = 5,600$, $11,200$, . . . , and adjust scales accordingly.)

30. The half-life of radium is 1,600 years. Sketch the graph for radium the way you sketched the graph in Problem 29, where $A_0 = 100$.

Mind Boggler

31. Set up two coordinate grids. On one, label the x-axis 1, 2, 3, 4, . . . at equal intervals. Label the y-axis 2, 4, 8, 16, . . . at equal divisions (see the figure on the left). On the second grid, label both axes with 2, 4, 8, 16, 32, . . . (see the figure on the right). Now sketch $y = x^2$ and $y = 2^x$ on both grids and comment on the results.

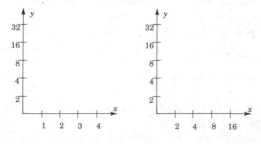

10.2   Exponentials and the Natural Base

Exponential functions have a great many applications. Here we consider a variety of examples, including growth and decay. Radioactive substances, for example, decompose or decay at varying rates. The decay is measured by the *half-life* of the substance, which is the time required for one-half of the material to decompose. The amount, A, remaining after time t is given by the exponential equation

$$A = A_0(\tfrac{1}{2})^{t/h}$$

where A_0 is the original amount and h is the half-life. Notice that since $0 < \tfrac{1}{2} < 1$, this is a decreasing (or decaying) function.

Example 1   The half-life of radium-226 (^{226}Ra) is 1,622 years. How much of 100 g of ^{226}Ra remains after ten thousand years?

Solution
$$A = A_0(\tfrac{1}{2})^{t/h}$$
$$A_0 = 100 \qquad t = 10,000 \qquad h = 1,622$$

$$A = 100(\tfrac{1}{2})^{10,000/1,622}$$
$$\approx 100(.0139342)$$
$$\approx 1.39342$$

Approximately 1.4 g of the 100 g remains.   □

Note the use of "≈." At nearly every point where a table or a calculator is used, you obtain an approximation. The tables are accurate, but only to the number of places shown. Calculators are more accurate, but are also limited by their display and, in fact, may be incorrect in the last one or two places.

Note that Table 10.1 (Powers of 2 and 3) is insufficient for Example 1. A calculator with a y^x key is much more efficient here and for later examples. However, $10,000 \div 1,622$ must be computed separately. If your calculator has parentheses, the following scheme may be followed:

$$\boxed{.5}\ \boxed{y^x}\ \boxed{(}\ \boxed{10000}\ \boxed{\div}\ \boxed{1622}\ \boxed{)}\ \boxed{=}\ \boxed{\times}\ \boxed{100}\ \boxed{=}$$

Without parentheses, $10,000 \div 1,622$ will most likely have to be stored as shown in this alternate scheme:

$$\boxed{10000}\ \boxed{\div}\ \boxed{1622}\ \boxed{=}\ \boxed{STO}\ \boxed{.5}\ \boxed{y^x}\ \boxed{RCL}\ \boxed{=}\ \boxed{\times}\ \boxed{100}\ \boxed{=}$$

Now, let's turn from decay to growth—that is, from a decreasing function to an increasing function. Population growth is sometimes measured by the frequency with which it doubles in size. If the population of a city doubles every n years, then the population P after t years is given by

$$P = P_0 2^{t/n}$$

where P_0 is the initial population.

Example 2   If Arlington, Texas, continued to grow at its 1970–1975 rate, it would double every 17 years (approximately). If the population of Arlington was 90,229 in 1970, estimate its 1975 population to the nearest thousand.

Solution

$P = P_0 2^{t/n}$
$P_0 = 90{,}229 \qquad n = 17 \qquad t = 1975 - 1970 = 5$
$P = 90{,}229(2^{5/17})$
$\approx 90{,}229(1.22613)$
$\approx 110{,}632.92$
$\approx 111{,}000$

This typical key scheme should give a check on your calculation.

Key	Display
2	2
y^x	2
(	2
5	5
÷	5
17	17
)	.29411765
=	1.2261348
×	1.2261348
90229	90229
=	110632.92

The 1975 population was approximately 111,000. □

A very practical application of an exponential function is the growth of money at compound interest. In computing compound interest, the principal on which interest is computed is increased by the addition of interest at the end of each interest period of the term. Whenever interest is not actually paid at the end of a period, but instead is added to the principal, it is said to be *compounded*. If a principal of P dollars is invested at annual rate r compounded n times a year for t years, then the amount A accumulated is given by

$$A = P\left(1 + \frac{r}{n}\right)^{nt}$$

Example 3 How much is in an account earning 6% compounded quarterly for five years, if $1,500 was the initial balance?

Solution

$$A = P\left(1 + \frac{r}{n}\right)^{nt}$$

$P = 1{,}500 \qquad r = .06 \qquad n = 4 \qquad t = 5$

Key	Display
1.015	1.015
y^x	1.015
20	20
=	1.34686
×	1.34686
1500	1500
=	2020.2825

$$A = 1{,}500\left(1 + \frac{.06}{4}\right)^{4(5)}$$
$$= 1{,}500(1.015)^{20}$$
$$\approx 1{,}500(1.347)$$
$$= 2{,}020.28$$

Thus, $2,020.28 is accumulated after five years. □

The Natural Base

Compound interest gives us an opportunity to investigate an important and interesting quantity. To do so, reconsider the formula

$$A = P\left(1 + \frac{r}{n}\right)^{nt}$$

If you let $P = 1$, $t = 1$, and $r = 1$, you have

$$A = \left(1 + \frac{1}{n}\right)^n$$

What happens as n increases? That is, if you invest one dollar for one year at 100%, how much difference does it make how often the interest is compounded? You hear a great deal about interest being compounded monthly, daily, or even instantaneously. Find the amount earned if compounded yearly, semiannually, quarterly, monthly, weekly, daily, hourly, and so on, by letting $n = 1, 2, 4, 12, 52, 365, 8{,}760, \ldots$

Table 10.2

n	$\left(1 + \frac{1}{n}\right)$	$\left(1 + \frac{1}{n}\right)^n$
1	2	2
2	1.5	2.25
4	1.25	2.44140625
12	1.08333333	2.61303529
52	1.019230769	2.692596954
365	1.002739726	2.714567475
8,760	1.000114155	2.718126665
525,600	1.000001903	2.718268514
31,536,000	1.000000032	2.718281829

Table 10.2 shows that you receive substantial increases until weekly or daily calculation; beyond that, the increases are very small. In fact, no matter how often the interest is compounded, the amount accumulated doesn't exceed a number that is approximately 2.7182818. This number

is denoted by the symbol e. It is used as a base for exponential functions, and has a great many applications since it describes continuous growth. The irrational number e is called the **natural base.** If interest were compounded continuously—that is, every instant—you could rewrite the compound interest formula as

$$A = Pe^{tr}$$

Consider the difference in Example 3 if the interest were compounded continuously.

Example 4 How much is in an account earning 6% compounded continuously for five years, if $1,500 was the initial balance?

Solution

You may use Table II in Appendix A to find e^x if your calculator doesn't have that function. However, if your calculator has exponential and logarithmic functions, your results will vary from our examples. Compare your calculation with the key scheme shown below.

$$A = Pe^{tr}$$
$$P = 1,500 \qquad t = 5 \qquad r = .06$$
$$A = 1,500e^{5(.06)}$$
$$= 1,500e^{.3}$$
$$\approx 1,500(1.3498588)$$
$$\approx 2,024.7882$$

Thus, $2,024.79 is accumulated after five years. □

Key	Display
5	5
×	5
.06	.06
=	.3
e^x	1.3498588
×	1.3498588
1500	1500
=	2024.7882

Interest, of course, is generally compounded a finite number of times (discretely) over any time period. There are many natural phenomena, however, that grow continuously rather than discretely. Many kinds of growth or decay are described or approximated by an exponential function of the form

$$y = y_0 e^{kt}$$

where t is the time and k is a constant that depends on the particular phenomenon. If $t = 0$, then the beginning amount is found by substitution.

$$y = y_0 e^{k(0)}$$
$$= y_0 e^0$$
$$= y_0 \cdot 1$$
$$= y_0$$

Thus, y_0 is the initial amount present when $t = 0$.

Example 5 A city has a population of 15,000 in 1980. If the population is approximated by $y = y_0 e^{.04t}$, where t is given in years, what will the population be in the year 2000?

Solution Taking $t = 0$ for the year 1980, the initial population is 15,000, so

$$y_0 = 15,000$$

.09077

The time is 20 years from 1980 to 2000, so

$$t = 20$$

Then,

$$y = 15{,}000e^{.04(20)}$$
$$= 15{,}000e^{.80}$$
$$\approx 15{,}000(2.226)$$
$$= 33{,}390$$

The population will be approximately 33,000 in the year 2000. $\square$

Recall the comparison of $y = b^x$ and $y = b^{-x}$. If $y = y_0e^{kt}$, $kt > 0$, represents growth (an increasing function), then $y = y_0e^{-kt}$ represents decline or decay. A common application we've already mentioned is the radioactive decay or half-life of a substance. Recall that if a substance has a half-life of time t, then in that time one-half of the substance will disintegrate due to radioactive decay.

Example 6   The decay of radioactive argon-39 is described by

$$A = A_0e^{-.173\,t}$$

where A mg of the argon remains out of A_0 mg after t minutes. If you begin with 100 mg of argon-39, then how much is left after 10 minutes?

Solution   We are given $A_0 = 100$ and $t = 10$, so

$$A = 100e^{-.173(10)}$$
$$= 100e^{-1.73}$$
$$\approx 100(.177)$$
$$= 17.7$$

17.7 mg are left after 10 minutes of decay. $\square$

Example 7   The atmospheric pressure P in psi (pounds per square inch) is approximated by $P = 14.7e^{-.21\,a}$, where a is the altitude above sea level in miles. What is the pressure:
a. At sea level?   **b.** At Denver, the "mile-high city"?
c. In space 10 miles from earth?

Solution   **a.** $P = 14.7e^{-.21(0)}$ $a = 0$ at sea level
            $= 14.7e^0$
            $= 14.7$
            14.7 psi at sea level
      b. $P = 14.7e^{-.21(1)}$ $a = 1$ mile
            $= 14.7e^{-.21}$
            $\approx 14.7(.811)$
            $= 11.9$
            11.9 psi in Denver

c. $P = 14.7e^{-.21(10)}$ $a = 10$ miles
$= 14.7e^{-2.10}$
$\approx 14.7(.122)$
$= 1.79$
1.8 psi in space (10 miles)   □

Notice that exponential functions can be used to model a wide variety of phenomena. Many examples are presented in Problem Set 10.2.

One last remark on the definition of the natural base, e. Recall that as you take larger and larger values of n, the expression $\left(1+\frac{1}{n}\right)^n$ gets closer and closer to the value of e. Thus, the *limit*, or the limiting value, of the expression is e, and it may be written as shown below. (This notation is considered in the next chapter.)

Definition of e

$$e = \lim_{n\to\infty}\left(1+\frac{1}{n}\right)^n \approx 2.7182818284\ldots$$

Cal. [ENM] [LOG] [INV] [lnx]

Problem Set 10.2

A   *Chemistry. The following formula is necessary for Problems 1–6: The amount A of a radioactive substance remaining after time t is given by*

$$A = A_0(\tfrac{1}{2})^{t/h}$$

where A_0 is the original amount and h is the half-life (given in the same units as t).

See Example 1.

1. The half-life of ^{234}U (uranium-234) is $2.52 \cdot 10^5$ years. How much of a 100 g sample remains after ten thousand years?
2. How much of a 100 g specimen of ^{22}Na (sodium-22) remains after seven years if its half-life is 2.6 years?
3. Curium-242 (^{242}Cm) has a half-life of 163 days. How much remains of 10 g after two years? [*Hint:* Be careful with the units of time.]
4. Neptunium-239 (^{239}Np) has a half-life of 2.34 days. How much remains of 10 g after one week? [*Hint:* Be careful with the units of time.]
5. How much of 10 g of ^{198}Pb (lead-198) remains after a day if its half-life is 2.4 hours? [*Hint:* Be careful with the units of time.]
6. How much of 25 g of ^{243}Pu (plutonium-243) remains after a day if its half-life is 4.98 hours? [*Hint:* Be careful with the units of time.]

Sociology.   The following formula is necessary for Problems 7–10: The population P of a city after t years is given by

$$P = P_0 2^{t/n}$$

where P_0 is the initial population and n is the number of years necessary for it to double.

See Example 2.   **7.**   If Anchorage, Alaska, continued to grow at its 1970–1975 rate, it would double in approximately 14.3 years. Estimate its 1995 population if it was 126,385 in 1970.

8.   Aurora, Colorado, would double in size every 8 years if it continued to grow at its 1970–1975 rate. Estimate its 1990 population if it was 76,477 in 1970.

9.   Every 38.6 years, Little Rock, Arkansas, would double in population if it continued to grow at its 1960–1975 rate. Estimate its 1985 population if Little Rock was 107,813 in 1960.

10.   Springfield, Missouri, had a population of 95,865 in 1960. It grew from 1960 to 1975 at a rate that would cause it to double every 32.85 years. Estimate Springfield's 1995 population.

Finance.   Problems 11–20 require the following formulas: If P represents the principal invested at annual interest rate, r, and compounded n times a year, then A is the amount accumulated in t years.

$$A = P\left(1 + \frac{r}{n}\right)^{nt}$$

If interest were compounded continuously, we could rewrite the formula as

$$A = Pe^{tr}$$

See Example 3.   **11.**   A thousand dollars is left in a bank savings account drawing 7% interest compounded quarterly for 10 years. What is the balance at the end of that time?

12.   A thousand dollars is left in a credit union drawing 7% compounded monthly. What is the balance at the end of ten years?

13.   Suppose $1,750 is invested in an account earning $13\frac{1}{2}$% compounded monthly for a two year period. What is the account worth at the end of that time?

14.   You lend $5,500 at 10% compounded monthly. If the debt is repaid in 18 months, what was the total owed at the time of repayment?

15.   A $10,000 Treasury bill earned 16% compounded monthly. If the bill matured in two years, what was it worth at maturity?

16.   You borrow $25,000 at $12\frac{1}{4}$% compounded monthly. If you are unable to make any payments the first year, how much do you owe (excluding penalties)?

See Examples 3 and 4.

17. A savings institution advertises 7% annual interest compounded daily. How much more interest would you earn over the bank savings account in Problem 11 or the credit union in Problem 12?

18. An $8\frac{1}{2}$% account earns continuous interest. If $2,500 is deposited for five years, what is the total accumulated?

19. You lend $100 at 10% continuous interest. If you are repaid two months later, what was owed?

20. If you had a million dollars for just two months, how much interest could be earned in an account earning 10% compounded monthly?

Problems 21–30 require the use of a calculator or Table II (in Appendix A) for powers of e.

Sociology. The following formula is necessary for Problems 21–26: Human population growth can be approximated by

$$P = P_0 e^{rt}$$

where a population of P_0 grows at an annual rate of r to P after t years.

See Example 5.

21. The population of the city of Los Angeles grew from 1970 to 1980 at an annual rate of approximately .48%. If the population in 1970 was 2,811,801, what was the population in 1980, to the nearest ten thousand?

22. Estimate the population of Los Angeles in the year 2000, if it continues to grow at the rate described in Problem 21.

23. Columbus, Ohio, grew in population from 1970 to 1980 at an annual rate of .40%. If the population was 540,025 in 1970, what was the population in 1980, to the nearest ten thousand?

24. Estimate the population of Columbus in the year 2000, if it continues to grow at the rate described in Problem 23.

25. The city of Indianapolis, Indiana, had a 1980 population of 695,040. It had declined in population at an annual rate of .488% between 1970 and 1980. If this decline continues, estimate its population in 1990 and 2000.

26. The population of San Francisco, California, was 647,063 in 1980. The city declined in population between 1960 and 1980 at an annual rate of .469%. If the decline continues at this rate, estimate the 1990 and 2000 populations.

Chemistry. The following formula is necessary for Problems 27 and 28: The radioactive decay of a substance is expressed by $A = A_0 e^{-kt}$, where the initial amount A_0 decays to an amount A after t years. The positive constant k differs for each substance.

See Example 6.

27. Strontium-90 is used in nuclear reactors. How much of an original amount of 250 mg of strontium-90 is present after five years if $k = .0248$?

28. Radium decays such that $k = .0004$. Find out how much of 1,000 mg of radium remains after a century.

Geoscience. *The following formula is necessary for Problems 29 and 30: The atmospheric pressure P, in psi, is approximated by $P = 14.7e^{-.21a}$ where a is the altitude above sea level in miles.*

See Example 7. 29. Mount McKinley, in Alaska, is the highest point in North America. The altitude is 20,320 feet or 3.85 miles. What is the pressure on top?

30. The lowest land point in the world is the Dead Sea (between Israel and Jordan), where the altitude is 1,299 feet below sea level ($-.25$ mile). What is the atmospheric pressure at this point?

B *Problems 31–38 require the use of a calculator or Table II (in Appendix A) for powers of e.*

31. *Medicine.* A healing law for skin wounds states that

$$A = A_0 e^{-.1t}$$

where A is the number of square centimeters of unhealed skin after t days when the original area of the wound was A_0. How many days does it take for half of the wound to heal? Theoretically, the wound never completely heals. Practically, however, after a given number of days the unhealed area is infinitesimal.

32. *Physics.* A law of light absorption of a medium for a beam of light passing through is given by

$$I = I_0 e^{-rt}$$

where I_0 is the original intensity of the beam in lumens, and I is the intensity after passing through t cm of a medium with an absorption coefficient of r. Find the intensity of a 100 lumen beam after it passes through 2.54 cm of a medium with absorption coefficient .095.

33. *Psychology.* A *learning curve* describes the rate at which a person learns certain specific tasks. If N is the number of words per minute typed by a student, then

$$N = 80(1 - e^{-.016n})$$

where n is the number of days of instruction. Assuming that Joe Cool is an average student, what is his typing rate after 20 days (4 weeks) of instruction?

34. *Psychology.* Members of a discussion group are ranked exponentially by the number of times they participate in the discussion. For a group of ten, the number of times the nth-ranked participant takes part is P_n times, as given by

$$P_n = P_1 e^{.11(1-n)}$$

where P_1 is the number of times the 1st-ranked person participates in the discussion. For each 100 times the top-ranked participant enters the discussion, how many times should the bottom-ranked person be expected to participate?

35. *Psychology.* Sketch the *learning curve* in Problem 33. First evaluate the rate for every two weeks of instruction ($n = 10, 20, 30, \ldots$).

36. *Psychology.* Sketch the *discussion curve* for the ten person group of Problem 34. (Note that the domain here is the counting numbers less than eleven.)

37. *Business.* Without benefit of promotion, the yearly sales, S, of a particular product will decrease at a constant yearly rate. After t years,

$$S = S_0 e^{-kt}$$

where S_0 is the sales in the initial year, and k is called the *sales decay constant*. Sketch the graph of the sales decline curve by computing and plotting several points where $S_0 = 1{,}000{,}000$ and $k = .18$.

38. *Physics.* The current I (in amps) in an electrical circuit is

$$I = \frac{E}{R}(1 - e^{-Rt/L})$$

t seconds after the circuit is closed, where E is the voltage, R is the resistance in ohms, and L is the inductance in henrys. Sketch the graph of this function in which $E = 10$, $R = 5$, and $L = 2.1$. Begin by finding the current for each tenth of a second after the switch is flipped.

Mind Bogglers

39. *Physics.* Previously, we have ignored friction (or air resistance) when considering the height, s, of an object after t seconds,

a. $s = v_0 t - 16 t^2$

where v_0 is the starting velocity. Actually, this formula is valid only in a vacuum. The following formula more accurately describes the path of the projectile:

b. $s = \dfrac{m}{k}\left[\left(v_0 + \dfrac{32m}{k}\right)(1 - e^{-kt/m}) - 32t\right]$

where m is the mass and k is a constant for air resistance.

Since the graph of equation a is a parabola, the graph of equation b can't be too different. Let $m = 1$, $k = .001$, and $v_0 = 160$, and sketch each. Now compare the two graphs, and conjecture the reasons for the differences.

40. Estimate and make a conjecture about the actual value of the continued fraction shown at the top of the next page.

$$2 + \cfrac{1}{1 + \cfrac{1}{2 + \cfrac{1}{1 + \cfrac{1}{1 + \cfrac{1}{4 + \cfrac{1}{1 + \cfrac{1}{1 + \cfrac{1}{6 + \ldots}}}}}}}}$$

First evaluate $2 + \frac{1}{1}$, then $2 + \dfrac{1}{1 + \frac{1}{2}}$, continuing to take another term each time. See if you observe a pattern emerging. [*Hint:* See Problem Set 5.5, Problems 28–31.]

10.3 Logarithmic Functions

Exponential equations require methods quite different from those used with polynomial and rational equations. First, we must find some way of solving for the exponent itself. Consider

$x = b^y$ with $b > 0,$ $b \ne 1$

Then, what is y? Can it be expressed simply?

First,

y is the exponent of b that yields x

but this is very wordy. We can say

$y = Exponent_b\ x$

which is shorter, but historically this new function has been called the **logarithm function,** and it is written as follows:

$y = \log_b x$

This is read "y is log base b of x" and means y is the exponent of b that yields x.

Our need to solve the exponential equation for the exponent leads to the following definition.

LOGARITHM
FUNCTION

> **Logarithm Function**
> For $b > 0,\ b \ne 1$
>
> $y = \log_b x$ is equivalent to $x = b^y$
>
> The logarithm to base b of x is the exponent y to which b must be raised to equal x.

The functions $y = \log_b x$ and $x = b^y$ may be used interchangeably. An exponential may be rewritten in logarithmic form, and vice versa.

Example 1 Change from exponential to logarithmic form.

  a. $8 = 2^3 \rightarrow \log_2 8 = 3$ **b.** $\frac{1}{9} = 3^{-2} \rightarrow \log_3 \frac{1}{9} = -2$

  c. $64 = 16^{3/2} \rightarrow \log_{16} 64 = \frac{3}{2}$ □

Example 2 Change from logarithmic to exponential form.

  a. $\log_{10} 1{,}000 = 3 \rightarrow 1{,}000 = 10^3$ **b.** $\log_5 1 = 0 \rightarrow 1 = 5^0$

  c. $\log_4 8 = \frac{3}{2} \rightarrow 8 = 4^{3/2}$ □

Example 3 Rewrite $\log_3 9\sqrt{3} = y$ in exponential form and solve for y.

Solution
$$3^y = 9\sqrt{3}$$
$$3^y = 3^2 \cdot 3^{1/2}$$
$$3^y = 3^{2.5}$$
$$y = 2.5$$ □

Graph of the Logarithm Function

Examining the graph of this new function can focus attention on its most important features. Keep in mind that as in Example 4, for instance, $y = \log_2 x$ is equivalent to $x = 2^y$. Using this equivalence will make it easier to compile pairs of values for the graph.

Example 4 Sketch $y = \log_2 x$.

Solution Since $y = \log_2 x$ is equivalent to $x = 2^y$, we compile a table with $y = -2$, $-1, 0, 1, 2, 3$, and plot the corresponding points.

x	y
$\frac{1}{4}$	-2
$\frac{1}{2}$	-1
1	0
2	1
4	2
8	3

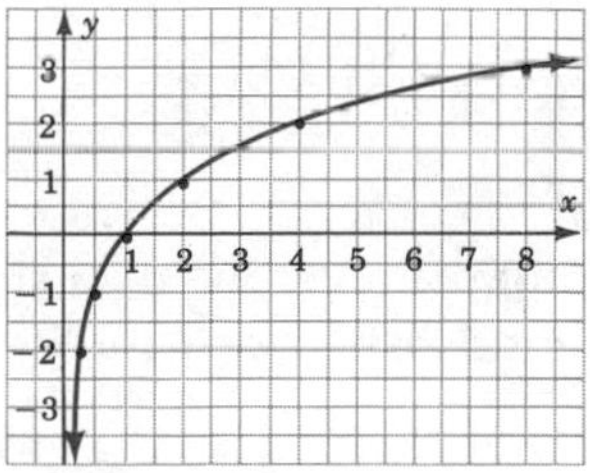

Figure 10.8 □

Example 5 Sketch $y = \log_{1/3} x$.

Solution The graph is identical to the graph of $x = (\frac{1}{3})^y$. First, compile a table using convenient values of y, plot these points, and finally, sketch a smooth curve through the points, as shown in Figure 10.9 on page 350.

From these sketches, note the following:

1. $y = \log_b x$ is increasing if $b > 1$ and decreasing if $0 < b < 1$.
2. $y = \log_b x$ is not defined for $x \leq 0$.
3. $y = \log_b x$ is 0 if and only if $x = 1$; that is, $\log_b 1 = 0$.
4. $y = \log_b x$ is 1 if and only if $x = b$; that is, $\log_b b = 1$.

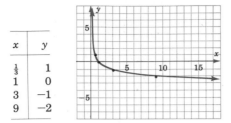

x	y
$\frac{1}{3}$	1
1	0
3	-1
9	-2

Figure 10.9 Graph of $y = \log_{1/3} x$

Properties of Logarithms

Since each logarithm function is equivalent to an exponential, each law of exponents has a counterpart for logarithms. For example, consider the first law: $b^x b^y = b^{x+y}$. Let

$$A = b^x \quad \text{and} \quad B = b^y$$

Then

$$x = \log_b A, \qquad y = \log_b B$$

The product

$$AB = b^x b^y$$
$$= b^{x+y}$$

can be written in logarithmic form as

$$\log_b AB = x + y$$

and we can substitute for x and y:

$$\log_b AB = \log_b A + \log_b B$$

The other laws of exponents yield corresponding properties for logarithms, which are summarized below.

Properties of Logarithms

If A, B, and b are positive real numbers, $b \neq 1$, then:

I. $\log_b AB = \log_b A + \log_b B$ $b^x b^y = b^{x+y}$

The log of the product of two numbers is the sum of the logs of the numbers.

II. $\log_b \dfrac{A}{B} = \log_b A - \log_b B$ $\dfrac{b^x}{b^y} = b^{x-y}$

The log of the quotient of two numbers is the log of the numerator minus the log of the denominator.

III. $\log_b A^n = n \cdot \log_b A$ $\qquad\qquad\qquad (b^x)^y = b^{xy}$

The log of the nth power of a number is n times the log of the number.

IV. $\log_b 1 = 0$ $\qquad\qquad\qquad\qquad\qquad\qquad b^0 = 1$

The log of 1 is zero for any base.

V. $\log_b \dfrac{1}{A} = -\log_b A$ $\qquad\qquad\qquad\qquad b^{-1} = \dfrac{1}{b}$

The log of the reciprocal of a number is the negative of the log of the number.

These properties allow you to convert multiplication problems to addition, division to subtraction, and powers and roots to multiplication. That is,

$$\log_b (1{,}745 \cdot 423) = \log_b 1{,}745 + \log_b 423$$

Instead of multiplying these numbers, you can add their logarithms. The examples below illustrate the use of the properties to expand expressions.

In Examples 6–11 use the properties of logarithms to expand.

Example 6 $\log_b 21 = \log_b(3 \cdot 7)$
$\qquad\qquad\quad = \log_b 3 + \log_b 7$ $\qquad\qquad\qquad\qquad\qquad$ □

Example 7 $\log_b \frac{2}{3} = \log_b 2 - \log_b 3$ $\qquad\qquad\qquad\qquad\qquad$ □

Example 8 $\log_b 12 = \log_b(3 \cdot 4) = \log_b(3 \cdot 2^2)$
$\qquad\qquad\quad = \log_b 3 + \log_b 2^2$
$\qquad\qquad\quad = \log_b 3 + 2\log_b 2$ $\qquad\qquad\qquad\qquad\qquad$ □

Example 9 $\log_b 5\sqrt{33} = \log_b 5(3 \cdot 11)^{1/2}$
$\qquad\qquad\qquad = \log_b 5 + \log_b(3 \cdot 11)^{1/2}$
$\qquad\qquad\qquad = \log_b 5 + \frac{1}{2}\log_b(3 \cdot 11)$
$\qquad\qquad\qquad = \log_b 5 + \frac{1}{2}(\log_b 3 + \log_b 11)$ $\qquad\qquad$ □

Example 10 $\log_d \dfrac{1}{k^3} = \log_d k^{-3}$ $\qquad \dfrac{1}{b} = b^{-1}$
$\qquad\qquad\quad = -3\log_d k$ $\qquad \log_b A^B = B\log_b A$ $\qquad\qquad$ □

Example 11 $\log_B \dfrac{a\sqrt[3]{b}}{c^2 d} = \log_B \dfrac{ab^{1/3}}{c^2 d}$ $\qquad\qquad \sqrt[n]{b} = b^{1/n}$

$\qquad\qquad\quad = \log_B(ab^{1/3}) - \log_B(c^2 d)$ $\qquad \log_b(A/B) = \log_b A - \log_b B$
$\qquad\qquad\quad = \log_B a + \log_B b^{1/3} - \log_B c^2 - \log_B d$ $\qquad \log_b AB = \log_b A + \log_b B$
$\qquad\qquad\quad = \log_B a + \frac{1}{3}\log_B b - 2\log_B c - \log_B d$ $\qquad \log_b A^B = B\log_b A$ $\qquad$ □

The Scot John Napier (1550–1617) was the inventor of logarithms. He originally used the term *artificial number,* but later adopted *logarithm,* a word from Greek meaning "ratio number." Napier used the base $.9999999 = 1 - 10^{-7}$. Henry Briggs (1561–1631) was responsible for the base of ten and constructed the first tables. Leonhard Euler (1707–1783) later introduced the letter e to represent the natural constant $2.71828\ldots$.

These properties allow you to work more effectively and efficiently with the logarithm function and its inverse, the exponential function. Historically, these properties made logarithms an important aid to science. Logarithms were devised to lift some of the burden of calculation found in science, especially in astronomy. Using properties of logarithms and tables of values for logarithms, numerical problems may be greatly simplified. It is paradoxical that logarithms were invented before exponents were widely used. Since our number system is base 10, logarithms with base 10 are convenient for numerical calculations. If base 10 is used, the logarithms are called **common logarithms** and are written $y = \log x$ with no indication of base. For scientific purposes, the natural base e is widely used; such logarithms are called **natural logarithms** and are written $y = \ln x$.

To apply logarithms more broadly, we can state one more property. This particular property will be applied to solve logarithmic and exponential equations, as illustrated by the examples below.

Equality Property of Logarithms

Let m and n be positive real numbers and $b > 0$, $b \neq 1$:

If $\log_b m = \log_b n$,   then $m = n$.

If the logs are equal, then the numbers are equal.

If $m = n$,   then $\log_b m = \log_b n$.

If the numbers are equal, then their logs are also equal.

Finally, reconsider the formulas of the last section. In general, a formula is not always in the form that would be most useful. You often have to solve for one of the other variables before proceeding. It is now possible to solve for variables that occur within the exponent.

Example 12   Solve for t: $A = A_0(\tfrac{1}{2})^{t/h}$

Solution $\dfrac{A}{A_0} = (\tfrac{1}{2})^{t/h}$ First arrange in exponential form.

$\dfrac{t}{h} = \log_{1/2} \dfrac{A}{A_0}$ Now rewrite in logarithmic form.

$t = h \log_{1/2} \dfrac{A}{A_0}$ Multiply by h.

Example 13   Solve for r: $A = Pe^{rt}$

Solution

$$\frac{A}{P} = e^{rt} \qquad \text{Divide by } P.$$

$$rt = \log_e \frac{A}{P} \qquad \text{Rewrite.}$$

$$rt = \ln \frac{A}{P} \qquad \text{Base } e \text{ is natural logarithm.}$$

$$r = \frac{1}{t} \ln \frac{A}{P} \qquad \text{Solve for } r.$$

□

Example 14   Solve for L: $I = \dfrac{E}{R}(1 - e^{-Rt/L})$

Solution

$$\frac{RI}{E} = 1 - e^{-Rt/L} \qquad \text{Multiply by } R/E.$$

$$\frac{RI}{E} - 1 = - e^{-Rt/L} \qquad \text{Subtract 1.}$$

$$1 - \frac{RI}{E} = e^{-Rt/L} \qquad \text{Multiply by } -1.$$

$$-\frac{Rt}{L} = \ln\left(1 - \frac{RI}{E}\right) \qquad \text{Logarithmic form.}$$

$$-Rt = L \ln\left(1 - \frac{RI}{E}\right) \qquad \text{Multiply by } L.$$

$$L = \frac{-Rt}{\ln\left(1 - \dfrac{RI}{E}\right)} \qquad \text{Divide.}$$

□

Problem Set 10.3

A   *Rewrite Problems 1–10 in logarithmic form.*

See Example 1.

1. $125 = 5^3$ **2.** $243 = 3^5$ **3.** $\frac{1}{9} = 3^{-2}$ **4.** $4 = (\frac{1}{2})^{-2}$

5. $8 = 4^{3/2}$ **6.** $9 = 27^{2/3}$ **7.** $\frac{4}{9} = (\frac{3}{2})^{-2}$ **8.** $\frac{1}{3} = 81^{-1/4}$

9. $a = b^c$ **10.** $u = v^w$

Rewrite Problems 11–20 in exponential form.

See Example 2.

Recall that $\log x$ is base 10 and $\ln x$ is base e; $\ln x$ is read "lon x."

11. $\log_2 8 = 3$ **12.** $\log_3 81 = 4$ **13.** $\log .01 = -2$

14. $\ln e^2 = 2$ **15.** $\log_4 2 = .5$ **16.** $\log_{27} 3 = \frac{1}{3}$

17. $\log_{1/3} 9 = -2$ **18.** $\log_{1/4} 8 = -\frac{3}{2}$ **19.** $\log_k h = c$

20. $\log_x y = z$

Determine the values of the variables in Problems 21–36.

See Examples 2 and 3.

21. $\log_2 8 = x$ 22. $\log_3 9 = y$ 23. $\log 100 = x$
24. $\log .0001 = y$ 25. $\log_{27} 9 = x$ 26. $\log_4 8 = y$
27. $\log_3 x = 2$ 28. $\log_5 x = 3$ 29. $\log_b 16 = 4$
30. $\log_b 125 = 3$ 31. $\log_7 49 = y$ 32. $\log_8 2\sqrt{2} = y$
33. $\log_y 27 = y$ 34. $\log_b 4 = b$ 35. $\log_b 1 = 0$
36. $\log_x x = 1$

In Problems 37–40 sketch each set of functions on a single set of coordinate axes.

See Examples 4 and 5.

37. $y = \log_2 x, \quad y = \log_{1/2} x, \quad y = 2^x$
38. $y = \log_3 x, \quad y = \log_{1/3} x, \quad y = 3^x$
39. $y = \ln x, \quad y = e^x, \quad y = \log_5 x$
40. $y = \log x, \quad y = 10^x, \quad y = \log_5 x$

B   *Use the properties of logarithms to expand the expressions in Problems 41–50.*

See Examples 6–11.

41. $\log_b 4ac$ 42. $\log_b \frac{1}{2} lw$ 43. $\log \pi r^2$ 44. $\log 2\pi r$

45. $\log_b P\sqrt{Q}$ 46. $\log_b A^2 B^3$ 47. $\log_b \frac{rs^2}{\sqrt[3]{t}}$ 48. $\log_b \frac{r^3\sqrt{s}}{t^2}$

49. $\ln Pe^{-rt}$ 50. $\ln Ae^{kt}$

Solve for the indicated variable in Problems 51–60.

See Examples 12–14.

51. $P = P_0 e^{rt}; \quad$ for t 52. $I = I_0 e^{-rt}; \quad$ for t
53. $P = 14.7 e^{-.21a}; \quad$ for a 54. $A = 250 e^{-.0248t}; \quad$ for t
55. $A = A_0(\frac{1}{2})^{t/h}; \quad$ for h 56. $I = I_0(10)^{N/10}; \quad$ for N
57. $P_n = P_1 e^{.11(1-n)}; \quad$ for n 58. $N = 80(1 - e^{-.016n}); \quad$ for n
59. $I = \frac{E}{R}(1 - e^{-Rt/L}); \quad$ for t 60. $T = A + (B - A)10^{-kt}; \quad$ for k

Mind Boggler   61. Find the fallacy in the following development:

$$3 > 2$$
$$3 \log \tfrac{1}{2} > 2 \log \tfrac{1}{2}$$
$$\log(\tfrac{1}{2})^3 > \log(\tfrac{1}{2})^2$$
$$(\tfrac{1}{2})^3 > (\tfrac{1}{2})^2$$
$$\tfrac{1}{8} > \tfrac{1}{4}$$

10.4   Logarithmic Equations

The common scientific hand-held calculator has both the common and natural logarithm functions. Computing values for these functions is accomplished by entering the given number and pressing the appropriate key.

Example 1 Evaluate: log 453

Solution   453̲ L̲O̲G̲

log 453 ≈ 2.6560982

Notice that "≈" is used to indicate that the value is correct to eight places. Your calculator may display fewer (or more) places. In any event, it will probably be sufficient for our applications. □

Example 2 Evaluate: ln 7.831

Solution   7̲.̲8̲3̲1̲ L̲N̲

ln 7.831 ≈ 2.0580902 □

Example 3 Evaluate: log 3,406,000,000

Solution   3̲4̲0̲6̲0̲0̲0̲0̲0̲0̲ L̲O̲G̲

log 3,406,000,000 ≈ 9.5322446 □

It is likely that your calculator would not accept the number in the last example in the form given. In general, very large or very small numbers are written in a more convenient form. Any number may be written as a number between 1 and 10, times a power of 10, the familiar **scientific notation.**

SCIENTIFIC
NOTATION

Scientific Notation

For any real number n,

$$n = m \cdot 10^C \qquad \text{where} \quad 1 \le m < 10, \quad C \text{ is an integer}$$

A calculator will accept a number in this form if it has an E̲E̲X̲, E̲E̲, or S̲C̲I̲ key. Reconsider the number in Example 3.

Example 4 Evaluate: $\log 3{,}406{,}000{,}000 = \log(3.406 \cdot 10^9)$

Solution   3̲.̲4̲0̲6̲ E̲E̲X̲ 9̲ L̲O̲G̲

$\log(3.406 \cdot 10^9) \approx 9.5322446$ □

Example 5 Evaluate: $\ln .00000006572 = \ln(6.572 \cdot 10^{-8})$

Solution   6̲.̲5̲7̲2̲ E̲E̲X̲ 8̲ +̲/̲−̲ L̲N̲

$\ln(6.572 \cdot 10^{-8}) \approx -16.5378625$ □

Example 6   Evaluate: $\ln(6.023 \cdot 10^{23})$

Solution | 6.023 | | EEX | | 23 | | LN |

6.023 · 10²³ is called
Avogadro's number; it
is the number of
molecules in one gram-
molecule of a
substance or the
number of atoms in
one gram-atom of a
pure element.

$\ln(6.023 \cdot 10^{23}) \approx 54.755042$

Example 7   The *hydrogen potential,* or pH, of a solution is

$-\log[H^+]$

where $[H^+]$ is the concentration of hydrogen ions in aqueous solution given in moles per liter. A solution is considered neutral if its pH is 7. When the pH exceeds 7, the solution is alkaline. When it's less than 7, the solution is acid. Grapefruit has a $[H^+]$ of $7.9 \cdot 10^{-4}$. Find its pH to the nearest tenth.

Solution
$$pH = -\log[H^+]$$
$$= -\log(7.9 \cdot 10^{-4})$$

| 7.9 | | EEX | | 4 | | +/− | | LOG | | +/− |

$$\approx 3.1023729$$
$$\approx 3.1$$

The pH of grapefruit is approximately 3.1.

In the previous section we used the properties of logarithms to expand logarithmic expressions. These properties can likewise be used to simplify expressions in order to solve logarithmic equations.

Example 8   Solve for x.

Solution
$$\log_b 2x + \tfrac{1}{3}\log_b 27 = \tfrac{2}{5}\log_b 243 + 2\log_b 2$$
$$\log_b 2x + \log_b 27^{1/3} = \log_b 243^{2/5} + \log_b 2^2$$
$$\log_b 2x + \log_b 3 = \log_b 9 + \log_b 4$$
$$\log_b 6x = \log_b 36$$
$$6x = 36$$
$$x = 6$$

Simplify both sides of the equation first.

Since $\log_b m = \log_b n$, then $m = n$.

Example 9   Solve for b.

Solution

$$3 \log_b 2 - \tfrac{1}{2}\log_b 12 = 1 - \tfrac{1}{2}\log_b 3$$

$$\log_b 2^3 - \log_b\sqrt{12} = \log_b b - \log_b\sqrt{3}$$

Simplify first.
Note that $1 = \log_b b$.

$$\log_b \frac{2^3}{\sqrt{12}} = \log_b \frac{b}{\sqrt{3}}$$

Since $\log_b m = \log_b n$, then $m = n$.

$$\frac{2^3}{\sqrt{12}} = \frac{b}{\sqrt{3}}$$

$$4 = b$$

$\square$

Notice that the solution is generally independent of the base b. The ordinary calculator has both common and natural logarithm functions, but it is sometimes necessary to evaluate a logarithm with a base other than 10 or e.

Logarithms in Other Bases

Common or natural logarithms are sufficient to find the logarithm of a number in any acceptable base. Recall that

$$\log_b x = y$$

is equivalent to

$$b^y = x$$

and thus,

$$\log b^y = \log x \qquad \text{or} \qquad \ln b^y = \ln x$$

$$y \cdot \log b = \log x \qquad\qquad y \cdot \ln b = \ln x$$

$$y = \frac{\log x}{\log b} \qquad\qquad y = \frac{\ln x}{\ln b}$$

$$\log_b x = \frac{\log x}{\log b} \qquad\qquad \log_b x = \frac{\ln x}{\ln b}$$

CHANGE OF BASE PROPERTY

$$\log_b x = \frac{\log x}{\log b} \qquad \text{or} \qquad \frac{\ln x}{\ln b}$$

The logarithm of a number in any valid base may be found by dividing the log (or the ln) of the number by the log (or the ln) of the base.

In Examples 10–12 find the logarithm of each number correct to four decimal places.

Example 10

$$\log_3 14 = \frac{\log 14}{\log 3}$$

$$\approx \frac{1.1461280}{.47712125}$$

$$\approx 2.4021735$$

$$\approx 2.4022$$

Key	Display
14	14
LOG	1.1461280
÷	1.1461280
3	3
LOG	.47712125
=	2.4021735

Alternately, you can use ln.

$$\log_3 14 = \frac{\ln 14}{\ln 3}$$

$$\approx \frac{2.6390573}{1.0986123}$$

$$\approx 2.4021735$$

$$\approx 2.4022$$ □

Example 11

$$\log_\pi \sqrt{2} = \frac{\log \sqrt{2}}{\log \pi}$$

$$\approx \frac{.15051499}{.49714987}$$

$$\approx .30275578$$

$$\approx .3028$$ □

Example 12

$$\log_5 e = \frac{\ln e}{\ln 5}$$

$$\approx \frac{1}{1.6094379}$$

$$\approx .62133493$$

$$\approx .6213$$ □

Example 13   If a certain sum of money is invested at 8% and compounded semiannually, how long does it take the money to double?

Solution

$$A = P\left(1 + \frac{r}{n}\right)^{nt}$$

$$2P = P\left(1 + \frac{.08}{2}\right)^{2t}$$

$$2 = (1.04)^{2t}$$

$$2t = \log_{1.04} 2$$

$$t = \frac{\log 2}{2 \log 1.04}$$

$$\boxed{2}\ \boxed{\text{LOG}}\ \boxed{\div}\ \boxed{2}\ \boxed{\div}\ \boxed{1.04}\ \boxed{\text{LOG}}\ \boxed{=}$$

$$t \approx 8.8364938$$

$$t \approx 8.84$$

So it takes 8.84 years, or about 8 years and 10 months, to double the money at 8% compounded semiannually.   □

Example 14   Compute the number of years necessary for a $1,000 investment to grow to $2,500 at 8% compounded quarterly.

Solution

$$A = P\left(1 + \frac{r}{n}\right)^{nt}$$

	Key	*Display*
$2{,}500 = 1{,}000\left(1 + \dfrac{.08}{4}\right)^{4t}$	$\boxed{2.5}$	2.5
$2.5 = (1.02)^{4t}$	$\boxed{\text{LOG}}$	$.39794000$
$4t = \dfrac{\log 2.5}{\log 1.02}$	$\boxed{\div}$	$.39794000$
	$\boxed{4}$	4
$t = \dfrac{\log 2.5}{4 \log 1.02}$	$\boxed{\div}$	$.099485002$
	$\boxed{1.02}$	1.02
≈ 11.567792	$\boxed{\text{LOG}}$	$.0086001717$
$t \approx 11.6$	$\boxed{=}$	11.567792

Approximately 11.6 years is required for the investment to grow to $2,500.   □

Problem Set 10.4

A   *Find the logarithm of each number in Problems 1–12.*

See Examples 1–3.
  1. log 45.6   **2.** log 981   **3.** ln .0639

  4. ln .00254   **5.** log 19,800   **6.** ln 566,000

See Examples 4–6.
  7. ln .3170   **8.** log .1980   **9.** $\log(3.16 \cdot 10^{-10})$

  10. $\ln(5.23 \cdot 10^{-6})$ **11.** $\ln(4.57 \cdot 10^{8})$ **12.** $\log(7.09 \cdot 10^{6})$

Chemistry.   The following is needed for Problems 13–20: The hydrogen potential, or pH, of a solution is

$$-\log [H^{+}]$$

where $[H^{+}]$ is the concentration of hydrogen ions in aqueous solution given in moles per liter.

In Problems 13–20 find the pH to the nearest hundredth, where the $[H^{+}]$ for the substance named is given.

See Example 7.
  13. Vinegar; $1.26 \cdot 10^{-3}$ **14.** Tomatoes; $6.31 \cdot 10^{-5}$

  15. Rainwater; $6.31 \cdot 10^{-7}$ **16.** Soft drink; $1.0 \cdot 10^{-3}$

  17. Milk of magnesia; $3.16 \cdot 10^{-11}$ **18.** Seawater; $3.16 \cdot 10^{-9}$

  19. Milk; $3.98 \cdot 10^{-7}$ **20.** Bread; $3.16 \cdot 10^{-6}$

B   *Use the laws of logarithms to solve for x in Problems 21–30.*

See Examples 8 and 9.
  21. $\log_b 2 + \frac{1}{2}\log_b 3 + 4 \log_b 5 = \log_b x$

  22. $\log_b x = \log_b 5 - 3 \log_b 2 + \frac{1}{4}\log_b 3$

  23. $\frac{1}{2}\log_b x = 3 \log_b 5 - \log_b x$ **24.** $\log_b x - \frac{1}{2}\log_b 2 = \frac{1}{2}\log_b(3x - 4)$

  25. $\log 2 = \frac{1}{4}\log 16 - \log x$ **26.** $\ln e = \ln \dfrac{\sqrt{2}}{x} - \ln e$

  27. $\ln \sqrt{2e} = \ln 1 + \ln x$ **28.** $\log 10 = \log\sqrt{1,000} - \log x$

  29. $\frac{1}{2}\log x - \log 100 = 2$ **30.** $2 = \ln \dfrac{e^{2}}{2} + \ln x$

Find the logarithm of each number in Problems 31–40.

See Examples 10–12
  31. $\log_\pi e$ **32.** $\log_e \pi$ **33.** $\log_3 e$

  34. $\log_2 \pi$ **35.** $\log_{1.03} 3$ **36.** $\log_{1.05} 2$

  37. $\log_{1.44} .000379$ **38.** $\log_{1.97} 1,237,000$ **39.** $\log_{.569}(2.63 \cdot 10^{11})$

  40. $\log_{4.58}(3.74 \cdot 10^{-8})$

Physics.   The following is needed for Problems 41–44.

The intensity of sound is measured in decibels. The number of decibels, N, is given by

Historical Note

The unit of intensity, the *decibel,* is named after Alexander Graham Bell, the inventor of the telephone.

$$N = \log\left(\frac{I}{I_0}\right)^{10} \quad or \quad 10 \cdot \log\frac{I}{I_0}$$

where I is the power of the sound in watts per square centimeter and I_0 is the power of sound just below the threshold of hearing (I_0 is approximately 10^{-16} watt/cm^2).

In Problems 41–44 find the number of decibels for the power of the given sound.

41. Whisper; 10^{-13} watt/cm^2 42. Traffic jam; 10^{-8} watt/cm^2
43. Rock concert; $5.23 \cdot 10^{-6}$ watt/cm^2
44. Normal conversation; $3.16 \cdot 10^{-10}$ watt/cm^2

Finance.   The following is needed for Problems 45–50: If P represents the principal invested at r percent annual interest and compounded n times a year, then A is the amount accumulated in t years,

$$A = P\left(1 + \frac{r}{n}\right)^{nt}$$

See Examples 13 and 14.

45. How long does it take (to the nearest $\frac{1}{10}$ year) a sum of money to double if it is earning $9\frac{1}{4}\%$ compounded quarterly?
46. A sum of money doubles in how many years (to the nearest $\frac{1}{10}$ year) while earning $5\frac{1}{2}\%$ compounded quarterly?
47. How long does it take an investment (to the nearest $\frac{1}{10}$ year) of $1,450 to grow to $2,000 if it earns 10% compounded monthly?
48. How long does it take (to the nearest $\frac{1}{10}$ year) to obtain $5,400 from an investment of $2,100 at 12% compounded monthly?
49. What rate (to the nearest $\frac{1}{10}$ percent) is necessary for an investment to double in 5 years if compounded quarterly?
50. What rate (to the nearest $\frac{1}{10}$ percent) is necessary for an investment to double in five years if compounded monthly?

Physics.   The following is needed for Problems 51–56: If an object at temperature B is surrounded by air at temperature A, it will gradually cool so that the temperature T, t minutes later, is given by

$$T = A + (B - A)10^{-kt}$$

This is Newton's law of cooling. The constant k depends on the particular object. If we restate the formula, the cooling constant is given by

$$k = \frac{1}{t}\log\frac{B - A}{T - A}$$

51. You draw a tub of hot water ($k = .01$) for a bath. The water is 100°F when drawn, and the room is 72°F. If you are called away to the phone, what is the temperature of the water 20 minutes later when you are able to get in?

52. You take a batch of chocolate chip cookies from the oven (250°F), and the room temperature is 74°F. If the cookies cool for 20 minutes and $k = .075$, what is their temperature?

53. It is known that the temperature of a given object fell from 120°F to 70°F in an hour when placed in 20°F air. What was the temperature of the object after 30 minutes?   *Hint:*   First find the cooling constant for this object.

54. An object is initially 100°F. In air of 40°F, it cools to 45°F in 20 minutes. What is its temperature in 30 minutes?

55. Using the information of Problem 53, how long will it take the object to cool to 40°F?

56. Using the information in Problem 54, how long will it take this object to cool to 75°F?

57. *Geoscience.* The *Richter scale* is a well-known means of measuring the magnitude, M, of an earthquake:

$$M = \log \frac{A}{A_0}$$

where A and A_0 are the amplitudes of the seismic (shock) waves of the measured earthquake and a quake that is taken as the norm. The size of an earthquake is properly measured by the energy released, E, in ergs. An approximation for this energy is given by

$$\log E = 11.8 + 1.5M$$

What was the energy released by the 1906 San Francisco quake that measured 8.3 on the Richter scale? Write the answer in scientific notation. (This energy, it is estimated, would be sufficient to provide the entire world's food requirements for a day.)

Mind Bogglers

58. *Physics.* A vertically fired projectile will reach a maximum height, H, as given by

$$H = \frac{1}{K}\left[V_0 - \frac{g}{K}\ln\left(1 + \frac{V_0 K}{g}\right)\right]$$

where V_0 is the initial velocity, the gravitational constant g is approximately 32 ft/sec², and K is a coefficient of air resistance. Let $K = 2.4$ and sketch the graph of the function $h(V_0) = H$. Use the graph as a basis to discuss the relationship of initial speed to the height attained.

59. Construct a logarithmic scale. On a sheet of paper, draw a line 10 inches long and mark it in tenths and hundredths. Place the edge of a second sheet along this line and use the first as a ruler to mark off logs on the second. At 0, mark 1 since $\log 1 = 0$. Mark 2 at .301,

3 at .477, and so on until you have something similar to the following illustration:

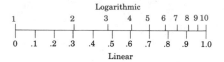

Fill in the scale between 1 and 2 for every tenth, and the others at least at the halves. Using two of these log scales, can you make a simple slide rule? *Explain* how your slide rule multiplies and divides.

60. Construct a coordinate system using logarithmic scales instead of the usual linear scales. The divisions will be irregular instead of evenly spaced. Sketch the graph of $y = x^2$ and explain the result.
61. Using the logarithmic coordinate system from Problem 60, sketch $y = x$ and explain the result.
62. Construct a coordinate system using the logarithmic scale on the vertical axis and a usual linear scale on the horizontal axis. Sketch $y = 2^x$ and explain the result.
63. Construct a coordinate system with a vertical linear scale and a horizontal logarithmic scale. Sketch the graph of $y = \log x$ and explain the result.

10.5 Additional Applications

There are many applications for the exponential and logarithmic functions. All the applied problems discussed in this section require a considerable amount of computation, and a calculator is needed to perform much of this computation.

The next couple of examples use the following: For budgeting, inventory, or tax purposes, businesses must depreciate equipment. An item may not be useful to a company even though it still functions, since it might have become too expensive to maintain. Perhaps it has become obsolete after n years. The value of an item at the end of its useful life is called its *scrap value, S,* given by

$$S = P(1 - r)^n$$

where P is the purchase price and r is the annual rate of depreciation.

Example 1 A small contractor in light construction depreciates a $40,000 tractor at the rate of 20% a year. What is the scrap value of the equipment in eight years?

Solution $P = 40{,}000 \qquad r = .20 \qquad n = 8$
$$S = 40{,}000(1 - .20)^8$$
$$= 40{,}000(.80)^8$$

| .8 | y^x | 8 | = | × | 40000 | = |

$$S \approx 6{,}710.8864$$
$$\approx 6{,}700$$

The scrap value is approximately $6,700.   □

Example 2   An $8,000 pickup truck is depreciated to $1,500 over five years of use. What is the rate of depreciation?

Solution $S = 1{,}500 \qquad P = 8{,}000 \qquad n = 5$
$$1{,}500 = 8{,}000(1 - r)^5$$
$$\frac{1{,}500}{8{,}000} = (1 - r)^5$$
$$\left(\frac{3}{16}\right)^{1/5} = 1 - r$$
$$r = 1 - \left(\frac{3}{16}\right)^{1/5}$$
$$= 1 - \left(\frac{3}{16}\right)^{.2}$$

| 3 | ÷ | 16 | = | y^x | .2 | = | +/− | + | 1 | = |

$$\approx .28451546$$
$$\approx .285$$

The rate of depreciation is approximately 28.5%.   □

More About Growth

Population growth is similar to other types of exponential growth. The population P_0 will grow to P in t years as approximated by

$$P = P_0 e^{kt}$$

where k is the growth rate. The constant k may be determined empirically. That is, given population figures from two years, you can calculate the rate of growth during that period of time.

City	1950	1960	1970	1980
Las Vegas, Nevada	24,624	64,405	125,787	164,275

The population figures show that Las Vegas has been an extremely fast-growing young city. How fast? Consider the following examples.

Example 3 Find the annual rate of growth for Las Vegas from 1970 to 1980.

Solution $P = 164{,}275 \qquad P_0 = 125{,}787 \qquad t = 10$

$$164{,}275 = 125{,}787 e^{10k}$$

$$\frac{164{,}275}{125{,}787} = e^{10k}$$

$$10k = \ln \frac{164{,}275}{125{,}787}$$

$$k = \frac{1}{10} \ln \frac{164{,}275}{125{,}787}$$

$$\boxed{164275} \;\boxed{\div}\; \boxed{125787} \;\boxed{=}\; \boxed{\text{LN}} \;\boxed{\div}\; \boxed{10} \;\boxed{=}$$

$$k \approx .026695185$$
$$k \approx .0267$$

Las Vegas grew at the rate of 2.67% per year during the ten year period 1970–1980. □

Example 4 Predict the population of Las Vegas in the year 2000, assuming it continues to grow at its 1970–1980 rate.

Solution $P_0 = 164{,}275 \qquad k = .0267 \qquad t = 20$

$$P = 164{,}275 e^{.0267(20)}$$
$$= 164{,}275 e^{.534}$$
$$\approx 280{,}210.70$$
$$\approx 280{,}000$$

The population will be about 280,000 in the year 2000. □

More About Interest

Compound interest earned on invested principal is an important application. An equally important application involves borrowing money, where you pay interest on a diminishing principal instead of earning interest on an increasing principal. Such loans are usually repaid in equal monthly installments. If P dollars are borrowed for n months at i monthly interest rate, the monthly payment, M, on the loan is given by

$$M = \frac{Pi}{1 - (1+i)^{-n}}$$

Example 5   What is the monthly house payment for a 30 year loan at 12% on $60,000?

Solution $P = 60,000 \qquad i = \dfrac{.12}{12} = .01 \qquad n = 30 \cdot 12 = 360$

$$M = \frac{60,000(.01)}{1 - (1 + .01)^{-360}}$$

$$= \frac{600}{1 - 1.01^{-360}}$$

$$\approx 617.16755$$

Key	Display
1.01	1.01
y^x	1.01
360	360
+/−	−360
=	.027816689
+/−	−.027816689
+	−.027816689
1	1
=	.972183311
1/x	1.0286126
×	1.0286126
600	600
=	617.16755

The monthly payment would be $617.17.   □

Calculating the result in Example 5 is definitely nontrivial and should put your understanding of your calculator to the test. The sequence of calculations may differ slightly from those on your particular model. Nonetheless, notice that +/− + changes the signs and adds for subtraction and that 1/x × takes the reciprocal and multiplies for division.

Is the result what you expected? The monthly payment of $617.17 for 30 years will total $222,181.20 for the $60,000 loan. Of this total, $162,181.20 is interest, which is rent on the borrowed money. You might compare this with a lower interest rate or a shorter-term loan.

Example 6   Find the monthly payment and the total paid on $60,000 borrowed for 20 years at 12%.

$$P = 60,000 \qquad i = .01 \qquad n = 20 \cdot 12 = 240$$

$$M = \frac{60,000(.01)}{1 - (1 + .01)^{-240}}$$

$$= \frac{600}{1 - (1.01)^{-240}}$$

$$\approx 660.65$$

$$240M \approx 158,556.40$$

Notice the increased monthly payment, but there is a substantial savings in total cost over the shorter period.

The monthly payment is $660.65, and the total paid is $158,556.   □

Example 7 What is the monthly payment and the total amount paid on a $60,000 loan at 9% for 30 years?

Solution $P = 60,000$ $i = \dfrac{.09}{12} = .0075$ $n = 30 \cdot 12 = 360$

$$M = \frac{60,000(.0075)}{1 - (1 + .0075)^{-360}}$$

$$= \frac{450}{1 - (1.0075)^{-360}}$$

$$\approx 482.77$$

$$360M = 173,797.20$$

$173,797.20 is paid in monthly payments of $482.77 each.   □

Problem Set 10.5

A *Business.   The following is required for Problems 1–6. The scrap value, S, of an item with a useful life of n years is given by*

$$S = P(1 - r)^n$$

where P is the original purchase price and r is the annual rate of depreciation.

See Example 1.

1. A delivery truck costs $12,500 and is used for six years. If it is depreciated at a rate of 15%, what is the scrap value?
2. An electric generator costs $39,000 and has an estimated life of 12 years. What is its scrap value if it is depreciated at 10%?

See Example 2.

3. A sand and gravel company purchases a piece of property for $215,000. It is estimated that the property will have a resale value of $35,000 after ten years. What is the rate of depreciation?
4. An apartment building is purchased for $382,000 and has an effective life of 40 years. If the site is still worth $50,000 after that period, what is the rate of depreciation?
5. A $15,000 machine has an expected life of eight years and a scrap value of $1,000. If the machine is replaced after five years, what is its value at the time of replacement?
6. A sales representative depreciates her car over five years. If it is purchased for $8,400 and presumed to have a scrap value of $950, what is its depreciated value after two years?

Sociology.   The following is required for Problems 7–14: The population P after t years is given by

$$P = P_0 e^{kt}$$

where P_0 is the initial population and k is the growth rate.

Populations of Eight
U.S. Cities

City	1950	1960	1970	1980
Cleveland, Ohio	914,804	876,050	750,879	572,532
Boston, Massachusetts	801,444	697,197	641,071	562,118
Pittsburgh, Pennsylvania	676,806	604,332	520,089	423,962
Milwaukee, Wisconsin	637,392	741,324	717,372	632,989
Denver, Colorado	415,786	493,887	514,678	488,765
San Antonio, Texas	408,442	587,718	654,153	783,296
Memphis, Tennessee	396,000	497,524	623,988	644,838
San Jose, California	95,280	204,196	459,913	625,763

See Example 3.

7. Determine the rate of growth for San Antonio, Texas, over the periods 1950–1960, 1960–1970, and 1970–1980.

8. Find the rates of growth for Cleveland, Ohio, over the periods 1950–1960, 1960–1970, and 1970–1980. (Note that the population is decreasing and will have a negative rate of growth.)

See Example 4.

9. If Boston, Massachusetts, had continued to decline at its 1950–1970 rate, what would the population have been in 1980? (Note that the decline actually accelerated.)

10. If Denver, Colorado, had continued to grow at its 1960–1970 rate, what would its 1980 population have been? (Note that it actually declined.)

11. If San Jose, California, continues to grow at its 1970–1980 rate, estimate its population in the year 2000.

12. If Pittsburgh, Pennsylvania, continues to decline at its 1970–1980 rate, estimate its population in 1990.

13. If Memphis, Tennessee, grew uniformly during the decade 1960–1970, estimate its population in 1964.

14. Estimate the 1977 population of Milwaukee, Wisconsin. Assume that its population change was uniform during the 1970–1980 period.

B *Finance. The following is required for Problems 15–20: If P dollars are borrowed for n months at i monthly interest rate, the monthly payment, M, on the loan is given by* How much payed back is ∧ (M)

$$M = \frac{Pi}{1 - (1 + i)^{-n}}$$

See Examples 5–7.

15. A home loan is for $45,000 at 9% for 30 years. Find the monthly payment.

16. Find the monthly payment for a $70,000 home loan at 10% for 30 years.

17. The total cost of a new car is $9,673.54. Suppose that $873.54 is given as a down payment, and the remainder is financed at $11\frac{3}{4}$% for five years. What is the monthly payment on the new car loan?

18. New furniture is purchased for a total cost of $2,040.47. If a down payment of $340.47 is made, what is the monthly payment on a loan at $12\frac{1}{2}$% for four years?

19. An engagement ring is purchased on time. If the $1,100 cost is financed at 11.5% for six years, what is the monthly payment?

20. If the ring in Problem 19 is put on a credit card with a 21% charge, what monthly installment would be necessary to pay off the debt in the same time?

Sociology. *The following article is needed for Problems 21–25.*

THE PRESS DEMOCRAT

The Redwood Empire's Leading Newspaper **25** *cents*

SANTA ROSA, CALIF., SUNDAY, MARCH 28, 1976

World population 4 billion tonight

By EDWARD K. DeLONG

WASHINGTON (UPI) — By midnight tonight, the Earth's population will reach the 4 billion mark, twice the number of people living on the planet just 46 years ago, the Population Reference Bureau said Saturday.

The bureau expressed no joy at the new milestone.

It said global birth rates are too high, placing serious pressures on all aspects of future life and causing "major concern" in the world scientific community, and more than one-third of the present population has yet to reach child-bearing age.

The PRB found cause for optimism, however, in that some governments are stressing birth control to blunt the impact of "explosive growth" and the population growth rate dropped slightly in the past year.

"In 1976, each new dawn brings a formidable increase of approximately 195,000 newborn infants to share the resources of our finite world," it said.

One expert warned that a lack of jobs, rather than too little food, may be the "ultimate threat" facing society as the planet becomes more and more crowded.

It took between two and three million years for the human race to hit the one billion mark in 1850, the PRB said. By 1930, 80 years later, the population stood at 2 billion. A mere 31 years after that, in 1961, it was 3 billion. The growth from 3 to the present 4 billion took just 16 years.

The world could find it has 5 billion people by 1989 — just 13 years from now — if population growth continues at the present rate of 1.8 per cent a year, said Dr. Leon F. Bouvier, vice president of the private, nonprofit PRB.

Bouvier said the newly calculated growth rate is a little lower than the 1.9 per cent estimated last year. Thanks to that slowdown, the passing of the 4 billion milestone came a year later than some demographers had predicted.

"I really think the rate of growth is going to start declining ever so slightly because of declining fertility," Bouvier said. "I think there is some evidence of progress — ever so slow, much too slow."

The new PRB figures show there were 3,982,815,000 people on Earth on Jan. 1. By March 1 the number had grown to 3,994,812,000, the organization said, and by April 1 the total will be 4,000,824,000.

The bureau said its calculations are based on estimates of 328,000 live births per day minus 133,000 deaths.

A growing number of governments are taking steps to slow growth rates, the PRB said.

Singapore appears likely to meet the goal of the two-child family "well before the target date of 1980," it said, and several states in India, which yearly adds the equivalent of the population of Australia, are considering financial incentives to birth control and mandatory sterilization after the birth of two children.

Dr. Paul Ehrlich of Stanford University, one of several population experts contacted by PRB, said he was sad to realize at the age of 44 he had lived through a doubling of Earth's population. He expressed fear the next 44 years could see population growth halted "by a horrifying increase in death rates."

"At this point, hunger does not seem the greatest issue presented by the ever growing number of people," said Dr. Louis M. Hellman, chief of population staff at the Health, Education and Welfare Department.

"Rather, the threat appears to lie in the increasing numbers who can find no work. As these masses of unemployed migrate toward the cities, they create a growing impetus toward political unrest and instability."

21. According to the article, it took 80 years for the world's population to double from 1 to 2 billion. What was the rate of growth during that period?

22. The article mentions that the number of people in the world doubled from 2 billion in 1930 to 4 billion in 1976. What was the rate of growth over that period?

23. Using the current rate of growth, estimate the years in which the world population will be 5, 6, 7, and 8 billion.

24. Information subsequent to the article indicates that world population growth is slowing. From 1975 to 1980, the rate was estimated at 1.7%. If this rate continues, in what year will the world figures reach 5, 6, 7, and 8 billion?

25. Using the information in the article, estimate the world population in the year 2001 to the nearest ten million.

Mind Bogglers **26.** If $a^2 + b^2 = 7ab$, show that

$$\log(a + b) - \log 3 = \tfrac{1}{2}(\log a + \log b)$$

Geoscience. *Use the table below and a recent Almanac listing of oil consumption to answer the questions posed in Problems 27–31.*

World Consumption of Petroleum Products

Year	Millions of Barrels
1915	43
1920	68
1925	110
1930	150
1935	170
1940	220
1945	260
1950	340
1955	480
1960	780
1965	1,130
1970	1,670

27. Establish that the use of petroleum has grown exponentially.

28. Estimate the rate of growth of the worldwide use of petroleum.

29. Forecast figures for 1975, 1980, 1990, ...

30. Verify forecast figures for years for which data are available.

31. How do these figures compare to estimated world petroleum reserves? Graph use and remaining reserves on one grid. What conclusions do you reach?

10.6 Review Problems

Fill in the word or words that make the statements in Problems 1–10 complete and correct.

(10.1) **1.** The equation $f(x) = b^x$, $b > 0$, $b \neq 1$, defines an _____ function.

(10.1) **2.** For nonzero real x and y and $a > 0$, $a \neq 1$, if $a^x = a^y$, then _____.

(10.2) **3.** If n increases, $\left(1 + \dfrac{1}{n}\right)^n$ _____ the number e, which is approximately 2.7182818.

(10.3) **4.** If r is the exponent of s that yields t, then _____ or _____.

(10.3) **5.** For $b > 0$, $b \neq 1$, $x = b^y$ is equivalent to $y =$ _____.

(10.3) **6.** The log of the product of two numbers is the _____ of the numbers.

(10.3) **7.** The log of _____ is _____ for any base.

(10.3) **8.** If the base is 10, the logarithms are called _____ logarithms.

(10.4) **9.** If $n = b \cdot 10^C$, $1 \leq b < 10$, and C an integer, then n is in _____.

(10.3) **10.** If $\log_b x = \log_b y$, then _____.

(10.1) **11.** Sketch the graphs.
  a. $y = e^x$ **b.** $y = 2^{-x^2}$ **c.** $y = \log x$

(10.1) **12.** Solve for x.
  a. $13^x = 169$ **b.** $343^x = \frac{1}{49}$ **c.** $x^{-2/3} = \frac{100}{121}$

(10.3) **13.** Rewrite $2^3 = 8$ in logarithmic form.

(10.3) **14.** Rewrite $\log_8 4 = \frac{2}{3}$ in exponential form.

(10.3, 10.5) **15.** Find the value of the variable.
  a. $\log 31.7 = a$ **b.** $b = \log .00683$ **c.** $\log c = 2.4536$
  d. $d = \ln 1.05$ **e.** $x = \log_\pi e$ **f.** $-.3245 = \log f$
  g. $\log_2 g = 3$ **h.** $\log_h 16 = -.25$ **i.** $\log_\pi 1 = y$

(10.3) **16.** Use the laws of logarithms to expand.
  a. $\log ab$ **b.** $\log_b c\sqrt{d}$ **c.** $\ln ke^{-ht}$ **d.** $\log \dfrac{5(6)^3}{\sqrt{160}}$

(10.4) **17.** Find the logarithms.
  a. $\log 1730$ **b.** $\log .0000731$ **c.** $\ln 31.7 \cdot 10^9$

(10.2, 10.5) **18.** *Finance.* For continuously compounded interest, the amount, A, accumulated after t years is

$$A = Pe^{rt}$$

where P is the principal and r is the annual rate.
  a. Calculate the amount after eight years at 5% on a $1,500 investment.
  b. Let $P = 1$, $t = 10$ and sketch $A = f(r)$.
  c. Find the rate at which the investment doubles in 12 years.

(10.4)   **19.**   *Astronomy.*   The *limiting magnitude, LM,* of an optical telescope is a function of its diameter, d (in inches):

$$LM = 8.8 + 51 \log d$$

Find the *LM* for:
a. The 200 inch reflecting telescope at Hale Observatory on Mt. Palomar, California
b. The 120 inch reflector at Lick Observatory on Mt. Hamilton near San Jose, California
c. An amateur's home six-incher

(10.5)   **20.**   *Finance.*   If P dollars are borrowed for n months at i monthly interest rate, the monthly payment, M, on the loan is given by

$$M = \frac{Pi}{1 - (1 + i)^{-n}}$$

What is the monthly house payment for a 30 year loan at 14% on an $80,000 loan?

CHAPTER

11

Sequences, Series, and the Binomial Theorem

Contents

11.1   **Arithmetic and Geometric Sequences**

ARE YOU A GENIUS?

EACH problem is a series of some sort—that is, a succession of either letters, numbers or drawings—with the last item in the series missing. Each series is arranged according to a different rule and, in order to identify the missing item, you must figure out what that rule is.

Now, it's your turn to play. Give yourself a maximum of 20 minutes to answer the 15 questions. If you haven't finished in that time, stop anyway. In the test problems done with drawings, it is always the top row or group that needs to be completed by choosing one drawing from the bottom row.

PROBLEM 1

A D G J . . .

PROBLEM 2

1 3 6 10 . . .

PROBLEM 3

1 1 2 3 5 . . .

PROBLEM 4

21 20 18 15 11 . . .

PROBLEM 5

8 6 7 5 6 4 . . .

PROBLEM 6

40 35 34 29 28 23 . . .

PROBLEM 7

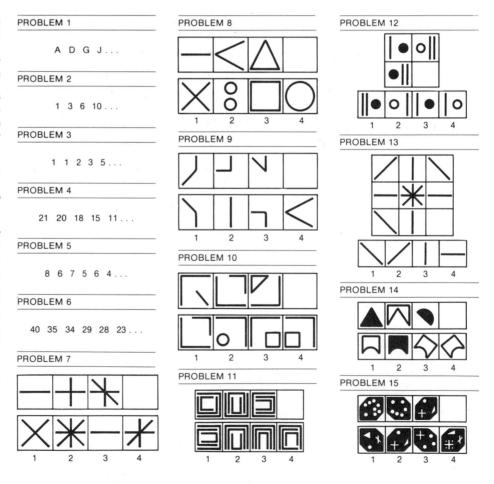

PROBLEM 8

PROBLEM 9

PROBLEM 10

PROBLEM 11

PROBLEM 12

PROBLEM 13

PROBLEM 14

PROBLEM 15

Have you ever taken an IQ test where you were asked to fill in the blanks to complete a given pattern? For example, try to fill in each blank space with the result of a pattern you see. There may be more than one answer. (Solutions will be given later.)

1. 1, 4, 7, 10, 13, _____
2. 20, 14, 8, 2, −4, −10, _____
3. a, $a+d$, $a+2d$, $a+3d$, $a+4d$, _____
4. 2, 4, 8, 16, 32, _____
5. 10, 5, $\frac{5}{2}$, $\frac{5}{4}$, $\frac{5}{8}$, _____
6. a, ar, ar^2, ar^3, ar^4, _____
7. 1, 2, 1, 1, 2, 1, 1, _____
8. 1, 1, 2, 3, 5, 8, 13, _____
9. 1, 2, 4, 7, 11, 16, _____
10. 1, 3, 4, 7, 11, 18, _____

Did you find some examples easier than others? The reason for the ease of working some of the problems and the difficulty of others has to do with the way in which the pattern is constructed.

The easiest types of patterns to discover are those that are special types of functions called **sequences** or **progressions.**

INFINITE
SEQUENCE

> An **infinite sequence** is a function whose domain is the set of counting numbers.

Precisely, an infinite sequence is the *range* of a function whose domain is the set of natural numbers.

Remember that the set of counting numbers is

$$N = \{1, 2, 3, \ldots, n, \ldots\}$$

For convenience, we sometimes refer to an infinite sequence simply as a *sequence* or *progression.*

Sometimes we talk of a *finite sequence*, which means that we are considering as the domain the finite set

$$\{1, 2, 3, \ldots, n-1, n\}$$

There are two special types of sequences studied in this chapter. The first is an **arithmetic sequence** and is illustrated by the first three examples. In any arithmetic sequence, there is a common difference between successive terms. That is, if any term is subtracted from the next term, the result is always the same, and this number is called the **common difference.**

Example 1   1, 4, 7, 10, 13, _____

Solution
$$4 - 1 = 3$$
$$7 - 4 = 3$$
$$10 - 7 = 3$$
$$13 - 10 = 3$$

The common difference is 3.

$$x - 13 = 3$$ Where x is the missing term.
$$x = 16$$

Thus, 16 is the next term.   □

Example 2   20, 14, 8, 2, −4, −10, _____

Solution   The common difference is −6, so

$$x - (-10) = -6$$

where x is the missing term.

$$x = -16$$

Thus, −16 is the next term.   □

Example 3 $a, a + d, a + 2d, a + 3d, a + 4d,$ _____

Solution   The common difference is d, so

$$x - (a + 4d) = d$$
$$x = a + 5d$$

Thus, the next term is $a + 5d$.   □

Examples 4–6 are examples of **geometric sequences.** There is a common ratio between successive terms. If any term is divided into the next term, the result is always the same, and this number is called the **common ratio.**

Example 4   2, 4, 8, 16, 32, _____

Solution
$$\frac{4}{2} = 2$$
$$\frac{8}{4} = 2$$
$$\frac{16}{8} = 2$$
$$\frac{32}{16} = 2$$

The common ratio is 2.

$$\frac{x}{32} = 2$$ Where x is the next term.

$$x = 64$$

Thus, $x = 64$ is the next term.   □

Example 5 $10, 5, \frac{5}{2}, \frac{5}{4}, \frac{5}{8}, \underline{\hspace{1.5cm}}$

Solution   The common ratio is $\frac{1}{2}$, so

$$\frac{x}{\frac{5}{8}} = \frac{1}{2} \qquad \text{Where } x \text{ is the missing term.}$$

$$x = \frac{5}{16}$$

Thus, $x = \frac{5}{16}$ is the next term. $\square$

Example 6 $a, ar, ar^2, ar^3, ar^4, \underline{\hspace{1.5cm}}$

Solution   The common ratio is r, so

$$\frac{x}{ar^4} = r$$

$$x = ar^5$$

The next term is ar^5. $\square$

Examples 7–10 illustrate patterns that are neither arithmetic nor geometric. You can verify this by trying to find a common difference or a common ratio for each. We will not develop any formal methods for these other types of patterns, but rather we'll focus attention on arithmetic and geometric sequences.

In Examples 7–10 show the next few terms of each sequence.

Example 7 $1, 2, 1, 1, 2, 1, 1, \underline{\hspace{1.5cm}}$

Solution $1, 2, 1, 1, 2, 1, 1, \mathbf{1, 2, 1, 1, 1, 1, 2,} \ldots$
or
$1, 2, 1, 1, 2, 1, 1, \mathbf{2, 1, 1, 2, 1, 1, 2,} \ldots$

The pattern of the first few terms doesn't have to specify a unique sequence. Can you think of another pattern? $\square$

Example 8 $1, 1, 2, 3, 5, 8, 13, \underline{\hspace{1.5cm}}$

Solution $1, 1, 2, 3, 5, 8, 13, \mathbf{21, 34, 55, 89,} \ldots$

Historical Note

The sequence in Example 8 is known as the *Fibonacci numbers*. See the Historical Note on page 381.

Notice:

$1 + 1 = 2$	$3 + 5 = 8$
$1 + 2 = 3$	$5 + 8 = 13$
$2 + 3 = 5$	$8 + 13 = \mathbf{21}$

Each term, after the first two, is obtained by adding the two preceding terms. $\square$

Example 9   1, 2, 4, 7, 11, 16, _____

Solution   1, 2, 4, 7, 11, 16, **22, 29, 37, 46, . . .**

Look at the differences between terms:

$$2 - 1 = 1 \qquad 11 - 7 = 4$$
$$4 - 2 = 2 \qquad 16 - 11 = 5$$
$$7 - 4 = 3 \qquad \vdots$$

Each difference is one greater. ☐

Example 10   1, 3, 4, 7, 11, 18, _____

Solution   1, 3, 4, 7, 11, 18, **29, 47, 76, . . .**

Compare with Example 8. ☐

A new notation is usually used with sequences. Remember that the domain is the set of counting numbers, so we might define a sequence by

$$s(n) = 3n - 2 \qquad \text{where } n \in \{1, 2, 3, \ldots\}$$

Thus,

$$s(1) = 3(1) - 2 = 1$$
$$s(2) = 3(2) - 2 = 4$$
$$s(3) = 3(3) - 2 = 7$$
$$\vdots$$

However, instead of writing $s(1)$, write s_1; in place of $s(2)$, use s_2; and so on. In place of $s(n)$, write s_n. Thus, s_{15} means the 15th term of the sequence, and you find s_{15} in the same fashion as if you used the notation $s(15)$.

$$s_{15} = 3(15) - 2$$
$$= 43$$

In Examples 11–15 find the first four terms of the sequences whose nth terms are given.

Example 11 $s_n = 26 - 6n$

Solution $s_1 = 26 - 6 = 20$
$s_2 = 26 - 6(2) = 14$
$s_3 = 26 - 6(3) = 8$
$s_4 = 26 - 6(4) = 2$

The sequence is 20, 14, 8, 2, ... ☐

Example 12 $s_n = (-1)^n n^2$

Solution $s_1 = (-1)^1(1)^2 = -1$
$s_2 = (-1)^2(2)^2 = 4$
$s_3 = (-1)^3(3)^2 = -9$
$s_4 = (-1)^4(4)^2 = 16$

The sequence is $-1, 4, -9, 16, \ldots$ $\square$

Example 13 $s_n = s_{n-1} + s_{n-2}$, $n \geq 3$, where $s_1 = 1$ and $s_2 = 2$

Solution $s_1 = 1$ Given
$s_2 = 2$ Given
$s_3 = s_2 + s_1$
$\quad = 2 + 1$ By substitution
$\quad = 3$
$s_4 = s_3 + s_2$
$\quad = 3 + 2$
$\quad = 5$

The sequence is $1, 2, 3, 5, \ldots$ (Compare with Example 8.) $\square$

Example 14 $s_n = 2n$

Solution $s_1 = 2$
$s_2 = 4$
$s_3 = 6$
$s_4 = 8$

The sequence is $2, 4, 6, 8, \ldots$ $\square$

Example 15 $s_n = 2n + (n - 1)(n - 2)(n - 3)(n - 4)$

Solution $s_1 = 2(1) + 0 = 2$
$s_2 = 2(2) + 0 = 4$
$s_3 = 2(3) + 0 = 6$
$s_4 = 2(4) + 0 = 8$

The sequence is $2, 4, 6, 8, \ldots$ $\square$

Notice from Examples 14 and 15 above that if only a finite number of successive terms are known and the nth term is not given, then a *unique* nth term cannot be given. Sometimes the nth term is called the **general term.** That is, if you are given the sequence

$2, 4, 6, 8, \underline{\hspace{2cm}}$

the next term is probably 10 (if you are thinking of the general term of Example 14), but it *may* be something different. In Example 15,

$$s_5 = 2(5) + (5-1)(5-2)(5-3)(5-4)$$
$$= 10 + (4)(3)(2)(1)$$
$$= 34$$

You are usually looking for the simplest general term, but nevertheless, remember that answers aren't unique *unless you are given* the general term.

Problem Set 11.1

A *Classify the sequences in Problems 1–15 as arithmetic, geometric, or neither, and then supply the missing term.*

See Examples 1–10.

1. $2, 5, 8, 11, 14,$ _____
2. $1, 2, 1, 1, 2, 1, 1, 1, 2, 1, 1, 1, 1,$ _____
3. $3, 6, 12, 24, 48,$ _____
4. $5, -15, 45, -135, 405,$ _____
5. $100, 99, 97, 94, 90,$ _____
6. $1, 1, 2, 3, 5, 8, 13,$ _____
7. $p, pq, pq^2, pq^3, pq^4,$ _____
8. $97, 86, 75, 64,$ _____
9. $8, 12, 18, 26,$ _____
10. $5^5, 5^4, 5^3, 5^2,$ _____
11. $2, 5, 2, 5, 5, 2, 5, 5, 5,$ _____
12. $5, -5, -15, -25, -35,$ _____
13. $1, \frac{1}{2}, \frac{1}{3}, \frac{2}{3}, \frac{1}{4}, \frac{3}{4}, \frac{1}{5}, \frac{2}{5}, \frac{3}{5}, \frac{4}{5}, \frac{1}{6},$ _____
14. $\frac{4}{3}, 2, 3, 4\frac{1}{2},$ _____
15. $1, 8, 27, 64, 125,$ _____

Find the first three terms of the sequences whose nth terms are given in Problems 16–27.

See Examples 11–15.

16. $s_n = 4n - 3$ 17. $s_n = -3 + 3n$ 18. $s_n = \dfrac{10}{2^{n-1}}$

19. $s_n = a + nd$ 20. $s_n = ar^{n-1}$ 21. $s_n = \dfrac{n-1}{n+1}$

22. $s_n = (-1)^n$ 23. $s_n = (-1)^n(n+1)$ 24. $s_n = 1 + \dfrac{1}{n}$

25. $s_n = \dfrac{n+1}{n}$ 26. $s_n = 2$ 27. $s_n = -5$

B   28. Find the 15th term of the sequence $s_n = 4n - 3$.

See Examples 11–15.   29. Find the 102nd term of the sequence $s_n = -3 + 3n$.

30. Find the 10th term of the sequence $s_n = 10/2^{n-1}$.

31. Find the 20th term of the sequence $s_n = (-1)^n(n+1)$.
32. Find the 3rd term of the sequence $(-1)^{n+1}5^{n+1}$.
33. Find the 2nd term of the sequence $(-1)^{n-1}7^{n-1}$.
34. Find the first five terms of the sequence where $s_1 = 2$ and $s_n = 3s_{n-1}$, $n \geq 2$.
35. Find the first five terms of the sequence where $s_1 = 3$ and $s_n = \frac{1}{3}s_{n-1}$, $n \geq 2$.
36. Find the first five terms of the sequence where $s_1 = 1$, $s_2 = 1$, and $s_n = s_{n-1} + s_{n-2}$, $n \geq 3$.
37. Find the first five terms of the sequence where $s_1 = 1$, $s_2 = 3$, and $s_n = s_{n-1} + s_{n-2}$, $n \geq 3$.

Mind Bogglers *Find the next term for each sequence in Problems 38–41.*

38. $1, 3, 4, 7, 11, 18, 29,$ _____
39. $225, 625, 1225, 2025,$ _____
40. $8, 5, 4, 9, 1,$ _____
41. $3, 3, 5, 4, 4, 3, 5, 5, 4, 3,$ _____

11.2 Arithmetic Series and Sequences

Historical Note

Fibonacci was born about 1175 in Pisa, Italy. His famous work *Liber abaci* did much to promote the introduction of Hindu–Arabic notation in Europe. The sequence arises from the problem: "How many pairs of rabbits can be produced in a year from an initial pair, if each pair produces a new pair which from the second month on becomes productive?" Curiously, the sequence has many interesting applications, including art, biology, and the logarithmic spiral.

Let's concentrate on *arithmetic* sequences and for convenience denote the terms of an arithmetic sequence by $a_1, a_2, a_3, a_4, \ldots, a_n$. The a will remind us that the sequence is *arithmetic*. Recall that an arithmetic sequence has a *common difference* between successive terms, denoted by d:

$$a_n - a_{n-1} = d \qquad \text{for every} \quad n > 1$$

If you write this as

$$a_n = a_{n-1} + d$$

and let $n = 2$, then

$$a_2 = a_1 + d$$

and

$$\begin{aligned}
a_3 &= a_2 + d \\
&= (a_1 + d) + d \\
&= a_1 + 2d \\
a_4 &= a_3 + d \\
&= (a_1 + 2d) + d \\
&= a_1 + 3d \\
&\ \vdots \\
a_n &= a_1 + (n-1)d
\end{aligned}$$

This formula gives the nth term when the first term and common difference are known.

For an arithmetic sequence $a_1, a_2, a_3, a_4, \ldots, a_n$, with common difference d:

$$a_n = a_1 + (n-1)d \qquad \text{for every} \quad n \geq 1$$

Example 1   Find an expression for the general term of the arithmetic sequence 18, 14, 10, 6, ...

Solution $a_1 = 18 \qquad d = 14 - 18 = -4$
$a_n = 18 + (n-1)(-4)$
$\quad = 18 - 4n + 4$
$\quad = 22 - 4n$ □

In Examples 2–4 find the missing quantities.

Example 2 $a_1 = 5 \qquad d = 3 \qquad a_{10} = ?$

Solution   Find a_n, where $n = 10$:

$a_n = a_1 + (n-1)d$
$a_{10} = 5 + (10-1)3$
$a_{10} = 5 + 27$
$a_{10} = 32$ □

Example 3 $a_1 = -4 \qquad a_{12} = 51 \qquad d = ?$

Solution   Find the common difference:

$a_n = a_1 + (n-1)d$
$51 = -4 + (12-1)d$
$51 = -4 + 11d$
$55 = 11d$
$5 = d$ □

Example 4 $a_1 = 43 \qquad a_{10} = 7 \qquad a_{25} = ?$

Solution   First, find the common difference:

$a_{10} = a_1 + (n-1)d$
$7 = 43 + 9d$
$-36 = 9d$
$-4 = d$

Now, find the twenty-fifth term:

$a_{25} = 43 + 24(-4)$
$a_{25} = 43 - 96$
$a_{25} = -53$ □

Arithmetic Series

What is the total number of blocks in the diagram shown in Figure 11.1?

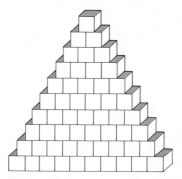

Figure 11.1

There are 10 blocks on the bottom row, 9 on the next row, . . . , and 1 on the top row. Thus, the number of blocks in each row is an arithmetic sequence,

$$1, 2, 3, 4, 5, 6, 7, 8, 9, 10$$

and the answer is the sum

$$1 + 2 + 3 + 4 + 5 + 6 + 7 + 8 + 9 + 10$$

Such a sum is called a **series,** and in this case, an *arithmetic series.*

SERIES

> The indicated sum of the terms of a sequence $s_1, s_2, s_3, \ldots, s_n$ is a **series,**
>
> $$S_n = s_1 + s_2 + s_3 + \cdots + s_n$$

To answer the question about the blocks, consider the series

$$1 + 2 + 3 + \cdots + 9 + 10 = 55$$

However, if the bottom row of blocks contained 100 blocks, direct addition would be very tedious, so investigate some other method for finding the sum of a series. Consider the sum A_n of the first n terms of an arithmetic sequence:

$$A_n = a_1 + a_2 \ + a_3 \ + \cdots + a_{n-2} + a_{n-1} + a_n$$

$$A_n = a_n + a_{n-1} + a_{n-2} + \cdots + a_3 \ + a_2 \ + a_1$$

We have simply reversed the order of the terms.

If these equations are added term-by-term as shown, you obtain

$$2A_n = (a_1 + a_n) + (a_2 + a_{n-1}) + (a_3 + a_{n-2})$$
$$+ \cdots + (a_{n-2} + a_3) + (a_{n-1} + a_2) + (a_n + a_1)$$

Now each of the quantities within parentheses can be rewritten.

$$a_1 + a_n = a_1 + [a_1 + (n-1)d]$$
$$= 2a_1 + (n-1)d$$

$$a_2 + a_{n-1} = (a_1 + d) + [a_1 + (n-2)d]$$
$$= 2a_1 + (n-1)d \longleftarrow \text{Notice that this is the same result as } a_1 + a_n.$$

$$a_3 + a_{n-1} = (a_1 + 2d) + [a_1 + (n-3)d]$$
$$= 2a_1 + (n-1)d \longleftarrow \text{Aha! The same result again.}$$

There is a total of n such sums, so

$$2A_n = n[2a_1 + (n-1)d]$$

$$A_n = \frac{n}{2}[2a_1 + (n-1)d]$$

Or, replacing $2a_1 + (n-1)d$ by $a_1 + a_n$, you obtain

$$A_n = \frac{n}{2}(a_1 + a_n)$$

which is n times the average of the first and last terms.

First Last
term term
↓ ↓
$$A_n = n\left(\frac{a_1 + a_n}{2}\right)$$

Average of
first and
last terms

For the question of the number of blocks,

$$A_{10} = 1 + 2 + 3 + \cdots + 9 + 10$$

First   Last
term   term
↓   ↓
$$= 10\left(\frac{1 + 10}{2}\right)$$

└─Number of terms

$$= 10\left(\frac{11}{2}\right)$$

$$= 55$$

If the bottom row contained 100 blocks, the total number of blocks, A_{100}, is found by

$$A_{100} = 100\left(\frac{1+100}{2}\right)$$

$$= 50(101)$$

$$= 5{,}050$$

ARITHMETIC SERIES

For an arithmetic sequence $a_1, a_2, a_3, a_4, \ldots, a_n$, with common difference d,

$$A_n = \frac{n}{2}(a_1 + a_n) \qquad \text{or} \qquad A_n = \frac{n}{2}[2a_1 + (n-1)d]$$

Example 5 Find the sum of the first 50 terms of the arithmetic sequence whose first term is -10 and whose common difference is 4.

Solution $a_1 = -10 \qquad n = 50 \qquad d = 4$

$$A_n = \frac{n}{2}[2a_1 + (n-1)d]$$

$$A_{50} = \frac{50}{2}[2(-10) + 49(4)]$$

$$= 25(-20 + 196)$$

$$= 4{,}400 \qquad \qquad \square$$

Example 6 Find the sum of the first 100 even integers.

Solution The finite sequence is 2, 4, 6, . . . , 200.

$$a_1 = 2 \qquad a_{100} = 200$$

$$A_{100} = 100\left(\frac{2+200}{2}\right)$$

$$= 100(101)$$

$$= 10{,}100 \qquad \qquad \square$$

Alternate Solution The last term doesn't have to be used since it is known that $n = 100$, $a_1 = 2$, and $d = 2$. You can also use

$$A_n = \frac{n}{2}[2a_1 + (n-1)d]$$

$$A_{100} = \frac{100}{2}[2(2) + (99)(2)]$$

$$= 50(4 + 198)$$

$$= 10{,}100 \qquad \qquad \square$$

Example 7   Find the missing quantity:

$$a_1 = -10 \qquad a_9 = -66 \qquad A_{20} = ?$$

Solution   First find d; then find A_{20}.

$$a_9 = a_1 + (n-1)d$$
$$-66 = -10 + (9-1)d$$
$$-56 = 8d$$
$$-7 = d$$

$$A_n = \frac{n}{2}[2a_1 + (n-1)d]$$

$$A_{20} = \frac{20}{2}[2(-10) + 19(-7)]$$

$$= 10(-20 - 133)$$
$$= 10(-153)$$
$$= -1{,}530$$

Problem Set 11.2

A *Use the formula $a_n = a_1 + (n-1)d$ to find an expression for the general term of each arithmetic sequence in Problems 1–10.*

See Examples 1–3.

1. 3, 7, 11, 15, . . .

2. 2, 7, 12, 17, . . .

3. 6, 11, 16, . . .

4. 35, 46, 57, . . .

5. −8, −1, 6, . . .

6. −1, 1, 3, . . .

7. 151, 142, 133, . . .

8. 76, 89, 102, . . .

9. $x, 2x, 3x, \ldots$

10. $x - 5a, \ x - 3a, \ x - a$

Write out the first four terms of the arithmetic sequences in Problems 11–20, where the first element is a_1 and the common difference is d. Also, find the general term.

See Examples 2–4.

11. $a_1 = 5; \quad d = 4$

12. $a_1 = 85; \quad d = 3$

13. $a_1 = -15; \quad d = 8$

14. $a_1 = -22; \quad d = 7$

15. $a_1 = 100; \quad d = -5$

16. $a_1 = 20; \quad d = -4$

17. $a_1 = \frac{1}{2}; \quad d = \frac{3}{2}$

18. $a_1 = \frac{5}{3}; \quad d = -\frac{2}{3}$

19. $a_1 = 5; \quad d = x$

20. $a_1 = x; \quad d = y$

B *Find the missing quantities in Problems 21–40 for the given arithmetic sequences.*

See Examples 2–7.

21. $a_1 = 6; \quad d = 5; \quad a_{20} = ?$

22. $a_1 = 35; \quad d = 11; \quad a_{10} = ?$

23. $a_1 = -30; \quad d = 4; \quad a_{12} = ?$

24. $a_1 = 19; \quad d = -8; \quad a_{10} = ?$

25. $a_1 = -5; \quad a_{30} = -63; \quad d = ?$

26. $a_1 = 4; \quad a_6 = 24; \quad d = ?$

27. $a_1 = \frac{1}{2}; \quad a_7 = \frac{13}{2}; \quad d = ?$

28. $a_1 = -\frac{7}{3}; \quad a_{12} = \frac{4}{3}; \quad d = ?$

29. $a_1 = 35$; $d = 11$; $A_{10} = ?$ **30.** $a_1 = -7$; $d = -2$; $A_{100} = ?$
31. $a_1 = 17$; $a_{10} = -55$; $A_{10} = ?$ **32.** $a_1 = -29$; $a_8 = 20$; $A_8 = ?$
33. $a_1 = 4$; $a_6 = 24$; $A_{15} = ?$ **34.** $a_1 = -5$; $a_{30} = -63$; $A_{10} = ?$
35. $a_1 = -8$; $a_5 = 12$; $A_{10} = ?$ **36.** $a_1 = 12$; $a_5 = -8$; $A_{10} = ?$
37. $a_1 = 100$; $a_{11} = 30$; $A_{25} = ?$ **38.** $a_1 = 125$; $a_6 = 90$; $A_{19} = ?$
39. $a_1 = -1$; $a_7 = 2$; $A_{100} = ?$ **40.** $a_1 = 2$; $a_7 = -1$; $A_{100} = ?$

See Examples 5 and 6.

41. Find the sum of the first 20 terms of the arithmetic sequence whose first term is 100 and whose common difference is 50.

42. Find the sum of the first 50 terms of the arithmetic sequence whose first term is −15 and whose common difference is 5.

43. Find the sum of the even integers between 41 and 99.

44. Find the sum of the odd integers between 100 and 80.

45. Find the sum of the odd integers between 48 and 136.

46. Find the sum of the first n odd integers.

47. Find the sum of the first n even integers.

48. How many blocks are in a stack like those in the figure, where the bottom row has 28 blocks?

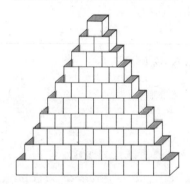

49. How many blocks are in a stack like those in the figure, where the bottom row has 87 blocks?

50. A sequence $s_1, s_2, \ldots, s_n$ is a *harmonic sequence* if and only if its reciprocals form an arithmetic sequence. Which of the following are harmonic sequences?

a. $1, \frac{1}{2}, \frac{1}{3}, \frac{1}{4}, \frac{1}{5}, \ldots$ **b.** $\frac{1}{2}, \frac{1}{5}, \frac{1}{8}, \frac{1}{11}, \frac{1}{14}, \ldots$ **c.** $2, \frac{2}{3}, \frac{2}{5}, \frac{2}{7}, \ldots$

d. $\frac{1}{5}, -\frac{1}{5}, -\frac{1}{15}, -\frac{1}{25}, \ldots$ **e.** $\frac{3}{4}, \frac{1}{2}, \frac{1}{3}, \frac{2}{9}, \ldots$

51. Consider the arithmetic sequence s_1, x, s_2. The number x can be found by considering

$$x = s_1 + d$$
$$\underline{x = s_2 - d}$$
$$2x = s_1 + s_2 \qquad \text{By adding}$$

$$x = \frac{s_1 + s_2}{2}$$

x is called the **arithmetic mean** between s_1 and s_2. Find the arithmetic mean between each pair of numbers.

    a. 1, 8   **b.** 1, 7   **c.** −5, 3   **d.** 80, 88   **e.** 40, 56

52. Find the arithmetic mean (see Problem 51) between each pair of numbers.

    a. 4, 20   **b.** 4, 15   **c.** $\frac{1}{2}, \frac{1}{3}$ **d.** −10, −2   **e.** $-\frac{2}{3}, \frac{4}{5}$

53. How many blocks are there in the solid figure shown here?

Mind Boggler   **54.** Fill in the missing term.

    a. A, A, B, Ꞵ, C, Ɔ, D, ᗡ, _____

    b. A, C, E, G, I, K, _____

    c. A, E, F, H, I, K, L, M, N, _____

    d. CAT, THREE, ALLIGATOR, NINE, WOLF, FOUR, ELEPHANT, _____

    e. 679, 378, 168, 48, 32, _____

11.3 Geometric Series and Sequences

Let's now turn our attention to *geometric* sequences and for convenience denote the terms of a geometric sequence by $g_1, g_2, g_3, g_4, \ldots, g_n$. The g will remind us that the sequence is *geometric*. Recall that a geometric sequence has a *common ratio*, denoted by r:

$$\frac{g_n}{g_{n-1}} = r \quad \text{or} \quad g_n = g_{n-1} r$$

And, similar to the development of the general term of an arithmetic sequence,

$$g_2 = g_1 r$$
$$g_3 = g_1 r^2$$
$$g_4 = g_1 r^3$$
$$\vdots$$
$$g_n = g_1 r^{n-1}$$

This formula gives the nth term when the first term and the common ratio are known.

GENERAL TERM OF A GEOMETRIC SEQUENCE	For a geometric sequence $g_1, g_2, g_3, g_4, \ldots, g_n$ with common ratio r, $$g_n = g_1 r^{n-1} \qquad \text{for every} \quad n \geq 1$$

Example 1 Find an expression for the general term of the geometric sequence 200, 400, 800, ...

Solution $g_1 = 200 \qquad r = \dfrac{400}{200} = 2$

$$g_n = g_1 r^{n-1}$$
$$= 200(2)^{n-1}$$
$$= 2 \cdot 10^2 \cdot 2^{n-1}$$
$$= 2^n \cdot 10^2 \qquad \square$$

In Examples 2–4 find the missing quantities.

Example 2 $g_1 = 3 \qquad r = 2 \qquad g_{10} = ?$

Solution Find g_n, where $n = 10$:

$$g_n = g_1 r^{n-1}$$
$$g_{10} = 3 \cdot 2^{10-1}$$
$$= 3 \cdot 2^9$$
$$= 3 \cdot 512$$
$$= 1{,}536 \qquad \square$$

Example 3 $g_1 = 486 \qquad g_6 = 2 \qquad r = ?$

Solution Find the common ratio:

$$g_6 = g_1 r^5$$
$$2 = 486 \cdot r^5$$
$$\frac{1}{243} = r^5$$
$$\left(\frac{1}{3}\right)^5 = r^5$$
$$\frac{1}{3} = r \qquad \square$$

Example 4 $g_1 = \dfrac{16}{27} \qquad g_6 = -\dfrac{9}{2} \qquad g_9 = ?$

Solution First, find the common ratio:

$$g_6 = g_1 r^5$$

$$-\frac{9}{2} = \frac{16}{27} r^5$$

$$-\frac{243}{32} = r^5$$

$$\left(-\frac{3}{2}\right)^5 = r^5$$

$$-\frac{3}{2} = r$$

Now find the ninth term:

$$g_9 = g_1 r^8$$

$$= \frac{16}{27}\left(-\frac{3}{2}\right)^8$$

$$= \frac{2^4}{3^3}\left(\frac{3^8}{2^8}\right)$$

$$= \frac{3^5}{2^4}$$

$$= \frac{243}{16}$$

☐

Geometric Series

Suppose you receive the following letter:

Dear Friend,

This is a chain letter . . .

Copy this letter six times and send it to six of your friends. In twenty days, you will have good luck.

If you break this chain, you will have bad luck! . . .

Consider the number of people that could become involved with this chain letter if we assume that everyone carries out their task and doesn't break the chain. The first mailing would consist of 6 letters with 7 people involved:

$$1 + 6 = 7$$

The second mailing would involve 43 people since the second mailing of 36 letters (each of the 6 people receiving a letter send out 6 more letters) is added to the total:

$$1 + 6 + 36 = 43$$

The number of letters in each successive mailing is a number of a geometric sequence:

1st mailing	$6 = 6$
2nd mailing	$6^2 = 36$
3rd mailing	$6^3 = 216$
4th mailing	$6^4 = 1{,}296$
$\vdots$	
10th mailing	$6^{10} = 60{,}466{,}176$
11th mailing	$6^{11} = 362{,}797{,}056$

By the 11th mailing, more letters would have to be sent than there are people in the United States! The number of letters in only two more mailings would exceed the number of men, women, and children in the whole world.

How many people are involved in 11 mailings assuming that no person receives a letter more than once? To answer this question, consider the series associated with the geometric sequence. The G_n represents the sum of the first n terms of the geometric series, then in this problem you need to find G_{11}:

$$G_{11} = 1 + 6 + 36 + 216 + \cdots + 60{,}466{,}176 + 362{,}797{,}056$$

You could add these on your calculator, but that would take a long time; instead, write these numbers using exponents.

$$G_{11} = 1 + 6 + 6^2 + 6^3 + \cdots + 6^{10} + 6^{11}$$

Next, multiply both sides by 6:

$$6G_{11} = 6 + 6^2 + 6^3 + 6^4 + \cdots + 6^{11} + 6^{12}$$

Finally, consider $G_{11} - 6G_{11}$:

$$G_{11} - 6G_{11} = 1 - 6^{12}$$
$$-5G_{11} = 1 - 6^{12}$$
$$G_{11} = \frac{1 - 6^{12}}{-5} \qquad \text{or} \qquad \frac{1}{5}(6^{12} - 1)$$

This number is easier to find on your calculator. But more important, it leads to a procedure for finding G_n in general.

$$G_n = g_1 + g_1 r + g_1 r^2 + g_1 r^3 + \cdots + g_1 r^{n-1}$$

$$rG_n = g_1 r + g_1 r^2 + g_1 r^3 + g_1 r^4 + \cdots + g_1 r^n \qquad \text{Multiply both sides by } r.$$

Notice that, except for the first and last terms, all the terms in the expressions for G_n and rG_n are the same, so that

$$G_n - rG_n = g_1 - g_1 r^n$$

Now solve for G_n:

$$(1 - r)G_n = g_1(1 - r^n)$$

$$G_n = \frac{g_1(1 - r^n)}{1 - r} \qquad r \neq 1$$

GEOMETRIC SERIES

For a geometric series $g_1 + g_2 + g_3 + \cdots + g_n$ with common ratio $r \neq 1$,

$$G_n = \frac{g_1(1 - r^n)}{1 - r}$$

Example 5 Find the sum of the first six terms of the geometric sequence with $g_1 = -3$ and $r = 2$.

Solution

$$G_n = \frac{g_1(1 - r^n)}{1 - r}$$

$$G_6 = \frac{(-3)(1 - 2^6)}{1 - 2}$$

$$= \frac{(-3)(-63)}{-1}$$

$$= -189 \qquad \square$$

Example 6 Find the sum of the first ten terms of the geometric sequence with $g_1 = \frac{1}{2}$ and $r = \frac{1}{2}$.

Solution

$$G_n = \frac{g_1(1 - r^n)}{1 - r}$$

$$G_{10} = \frac{\frac{1}{2}[1 - (\frac{1}{2})^{10}]}{1 - \frac{1}{2}}$$

$$= 1 - \left(\frac{1}{2}\right)^{10}$$

$$= 1 - \frac{1}{1,024}$$

$$= \frac{1,023}{1,024} \qquad \square$$

Example 7 If $g_1 = \frac{9}{4}$ and $g_4 = -\frac{1}{12}$, find G_7.

Solution First find r:

$$g_4 = g_1 r^3$$

$$-\frac{1}{12} = \frac{9}{4} r^3$$

$$-\frac{1}{27} = r^3$$

$$-\frac{1}{3} = r$$

Now find G_n for $n = 7$:

$$G_7 = \frac{g_1(1 - r^7)}{1 - r}$$

$$= \frac{\frac{9}{4}[1 - (-\frac{1}{3})^7]}{1 - (-\frac{1}{3})}$$

$$= \frac{\frac{9}{4}[1 + \frac{1}{2,187}]}{\frac{4}{3}}$$

$$= \frac{27}{16}\left[\frac{2,188}{2,187}\right]$$

$$= \frac{547}{324}$$

Problem Set 11.3

A *Write out the first four terms of the geometric sequences in Problems 1–10 where the first element is g_1 and the common ratio is r. Also, find the general term.*

See Examples 1–4.

1. $g_1 = 5;\quad r = 3$ **2.** $g_1 = -12;\quad r = 3$ **3.** $g_1 = 1;\quad r = -2$

4. $g_1 = 1;\quad r = 2$ **5.** $g_1 = -15;\quad r = \frac{1}{5}$ **6.** $g_1 = 625;\quad r = -\frac{1}{5}$

7. $g_1 = 54;\quad r = -\frac{2}{3}$ **8.** $g_1 = 128;\quad r = \frac{3}{2}$ **9.** $g_1 = 8;\quad r = x$

10. $g_1 = x;\quad r = y$

Find g_1 and r for each sequence in Problems 11–20.

11. 3, 6, 12, . . .   **12.** 7, 14, 28, . . .

13. 1, $\frac{1}{2}$, $\frac{1}{4}$, . . .   **14.** 100, 50, 25, . . .

15. 3,125, −625, 125, . . .   **16.** 3, −1, $\frac{1}{3}$, −$\frac{1}{9}$, . . .

17. 100, 150, 225, . . .   **18.** 625, 250, 100, . . .

19. x, x^2, x^3, . . .   **20.** xyz, xy, . . .

B *Use the formula $g_n = g_1 r^{n-1}$ to find an expression for the general term of each of the geometric sequences in Problems 21–30. Notice that you found g_1 and r for each of these in Problems 11–20.*

See Examples 1–4.   **21.** 3, 6, 12, . . .   **22.** 7, 14, 28, . . .
                23. 1, $\frac{1}{2}$, $\frac{1}{4}$, . . .   **24.** 100, 50, 25, . . .
                25. 3,125, −625, 125, . . .   **26.** 3, −1, $\frac{1}{3}$, −$\frac{1}{9}$, . . .
                27. 100, 150, 225, . . .   **28.** 625, 250, 100, . . .
                29. x, x^2, x^3, . . .   **30.** xyz, xy, . . .

Find the missing quantities in Problems 31–50 for the given geometric sequences.

See Examples 1–4.   **31.** $g_1 = 6$; $r = 3$; $g_5 = ?$ **32.** $g_1 = 5$; $r = 2$; $g_7 = ?$
                33. $g_1 = 1{,}024$; $r = \frac{1}{2}$; $g_9 = ?$ **34.** $g_1 = 100$; $r = \frac{1}{10}$; $g_{10} = ?$
                35. $g_1 = 27$; $g_4 = -1$; $g_7 = ?$ **36.** $g_1 = 72$; $g_4 = -\frac{1}{3}$; $g_6 = ?$
                37. $g_1 = 8$; $g_3 = \frac{3}{2}$; $g_5 = ?$ **38.** $g_1 = 9$; $g_4 = \frac{8}{3}$; $g_7 = ?$
See Examples 5–7.   **39.** $g_1 = 6$; $r = 3$; $G_5 = ?$ **40.** $g_1 = 5$; $r = 2$; $G_7 = ?$
                41. $g_1 = 1{,}024$; $r = \frac{1}{2}$; $G_9 = ?$ **42.** $g_1 = 100$; $r = \frac{1}{10}$; $G_{10} = ?$
                43. $g_1 = 512$; $r = \frac{3}{2}$; $G_8 = ?$ **44.** $g_1 = 729$; $r = -\frac{4}{3}$; $G_7 = ?$
                45. $g_1 = \frac{1}{3}$; $r = -\frac{1}{3}$; $G_5 = ?$ **46.** $g_1 = \frac{1}{2}$; $r = -\frac{1}{2}$; $G_6 = ?$
                47. $g_1 = \frac{1}{8}$; $g_8 = -16$; $G_6 = ?$ **48.** $g_1 = 81$; $g_5 = 16$; $G_7 = ?$
                49. $g_1 = 12$; $g_4 = -\frac{4}{9}$; $G_8 = ?$ **50.** $g_1 = 9$; $g_4 = \frac{8}{3}$; $G_9 = ?$

51. If a chain letter requires that you send copies to five friends, what is the total number of letters mailed with five mailings?

52. Answer Problem 51 for 15 mailings.

53. If a chain letter requires that you send copies to ten friends, what is the total number of letters mailed with four mailings?

54. Answer Problem 53 for ten mailings.

55. *Sociology.* According to the 1970 census, the population of Hawaii is about 800,000. If the population increases 20% every five years, what will the population be in the year 2000? [*Hint:* This means that the population each five years is 120% of the previous total.]

56. Consider the geometric sequence g_1, x, g_2. The number x can be found by considering

$$\frac{x}{g_1} = r$$

$$\frac{g_2}{x} = r$$

So,

$$\frac{x}{g_1} = \frac{g_2}{x}$$

$$x^2 = g_1 g_2$$

This equation has two solutions:

$$x = \sqrt{g_1 g_2}$$
$$x = -\sqrt{g_1 g_2}$$

If g_1 and g_2 are both positive, then $\sqrt{g_1 g_2}$ is called the **geometric mean** of g_1 and g_2. If g_1 and g_2 are both negative, then $-\sqrt{g_1 g_2}$ is the geometric mean. Find the geometric mean of each pair of numbers.
a. 1, 8   **b.** 2, 8   **c.** −5, −3   **d.** −10, −2   **e.** 4, 20

Mind Bogglers   **57.** Find three distinct numbers whose sum is 9 so that these numbers form an arithmetic sequence and their squares form a geometric sequence.

58. Give an example of an arithmetic sequence that is also a geometric sequence.

59. Fill in the blanks so that the sequence

_____,   8,   _____,   _____,   27,   _____,   · · ·

is:

a.   An arithmetic sequence
b.   A geometric sequence
c.   A sequence that is neither arithmetic nor geometric, but for which you are able to write a general term.

11.4   Infinite Series

In the previous section you found the sum of the first n terms of a geometric series. Sometimes it is possible to find the sum of the entire infinite geometric series. For example, in the previous section you found the first 10 terms of the geometric series with $g_1 = \frac{1}{2}$ and $r = \frac{1}{2}$. Let's take a closer look at this series.

Sequence $\frac{1}{2}, \frac{1}{4}, \frac{1}{8}, \frac{1}{16}, \frac{1}{32}, \frac{1}{64}, \frac{1}{128}, \cdots$

Series $G_1 = \frac{1}{2}$
$G_2 = \frac{1}{2} + \frac{1}{4} = \frac{3}{4}$
$G_3 = \frac{1}{2} + \frac{1}{4} + \frac{1}{8} = \frac{7}{8}$
$G_{10} = \frac{1}{2} + \frac{1}{4} + \frac{1}{8} + \cdots + \frac{1}{1,024} = \frac{1,023}{1,024}$ See Example 6, page 392.

Does this series have a sum if you add *all* its terms? It does seem that as you take more terms of the series, the sum is closer and closer to 1. Graphically, it is seen that if the terms are laid out end-to-end as lengths on a number line, then each term is half of the remaining distance to 1. That is, $\frac{1}{2} + \frac{1}{4} = \frac{3}{4}$ and the next term is $\frac{1}{8}$, just half of the remaining $\frac{1}{4}$. However,

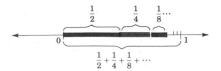

Figure 11.2

the remaining length is shrinking quickly, $\frac{1}{2}$, $\frac{1}{4}$, $\frac{1}{8}$, $\frac{1}{16}$, $\frac{1}{32}$, . . . , and you can see that as n becomes large, $(\frac{1}{2})^n$ will become and remain as close to 0 as we please. We say that *0 is the limit of* $(\frac{1}{2})^n$ *as n increases without bound.* Symbolically,

$$\lim_{n\to\infty} (\tfrac{1}{2})^n = 0$$

The arrow means "approaches"; write $k \to 3$ to mean *"k approaches 3"* and $n \to \infty$ to indicate that n increases without bound. In general, it may be said that

$$\lim_{n\to\infty} r^n = 0 \qquad \text{if} \quad |r| < 1$$

That is, any number between -1 and 1 raised to large powers will approach 0 as a limit.

Now return to the original question of the sum of *all* the terms of a geometric series. Does G_n have a limit as $n \to \infty$?

$$G_n = \frac{g_1(1 - r^n)}{1 - r}$$

$$G_n = \frac{g_1}{1 - r}(1 - r^n)$$

Notice that as $n \to \infty$, r^n decreases and approaches 0 if $|r| < 1$. That is,

$$\lim_{n\to\infty} G_n = \lim_{n\to\infty} \frac{g_1}{1 - r}(1 - r^n)$$

$$= \frac{g_1}{1 - r}(1 - 0)$$

$$= \frac{g_1}{1 - r}$$

Thus, in the example with $g_1 = \frac{1}{2}$ and $r = \frac{1}{2}$,

$$\lim_{n\to\infty} G_n = \frac{\frac{1}{2}}{1 - \frac{1}{2}}$$

$$= \frac{\frac{1}{2}}{\frac{1}{2}}$$

$$= 1$$

In general, we define the limit of the sum of an infinite geometric series to be $\lim_{n \to \infty} G_n$, and we call this limit G_∞.

INFINITE
GEOMETRIC SERIES

If $G_n = g_1 + g_1 r + g_1 r^2 + g_1 r^3 + \cdots$, then

$$\lim_{n \to \infty} G_n = G_\infty = \frac{g_1}{1 - r}$$

for $|r| < 1$. If $|r| \geq 1$, the infinite geometric series has no sum.

Not all infinite geometric series have sums. Our earlier chain-letter problem gave rise to a geometric series with $g_1 = 6$ and $r = 6$. Thus,

$$G_n = \frac{g_1}{1 - r} - \frac{g_1 r^n}{1 - r}$$

$$= \frac{6}{1 - 6} - \frac{6(6^n)}{1 - 6}$$

$$= -\frac{6}{5} + \frac{6}{5}(6^n)$$

Notice that G_n becomes large without limit as n becomes large.

In Examples 1–4 find the sum of the infinite geometric series, if possible.

Example 1 $\dfrac{1}{3} + \dfrac{1}{9} + \dfrac{1}{27} + \dfrac{1}{81} + \cdots$

Solution $g_1 = \dfrac{1}{3} \qquad r = \dfrac{1}{3}$

$$G_\infty = \frac{\frac{1}{3}}{1 - \frac{1}{3}}$$

$$= \frac{\frac{1}{3}}{\frac{2}{3}}$$

$$= \frac{1}{2}$$

□

Example 2 $100 + 50 + 25 + \cdots$

Solution $g_1 = 100 \qquad r = \frac{1}{2}$

$$\lim_{n \to \infty} G_n = \frac{100}{1 - \frac{1}{2}}$$

$$= 200$$

□

Example 3 $1-\dfrac{2}{3}+\dfrac{4}{9}-\dfrac{8}{27}+-+\cdots$

Solution $g_1=1 \qquad r=-\dfrac{2}{3}$

$$G_\infty=\dfrac{1}{1-(-\frac{2}{3})}$$

$$=\dfrac{1}{1+\frac{2}{3}}$$

$$=\dfrac{1}{\frac{5}{3}}$$

$$=\dfrac{3}{5}$$

Example 4 $-5+10-20+\cdots$

Solution $g_1=-5 \qquad r=-2$

Since $|r|\geq 1$, this infinite series doesn't have a sum.

Repeating Decimal Representation

The repeating decimal .4444 ... or $.\overline{4}$ is rational and can therefore be written as the quotient of two integers. Moreover, it may be written as an infinite series:

$$.4444\ldots = .4+.04+.004+.0004+\cdots$$
$$=.4+.4(.1)+.4(.01)+.4(.001)+\cdots$$
$$=.4+.4(.1)+.4(.1)^2+.4(.1)^3+\cdots$$

Notice that $g_1=.4$ with $r=.1$, so

$$G_\infty=\dfrac{.4}{1-.1}$$

$$=\dfrac{.4}{.9}$$

$$=\dfrac{4}{9}$$

Thus, $.4444\ldots=\frac{4}{9}$.

Example 5   Express .727272 ... as the quotient of two integers.

Solution $.727272\ldots = .72+.0072+.000072+\cdots$
$$=.72+.72(.01)+.72(.0001)+\cdots$$
$$=.72+.72(.01)+.72(.01)^2+\cdots$$

We see that $g_1 = .72$, $r = .01$, and

$$\lim_{n \to \infty} G_n = \frac{.72}{1 - .01}$$

$$= \frac{.72}{.99} \qquad \text{Write this as a fraction, not a decimal.}$$

$$= \frac{\frac{72}{100}}{\frac{99}{100}}$$

$$= \frac{72}{99}$$

$$= \frac{8}{11}$$

□

Example 6 The path of each swing of a pendulum bob is .85 as long as the path of the previous swing (after the first). If the path of the first swing is 30 cm long, how far does the bob travel before eventually coming to rest?

Solution Notice that $g_1 = 30$ and $r = .85$, so that

$$\left(\begin{array}{c} \text{TOTAL} \\ \text{DISTANCE} \end{array}\right) = 30 + 30(.85) + 30(.85)^2 + \cdots$$

$$= \frac{30}{1 - .85}$$

$$= \frac{30}{.15}$$

$$= 200$$

The pendulum bob travels 200 cm.

□

Problem Set 11.4

A *Find the sum, if possible, of each infinite geometric series in Problems 1–10.*

See Examples 1–4.

1. $1 + \frac{1}{2} + \frac{1}{4} + \cdots$ **2.** $1 + \frac{1}{3} + \frac{1}{9} + \cdots$

3. $1 + \frac{3}{4} + \frac{9}{16} + \cdots$ **4.** $1 + \frac{3}{2} + \frac{9}{4} + \cdots$

5. $1{,}000 + 500 + 250 + \cdots$ **6.** $100 + 50 + 25 + \cdots$

7. $-20 + 10 - 5 + \cdots$ **8.** $-45 - 15 - 5 - \cdots$

9. $\frac{1}{3} + \frac{1}{9} + \frac{1}{27} + \cdots$ **10.** $\frac{1}{4} + \frac{1}{16} + \frac{1}{64} + \cdots$

Represent the repeating decimals in Problems 11–20 as quotients of two integers by considering an infinite geometric series.

See Example 5.

11. $.\overline{4}$ **12.** $.\overline{5}$ **13.** $.\overline{27}$ **14.** $.\overline{18}$ **15.** $2.\overline{45}$

16. $1.\overline{34}$ **17.** $.9\overline{23}$ **18.** $.4\overline{18}$ **19.** $.\overline{4182}$ **20.** $.\overline{2185}$

B   *Find the sum of each infinite geometric series in Problems 21–30, if possible.*

See Examples 1–4.   **21.** $\frac{16}{27} + \frac{8}{9} + \frac{4}{3} + \cdots$ **22.** $\frac{625}{256} + \frac{125}{64} + \frac{25}{16} + \cdots$

23. $1 + (1.08)^{-1} + (1.08)^{-2} + \cdots$ **24.** $1 + (1.10)^{-1} + (1.10)^{-2} + \cdots$

25. $2 + \sqrt{2} + 1 + \cdots$ **26.** $3 + \sqrt{3} + 1 + \cdots$

27. $(1 + \sqrt{2}) + 1 + (-1 + \sqrt{2}) + \cdots$ **28.** $(\sqrt{2} - 1) + 1 + (\sqrt{2} + 1) + \cdots$

See Example 5.   **29.** $5.03\overline{1}$ **30.** $2.25\overline{34}$

See Example 6.   **31.** *Physics.*   A pendulum is swung 20 cm and allowed to swing free until it eventually comes to rest. Each subsequent swing of the bob of the pendulum is 90% as far as the preceding swing. How far will the bob travel before coming to rest?

32. *Physics.*   The initial swing of the bob of a pendulum is 25 cm. If each swing of the bob is 75% of the preceding swing, how far does the bob travel before eventually coming to rest?

33. *Physics.*   A flywheel is brought to a speed of 375 revolutions per minute (rpm) and allowed to slow and eventually come to rest. If, in slowing, it rotates three-fourths as fast each subsequent minute, how many revolutions will the wheel make before returning to rest?

34. *Physics.*   A rotating flywheel is allowed to slow to a stop from a speed of 500 rpm. While slowing, each minute it rotates two-thirds as many times as in the preceding minute. How many revolutions will the wheel make before coming to rest?

35. *Sports.*   A new type of superball advertises that it will rebound $\frac{9}{10}$ of its original height. If it is dropped from a height of 10 feet, how far will the ball travel before coming to rest?   [*Hint:* Find the distance traveled from the time it hits the ground the first time and then add 10 feet.]

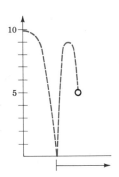

36. *Sports.*   A tennis ball is dropped from a height of 10 feet. If the ball rebounds $\frac{2}{3}$ of its height on each bounce, how far will the ball travel before coming to rest?

Mind Bogglers

37. The sum of an infinite geometric series is thirty. Each term is exactly four times the sum of the remaining terms. Determine the series with these properties.

38. Each term is five times the sum of all the terms that follow it. Determine the infinite geometric series if the sum of the series is twenty.

39. **a.** Find .333 . . . as the quotient of two integers by considering an infinite geometric series.

b. Find .999 . . . as the quotient of two integers by considering an infinite geometric series.

c. Are your results to parts a and b consistent? That is, is your answer to part b three times your answer to part a?

d. Do you agree with the results of this problem? Why or why not?

40. An equilateral triangle of side a is cut out of paper, as shown in Figure a. Next, three equilateral triangles, each of side $a/3$, are cut out and placed in the middle of each side of the first triangle, as shown in Figure b. Then 12 equilateral triangles, each of side $a/9$, are placed halfway along each of the sides of this figure, as shown in Figure c. Figure d shows the result of adding 48 equilateral triangles, each of side $a/27$, to the previous figure. Assume that this procedure is repeated indefinitely. Find:

a. The perimeter of the figure obtained

b. The area of the figure obtained

[*Hint:* The height of an equilateral triangle is $\frac{1}{2}a\sqrt{3}$, where a is the length of the side.]

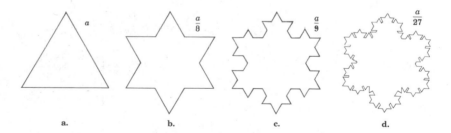

a.   b.   c.   d.

11.5 Summation, Factorial, and Pascal

This section will introduce some notation that is quite useful not only when working with series but also in future work in mathematics. While introducing this notation the concepts of arithmetic and geometric series will be reviewed.

Summation Notation

Recall that a finite sequence is a function whose domain is the set of counting numbers less than some given number. Consider the function $s(k) = 2k$

and $N = \{1, 2, 3, 4\}$ for which the following table can be compiled:

k	$s(k) = 2k$
1	2
2	4
3	6
4	8

The sum of this finite arithmetic sequence is

$2 + 4 + 6 + 8$

This sum can be denoted by the Greek letter Σ (sigma).

This is the last natural number in the domain.

$$\sum_{k=1}^{4} 2k = 2 + 4 + 6 + 8$$

This is the function that is evaluated.

This is the first natural number in the domain.

The Greek letter sigma means that the function is evaluated for each number in the domain and the results are added.

Thus,

$$\sum_{k=1}^{4} 2k = 20$$

Example 1   Let $s(k) = (2k + 1)$ and $N = \{3, 4, 5, 6\}$. Then:

	k	$s(k) = 2k + 1$
First natural number in domain; $k = 3$. →	3	7
	4	9
	5	11
Last natural number in domain; $k = 6$. →	6	13

The sigma means that these values are added.

Thus,

$$\sum_{k=3}^{6} (2k + 1) = 7 + 9 + 11 + 13$$

$$k = 4 \qquad k = 5 \qquad k = 6$$

Obtained by letting $k = 3$ and evaluating $(2k + 1)$.

Example 2   Evaluate: $\sum\limits_{k=1}^{5} (3k-2)$

Solution $\sum\limits_{k=1}^{5} (3k-2) = 1 + 4 + 7 + 10 + 13$

$$= \frac{n}{2}(a_1 + a_n)$$

$$= \frac{5}{2}(1 + 13)$$

$$= 35 \qquad \square$$

Example 3   Evaluate: $\sum\limits_{k=1}^{20} (15 - 2k)$

Solution $\sum\limits_{k=1}^{20} (15 - 2k) = 13 + 11 + 9 + \cdots + (-23) + (-25)$

$$= \frac{20}{2}(13 - 25)$$

$$= 10(-12)$$

$$= -120 \qquad \square$$

Example 4   Write the sum of the arithmetic series

$$A_n = a_1 + a_2 + \cdots + a_n$$

using sigma notation.

Solution $A_n = \sum\limits_{k=1}^{n} a_k$

By formula,

$$A_n = \sum\limits_{k=1}^{n} a_k = \frac{n}{2}(a_1 + a_n) \qquad \square$$

Example 5   Let $s(k) = 1/2^k$ and $N = \{1, 2, 3, 4, \ldots, n\}$. Then

$$\sum\limits_{k=1}^{n} \frac{1}{2^k} = \underset{\underset{k=1}{\uparrow}}{\frac{1}{2}} + \underset{\underset{k=2}{\uparrow}}{\frac{1}{4}} + \underset{\underset{k=3}{\uparrow}}{\frac{1}{8}} + \cdots + \underset{\underset{k=n}{\uparrow}}{\frac{1}{2^n}} \qquad \square$$

Example 6   Evaluate: $\displaystyle\sum_{k=1}^{5} 3^{1-k}$

Solution $\displaystyle\sum_{k=1}^{5} 3^{1-k} = 3^0 + 3^{-1} + 3^{-2} + 3^{-3} + 3^{-4}$

$$= 1 + \frac{1}{3} + \frac{1}{9} + \frac{1}{27} + \frac{1}{81}$$

Use

$$G_n = \frac{g_1(1 - r^n)}{1 - r}$$

where $g_1 = 1$, $r = \frac{1}{3}$, and $n = 5$:

$$G_5 = \frac{1(1 - \frac{1}{243})}{1 - \frac{1}{3}}$$

$$= \frac{3}{2}\left(\frac{242}{243}\right)$$

$$= \frac{121}{81}$$ □

Example 7   Write the sum of the geometric series

$$G_n = g_1 + g_1 r + g_1 r^2 + \cdots + g_1 r^{n-1}$$

using sigma notation.

Solution $\displaystyle G_n = \sum_{k=1}^{n} g_1 r^{k-1}$

By formula,

$$G_n = \sum_{k=1}^{n} g_1 r^{k-1} = \frac{g_1(1 - r^n)}{1 - r} \qquad r \neq 1$$ □

Example 8   Write the sum of the geometric series

$$G_n = g_1 + g_1 r + g_1 r^2 + \cdots$$

where $|r| < 1$.

Solution $\displaystyle \lim_{n \to \infty} G_n = \lim_{n \to \infty} \sum_{k=1}^{n} g_1 r^{k-1}$

By formula,

$$\lim_{n \to \infty} G_n = \lim_{n \to \infty} \sum_{k=1}^{n} g_1 r^{k-1} = \frac{g_1}{1 - r}$$ □

Factorial Notation

There are occasions when you wish to know the *product* of the first n natural numbers. We symbolize this by $n!$ and call it **n-factorial.**

FACTORIAL

$$n! = 1 \cdot 2 \cdot 3 \cdot \ldots \cdot (n-1) \cdot n$$

is called **n-factorial** (n a natural number). Also, we define $0! = 1$ and $1! = 1$.

In Examples 9–14 evaluate each expression.

Example 9
$0! = 1$
$1! = 1$
$2! = 1 \cdot 2 = 2$
$3! = 1 \cdot 2 \cdot 3 = 6$
$4! = 1 \cdot 2 \cdot 3 \cdot 4 = 24$
$5! = 1 \cdot 2 \cdot 3 \cdot 4 \cdot 5 = 120$
$6! = 1 \cdot 2 \cdot 3 \cdot 4 \cdot 5 \cdot 6 = 720$
$7! = 1 \cdot 2 \cdot 3 \cdot 4 \cdot 5 \cdot 6 \cdot 7 = 5{,}040$
$8! = 1 \cdot 2 \cdot 3 \cdot \ldots \cdot 7 \cdot 8 = 40{,}320$
$9! = 1 \cdot 2 \cdot 3 \cdot \ldots \cdot 8 \cdot 9 = 362{,}880$
$10! = 1 \cdot 2 \cdot 3 \cdot \ldots \cdot 9 \cdot 10 = 3{,}628{,}800$ □

Example 10
$$5! - 4! = 120 - 24$$
$$= 96$$ □

Example 11
$$(5 - 4)! = 1!$$
$$= 1$$ □

Example 12
$$\frac{8!}{4!} = \frac{8 \cdot 7 \cdot 6 \cdot 5 \cdot \cancel{4} \cdot \cancel{3} \cdot \cancel{2} \cdot \cancel{1}}{\cancel{4} \cdot \cancel{3} \cdot \cancel{2} \cdot \cancel{1}}$$
$$= 8 \cdot 7 \cdot 6 \cdot 5$$
$$= 1{,}680$$ □

Example 13
$$(2 \cdot 3)! = 6!$$
$$= 720$$ □

Example 14
$$\frac{10!}{8!} = \frac{10 \cdot 9 \cdot \cancel{8!}}{\cancel{8!}}$$

Notice that $10! = 10 \cdot 9!$
$= 10 \cdot 9 \cdot 8!$
$= 10 \cdot 9 \cdot 8 \cdot 7!$
$\vdots$

$$= 90$$ □

Pascal's Triangle Notation

Consider the following pattern, called **Pascal's triangle.**

Row 0						1		$(x+y)^0$				
Row 1					1		1	$(x+y)^1$				
Row 2				1		2		1				
Row 3			1		3		3		1			
Row 4		1		4		6		4		1		
Row 5	1		5		10		10		5		1	
Row 6	1	6		15		20		15		6		1

$$\vdots$$

There are many interesting relationships associated with this pattern, but we are concerned with an expression representing the entries of this pattern. Do you see how to generate additional rows of the triangle?

1. Each row begins and ends with a 1.
2. Notice that we have begun counting the rows with row 0. This is because after row 0, the second entry in the row is the same as the row number. Thus, row 7 would begin 1, 7, and so on.
3. The triangle is symmetric about the middle. This means that the entries of each row are the same at the beginning and the end. Thus, row 7 ends with 7, 1.
4. To find new entries simply add the two entries just above in the preceding row. Thus, the 7th row is found by looking at the 6th row.

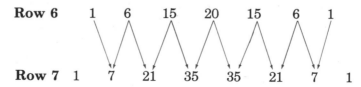

Row 6   1   6   15   20   15   6   1

Row 7 1   7   21   35   35   21   7   1

If you write Pascal's triangle in the form of rows and columns, as shown in Table 11.1, notice that you can locate any entry in the triangle by using an ordered pair.

Table 11.1

Row \ Column	0	1	2	3	4	...
0	1					
1	1	1				
2	1	2	1			
3	1	3	3	1		
4	1	4	6	4	1	
⋮						

We write $\binom{n}{r}$ to represent the element in the nth row and rth column of the triangle. Therefore,

$$\binom{0}{0} = 1$$

$$\binom{1}{0} = 1 \qquad \binom{1}{1} = 1$$

$$\binom{2}{0} = 1 \qquad \binom{2}{1} = 2 \qquad \binom{2}{2} = 1$$

$$\binom{3}{0} = 1 \qquad \binom{3}{1} = 3 \qquad \binom{3}{2} = 3 \qquad \binom{3}{3} = 1$$

$$\vdots$$

It is possible to show that

$${}_nC_R$$

$$\binom{n}{r} = \frac{n!}{r!(n-r)!}$$

In Examples 15–18 evaluate each expression.

Example 15 $\quad \binom{8}{3}$

Solution For small values of n, use Pascal's triangle. This is the entry in the 8th row, 3rd column.

$$\begin{array}{ccccccc} & 1 & & 7 & & 21 & & 35 & & 21 & \cdots \\ 1 & & 8 & & 28 & & \boxed{56} & & \cdots \end{array}$$

$$\binom{8}{3} = 56 \qquad \qquad \square$$

Example 16 $\quad \binom{52}{2} = \frac{52!}{2!(52-2)!}$

$$= \frac{52!}{2!50!}$$

$$= \frac{52 \cdot 51 \cdot 50!}{2 \cdot 1 \cdot 50!}$$

$$= 1{,}326 \qquad \qquad \square$$

Example 17 $\binom{n}{n}=\dfrac{n!}{n!(n-n)!}$

$\qquad\qquad =\dfrac{n!}{n!0!}$

$\qquad\qquad =1$

Example 18 $\binom{n}{n-1}=\dfrac{n!}{(n-1)![n-(n-1)]!}$

$\qquad\qquad =\dfrac{n!}{(n-1)!1!}$

$\qquad\qquad =\dfrac{n(n-1)!}{(n-1)!}$

$\qquad\qquad =n$

Problem Set 11.5

A *Evaluate the expressions in Problems 1–30.*

See Examples 1–8.

1. $X=\sum_{k=1}^{4}(4k-1)$ 2. $X=\sum_{k=1}^{5}(3k-1)$ 3. $X=\sum_{k=1}^{3}5(\tfrac{1}{2})^k$

4. $X=\sum_{k=1}^{2}10\,(\tfrac{1}{4})^k$ 5. $X=\sum_{k=1}^{5}3(2)^{k-1}$ 6. $X=\sum_{k=1}^{6}2(3)^k$

7. $A=\sum_{k=2}^{6}k$ 8. $B=\sum_{m=1}^{4}m^2$ 9. $C=\sum_{n=0}^{6}(2n+1)$

See Examples 9–14.   10. $D=\sum_{k=1}^{5}(3k+2)$ 11. $E=4!-2!$ 12. $F=5!-3!$

13. $G=(4-2)!$ 14. $H=(6-3)!$ 15. $I=\dfrac{9!}{7!}$

16. $J=\dfrac{10!}{6!}$ 17. $L=\dfrac{12!}{10!}$ 18. $M=\dfrac{10!}{4!6!}$

See Examples 15–18.   19. $N=\dfrac{12!}{3!(12-3)!}$ 20. $P=\dfrac{52!}{3!(52-3)!}$ 21. $Q=\binom{8}{1}$

22. $R=\binom{5}{4}$ 23. $S=\binom{8}{2}$ 24. $K=\binom{52}{2}$

25. $T=\binom{8}{3}$ 26. $U=\binom{7}{4}$ 27. $V=\binom{8}{4}$

28. $W=\binom{5}{5}$ 29. $Y=\binom{10}{1}$ 30. $Z=\binom{1000}{1}$

B
Algebra Adage

31. Use Problems 7–30 to complete the algebra adage. Replace the values within the parentheses with the capital letters from the problems. The letter O has been supplied as a further clue.

(22)(70)(22)(5)(10)(56)(6)(72)(220)(2)   (72)(28)
(132)(22)(2)(72)(56)(72)(210)(20)(56)(22)   (72)(220)
(210)(20)(56)(56)(22)(5)(28)   (22,100)(22)(5)(56)(20)(72)(220)(72)(220)(2)
(56)(O)   (20)(5)(55)(22)(220)(56)   (20)(114)(114)(22)(49)(56)(72)(O)(220)
(20)(220)(55)   (20)(5)(210)(22)(55)   (49)(O)(220)(114)(132)(72)(49)(56)
(30)(22)(56)(1)(22)(22)(220)   (220)(20)(56)(72)(O)(220)(28).

32. Translate the algebra adage above into the common proverb it paraphrases.

Write the expressions in Problems 33–42 using summation notation.

See Examples 1–8.

33. $\frac{1}{2} + \frac{1}{4} + \frac{1}{8} + \cdots + \frac{1}{128}$ **34.** $2 + 4 + 6 + \cdots + 100$
35. $1 + 6 + 36 + 216 + 1{,}296$ **36.** $5 + 15 + 45 + 135 + 405$
37. $1 + 11 + 21 + \cdots + 101$ **38.** $1 - 10 + 100 - \cdots + 1{,}000{,}000$
39. $\frac{1}{2} + \frac{5}{6} + \frac{7}{6} + \cdots + \frac{5}{2}$ **40.** $\frac{7}{3} + \frac{13}{6} + 2 + \cdots + \frac{1}{3}$

41. $8 - 4\sqrt{2} + 4 - \cdots + \frac{1}{2}$ **42.** $2\sqrt{3} + 3 + \dfrac{3\sqrt{3}}{2} + \cdots + \dfrac{27}{16}$

Write out the expressions in Problems 43 and 44 without using summation notation.

43. $\displaystyle\sum_{j=1}^{r} a_j b_j$ **44.** $\displaystyle\sum_{k=0}^{n} ka^k$

45. In Problem 43 let $b_j = k$ and show that: $\displaystyle\sum_{j=1}^{r} ka_j = k \sum_{j=1}^{r} a_j$

46. In Problem 45 let $a_j = 1$ and show that: $\displaystyle\sum_{j=1}^{r} k = kr$

47. Show that: $\displaystyle\sum_{k=1}^{n} (a_k + b_k) = \sum_{k=1}^{n} a_k + \sum_{k=1}^{n} b_k$

48. Examine Pascal's triangle carefully, look for patterns, and answer the following questions:
    a. What is the second number in the 100th row?
    b. What is the next-to-last number in the 200th row?

49. Which rows of Pascal's triangle contain only odd numbers?

50. Consider 11^0, 11^1, 11^2, 11^3, . . . and explain how the powers of 11 are related to Pascal's triangle.

Mind Bogglers   **51.**   How are the following numbers related to Pascal's triangle?

a. Square numbers

$$1, \quad 4, \quad 9, \quad 16, \cdots$$

b. Triangular numbers

$$1, \quad 3, \quad 6, \quad 10, \cdots$$

52.   Show that: $\binom{n-1}{r-1} + \binom{n-1}{r} = \binom{n}{r}$

53.   Show that: $\binom{n}{r} = \binom{n}{n-r}$

11.6 Binomial Theorem

In mathematics, it is frequently necessary to find $(a + b)^n$. If n is very large, direct calculation is tedious, so an easy pattern is sought that not only will help us find $(a + b)^n$ but also will allow us to find any given term in that expansion.

Consider the powers of $(a + b)$, which are found by direct multiplication:

$$
\begin{aligned}
(a + b)^0 &= 1 \\
(a + b)^1 &= 1 \cdot a + 1 \cdot b \\
(a + b)^2 &= 1 \cdot a^2 + 2 \cdot ab + 1 \cdot b^2 \\
(a + b)^3 &= 1 \cdot a^3 + 3 \cdot a^2 b + 3 \cdot ab^2 + 1 \cdot b^3 \\
(a + b)^4 &= 1 \cdot a^4 + 4 \cdot a^3 b + 6 \cdot a^2 b^2 + 4 \cdot ab^3 + 1 \cdot b^4 \\
(a + b)^5 &= 1 \cdot a^5 + 5 \cdot a^4 b + 10 \cdot a^3 b^2 + 10 \cdot a^2 b^3 + 5 \cdot ab^4 + 1 \cdot b^5 \\
&\qquad\qquad\qquad\qquad\qquad\qquad \vdots
\end{aligned}
$$

If the coefficients are ignored and attention is focused on the variables, a pattern can be seen:

$(a + b)^1$:	a	b		
$(a + b)^2$:	a^2	ab	b^2	
$(a + b)^3$:	a^3	$a^2 b$	ab^2	b^3
$(a + b)^4$:	a^4	$a^3 b$	$a^2 b^2$	ab^3	b^4

$$\vdots$$

Do you see the pattern? From left to right, the powers of a decrease and the powers of b increase. Notice that the sum of the exponents for each term is the same as the original power.

$(a+b)^n$: a^n $a^{n-1}b$ $a^{n-2}b^2$ $\cdots$ $a^{n-r}b^r$ $\cdots$ a^2b^{n-2} ab^{n-1} b^n

Next, consider the coefficients:

$(a+b)^0$:   1
$(a+b)^1$:   1   1
$(a+b)^2$:   1   2   1
$(a+b)^3$:   1   3   3   1
$(a+b)^4$:   1   4   6   4   1
$(a+b)^5$:   1   5   10   10   5   1
$$\vdots$$

Do you see the pattern? The coefficients are the numbers in Pascal's triangle. Using the notation for Pascal's triangle introduced in the last section,

$$(a+b)^n = \binom{n}{0}a^n + \binom{n}{1}a^{n-1}b + \binom{n}{2}a^{n-2}b^2 + \cdots + \binom{n}{r}a^{n-r}b^r$$

$$+ \cdots + \binom{n}{n-2}a^2b^{n-2} + \binom{n}{n-1}ab^{n-1} + \binom{n}{n}b^n$$

Using the summation notation, a more compact form is obtained, which is called the **binomial theorem.**

BINOMIAL
THEOREM

a+b

Binomial Theorem

For any positive integer n,

$$(a+b)^n = \sum_{k=0}^{n}\binom{n}{k}a^{n-k}b^k \qquad \text{where} \qquad \binom{n}{k} = \frac{n!}{k!(n-k)!}$$

The proof of the binomial theorem is by mathematical induction, which is beyond the scope of this course.

Example 1 Find $(x+y)^8$.

Solution For smaller powers, use Pascal's triangle to obtain the coefficients in the expansion. Thus,

$$(x+y)^8 = x^8 + 8x^7y + 28x^6y^2 + 56x^5y^3 + 70x^4y^4$$
$$+ 56x^3y^5 + 28x^2y^6 + 8xy^7 + y^8 \qquad \square$$

Example 2 Find $(x - 2y)^4$.

Solution In this example, $a = x$ and $b = -2y$, and the coefficients are in Pascal's triangle:

$$(x - 2y)^4 = 1 \cdot x^4 + 4 \cdot x^3(-2y) + 6 \cdot x^2(-2y)^2 + 4 \cdot x(-2y)^3 + 1 \cdot (-2y)^4$$
$$= x^4 - 8x^3y + 24x^2y^2 - 32xy^3 + 16y^4$$

Example 3 Find $(a + b)^{15}$.

Solution The power is rather large, so we use the binomial theorem to find the coefficients:

$$(a + b)^{15} = \binom{15}{0} a^{15} + \binom{15}{1} a^{14}b + \binom{15}{2} a^{13}b^2 + \cdots + \binom{15}{14} ab^{14} + \binom{15}{15} b^{15}$$

$$= \frac{15!}{0! \, 15!} a^{15} + \frac{15!}{1! \, 14!} a^{14}b + \frac{15!}{2! \, 13!} a^{13}b^2 + \cdots + \frac{15!}{14! \, 1!} ab^{14} + \frac{15!}{15! \, 0!} b^{15}$$

$$= a^{15} + 15a^{14}b + 105a^{13}b^2 + \cdots + 15ab^{14} + b^{15}$$

Example 4 Find the coefficient of the term x^2y^{10} in the expansion of $(x + 2y)^{12}$.

Solution We have $n = 12$, $k = 10$, $a = x$, and $b = 2y$; thus, the term we seek is

$$\binom{12}{10} x^2(2y)^{10} = \frac{12!}{10! \, 2!} (2)^{10}x^2y^{10}$$

$$= \frac{12 \cdot 11 \cdot \overset{6}{\cancel{10!}}}{\cancel{10!} \cdot \cancel{2} \cdot 1} 2^{10}x^2y^{10}$$

$$= 66 \cdot 2^{10}x^2y^{10}$$

$$= 66(1{,}024)x^2y^{10}$$

$$= 67{,}584x^2y^{10}$$

The coefficient is 67,584.

Problem Set 11.6

A *In Problems 1–10 expand using the binomial theorem.*

See Examples 1 and 2.
1. $(x - 1)^5$ 2. $(x + 1)^4$ 3. $(x + 1)^8$ 4. $(x - 1)^9$
5. $(x - y)^6$ 6. $(x + y)^5$ 7. $(x + 2)^5$ 8. $(x - 2)^6$
9. $(x - 3)^5$ 10. $(x + 4)^4$

Find the coefficient of the term in the expansion of the given binomial in Problems 11–20.

See Examples 3 and 4.

11. a^5b^6 in $(a-b)^{11}$ **12.** a^4b^7 in $(a+b)^{11}$
13. $x^{10}y^4$ in $(x+y)^{14}$ **14.** $x^{10}y^5$ in $(x-y)^{15}$
15. x^{12} in $(x-1)^{16}$ **16.** y^8 in $(y+1)^{12}$
17. r^5 in $(r+2)^9$ **18.** s^5 in $(s-2)^{10}$
19. a^7b in $(a-2b)^8$ **20.** a^4b^4 in $(a+2b)^8$

B *Find the first four terms in the expansions given in Problems 21–30.*

See Example 3.

21. $(x-y)^{15}$ **22.** $(x+2y)^{16}$ **23.** $(x+\sqrt{2})^8$ **24.** $(x-2y)^{12}$
25. $(x-3y)^{10}$ **26.** $(x+\sqrt{3})^9$ **27.** $(ab-2b)^{15}$ **28.** $(rs-3t)^{13}$
29. $(z^2+5k)^{11}$ **30.** $(z^3-k^2)^7$

31. Show that $\binom{n}{0} + \binom{n}{1} + \binom{n}{2} + \cdots + \binom{n}{n-1} + \binom{n}{n} = 2^n$. This says that the sum of the entries of the nth row of Pascal's triangle is 2^n. [*Hint:* Expand $(a+b)^n$, where $a=1$ and $b=1$.]

Mind Boggler **32.** Show that $\sum_{j=0}^{n} 2^j \binom{n}{j} = 3^n$ for every positive integer n.

11.7 Review Problems

Fill in the word or words to make the statements in Problems 1–5 complete and correct.

(11.1) **1.** A _____ is a function whose domain is the set of counting numbers.

(11.1) **2.** If the domain for a sequence is $N = \{1, 2, 3, \ldots, n, \ldots\}$, then we call it a(n) _____ sequence; and if the domain is $N = \{1, 2, 3, \ldots, n\}$, then we call it a _____ sequence.

(11.1) **3.** An arithmetic sequence is a sequence that has a common _____ between successive terms.

(11.5) **4.** $n! =$ _____ (formula)

(11.5) **5.** $\binom{n}{r} =$ _____ (formula)

(11.1, 11.2, 11.3) **6.** Classify the sequences as arithmetic, geometric, or neither. Also, find an expression for the general term if it is an arithmetic or geometric sequence. If it is neither, find the pattern, and give the next two terms.
 a. 1, 11, 21, 31, . . . **b.** 1, 11, 111, 1,111, . . .
 c. 1, 11, 121, 1,331, . . . **d.** 54, 18, 6, 2, . . .
 e. 1, 4, 9, 16, . . .

(11.2, 11.3) **7.** Find the missing quantities.
 a. $g_1 = 5$; $r = 2$; $g_{10} =$ _____ ; $G_5 =$ _____
 b. $a_1 = 50$; $d = -5$; $a_{10} =$ _____ ; $A_5 =$ _____

(11.2, 11.3)   **8.** Find the missing quantities.

a. $a_1 = 2$; $a_{10} = 20$; $d =$ _____; $A_{10} =$ _____

b. $g_1 = 512$; $g_{10} = 1$; $r =$ _____; $G_{10} =$ _____

(11.1)   **9.** Find the first four terms of the given sequences.

a. $a_n = 5n - 2$ b. $g_n = \dfrac{10^5}{2^{n-1}}$ c. $s_n = \dfrac{(-1)^n}{n}$

d. $s_n = \dfrac{(-1)^n}{n!}$ e. $s_1 = 1$, $s_2 = 2$, $s_n = s_{n-1} + s_{n-2}$; $n \geq 3$

(11.4)   **10.** a. Find $2.\overline{18}$ as the quotient of two integers by considering an infinite geometric series.

b. Find the sum of the infinite series $100 + 50 + 25 + \cdots$.

(11.5)   **11.** Evaluate the following:

a. $8! - 4!$ b. $(8 - 4)!$ c. $\dfrac{8!}{4!}$ d. $\left(\dfrac{8}{4}\right)!$ e. $\dbinom{8}{4}$

(11.5)   **12.** Write A_{10} using summation notation if $a_1 = 2$ and $a_{10} = 20$.

(11.5)   **13.** Write G_{10} using summation notation if $g_1 = 512$ and $g_{10} = 1$.

(11.5)   **14.** Evaluate:

a. $\dbinom{15}{0}$ b. $\dbinom{7}{3}$ c. $\dbinom{p}{q}$

(11.2, 11.3, 11.5)   **15.** Evaluate the following:

a. $\displaystyle\sum_{k=3}^{8} (2k - 3)$ b. $\displaystyle\sum_{k=1}^{100} [5 + (k-1)4]$ c. $\displaystyle\sum_{k=1}^{10} 2(3)^{k-1}$

(11.5)   **16.** Write out the given expressions without using summation notation.

a. $\displaystyle\sum_{k=0}^{r} \binom{n}{k}$ b. $\displaystyle\sum_{k=0}^{n} a^{n-k}b^k$ c. $\displaystyle\sum_{k=0}^{n} \binom{n}{k} a^{n-k}b^k$

(11.5)   **17.** Find:

a. $(x - y)^5$ b. $(2x + y)^5$

c. The coefficient of $x^8 y^4$ in the expansion of $(x + 2y)^{12}$

(11.2, 11.3)   **18.** *Sociology.* Suppose someone tells you she has traced her family tree back ten generations. How many ancestors does she have if there were no intermarriages?

(11.3)   **19.** *Biology.* A certain bacterium divides into two bacteria every 20 minutes. If there are 1,024 bacteria in the culture now, how many will there be in 24 hours assuming that no bacteria die? Leave your answer in exponential form.

(11.4)   **20.** *Physics.* A pendulum is swung 125 cm and allowed to swing free until it eventually comes to rest. Each subsequent swing of the bob of the pendulum is 80% as far as the preceding swing. How far will the bob travel before coming to rest?

APPENDIX

A

Tables

Contents

Table I
Squares and Square Roots (1 to 100)

No.	Sq.	Sq. Root	Prime Factors	No.	Sq.	Sq. Root	Prime Factors
1	1	1.000		51	2,601	7.141	$3 \cdot 17$
2	4	1.414	2	52	2,704	7.211	$2^2 \cdot 13$
3	9	1.732	3	53	2,809	7.280	53
4	16	2.000	2^2	54	2,916	7.348	$2 \cdot 3^3$
5	25	2.236	5	55	3,025	7.416	$5 \cdot 11$
6	36	2.449	$2 \cdot 3$	56	3,136	7.483	$2^3 \cdot 7$
7	49	2.646	7	57	3,249	7.550	$3 \cdot 19$
8	64	2.828	2^3	58	3,364	7.616	$2 \cdot 29$
9	81	3.000	3^2	59	3,481	7.681	59
10	100	3.162	$2 \cdot 5$	60	3,600	7.746	$2^2 \cdot 3 \cdot 5$
11	121	3.317	11	61	3,721	7.810	61
12	144	3.464	$2^2 \cdot 3$	62	3,844	7.874	$2 \cdot 31$
13	169	3.606	13	63	3,969	7.937	$3^2 \cdot 7$
14	196	3.742	$2 \cdot 7$	64	4,096	8.000	2^6
15	225	3.873	$3 \cdot 5$	65	4,225	8.062	$5 \cdot 13$
16	256	4.000	2^4	66	4,356	8.124	$2 \cdot 3 \cdot 11$
17	289	4.123	17	67	4,489	8.185	67
18	324	4.243	$2 \cdot 3^2$	68	4,624	8.246	$2^2 \cdot 17$
19	361	4.359	19	69	4,761	8.307	$3 \cdot 23$
20	400	4.472	$2^2 \cdot 5$	70	4,900	8.367	$2 \cdot 5 \cdot 7$
21	441	4.583	$3 \cdot 7$	71	5,041	8.426	71
22	484	4.690	$2 \cdot 11$	72	5,184	8.485	$2^3 \cdot 3^2$
23	529	4.796	23	73	5,329	8.544	73
24	576	4.899	$2^3 \cdot 3$	74	5,476	8.602	$2 \cdot 37$
25	625	5.000	5^2	75	5,625	8.660	$3 \cdot 5^2$
26	676	5.099	$2 \cdot 13$	76	5,776	8.718	$2^2 \cdot 19$
27	729	5.196	3^3	77	5,929	8.775	$7 \cdot 11$
28	784	5.292	$2^2 \cdot 7$	78	6,084	8.832	$2 \cdot 3 \cdot 13$
29	841	5.385	29	79	6,241	8.888	79
30	900	5.477	$2 \cdot 3 \cdot 5$	80	6,400	8.944	$2^4 \cdot 5$
31	961	5.568	31	81	6,561	9.000	3^4
32	1,024	5.657	2^5	82	6,724	9.055	$2 \cdot 41$
33	1,089	5.745	$3 \cdot 11$	83	6,889	9.110	83
34	1,156	5.831	$2 \cdot 17$	84	7,056	9.165	$2^2 \cdot 3 \cdot 7$
35	1,225	5.916	$5 \cdot 7$	85	7,225	9.220	$5 \cdot 17$
36	1,296	6.000	$2^2 \cdot 3^2$	86	7,396	9.274	$2 \cdot 43$
37	1,369	6.083	37	87	7,569	9.327	$3 \cdot 29$
38	1,444	6.164	$2 \cdot 19$	88	7,744	9.381	$2^3 \cdot 11$
39	1,521	6.245	$3 \cdot 13$	89	7,921	9.434	89
40	1,600	6.325	$2^3 \cdot 5$	90	8,100	9.487	$2 \cdot 3^2 \cdot 5$
41	1,681	6.403	41	91	8,281	9.539	$7 \cdot 13$
42	1,764	6.481	$2 \cdot 3 \cdot 7$	92	8,464	9.592	$2^2 \cdot 23$
43	1,849	6.557	43	93	8,649	9.644	$3 \cdot 31$
44	1,936	6.633	$2^2 \cdot 11$	94	8,836	9.695	$2 \cdot 47$
45	2,025	6.708	$3^2 \cdot 5$	95	9,025	9.747	$5 \cdot 19$
46	2,116	6.782	$2 \cdot 23$	96	9,216	9.798	$2^5 \cdot 3$
47	2,209	6.856	47	97	9,409	9.849	97
48	2,304	6.928	$2^4 \cdot 3$	98	9,604	9.899	$2 \cdot 7^2$
49	2,401	7.000	7^2	99	9,801	9.950	$3^2 \cdot 11$
50	2,500	7.071	$2 \cdot 5^2$	100	10,000	10.000	$2^2 \cdot 5^2$

Table II
Powers of e

x	e^x	e^{-x}	x	e^x	e^{-x}
0.00	1.0000	1.0000	1.5	4.4817	0.2231
0.01	1.0101	0.9901	1.6	4.9530	0.2019
0.02	1.0202	0.9802	1.7	5.4739	0.1827
0.03	1.0305	0.9705	1.8	6.0496	0.1653
0.04	1.0408	0.9608	1.9	6.6859	0.1496
0.05	1.0513	0.9512	2.0	7.3891	0.1353
0.06	1.0618	0.9418	2.1	8.1662	0.1225
0.07	1.0725	0.9324	2.2	9.0250	0.1108
0.08	1.0833	0.9331	2.3	9.9742	0.1003
0.09	1.0942	0.9139	2.4	11.023	0.0907
0.10	1.1052	0.9048	2.5	12.182	0.0821
0.11	1.1163	0.8958	2.6	13.464	0.0743
0.12	1.1275	0.8869	2.7	14.880	0.0672
0.13	1.1388	0.8781	2.8	16.445	0.0608
0.14	1.1503	0.8694	2.9	18.174	0.0550
0.15	1.1618	0.8607	3.0	20.086	0.0498
0.16	1.1735	0.8521	3.1	22.198	0.0450
0.17	1.1853	0.8437	3.2	24.533	0.0408
0.18	1.1972	0.8353	3.3	27.113	0.0369
0.19	1.2092	0.8270	3.4	29.964	0.0334
0.20	1.2214	0.8187	3.5	33.115	0.0302
0.21	1.2337	0.8106	3.6	36.598	0.0273
0.22	1.2461	0.8025	3.7	40.447	0.0247
0.23	1.2586	0.7945	3.8	44.701	0.0224
0.24	1.2712	0.7866	3.9	49.402	0.0202
0.25	1.2840	0.7788	4.0	54.598	0.0183
0.30	1.3499	0.7408	4.1	60.340	0.0166
0.35	1.4191	0.7047	4.2	66.686	0.0150
0.40	1.4918	0.6703	4.3	73.700	0.0136
0.45	1.5683	0.6376	4.4	81.451	0.0123
0.50	1.6487	0.6065	4.5	90.017	0.0111
0.55	1.7333	0.5769	4.6	99.484	0.0101
0.60	1.8221	0.5488	4.7	109.95	0.0091
0.65	1.9155	0.5220	4.8	121.51	0.0082
0.70	2.0138	0.4966	4.9	134.29	0.0074
0.75	2.1170	0.4724	5.0	148.41	0.0067
0.80	2.2255	0.4493	5.5	244.69	0.0041
0.85	2.3396	0.4274	6.0	403.43	0.0025
0.90	2.4596	0.4066	6.5	665.14	0.0015
0.95	2.5857	0.3867	7.0	1096.6	0.0009
1.0	2.7183	0.3679	7.5	1808.0	0.0006
1.1	3.0042	0.3329	8.0	2981.0	0.0003
1.2	3.3201	0.3012	8.5	4914.8	0.0002
1.3	3.6693	0.2725	9.0	8103.1	0.0001
1.4	4.0552	0.2466	10.0	22026	0.00005

Table III
Logarithms of
Numbers

x	0	1	2	3	4	5	6	7	8	9
1.0	0.0000	0.0043	0.0086	0.0128	0.0170	0.0212	0.0253	0.0294	0.0334	0.0374
1.1	0.0414	0.0453	0.0492	0.0531	0.0569	0.0607	0.0645	0.0682	0.0719	0.0755
1.2	0.0792	0.0828	0.0864	0.0899	0.0934	0.0969	0.1004	0.1038	0.1072	0.1106
1.3	0.1139	0.1173	0.1206	0.1239	0.1271	0.1303	0.1335	0.1367	0.1399	0.1430
1.4	0.1461	0.1492	0.1523	0.1553	0.1584	0.1614	0.1644	0.1673	0.1703	0.1732
1.5	0.1761	0.1790	0.1818	0.1847	0.1875	0.1903	0.1931	0.1959	0.1987	0.2014
1.6	0.2041	0.2068	0.2095	0.2122	0.2148	0.2175	0.2201	0.2227	0.2253	0.2279
1.7	0.2304	0.2330	0.2355	0.2380	0.2405	0.2430	0.2455	0.2480	0.2504	0.2529
1.8	0.2553	0.2577	0.2601	0.2625	0.2648	0.2672	0.2695	0.2718	0.2742	0.2765
1.9	0.2788	0.2810	0.2833	0.2856	0.2878	0.2900	0.2923	0.2945	0.2967	0.2989
2.0	0.3010	0.3032	0.3054	0.3075	0.3096	0.3118	0.3139	0.3160	0.3181	0.3201
2.1	0.3222	0.3243	0.3263	0.3284	0.3304	0.3324	0.3345	0.3365	0.3385	0.3404
2.2	0.3424	0.3444	0.3464	0.3483	0.3502	0.3522	0.3541	0.3560	0.3579	0.3598
2.3	0.3617	0.3636	0.3655	0.3674	0.3692	0.3711	0.3729	0.3747	0.3766	0.3784
2.4	0.3802	0.3820	0.3838	0.3856	0.3874	0.3892	0.3909	0.3927	0.3945	0.3962
2.5	0.3979	0.3997	0.4014	0.4031	0.4048	0.4065	0.4082	0.4099	0.4116	0.4133
2.6	0.4150	0.4166	0.4183	0.4200	0.4216	0.4232	0.4249	0.4265	0.4281	0.4298
2.7	0.4314	0.4330	0.4346	0.4362	0.4378	0.4393	0.4409	0.4425	0.4440	0.4456
2.8	0.4472	0.4487	0.4502	0.4518	0.4533	0.4548	0.4564	0.4579	0.4594	0.4609
2.9	0.4624	0.4639	0.4654	0.4669	0.4683	0.4698	0.4713	0.4728	0.4742	0.4757
3.0	0.4771	0.4786	0.4800	0.4814	0.4829	0.4843	0.4857	0.4871	0.4886	0.4900
3.1	0.4914	0.4928	0.4942	0.4955	0.4969	0.4983	0.4997	0.5011	0.5024	0.5038
3.2	0.5051	0.5065	0.5079	0.5092	0.5105	0.5119	0.5132	0.5145	0.5159	0.5172
3.3	0.5185	0.5198	0.5211	0.5224	0.5237	0.5250	0.5263	0.5276	0.5289	0.5302
3.4	0.5315	0.5328	0.5340	0.5353	0.5366	0.5378	0.5391	0.5403	0.5416	0.5428
3.5	0.5441	0.5453	0.5465	0.5478	0.5490	0.5502	0.5514	0.5527	0.5539	0.5551
3.6	0.5563	0.5575	0.5587	0.5599	0.5611	0.5623	0.5635	0.5647	0.5658	0.5670
3.7	0.5682	0.5694	0.5705	0.5717	0.5729	0.5740	0.5752	0.5763	0.5775	0.5786
3.8	0.5798	0.5809	0.5821	0.5832	0.5843	0.5855	0.5866	0.5877	0.5888	0.5899
3.9	0.5911	0.5922	0.5933	0.5944	0.5955	0.5966	0.5977	0.5988	0.5999	0.6010
4.0	0.6021	0.6031	0.6042	0.6053	0.6064	0.6075	0.6085	0.6096	0.6107	0.6117
4.1	0.6128	0.6138	0.6149	0.6160	0.6170	0.6180	0.6191	0.6201	0.6212	0.6222
4.2	0.6232	0.6243	0.6253	0.6263	0.6274	0.6284	0.6294	0.6304	0.6314	0.6325
4.3	0.6335	0.6345	0.6355	0.6365	0.6375	0.6385	0.6395	0.6405	0.6415	0.6425
4.4	0.6435	0.6444	0.6454	0.6464	0.6474	0.6484	0.6493	0.6503	0.6513	0.6522
4.5	0.6532	0.6542	0.6551	0.6561	0.6571	0.6580	0.6590	0.6599	0.6609	0.6618
4.6	0.6628	0.6637	0.6646	0.6656	0.6665	0.6675	0.6684	0.6693	0.6702	0.6712
4.7	0.6721	0.6730	0.6739	0.6749	0.6758	0.6767	0.6776	0.6785	0.6794	0.6803
4.8	0.6812	0.6821	0.6830	0.6839	0.6848	0.6857	0.6866	0.6875	0.6884	0.6893
4.9	0.6902	0.6911	0.6920	0.6928	0.6937	0.6946	0.6955	0.6964	0.6972	0.6981
5.0	0.6990	0.6998	0.7007	0.7016	0.7024	0.7033	0.7042	0.7050	0.7059	0.7067
5.1	0.7076	0.7084	0.7093	0.7101	0.7110	0.7118	0.7126	0.7135	0.7143	0.7152
5.2	0.7160	0.7168	0.7177	0.7185	0.7193	0.7202	0.7210	0.7218	0.7226	0.7235
5.3	0.7243	0.7251	0.7259	0.7267	0.7275	0.7284	0.7292	0.7300	0.7308	0.7316
5.4	0.7324	0.7332	0.7340	0.7348	0.7356	0.7364	0.7372	0.7380	0.7388	0.7396
x	0	1	2	3	4	5	6	7	8	9

x	0	1	2	3	4	5	6	7	8	9
5.5	0.7404	0.7412	0.7419	0.7427	0.7435	0.7443	0.7451	0.7459	0.7466	0.7474
5.6	0.7482	0.7490	0.7497	0.7505	0.7513	0.7520	0.7528	0.7536	0.7543	0.7551
5.7	0.7559	0.7566	0.7574	0.7582	0.7589	0.7597	0.7604	0.7612	0.7619	0.7627
5.8	0.7634	0.7642	0.7649	0.7657	0.7664	0.7672	0.7679	0.7686	0.7694	0.7701
5.9	0.7709	0.7716	0.7723	0.7731	0.7738	0.7745	0.7752	0.7760	0.7767	0.7774
6.0	0.7782	0.7789	0.7796	0.7803	0.7810	0.7818	0.7825	0.7832	0.7839	0.7846
6.1	0.7853	0.7860	0.7868	0.7875	0.7882	0.7889	0.7896	0.7903	0.7910	0.7917
6.2	0.7924	0.7931	0.7938	0.7945	0.7952	0.7959	0.7966	0.7973	0.7980	0.7987
6.3	0.7993	0.8000	0.8007	0.8014	0.8021	0.8028	0.8035	0.8041	0.8048	0.8055
6.4	0.8062	0.8069	0.8075	0.8082	0.8089	0.8096	0.8102	0.8109	0.8116	0.8122
6.5	0.8129	0.8136	0.8142	0.8149	0.8156	0.8162	0.8169	0.8176	0.8182	0.8189
6.6	0.8195	0.8202	0.8209	0.8215	0.8222	0.8228	0.8235	0.8241	0.8248	0.8254
6.7	0.8261	0.8267	0.8274	0.8280	0.8287	0.8293	0.8299	0.8306	0.8312	0.8319
6.8	0.8325	0.8331	0.8338	0.8344	0.8351	0.8357	0.8363	0.8370	0.8376	0.8382
6.9	0.8388	0.8395	0.8401	0.8407	0.8414	0.8420	0.8426	0.8432	0.8439	0.8445
7.0	0.8451	0.8457	0.8463	0.8470	0.8476	0.8482	0.8488	0.8494	0.8500	0.8506
7.1	0.8513	0.8519	0.8525	0.8531	0.8537	0.8543	0.8549	0.8555	0.8561	0.8567
7.2	0.8573	0.8579	0.8585	0.8591	0.8597	0.8603	0.8609	0.8615	0.8621	0.8627
7.3	0.8633	0.8639	0.8645	0.8651	0.8657	0.8663	0.8669	0.8675	0.8681	0.8686
7.4	0.8692	0.8698	0.8704	0.8710	0.8716	0.8722	0.8727	0.8733	0.8739	0.8745
7.5	0.8751	0.8756	0.8762	0.8768	0.8774	0.8779	0.8785	0.8791	0.8797	0.8802
7.6	0.8808	0.8814	0.8820	0.8825	0.8831	0.8837	0.8842	0.8848	0.8854	0.8859
7.7	0.8865	0.8871	0.8876	0.8882	0.8887	0.8893	0.8899	0.8904	0.8910	0.8915
7.8	0.8921	0.8927	0.8932	0.8938	0.8943	0.8949	0.8954	0.8960	0.8965	0.8971
7.9	0.8976	0.8982	0.8987	0.8993	0.8998	0.9004	0.9009	0.9015	0.9020	0.9025
8.0	0.9031	0.9036	0.9042	0.9047	0.9053	0.9058	0.9063	0.9069	0.9074	0.9079
8.1	0.9085	0.9090	0.9096	0.9101	0.9106	0.9112	0.9117	0.9122	0.9128	0.9133
8.2	0.9138	0.9143	0.9149	0.9154	0.9159	0.9165	0.9170	0.9175	0.9180	0.9186
8.3	0.9191	0.9196	0.9201	0.9206	0.9212	0.9217	0.9222	0.9227	0.9232	0.9238
8.4	0.9243	0.9248	0.9253	0.9258	0.9263	0.9269	0.9274	0.9279	0.9284	0.9289
8.5	0.9294	0.9299	0.9304	0.9309	0.9315	0.9320	0.9325	0.9330	0.9335	0.9340
8.6	0.9345	0.9350	0.9355	0.9360	0.9365	0.9370	0.9375	0.9380	0.9385	0.9390
8.7	0.9395	0.9400	0.9405	0.9410	0.9415	0.9420	0.9425	0.9430	0.9435	0.9440
8.8	0.9445	0.9450	0.9455	0.9460	0.9465	0.9469	0.9474	0.9479	0.9484	0.9489
8.9	0.9494	0.9499	0.9504	0.9509	0.9513	0.9518	0.9523	0.9528	0.9533	0.9538
9.0	0.9542	0.9547	0.9552	0.9557	0.9562	0.9566	0.9571	0.9576	0.9581	0.9586
9.1	0.9590	0.9595	0.9600	0.9605	0.9609	0.9614	0.9619	0.9624	0.9628	0.9633
9.2	0.9638	0.9643	0.9647	0.9652	0.9657	0.9661	0.9666	0.9671	0.9675	0.9680
9.3	0.9685	0.9689	0.9694	0.9699	0.9703	0.9708	0.9713	0.9717	0.9722	0.9727
9.4	0.9731	0.9736	0.9741	0.9745	0.9750	0.9754	0.9759	0.9763	0.9768	0.9773
9.5	0.9777	0.9782	0.9786	0.9791	0.9795	0.9800	0.9805	0.9809	0.9814	0.9818
9.6	0.9823	0.9827	0.9832	0.9836	0.9841	0.9845	0.9850	0.9854	0.9859	0.9863
9.7	0.9868	0.9872	0.9877	0.9881	0.9886	0.9890	0.9894	0.9899	0.9903	0.9908
9.8	0.9912	0.9917	0.9921	0.9926	0.9930	0.9934	0.9939	0.9943	0.9948	0.9952
9.9	0.9956	0.9961	0.9965	0.9969	0.9974	0.9978	0.9983	0.9987	0.9991	0.9996
x	0	1	2	3	4	5	6	7	8	9

Answers to Selected Problems

Chapter 1

Problem Set 1.1, Pages 8–10

1. {a, e, i, o, u}   **3.** At the time of this writing {Ford, Nixon, Carter}
5. {2, 3, 5, 7, 11, 13}

7. {2, 4, 6, 8}

9. {8, 9, 10, 12, 14, 15, 16, 18}

11. 14; sum   **13.** 8; sum   **15.** 4; difference   **17.** 17; difference   **19.** 8; difference   **21.** 13; sum
23. 2; quotient   **25.** 20; product   **27.** 8; quotient   **29.** 27; sum   **31.**
33. Answers vary   **35.** Oh BLISS

Problem Set 1.2, Pages 16–18

1. $x \cdot 3$ **3.** y **5.** $(x + y) + z$ **7.** 0   **9.** ba **11.** $a + (2 + b)$ **13.** $2a + 2b$ **15.** 0
17. $4(a + b)$ or $2(2a + 2b)$ **19.** $b + 0$ **21.** Not closed   **23.** Closed   **25.** Closed   **27.** Not closed
29. Closed   **31.** Commutative   **33.** Associative   **35.** Distributive   **37.** Identity   **39.** Inverse
41. Commutative   **43.** Commutative   **45.** Distributive   **47.** None (theorem)   **49.** Commutative

Problem Set 1.3, Pages 23–24

1. 4   **3.** 9   **5.** 2   **7.** -2 **9.** 8   **11.** -4 **13.** -1 **15.** -12 **17.** 3   **19.** -8
21. 2   **23.** 8   **25.** 5   **27.** 6   **29.** -15 **31.** 8   **33.** 10   **35.** 16   **37.** -15 **39.** -10
41. -12 **43.** -56 **45.** 27   **47.** -4 **49.** 15   **51.** 15   **53.** 24   **55.** 60   **57.** -2
59. 6   **61.** 1   **63.** 26   **65.** 19   **67.** 9   **69.** -5

Problem Set 1.4, Pages 26–27

1. $5a$ **3.** $8x$ **5.** $6a$ **7.** $16x$ **9.** $4x$ **11.** $-4x$ **13.** $5xy$ **15.** $-3x^2y$ **17.** $-2a + 8b$
19. $4x + 9$ **21.** -2 **23.** -4 **25.** 1   **27.** -1 **29.** 16   **31.** $3x - 2y$ **33.** $-m + 3n$
35. $x + 2y - 1$ **37.** $2x^2 - 3$ **39.** $-m^2 + m - 3$ **41.** 7   **43.** 30   **45.** -11 **47.** -2
49. 4

1.5 Review Problems, Pages 27–28

1. finite   **2.** integers   **3.** commutative   **4.** distributive   **5.** absolute value (or square)   **6.** opposite
7. reciprocal (or multiplicative inverse)   **8.** coefficient   **9.** exponent   **10.** similar (or like) terms
11. a. {Alabama, Alaska, Arizona, Arkansas}   **b.** {0, 2, 4, 6, 8}   **c.** {5, 6, 7, 8}   **12. a.** 13; sum
b. 1; quotient   **c.** 17; sum   **13. a.** $a(bc)$ **b.** $b + 0$ **c.** $a(b + c)$ **14.** Yes   **15. a.** Commutative
b. Identity   **c.** Distributive   **16. a.** 0; difference   **b.** -24; product   **c.** 9; difference
17. a. -5; quotient   **b.** 10; product   **c.** 6; product   **18. a.** $2a$ **b.** $-2a + b$ **c.** $4c - 1$
19. a. -1 **b.** -15 **c.** -4 **20. a.** $3a - 2$ **b.** $-b + 5c - 8$ **c.** $2c^2 + c - 8$

Chapter 2

Problem Set 2.1, Page 33

1. $x = 4$ **3.** $v = 6$ **5.** $r = 12$ **7.** $t = 4$ **9.** $v = 5$ **11.** $x = -9$ **13.** $x = 5$ **15.** $w = 5$
17. $m = 3$ **19.** $p = 10$ **21.** $r = -1$ **23.** $t = -2$ **25.** $x = 1$ **27.** $y = 4$ **29.** $z = -2$
31. $s = 5$ **33.** $a = 8$ **35.** $x = -2$ **37.** $y = 3$ **39.** $z = 1$ **41.** $x = 1$ **43.** $x = 1$ **45.** $x = 5$
47. $x = 1$

Problem Set 2.2, Pages 38–45

1. a. (1ST INTEGER + 2)   **b.** n **c.** $n+1$ **d.** $n+2$ **e.** 144   **f.** 48   **3. a.** WIDTH

b. 34   **c.** w **d.** $w+7$ **e.** 34   **f.** 34   **g.** 20   **h.** 5

5. a. 90   **b.** 150   **c.** 1,140   **d.** d **e.** $d+90$ **f.** $d-150$ **g.** 1,140   **h.** 1,140   **i.** 1,200

7. a. (NO. IN EACH HUNDRED-SIZE BOX)   **b.** (NO. OF HUNDRED-SIZE BOXES)   **c.** 2,000

d. (NO. OF DOZEN-SIZE BOXES)   **e.** 64 − (NO. OF DOZEN-SIZE BOXES)   **f.** 2,000   **g.** 64 − n **h.** 2,000

i. 2,000   **j.** −4,400   **k.** 50   **9. a.** (AMOUNT INVESTED AT 12.5%)   **b.** TOTAL EARNINGS   **c.** 10,000

d. (AMOUNT INVESTED AT 10%)   **e.** 1,100   **f.** 1,250 − .125A **g.** −150   **h.** 6,000   **i.** 4,000

11. $\begin{pmatrix} \text{1ST} \\ \text{INTEGER} \end{pmatrix} + \begin{pmatrix} \text{2ND} \\ \text{INTEGER} \end{pmatrix} + \begin{pmatrix} \text{3RD} \\ \text{INTEGER} \end{pmatrix} = \text{SUM}$

$\begin{pmatrix} \text{1ST} \\ \text{INTEGER} \end{pmatrix} + \begin{pmatrix} \text{1ST} \\ \text{INTEGER} +1 \end{pmatrix} + \begin{pmatrix} \text{1ST} \\ \text{INTEGER} +2 \end{pmatrix} = 66$

Let x = 1ST INTEGER.

$$x + \quad (x+1) + \quad (x+2) = 66$$
$$3x + 3 = 66$$
$$3x = 63$$
$$x = 21$$

And $x + 1 = 22$, $x + 2 = 23$.

Answer: The integers are 21, 22, and 23.

13. $\begin{pmatrix} \text{1ST ODD} \\ \text{INTEGER} \end{pmatrix} + \begin{pmatrix} \text{NEXT ODD} \\ \text{INTEGER} \end{pmatrix} + \begin{pmatrix} \text{LAST ODD} \\ \text{INTEGER} \end{pmatrix} = \text{SUM}$

$\begin{pmatrix} \text{1ST ODD} \\ \text{INTEGER} \end{pmatrix} + \begin{pmatrix} \text{1ST ODD} \\ \text{INTEGER} +2 \end{pmatrix} + \begin{pmatrix} \text{1ST ODD} \\ \text{INTEGER} +4 \end{pmatrix} = 69$

Let x = 1ST ODD INTEGER.

$$x + \quad (x+2) + \quad (x+4) = 69$$
$$3x + 6 = 69$$
$$3x = 63$$
$$x = 21$$

The first integer is 21.

15. $\begin{pmatrix} \text{1ST ODD} \\ \text{INTEGER} \end{pmatrix} + \begin{pmatrix} \text{2ND ODD} \\ \text{INTEGER} \end{pmatrix} + \begin{pmatrix} \text{3RD ODD} \\ \text{INTEGER} \end{pmatrix} + \begin{pmatrix} \text{4TH ODD} \\ \text{INTEGER} \end{pmatrix} = \text{SUM}$

$\begin{pmatrix} \text{1ST ODD} \\ \text{INTEGER} \end{pmatrix} + \begin{pmatrix} \text{1ST ODD} \\ \text{INTEGER} +2 \end{pmatrix} + \begin{pmatrix} \text{1ST ODD} \\ \text{INTEGER} +4 \end{pmatrix} + \begin{pmatrix} \text{1ST ODD} \\ \text{INTEGER} +6 \end{pmatrix} = 100$

Let x = 1ST ODD INTEGER.

$$x + \quad (x+2) + \quad (x+4) + \quad (x+6) = 100$$
$$4x + 12 = 100$$
$$4x = 88$$
$$x = 22$$

But x must be odd, so there are no such integers.

17. $2(\text{LENGTH}) + 2(\text{WIDTH}) = (\text{PERIMETER})$

$2(\text{WIDTH} + 2) + 2(\text{WIDTH}) = 36$

Let w = WIDTH.

$$2(w + 2) + \quad 2w = 36$$
$$4w + 4 = 36$$
$$4w = 32$$
$$w = 8$$

The width is 8 cm.

19. $\begin{pmatrix} \text{PERIMETER} \\ \text{OF SQUARE} \end{pmatrix} = \begin{pmatrix} \text{PERIMETER OF} \\ \text{RECTANGLE} \end{pmatrix}$

$4\begin{pmatrix} \text{SIDE OF} \\ \text{SQUARE} \end{pmatrix} = 2\begin{pmatrix} \text{WIDTH OF} \\ \text{RECTANGLE} \end{pmatrix} + 2\begin{pmatrix} \text{LENGTH OF} \\ \text{RECTANGLE} \end{pmatrix}$

$4\begin{pmatrix} \text{SIDE OF} \\ \text{SQUARE} \end{pmatrix} = 2\left[\tfrac{3}{4}\begin{pmatrix} \text{SIDE OF} \\ \text{SQUARE} \end{pmatrix}\right] + 2\left[\begin{pmatrix} \text{SIDE OF} \\ \text{SQUARE} \end{pmatrix} + 4\right]$

Let S represent the length of the side of the square.

$$4S = 2[\tfrac{3}{4}S] + 2[S+4]$$
$$4S = \tfrac{3}{2}S \quad + 2S + 8$$
$$\tfrac{1}{2}S = 8$$
$$S = 16$$

And $\tfrac{3}{4}S = \tfrac{3}{4}(16) = 12$, $S + 4 = 16 + 4 = 20$.

The square is 16 cm on a side and the rectangle is 12 by 20 cm.

21.
$$\begin{pmatrix} \text{NO. OF} \\ \text{BLOCKS FROM} \\ \text{COLLEGE TO ARENA} \end{pmatrix} + \begin{pmatrix} \text{NO. OF} \\ \text{BLOCKS FROM} \\ \text{ARENA TO DORM} \end{pmatrix} + \begin{pmatrix} \text{NO. OF} \\ \text{BLOCKS FROM} \\ \text{DORM TO THEATER} \end{pmatrix} = \begin{pmatrix} \text{NO. OF} \\ \text{BLOCKS FROM} \\ \text{COLLEGE TO THEATER} \end{pmatrix}$$

$$\begin{pmatrix} \text{NO. OF} \\ \text{BLOCKS FROM} + 1 \\ \text{ARENA TO DORM} \end{pmatrix} + \begin{pmatrix} \text{NO. OF} \\ \text{BLOCKS FROM} \\ \text{ARENA TO DORM} \end{pmatrix} + \begin{pmatrix} \text{NO. OF} \\ \text{BLOCKS FROM} + 3 \\ \text{ARENA TO DORM} \end{pmatrix} = 10$$

Let $N =$ NO. OF BLOCKS FROM ARENA TO DORM.

$$(N+1) + \qquad\qquad N + \qquad\qquad (N+3) = 10$$
$$3N + 4 = 10$$
$$3N = 6$$
$$N = 2$$

Then,

$$\begin{pmatrix} \text{NO. OF} \\ \text{BLOCKS FROM} \\ \text{COLLEGE TO DORM} \end{pmatrix} = \begin{pmatrix} \text{NO. OF} \\ \text{BLOCKS FROM} \\ \text{COLLEGE TO ARENA} \end{pmatrix} + \begin{pmatrix} \text{NO. OF} \\ \text{BLOCKS FROM} \\ \text{ARENA TO DORM} \end{pmatrix}$$
$$= \qquad (N+1) \qquad + N$$
$$= \qquad (2+1) \qquad + 2$$
$$= 5$$

It is 5 blocks from the college to the dorm.

23.
$$3\begin{pmatrix} \text{NO. OF} \\ \text{3-PACKS} \\ \text{SOLD} \end{pmatrix} + \begin{pmatrix} \text{NO. OF} \\ \text{SINGLE} \\ \text{CASSETTES SOLD} \end{pmatrix} = \begin{pmatrix} \text{TOTAL NUMBER} \\ \text{SOLD} \end{pmatrix}$$

$$3\left[5\begin{pmatrix} \text{NO. OF} \\ \text{SINGLE} \\ \text{CASSETTES SOLD} \end{pmatrix}\right] + \begin{pmatrix} \text{NO. OF} \\ \text{SINGLE} \\ \text{CASSETTES SOLD} \end{pmatrix} = 1,200$$

Let $n =$ NO. OF SINGLE CASSETTES SOLD.

$$15n + \qquad\qquad n = 1,200$$
$$16n = 1,200$$
$$n = 75$$

And $5n = 5(75) = 375$.

There were 375 3-packs sold.

25.
$$\begin{pmatrix} \text{RECEIPTS} \\ \text{FROM ADULT} \\ \text{TICKETS} \end{pmatrix} + \begin{pmatrix} \text{RECEIPTS} \\ \text{FROM CHILDREN} \\ \text{TICKETS} \end{pmatrix} = \begin{pmatrix} \text{TOTAL} \\ \text{RECEIPTS} \end{pmatrix}$$

$$1.50\begin{pmatrix} \text{ADULT} \\ \text{TICKETS} \end{pmatrix} + .75\begin{pmatrix} \text{CHILDREN} \\ \text{TICKETS} \end{pmatrix} = 321.75$$

$$1.50\begin{pmatrix} \text{ADULT} \\ \text{TICKETS} \end{pmatrix} + .75\left[9\begin{pmatrix} \text{ADULT} \\ \text{TICKETS} \end{pmatrix}\right] = 321.75$$

Let $A =$ ADULT TICKETS.

$$1.50A + \qquad\qquad .75(9A) = 321.75$$
$$8.25A = 321.75$$
$$A = 39$$

And $9A = 9(39) = 351$.

351 children attended.

27. $\left(\begin{array}{c}\text{INTEREST FROM}\\ 6\%\ \text{INVESTMENT}\end{array}\right) + \left(\begin{array}{c}\text{INTEREST FROM}\\ 8\%\ \text{INVESTMENT}\end{array}\right) = \left(\begin{array}{c}\text{TOTAL}\\ \text{INTEREST}\end{array}\right)$

$.06\left(\begin{array}{c}\text{AMT INVESTED}\\ \text{AT }6\%\end{array}\right) + .08\left(\begin{array}{c}\text{AMT INVESTED}\\ \text{AT }8\%\end{array}\right) = 119$

$.06\left(\begin{array}{c}\text{AMT INVESTED}\\ \text{AT }6\%\end{array}\right) + .08\left(1,500 - \begin{array}{c}\text{AMT INVESTED}\\ \text{AT }6\%\end{array}\right) = 119$

Let $S = $ AMT INVESTED AT 6%.

$$.06S + \qquad\qquad .08(1,500 - S) = 119$$
$$.06S + \qquad\qquad\quad 120 - .08S = 119$$
$$-.02 = -1$$
$$S = 50$$

And $1,500 - S = 1,500 - 50 = 1,450$.

$50 is invested at 6% and $1,450 at 8%.

29. $\left(\begin{array}{c}\text{AMT}\\ \text{BUTTERFAT}\\ \text{IN MILK}\end{array}\right) + \left(\begin{array}{c}\text{AMT}\\ \text{BUTTERFAT}\\ \text{IN CREAM}\end{array}\right) = \left(\begin{array}{c}\text{AMT BUTTERFAT}\\ \text{IN HALF-AND-HALF}\end{array}\right)$

$.10\left(\begin{array}{c}\text{AMT OF}\\ \text{MILK}\end{array}\right) + .80\left(\begin{array}{c}\text{AMT OF}\\ \text{CREAM}\end{array}\right) = .50\left(\begin{array}{c}\text{AMT OF}\\ \text{HALF-AND-HALF}\end{array}\right)$

$.10\left(\begin{array}{c}\text{AMT OF}\\ \text{MILK}\end{array}\right) + .80\left(140 - \begin{array}{c}\text{AMT OF}\\ \text{MILK}\end{array}\right) = .50(140)$

Let $m = $ AMT OF MILK.

$$.10m + \qquad\qquad .80(140 - m) = 70$$
$$.10m + \qquad\qquad\ \ 112 - .80m = 70$$
$$-.7m = -42$$
$$m = 60$$

And $140 - m = 140 - 60 = 80$.

60 gal of milk should be mixed with 80 gal of cream.

31. 24 people   **33.** He walked 2 miles in $\frac{1}{2}$ hour.

Problem Set 2.3, Pages 51–53

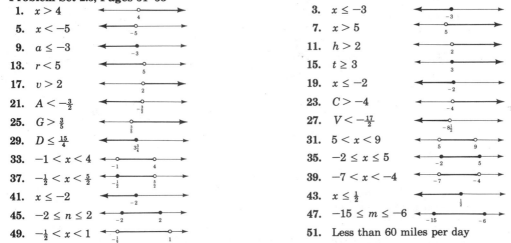

1. $x > 4$
3. $x \leq -3$
5. $x < -5$
7. $x > 5$
9. $a \leq -3$
11. $h > 2$
13. $r < 5$
15. $t \geq 3$
17. $v > 2$
19. $x \leq -2$
21. $A < -\frac{3}{2}$
23. $C > -4$
25. $G > \frac{3}{5}$
27. $V < -\frac{17}{2}$
29. $D \leq \frac{15}{4}$
31. $5 < x < 9$
33. $-1 < x < 4$
35. $-2 \leq x \leq 5$
37. $-\frac{1}{2} < x < \frac{5}{2}$
39. $-7 < x < -4$
41. $x \leq -2$
43. $x \leq \frac{1}{2}$
45. $-2 \leq n \leq 2$
47. $-15 \leq m \leq -6$
49. $-\frac{1}{2} < x < 1$
51. Less than 60 miles per day

53. At least $1,500 in sales   **55.** Price should be at least $18.60 but less than $20.00
57. Score should be between 57 and 77 (inclusive)   **59.** $\{10, 12, 14\}$; $\{12, 14, 16\}$; $\{14, 16, 18\}$
61. Possible values are $-4, -6, -8, \ldots$
63. Less than or equal to $6,000 should be invested at 6%, with the remainder invested at $8\frac{1}{2}\%$.

2.4 Review Problems, Pages 53–54
1. satisfy **2.** roots; solutions **3.** equivalent equations **4.** nonzero; the same solution set
5. $75 − 1ST SHARE **6.** two **7.** product **8.** order **9.** negative number **10.** intersection
11. $x = -3$ **12.** $y = 2$ **13.** $a = 7$ **14.** $b = 7$ **15.** 12 by 15 ft
16. $700 invested at 8% and $1,000 invested at $14\frac{1}{2}\%$ **17.** $x \geq 2$
18. $y < 7$
19. $-1 < z \leq 4$
20. Better than 76

Chapter 3

Problem Set 3.1, Pages 60–61
1. 11 **3.** 26 **5.** 2 **7.** −1 **9.** 3 **11.** 11 **13.** (−2, 3), (7, 0) **15.** (2, 1)
17. (3, 4), (3, 0), (3, −2) **19.** All real numbers **21.** All nonzero real numbers
23. Real numbers between −7 and −2, not including the end points **25.** 1, 2, 3, 4, 5, 6, 7, 8, 9
27. 0, 1, 2, 3, . . . , 14, 15 **29.** $\{(0, 2), (1, \frac{5}{3}), (2, \frac{4}{3}), (3, 1)\}$ **31.** $\{(0, 3), (1, -2), (2, -7), (3, -12)\}$
33. $\{(0, \frac{5}{2}), (1, 2), (2, \frac{3}{2}), (3, 1)\}$ **35.** $\{(0, -\frac{1}{2}), (1, \frac{1}{4}), (2, 1), (3, \frac{7}{4})\}$ **37–49.** Answers vary

Problem Set 3.2, Pages 69–70
1. 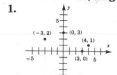 **3.** 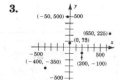 **5.**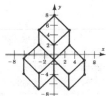
7. 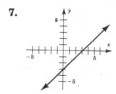 **9.** 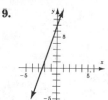 **11.**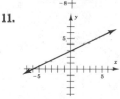
13. 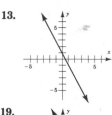 **15.** 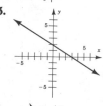 **17.**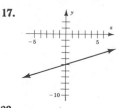
19. 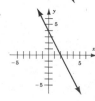 **21.** 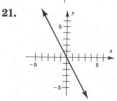 **23.**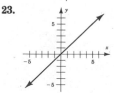

25.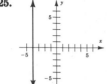

27.

29.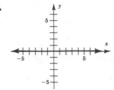

31.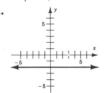

33.

35.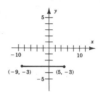

37.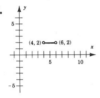

39.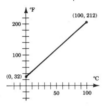

41.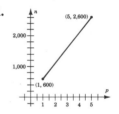

Problem Set 3.3, Pages 79–80

1. $m = 2$; $b = -3$ **3.** $m = 1$; $b = 2$ **5.** $m = -2$; $b = 5$ **7.** $m = -\frac{2}{3}$; $b = \frac{4}{3}$ **9.** $m = -\frac{2}{3}$; $b = 200$
11. $m = -1$; $b = -3$ **13.** $m = -\frac{2}{3}$; $b = \frac{4}{3}$ **15.** $m = -\frac{1}{3}$; $b = -\frac{2}{3}$ **17.** $m = 0$; $b = -2$
19. Slope undefined; no y-intercept   **21.** Slope undefined; no y-intercept   **23.** $m = -4$ **25.** $m = 1$
27. $m = -5$ **29.** $m = 0$

31.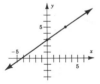

33.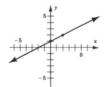

35.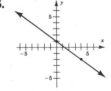

37.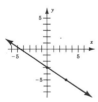

39.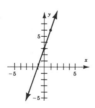

41.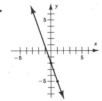

43.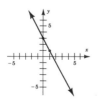

45.

47.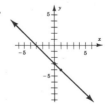

49.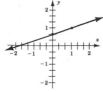

51.

53.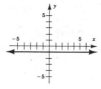

55.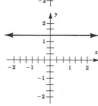

57.

59.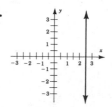

Problem Set 3.4, Pages 85–88

1. $5x - y + 6 = 0$ **3.** $2x + y + 3 = 0$ **5.** $x - 2y + 8 = 0$ **7.** $2x + 3y + 3 = 0$ **9.** $4x - 5y - 10 = 0$
11. $2x - y - 3 = 0$ **13.** $2x - 5y - 20 = 0$ **15.** $4x + 5y - 15 = 0$ **17.** $2x + 3y + 18 = 0$
19. $4x - 3y + 1 = 0$ **21.** $x - 2y + 2 = 0$ **23.** $y + 1 = 0$ **25.** Neither **27.** Parallel
29. Perpendicular **31.** Parallel **33.** Perpendicular
35. $2x + 5y - 4 = 0$ **37.** $y - 4 = 0$ **39.**

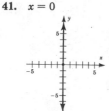

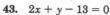

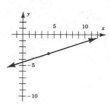

41. $x = 0$ **43.** $2x + y - 13 = 0$ **45.**

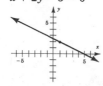

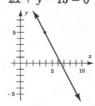

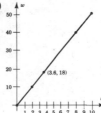

47. $x + 2y - 5 = 0$ **49.** Points $(2, 10)$ and $(0, 0)$; $m = 5$; $w = 5s$
If $s = 3.6$, then $w = 5(3.6)$
$\qquad = 18.0$
The weight is 18 kg.

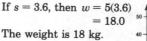

(3.6, 18)

51. Points $(10, 16.8)$ and $(20, 18.2)$; $m = .14$; $y - 16.8 = .14\,(x - 10)$
$\qquad 7x - 50y + 770 = 0$

53. Points (1.25, 25) and (2.00, 15); $m = -\frac{40}{3}$;
$$y - 15 = -\frac{40}{3}(x - 2)$$
$$40x + 3y - 125 = 0$$
$$40p + 3d - 125 = 0$$

55. No; (3, 2) is only *one* point satisfying the relationship, as shown by the graph.
$$\frac{y}{x} = \frac{2}{3}$$
$$y = \frac{2}{3}x, \quad x \neq 0$$

Problem Set 3.5, Page 93

1.
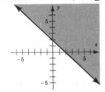

3.
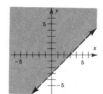

5.

7.
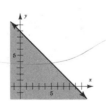

9.

11.

13.

15.
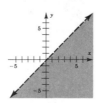

17.

19.

21.

23.
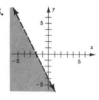

25.

27.
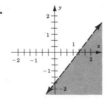

29.

3.6 Review Problems, Pages 93–94

1. independent; dependent   **2.** $Ax + By + C = 0$ **3.** y-intercept   **4.** half-planes; boundary
5. closed; open

6. 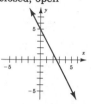   **7.** 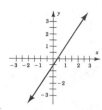   **8.**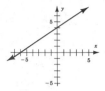

9.   **10.**   **11.**

12.   **13.** 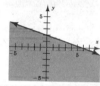   **14.**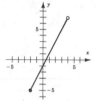

15. $2x - 3y - 9 = 0$ **16.** $3x + 2y + 21 = 0$ **17.** $x + 5 = 0$ **18.** $5x + 8y - 22 = 0$ **19.** $x - y - 3 = 0$

20. $3{,}000p + n - 23{,}000 = 0$

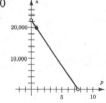

Chapter 4

Problem Set 4.1, Pages 99–101

1. x^6 **3.** x^2y^5 **5.** $2ab^3$ **7.** $3r^3 - s^4$ **9.** $-h^2k^3 - 7hk^2$ **11.** -49 **13.** 81 **15.** -8
17. -12 **19.** $9y^2$ **21.** $-x^2$ **23.** $-8y^3$ **25.** z^5 **27.** x^7 **29.** y^5 **31.** z^8 **33.** u^5v^2
35. $-6z^3$ **37.** x^{10} **39.** $6x^4y^3$ **41.** V   **43.** G   **45.** S   **47.** B   **49.** F   **51.** D   **53.** T
55. $-72x^5y^3$ **57.** $-a^6b^4$ **59.** h^7k^4 **61.** $18x^5y^3$ **63.** $x^5y^6z^7$ **65.** x^{a+b+3} **67.** $2x^{2n+2}$
69. $-x^{ab+c+3}$

Problem Set 4.2, Pages 105–106

1. $2x^3 - 6x^2 + 10x$ **3.** $x^3 - 6x^2 + 16x - 21$ **5.** $6x^3 + 7x^2 - 2x + 45$ **7.** $x^3 + 9x^2 + 27x + 27$
9. $4x^3 + 8x^2 - 3x - 9$ **11.** $15x^4$ **13.** $2x^5y^6$ **15.** $8x^5 - 12x^2$ **17.** $6x^3 - 2x^2 + 2x$ **19.** $x^2 + 2x - 3$
21. $x^2 + 5x + 6$ **23.** $xy - 5x - 4y + 20$ **25.** $2x^2 - 7x - 15$ **27.** $6x^2 + 19x - 7$ **29.** $8x^2 + 26x + 15$
31. $A = 2w^2 - 6w - 20$ sq ft   **33.** $A = 25s^2 - 20s + 4$ cm²   **35.** Distance $= 2x^2 - 5x - 3$
37. $6r^2 + 7r - 5$ trees   **39.** $7{,}500 + 400n - 3n^2$ dollars   **41.** $-9x + 19$ **43.** $7x^2 - x - 2$ **45.** x^2
47. $5xy + y^2$ **49.** $8x^2 + 10xy$ **51.** 15 **53.** 18×24 m

Problem Set 4.3, Pages 111–112

1. $x^2 - 2x + 3 + \dfrac{1}{x-1}$ 3. $2x^2 - 3x + 2 + \dfrac{-2}{x+3}$ 5. $3x^3 - 2x^2 - x - 6 + \dfrac{-6}{x-6}$ 7. $(x-2)(x^2 + 3x + 7)$

9. $(x+1)(x^2 - x + 1)$ 11.   Not a factor   13. $(x+3)(5x^2 - 3x - 3)$ 15. $(x-1)(3x^3 + x^2 + x + 5)$

17. $(x+2)(x^3 - 2x^2 + x - 2)$ 19. $(x+4)(2x^4 - x^3 + x^2 + 1)$ 21. $x + 1 + \dfrac{1}{x^2 + x + 1}$ 23. $x - 2$

25. $3x + 1$ 27. $2x - 1 + \dfrac{-2x}{3x^2 + 2x - 1}$ 29. $x^2 + x + 5 + \dfrac{21}{x^2 + 2x - 5}$

Problem Set 4.4, Pages 115–116

1. $2(x^2 + 1)$ 3. $3b(a + 2b)$ 5. $x(x^2 + x + 1)$ 7. $3rs(2s + 3r - 4)$ 9. $(x+2)(x+1)$
11. $(y-3)(y-2)$ 13. $(z-7)(z+5)$ 15. $(2t-3)(t+5)$ 17. $(3s+1)(s-2)$ 19. $(3v-2)(2v-1)$
21. $y(4x-1)(2x+3)$ 23. $2(x+3)(x-8)$ 25. $x(2x+7)(x-3)$ 27. $(3x-4)(4x+3)$
29. $x^2(3x+5)(4x-3)$ 31.   Width is $x + 3$ units   33.   Length is $w + 4$ cm
35.   Average rate is $2t + 1$ kph   37.   Rate is $(p + 4)$ 39. $3r - 1$ seats in each row   41. $(4x+3)(2x-3)$
43. $(8x+9)(3x-2)$ 45. $(3x-2)(2x-5)$ 47. $(2x-3y)(8x+5y)$ 49. $(7x^2-5)(2x^2+3)$
51. $3y^2(2x-1)(3x-1)$ 53. $(3x^2-2y)(x^2+y)$ 55. $(xy-z)^2$ 57. $(5x-yz)(4x-yz)$ 59. $x^2(4y+5z)(5y-2z)$

Problem Set 4.5, Pages 120–121

1. $(x-10)(x+10)$ 3. $(u-2v)(u+2v)$ 5. $(x+3)^2$ 7. $(y-1)(y^2 + y + 1)$ 9. $(2z-3)(2z+3)$
11. $(h+2)(h^2 - 2h + 4)$ 13. $(3r-1)^2$ 15. $2(2t-7)(2t+7)$ 17. $8(t-2)(t^2 + 2t + 4)$ 19. $3(2h+1)^2$
21. $(3x-2y)^2$ 23. $s(3s-11)(3s+11)$ 25. $9s(s-2)(s^2 + 2s + 4)$ 27. $x^2(3x+7)^2$ 29. $9(x^3+81)$
31. $(v-3)(v+3)(v-1)(v+1)$ 33. $(w^2+9)(w-3)(w+3)$ 35. $(x-3)(x+3)(x^2+3x+9)(x^2-3x+9)$
37. $y^2(y-2)(y+2)(y-3)(y+3)$ 39. $(z+2)(z-1)(z^2 - 2z + 4)(z^2 + z + 1)$ 41. $(x+4)(x-3)$
43. $(x-1)(x-4)$ 45. $2x^2 - 9x - 9$ 47. $(3x+2)(2x+1)$ 49. $(3x+4)(2x+3)$

Problem Set 4.6, Pages 126–127

1. $\{-7, -2\}$ 3. $\{-2, -3\}$ 5. $\{-\frac{1}{2}, 2\}$ 7. $\{-\frac{2}{3}, 5\}$ 9. $\{-9, 7\}$ 11. $\{\frac{1}{3}, \frac{1}{2}\}$ 13. $\{-\frac{1}{5}, \frac{4}{3}\}$ 15. $\{-1, \frac{13}{15}\}$

17.   19.   21.

23.   25.   27.

29.   31.   at least one   33.   critical value

35. $\{\frac{4}{3}, -\frac{3}{5}\}$ 37. $\{\frac{4}{9}, -\frac{3}{4}\}$ 39. $x < -\frac{4}{9}$ or $0 < x < \frac{2}{3}$ 41. $\{3, -4\}$ 43. $1 < x < 4$ 45. $\{\frac{3}{2}, 3\}$
47. $-\frac{2}{3} < x < -\frac{1}{2}$ 49. $-\frac{31}{4} \le x \le 0$

Problem Set 4.7, Pages 129–131

1.   3.   5. $\{-\frac{4}{3}\}$

7.   9. $\{\frac{5}{4}, \frac{5}{3}\}$ 11.

13. $\{\frac{2}{3}, -\frac{2}{3}, \frac{1}{2}, -\frac{1}{2}\}$ 15. $\{-4, -\frac{7}{4}\}$ 17. $\{-\frac{10}{3}, \frac{1}{4}\}$ 19.   1 second on the way up; 3 seconds on the way down
21.   Between $\frac{5}{8}$ and $\frac{11}{2}$ seconds   23. 3×7 m   25.   Length must be at least 5 ft
27.   Sheet must be 14×14 cm   29.   Cut out a 12 cm square

4.8 Review Problems, Pages 131–132

1.   binomial   2.   used as a factor   3.   quadratic   4.   quotient; remainder   5.   common monomial factor
6.   difference of squares   7.   sum   8. $A = 0$; $B = 0$ 9.   an even number of negative factors
10. $A \cdot B > 0$ 11.   a. $3x^2y^2 - 6xy^3$ b. $y^2 + y - 20$ c. $6z^3 + 7z^2 - 5z$
12. $3w^2 - w - 2$ square units   13.   a.   Yes   b.   No; remainder 10   c.   Yes   14.   a. $xy(2 - x^2 + 3y)$
b. $(y-7)(y-2)$ c. $(7z+5)(2z-1)$ 15. $2t + 3$ kph   16. $d + 5$ units   17.   a. $\{4, -2\}$ b. $\{0, 2, -2\}$
c. $\{-\frac{3}{2}, \frac{5}{2}\}$ 18. $3 \times 4 \times 6$ m   19.   a. $(5-x)(5+x)$ b. $y(y-4)^2$ c. $(2z+3)(4z^2 - 6z + 9)$
20.   a.   b.   c.

Chapter 5

Problem Set 5.1, Pages 140–141

1. Equal **3.** Equal **5.** Equal; $b \neq 0$ **7.** Not equal; $b \neq 0$ **9.** Equal; $x \neq 0$, $c \neq -d$ **11.** $\dfrac{3}{5}$

13. $\dfrac{-5}{7}$ **15.** $\dfrac{-x}{5}$ **17.** $\dfrac{3xy}{2z}$ **19.** $\dfrac{x}{y-2}$ $\left(\dfrac{-x}{2-y}\text{ is also acceptable, but less common}\right)$ **21.** $\dfrac{3}{5}$ **23.** $\dfrac{3}{2}$

25. $\dfrac{-3}{7}$ **27.** $\dfrac{-2}{15}$ **29.** $\dfrac{q}{s}$ **31.** $-p$ **33.** $\dfrac{-1}{x}$ **35.** $\dfrac{2}{3x}$ **37.** $\dfrac{2y}{xz}$ **39.** -1 **41.** $\dfrac{1}{2}$ **43.** $\dfrac{-3}{4}$

45. $\dfrac{-(2b+1)}{b+2}$ **47.** $\dfrac{1-d}{d+1}$ **49.** -1 **51.** $-(y+4)$

Problem Set 5.2, Pages 148–151

1. 60 **3.** $24xy^2$ **5.** $(x-3)(x+3)(2x+1)$ **7.** $(x-y)(x+y)$ **9.** $\dfrac{1}{10}$ **11.** $\dfrac{-5b}{2ac}$ **13.** $2(2x+8y^2-1)$

15. $\dfrac{5x+4y}{60}$ **17.** $\dfrac{5x-3y}{60}$ **19.** $\dfrac{18y-5x}{24xy^2}$ **21.** $\dfrac{25+4x}{5x}$ **23.** $\dfrac{x^2+1}{x}$ **25.** $\dfrac{5x+2}{(2x-1)(x+1)}$

27. $\dfrac{-9x^2-16x-2}{36x^3}$ **29.** $(x+5)(2x+1)$ or $2x^2+11x+5$ **31.** 1 **33.** $\dfrac{(3x-1)(x+4)}{x+2}$ **35.** $\dfrac{-3y+10}{2y-1}$

37. $\dfrac{x-y}{(x+y)(x-z)}$ **39.** $\dfrac{5x(x+2)}{(x-3)(x+3)(2x+1)}$ **41.** $\dfrac{4m-3n-3}{m-n}$ **43.** $\dfrac{x^2-12}{x-4}$ **45.** $\dfrac{1}{3x-1}$

47. $\dfrac{(-1)(x^2+xy+y^2)(x+y)^2}{x^2+y^2}$ **49.** $\dfrac{-4(y+2)(y+1)}{(y-5)(2y+3)}$ **51.** $\dfrac{m+1}{(m-n)^2}$ **53.** $\dfrac{x^2-x-h}{x^2h(x+h)}$
55. $10\frac{11}{16}$ inches **57.** $65\frac{11}{12}'$

Problem Set 5.3, Pages 157–161

1. y^4 **3.** $\dfrac{mp^4}{n^2}$ **5.** $\dfrac{-1}{2^4}$ or $\dfrac{-1}{16}$ **7.** 4 **9.** 4 **11.** $\dfrac{1}{5}$ **13.** $\dfrac{25x^4}{y^6}$ **15.** $\dfrac{x^4}{9y^6}$ **17.** $\dfrac{b^6}{a^6}$

19. $\dfrac{y^4}{3x^4z^5}$ **21.** $\dfrac{4a^2b^4}{c}$ **23.** $\dfrac{1}{(x+y)^2}$ **25.** 4.2×10^3 **27.** 1×10^{10} or 10^{10} **29.** 6.13×10^{-11}
31. 8.23 or 8.23×10^0 **33.** 8.23×10^2 **35.** .000002 **37.** 3,000,000,000,000 **39.** .05
41. 4,000,201,000,000 **43.** 1×10^4 or 10^4 **45.** 8×10^8 **47.** 1.2×10^{-3} **49.** 4×10^{-8}
51. 3 or 3×10^0 **53.** 9 cm **55.** 16 mi **57.** .25 ft³ **59.** 18 kg m/sec² **61.** 100 g
63. **a.** 10 **b.** 1,000 **c.** .001 **d.** 1,000,000 **e.** .001 **65.** See answers to Problems 43–45.

Problem Set 5.4, Pages 166–168

1. $D=-15$ **3.** $P=1$ **5.** $N=6$ **7.** $V=\frac{1}{2}$ **9.** $S=-2$ **11.** $L=5$ **13.** $J=4$ **15.** $T=9$
17. $U=\frac{-8}{5}$ **21.** $\{-3\}$ **23.** $\{\frac{12}{5}\}$ **25.** $\{4, 7\}$ **27.** 4 units of flour are needed
29. The longer side should be $3'4''$. **31.** It is $60'$ across the river.

Problem Set 5.5, Pages 171–172

1. $\dfrac{2}{5}$ **3.** $\dfrac{100}{9}$ **5.** 30 **7.** $\dfrac{11}{2(x+1)}$ **9.** $\dfrac{a(a+1)}{a-1}$ **11.** $\dfrac{5(3t+1)}{3t}$ **13.** $\dfrac{(n+1)(n-1)}{(n-4)(n+4)}$

15. $5(m+4)$ or $5m+20$ **17.** $\dfrac{y-2}{y-1}$ **19.** t **21.** $\dfrac{-2x-h}{x^2(x+h)^2}$ **23.** $\dfrac{-3(2x+h)}{(3x^2+6xh+3h^2+1)(3x^2+1)}$

25. $\dfrac{x+2y}{x-y}$ **27.** $\dfrac{(x^2-x-11)(x-5)}{(x-4)(x-2)(x-3)}$ **29.** $\dfrac{5}{7}$

5.6 Review Problems, Pages 173–174

1. rational **2.** $\dfrac{p}{q}, \dfrac{-p}{q}$ **3.** rational expression; nonzero **4.** proportion **5.** similar

6. a. =   **b.** =   **c.** =   **d.** =   **7.** $\dfrac{2x}{9zy^2}$ **8.** $\dfrac{6m-1}{m-1}$ **9.** $\dfrac{x^3y^3}{2}$ **10.** $\dfrac{s-37}{6(s-2)}$

11. $\dfrac{-9(a-1)}{a(a+9)}$ **12.** $\{2\}$ **13.** $\{2\}$ **14.** $\{\frac{21}{4}\}$ **15.** $\{-1\}$ **16.** $\{1.35 \times 10^{-25}\}$ **17.** $\{-2\}$ **18.** $\{\ \}$ or $\emptyset$

19. One will receive \$3,187.50 and the other will receive \$5,312.50.   **20.** It is 92.5′ across the canyon.

Chapter 6

Problem Set 6.1, Pages 181–183
1. 5; $b = 25$; $n = 2$ **3.** Not defined; $b = -25$; $n = 2$ **5.** -5; $b = 125$; $n = 3$ **7.** 3; $b = 729$; $n = 6$
9. 16 **11.** 16 **13.** -512 **15.** 4 **17.** 2 **19.** 18 **21.** 4 **23.** $3^{13/12}$ **25.** 9 **27.** $5^{1/6}$
29. Not defined   **31.** $\frac{1}{2}$ **33.** 25 **35.** 36 **37.** 4 **39.** $\dfrac{8}{125}$ **41.** $x^{8/7}$ **43.** $\dfrac{x^2}{y}$

45. $\dfrac{1}{x^{1/2}y^{3/2}}$ **47.** b **49.** $\dfrac{x}{y^7}$ **51.** x^3y^4 **53.** $x^2 + x$ **55.** $x - 2x^{1/2}y^{1/2} + y$
57. $s + 2(3^{1/2}s^{1/2}) + 3$ **59.** $x + y$ **61.** $(x + 1) + (x + 1)^{5/3}$

Problem Set 6.2, Pages 187–189
1. $\sqrt[3]{25^2}$ **3.** $2\sqrt{x}$ **5.** $4\sqrt[3]{x^2}$ **7.** $\sqrt[3]{(-2x)^2}$ **9.** $\sqrt[6]{3x^2y^3}$ **11.** $\sqrt{x^2 + y^2}$ **13.** $\dfrac{3}{\sqrt[3]{x}}$

15. $\dfrac{2}{\sqrt{x}} + \dfrac{3}{\sqrt{y}}$ **17.** $\dfrac{1}{4\sqrt{3x+2}}$ **19.** $\dfrac{1}{\sqrt[3]{(x^2 + 2xy + y^2)^2}}$ **21.** $5^{1/2}$ **23.** $2^{3/4}$ **25.** $(x + y)^{1/3}$

27. $(x^3 + y^3)^{1/3}$ **29.** $(-2x^3)^{1/5}$ **31.** $4(x^2y^3)^{1/4}$ **33.** $\dfrac{-2}{xy^{1/3}}$ **35.** $\dfrac{2 + 3x}{x^{1/2} + y^{1/2}}$ **37.** $\dfrac{-5x^2}{(x^2 - y^2)^{1/3}}$

39. $\dfrac{-5x^2}{(x - y)^{2/3}}$

41. Noninteger   **43.** Integer   **45.** Noninteger   **47.** Integer   **49.** Rational
51. Irrational   **53.** Irrational   **55.** Irrational   **57.** Irrational   **59.** Rational   **61.** Rational
63. Rational   **65.** (number line: $-\sqrt{7}$, $\sqrt{3}$, $\sqrt[3]{18}$ marked between -2 and 3)   **67.** (number line: $-11^{1/2}$, $15^{1/3}$, $15^{2/3}$ marked between -6 and 6)
69. $3.000000001493452864 \neq 3$
71. a. 14.42 **b.** 7.95 **73. a.** 3.54 **b.** 3.08

Problem Set 6.3, Pages 194–196
1. -3 **3.** $5\sqrt{5}$ **5.** $10\sqrt{10}$ **7.** $-21\sqrt{10}$ **9.** $20\sqrt{3}$ **11.** $-8\sqrt{3}$ **13.** $\frac{1}{2}\sqrt{2}$ **15.** $-\frac{1}{3}\sqrt{3}$
17. $-\frac{1}{5}\sqrt{10}$ **19.** $4\sqrt{3}$ **21.** $\frac{1}{2}\sqrt{2}$ **23.** $-\frac{1}{5}\sqrt{5}$ **25.** 5 **27.** $\sqrt{69}$ **29.** $2\sqrt{19}$ **31.** 0
33. $3 + \sqrt{3}$ **35.** $\dfrac{4 - \sqrt{2}}{3}$ **37.** $-2 - 3\sqrt{2}$ **39.** $1 - 3\sqrt{x}$ **41.** $1 - 4\sqrt{6}$ **43.** $\dfrac{2 + \sqrt{3}}{5}$ **45.** $\sqrt{13}$
47. $2\sqrt{10}$ **49.** $4\sqrt{2}$ **51.** $x - y$ **53.** $x + y$ **55.** $2x - y$ **57.** $18\sqrt{x^2 + 2x}$ **59.** $21(x + 3)\sqrt{x}$
61. $-30(x + 5)\sqrt{6}$ **63.** $\dfrac{3}{x}\sqrt{x}$ **65.** $\sqrt{x + 2}$ **67.** $\dfrac{2x}{5y}\sqrt{y}$ **69.** $\dfrac{16y^3}{x}\sqrt{2x}$ **71.** $\dfrac{5}{4}\sqrt{2}$ **73.** -1
75. $\dfrac{-5 - \sqrt{10}}{3}$

Problem Set 6.4, Pages 202–204
1. 4 **3.** $2\sqrt[3]{3}$ **5.** $6\sqrt[3]{2}$ **7.** $2\sqrt[4]{3}$ **9.** 100 **11.** $2\sqrt{2}$ **13.** $2\sqrt[5]{4}$ **15.** $xy\sqrt[3]{xy^2}$
17. $u^2t^2\sqrt[3]{ut^2}$ **19.** $y\sqrt[4]{x^3y^3}$ **21.** $\frac{3}{2}\sqrt{2}$ **23.** 1 **25.** $\frac{3}{5}\sqrt[3]{25}$ **27.** $\frac{1}{5}\sqrt[3]{5}$ **29.** $\frac{1}{2}\sqrt{2}$ **31.** $\frac{5}{4}\sqrt[3]{4}$
33. $\dfrac{1}{x}\sqrt{x}$ **35.** $\dfrac{1}{x}\sqrt[5]{x^3}$ **37.** $x^3\sqrt{x}$ **39.** $x\sqrt[4]{x^3}$ **41.** $\frac{1}{2}\sqrt{3}$ **43.** $\frac{1}{2}\sqrt[3]{5}$ **45.** $\frac{1}{5}\sqrt[3]{75}$ **47.** $\frac{1}{5}\sqrt[3]{5}$

49. $\frac{1}{2}\sqrt{2}$ **51.** $\frac{x}{6y}\sqrt{5y}$ **53.** $\sqrt[4]{2}$ **55.** $\sqrt{2x}$ **57.** $2x - y$ **59.** $28(x+1)\sqrt[3]{5}$ **61.** $2x^2\sqrt[3]{9x^2}$

63. $\frac{5}{2}\sqrt[3]{x+y}$ **65.** $\frac{x}{2}\sqrt[3]{2x^2}$ **67.** $(2x+y)\sqrt[3]{8x+4y}$ **69.** $\frac{x}{4}\sqrt[5]{8x^3}$ **71.** $\frac{1}{4x^2}\sqrt[5]{8}$ **73.** $\frac{2y^2}{x^2}\sqrt[5]{4x^4y}$

75. $\frac{2y^2}{x^2}\sqrt{2x}$ **77.** $80\sqrt{10}$ or about 253 m/sec

Problem Set 6.5, Pages 207–209
1. $7\sqrt{3}$ **3.** $4\sqrt{5}+3\sqrt{2}$ **5.** 2   **7.** 12   **9.** 45   **11.** $9+2\sqrt{6}$ **13.** $x+2\sqrt{x}+1$
15. $x+2y\sqrt{x}+y^2$ **17.** $y^2+4y\sqrt{x}+4x$ **19.** $\sqrt{2}+2\sqrt{5}$ **21.** $3\sqrt[3]{x}+\sqrt[3]{y}+\sqrt{y}$ **23.** $6\sqrt{2}$
25. $-4\sqrt{y}$ **27.** $7\sqrt[3]{4}-\sqrt[3]{2}$ **29.** $18\sqrt{2}-3\sqrt{3}$ **31.** $10\sqrt{3}+3\sqrt{2}$ **33.** $2\sqrt{3}/3$ **35.** $-12\sqrt{2}$
37. 2   **39.** $\sqrt[6]{200}$ **41.** $\frac{1}{2}\sqrt[6]{72}$ **43.** $\sqrt{3}+2$ **45.** $1-\sqrt{y}$ **47.** $-\sqrt[3]{3}+\sqrt[3]{9}$ **49.** $y-1$
51. $\frac{\sqrt{5}+1}{2}$ **53.** $-3-2\sqrt{2}$ **55.** $\frac{1-2\sqrt{x}+x}{1-x}$ **57.** $\frac{2\sqrt{x^2+5x}-5\sqrt{x+5}}{x+5}$ **59.** $\frac{y\sqrt{y}-2y}{y-4}$
61. $\frac{mn(\sqrt{m}-n)}{m-n^2}$ **63.** $B=15$ **65.** $D=-12$ **67.** $F=13$ **69.** $H=10$ **71.** $L=4$ **73.** $N=14$
75. $R=-6$ **77.** $T=11$ **79.** $W=-58$

Problem Set 6.6, Pages 214–216
1. $4i$ **3.** $3\sqrt{3}\,i$ **5.** $\sqrt{6}\,i$ **7.** $24i$ **9.** $3i$ **11.** $\frac{9+4\sqrt{5}}{2}$ **13.** $(-2+\sqrt{3})+\sqrt{2}\,i$

15. $3+(2\sqrt{2}+\sqrt{3})i$ **17.** $-1+\sqrt{2}\,i$ **19.** $8+6i$ **21.** $-1-i$ **23.** $-3+2i$ **25.** $10+15i$
27. $-12+9i$ **29.** $15-14i$ **31.** 1   **33.** $-i$ **35.** i **37.** $-3+2i$ **39.** $7+i$ **41.** $32-24i$
43. 7   **45.** $5+5i$ **47.** $-13+8\sqrt{3}\,i$ **49.** $-1+i$ **51.** $\frac{5}{17}+\frac{14}{17}i$ **53.** $-3i$ **55.** 5   **57.** $-i$
59. $25+4\sqrt{3}-8\sqrt{2}$

6.7 Review Problems, Pages 215–216
1. a. radical; index   **b.** complex   **c.** rationalizing the denominator   **d.** -1; imaginary unit
e. $a=c$ and $b=d$ **2. a.** -2 **b.** Not defined   **3. a.** 72   **b.** $y^{1/6}$
4. a. $2xy^{-1}$ or $\frac{2x}{y}$ **b.** x^{-1} or $\frac{1}{x}$ **5.**   **6. a.** $3\sqrt{3}$ **b.** $\frac{4}{5}\sqrt{5}$
7. a. $6+6\sqrt{3}$ **b.** $2-6\sqrt{2}$ **8. a.** $2+\sqrt{2}$ **b.** 2   **9. a.** 45   **b.** $11+6\sqrt{2}$
10. a. $\sqrt{x^2+y^2}$ **b.** $x+y$ **11. a.** $-\sqrt[3]{5}$ **b.** $-6\sqrt{2}+3\sqrt[3]{2}$ **12. a.** $2\sqrt[3]{25}$ **b.** $\frac{-2y^2\sqrt[3]{xy}}{x^2}$
13. a. $\sqrt{x^2+y^2}$ or $(x^2+y^2)^{1/2}$ **b.** $2x\sqrt[6]{2x^4}$ **14. a.** $\frac{\sqrt{3-y}}{3-y}$ **b.** $\frac{\sqrt{3y^2+9y}}{3y}$
15. a. $\sqrt{6}+2\sqrt[6]{2}$ **b.** $\frac{3\sqrt{2}}{2}$ **16. a.** $\frac{x(2-\sqrt{x})}{4-x}$ **b.** $\frac{x\sqrt{2+x}}{2+x}$ **17. a.** $\frac{\sqrt{6}-\sqrt{2}\,x}{3-x^2}$ **b.** $\frac{\sqrt{6+2x}}{3+x}$
18. a. $1-3i$ **b.** $5+5i$ **19. a.** -1 **b.** $-2i$ **20. a.** $7+6\sqrt{2}i$ **b.** $-\frac{6}{29}+\frac{15}{29}i$

Chapter 7

Problem Set 7.1, Pages 223–225
1. $u=\frac{1}{2}\sqrt{3}$ or $-\frac{1}{2}\sqrt{3}$ **3.** $v=8$ or -2 **5.** $w=2$ or $-\frac{8}{3}$ **7.** $x=3+\sqrt{3}$ or $3-\sqrt{3}$
9. $y=\frac{4+4\sqrt{3}}{5}$ or $\frac{4-4\sqrt{3}}{5}$ **11.** $a^2+12a+36=(a+6)^2$ **13.** $b^2-3b+(\frac{3}{2})^2=(b-\frac{3}{2})^2$

15. $c^2 + 11c + (\tfrac{11}{2})^2 = (c + \tfrac{11}{2})^2$ **17.** $d^2 + \tfrac{5}{3}d + (\tfrac{5}{6})^2 = (d + \tfrac{5}{6})^2$ **19.** $e^2 - 2\sqrt{3}\,e + 3 = (e - \sqrt{3})^2$
21. $x = 1$ or -5 **23.** $x = 2 + i$ or $2 - i$ **25.** $x = 2 + \sqrt{2}$ or $2 - \sqrt{2}$ **27.** $x = -4$ or 1
29. $x = 1 + \sqrt{2}$ or $1 - \sqrt{2}$ **31.** $x = 3 + \sqrt{7}$ or $3 - \sqrt{7}$ **33.** $x = 1$ or -7 **35.** $x = -\tfrac{1}{2}$ or $\tfrac{2}{3}$

37. $x = \tfrac{1}{2}$ or $-\tfrac{3}{2}$ **39.** $x = \dfrac{-2 + \sqrt{5}}{2}$ or $\dfrac{-2 - \sqrt{5}}{2}$ **41.** $h = 3$ or $-\tfrac{7}{4}$; 3.0 or -1.8 **43.** $m = \tfrac{7}{3}$ or 1; 2.3, 1.0

45. $v = \dfrac{-3 + \sqrt{13}}{7}$ or $\dfrac{-3 - \sqrt{13}}{7}$; .1 or $-.9$ **47.** $x = \dfrac{-1 + \sqrt{5}}{3}$ or $\dfrac{-1 - \sqrt{5}}{3}$; .4 or -1.1 **49.** $p = -\sqrt{5}$; -2.2

51. It is 15 ft from the source.   **53.** It is 4.2 ft from the source.
55. At 60 ft if the object is between the lights or at 300 ft if the object isn't between the lights.
57. The numbers are $2 \pm \sqrt{3}$.   **59.** A 20% interest rate is necessary.

Problem Set 7.2, Pages 232–234
Answers may vary in Problems 1–10.   **1.** $a = 1$, $b = 7$, $c = 2$, $d = 41$ **3.** $a = 1$, $b = 8$, $c = -3$, $d = 76$
5. $a = 2$, $b = -4$, $c = -3$, $d = 40$ **7.** $a = 3$, $b = -5$, $c = 0$, $d = 25$ **9.** $a = 2$, $b = \tfrac{1}{2}$, $c = -\sqrt{2}$, $d = \tfrac{1}{4} + 8\sqrt{2}$
11. $x - 11x - 102 = 0$; $b^2 - 4ac > 0$; 2 real roots   **13.** $6x^2 - x - 1 = 0$; $b^2 - 4ac > 0$; 2 real roots
15. $x^2 - 10x + 19 = 0$; $b^2 - 4ac > 0$; 2 real roots   **17.** $x^2 - 8x + 17 = 0$; $b^2 - 4ac < 0$; no real roots
19. $x^2 - 4x + 7 = 0$; $b^2 - 4ac < 0$; no real roots   **21.** $A = \tfrac{3}{4}$ or $-\tfrac{1}{3}$ **23.** $C = 2 + \sqrt{3}$ or $2 - \sqrt{3}$
25. $G = -7$ or -3 **27.** $I = \dfrac{3 \pm \sqrt{3}}{2}$ **29.** $L = \dfrac{-1 \pm \sqrt{13}}{5}$ **31.** $N = 2 \pm 2\sqrt{5}$ **33.** $P = 1 \pm i$

35. $R = 2\sqrt{2}$ or $\sqrt{2}$ **37.** $T = \dfrac{7 \pm \sqrt{13}}{6}$ **41.** $x = 7.98$ or 3.02   **43.** $x = 2.48$ or $-.90$

45. Let x = number; $x^2 + 9 = 5x$; $x^2 - 5x + 9 = 0$; the discriminant is $-45 < 0$, so there are no real roots.

47. The shortest side is $(-1 + \sqrt{35}) \approx 4.9$ cm.   **49.** The smaller cube has length $\left(\dfrac{1 + \sqrt{13}}{2}\right) \approx 1.3$ cm.

51. $\left(\dfrac{-1 + \sqrt{5}}{2}\right) \approx .6$ unit   **53.** $(9 + 9\sqrt{5}) \approx 29$ in.   **55.** The rate of the current is about 2.0 mph.

57. The faster ship is traveling at about 12 mph and the slower ship at about 7 mph.

Problem Set 7.3, Pages 239–240
1. 5   **3.** 3   **5.** $-4, -3$ **7.** 9   **9.** $\pm\sqrt{3}$ **11.** No roots   **13.** 1   **15.** 2, 1   **17.** 5, -2

19. 6   **21.** No roots   **23.** No roots   **25.** 37   **27.** $\pm\tfrac{1}{2}$ **29.** $6, -1, \dfrac{7 \pm \sqrt{73}}{2}$

Problem Set 7.4, Pages 242–244
1. $x = ky$ **3.** $s = kt^2$ **5.** $A = klw$ **7.** $V = kr^3$ **9.** $C = \dfrac{kt}{r}$ **11.** $V = kr^3$ **13.** $I = \dfrac{k}{R}$

15. $I = kPr$ **17.** $F = \dfrac{k}{d^2}$ **19.** $V = \dfrac{kT}{P}$ **21.** $E = kmv^2$ **23.** $H = ktRI^2$ **25.** $w = 21$ **27.** $p = \tfrac{5}{4}$
29. $A = 60$ **31.** $V = 288\pi$ cm³   **33.** $I = 20$ amp   **35.** $P = 1{,}200$ lb/ft²   **37.** $V = 3$ liters

7.5 Review Problems, Pages 244–245
1. $x^2 = a$ **2.** completing the square   **3.** $\dfrac{-b \pm \sqrt{b^2 - 4ac}}{2a}$ **4.** discriminant   **5.** 2 real   **b.** $-\dfrac{b}{a}$

7. $\dfrac{c}{a}$ **8.** extraneous   **9.** directly   **10.** $\dfrac{ky^2}{z^3}$ **11.** $2 \pm 2\sqrt{2}$ **12.** 4.8 or $-.8$ **13.** 41.42%
14. **a.** $x^2 - 2x - 15 = 0$ **b.** $x^2 - 2x - 1 = 0$ **c.** $x^2 - 8x + 17 = 0$
15. $b^2 - 4ac = (-16)^2 - 4(5)(13) < 0$; no real roots   **16.** $\dfrac{1 \pm \sqrt{5}}{4}$ **17.** The perimeter is 40 m.

18. **a.** -4 **b.** No roots   **19.** $S = kwd^2$ **20.** $h = \dfrac{32}{\pi}$ cm

Chapter 8

Problem Set 8.1, Pages 256–258

1. (3, 1)   **3.** (−2, −5)   **5.** Dependent system

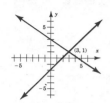   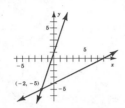   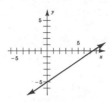

7. (13, 3)   **9.** (−3, 4)   **11.** Dependent system   **13.** (23, −43)   **15.** Dependent system   **17.** (13, 3)
19. (−6, 2); adding   **21.** (10, 4); adding   **23.** (1, 1); adding   **25.** (4, 1); substitution
27. (7, 8); substitution   **29.** (−5, 1); substitution   **31.** (9, −4)   **33.** (4, 2)   **35.** (2, 200)
37. $d = 84, q = 63$ **39.** Dependent system   **41.** (4, 400)   **43. a.** 40 mph   **b.** RATE AGAINST THE WIND
c. plus (or +)   **d.** (RATE OF BIRD) − (RATE OF WIND)   **e.** $b + w$ **f.** $b - w$ **g.** 25   **h.** 15

45.
$$\begin{cases} \text{RATE WITH THE CURRENT} & = 2 \\ \text{RATE AGAINST THE CURRENT} & = \tfrac{1}{2} \end{cases}$$

$$\begin{cases} (\text{RATE OF SWIMMER}) + (\text{RATE OF CURRENT}) = 2 \\ (\text{RATE OF SWIMMER}) - (\text{RATE OF CURRENT}) = .5 \end{cases}$$

Let s = RATE OF SWIMMER and c = RATE OF CURRENT.

$$\begin{cases} s + c = 2 \\ s - c = .5 \end{cases}$$
$$\overline{}$$
$$2s = 2.5$$
$$s = 1.25$$
$$1.25 + c = 2$$
$$c = .75$$

The rate of the current is $\frac{3}{4}$ mph.

47. The rate of the plane in still air is 525 mph.
49. 400 T-shirts at $4 (see the graph)

Problem Set 8.2, Pages 262–263

1. 5   **3.** 10   **5.** −16   **7.** 3   **9.** 0   **11.** $(\frac{2}{5}, \frac{4}{5})$ **13.** (−1, −4)   **15.** (2, 3)   **17.** (−2, −1)
19. (3, 2)   **21.** (43, −15)   **23.** (−3, 3)   **25.** $(3, -\frac{1}{2})$ **27.** (19, −7)   **29.** Inconsistent system
31. ~~Inconsistent~~ system   **33.** Dependent system

35. $\left(\dfrac{a}{a^2 - b^2}, \dfrac{-b}{a^2 - b^2}\right)$ *Dependent +*   **37.** The rate of the current is 5 mph.   **39.** The price is $390.

Problem Set 8.3, Pages 266–267

1. (4, 2, 1)   **3.** (4, 1, −4)   **5.** (2, 5, 7)   **7.** (2, −1, 1)   **9.** (3, 1, −4)   **11.** Inconsistent system
13. Inconsistent system   **15.** $(\frac{3}{5}, \frac{4}{5}, \frac{2}{5})$ **17.** $(\frac{1}{2}, \frac{2}{3}, \frac{5}{6})$ **19.** (31, −23, 29)

Problem Set 8.4, Pages 274–275

1. 2   **3.** −8   **5.** −2   **7.** −36   **9.** 96   **11.** 20   **13.** −33   **15.** −16

17. $D = -2; D_x = -4; D_y = 2; D_z = 4; (2, -1, -2)$ **19.** $D = -36; D_x = -6; D_y = 96; D_z = -36; (\frac{1}{6}, -\frac{8}{3}, 1)$

21. $D = 6; D_x = 24; D_y = 18; D_z = 30; (4, 3, 5)$ **23.** $D = -50; D_x = 50; D_y = -100; D_z = 150; (-1, 2, -3)$

25. $D = -25; D_x = 25; D_y = -50; D_z = 75; (-1, 2, -3)$

27. $D = 19; D_x = -19; D_y = -19; D_z = -38; (-1, -1, -2)$

29. $D = -11; D_x = -11; D_y = -22; D_z = -33; (1, 2, 3)$ **31.** $D = -16; D_x = -22; D_y = -4; D_z = -2; (\frac{11}{8}, \frac{1}{4}, \frac{1}{8})$

Problem Set 8.5, Pages 279–280

1.

3.
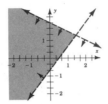

5.

7.

9.
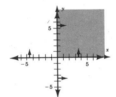

11.
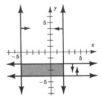

13.
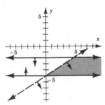

15.
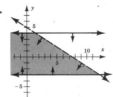

17.
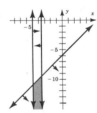

19.
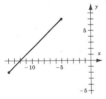

21.
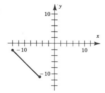

23.
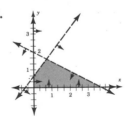

25.
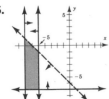

27.
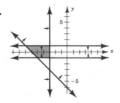

29.
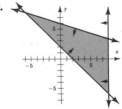

31. 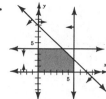   **33.**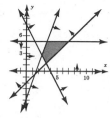

8.6 Review Problems, Pages 280–281

1. inconsistent; dependent   **2.** determinant; $ad - bc$ **3.** Cramer's rule   **4.** $\begin{vmatrix} a_1 & b_1 & c_1 \\ a_2 & b_2 & c_2 \\ a_3 & b_3 & c_3 \end{vmatrix}$; $\begin{vmatrix} a_1 & b_1 & d_1 \\ a_2 & b_2 & d_2 \\ a_3 & b_3 & d_3 \end{vmatrix}$

5. $-11; -20$ **6.** $(2, -2)$

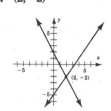

7. $3 \begin{cases} 2x + 5y = 27 \\ 3x - 15y = -117 \end{cases}$

$+ \begin{cases} 6x + 15y = 81 \\ \underline{3x - 15y = -117} \end{cases}$

$9x = -36$

$x = -4$

$-8 + 5y = 27$

$5y = 35$

$y = 7$

Solution: $(-4, 7)$

8. $5x - 7(8x - 37) = 4$

$5x - 56x + 259 = 4$

$-51x = -255$

$x = 5$

$y = 8(5) - 37$

$= 3$

Solution: $(5, 3)$

9. $x = \dfrac{\begin{vmatrix} 5 & 2 \\ -2 & -3 \end{vmatrix}}{\begin{vmatrix} 3 & 2 \\ 5 & -3 \end{vmatrix}}$ $y = \dfrac{\begin{vmatrix} 3 & 5 \\ 5 & -2 \end{vmatrix}}{-19}$

$= \dfrac{-15 + 4}{-9 - 10}$ $= \dfrac{-6 - 25}{-19}$

$= \dfrac{11}{19}$ $= \dfrac{31}{19}$

Solution: $\left(\dfrac{11}{19}, \dfrac{31}{19} \right)$

10. $(-1) \begin{cases} x + y + z = 2 \\ \underline{x + 2y - 2z = 1} \\ -y + 3z = 1 \end{cases}$ $(-1) \begin{cases} x + 2y - 2z = 1 \\ \underline{x + y + 3z = 4} \\ -y + 5z = 3 \end{cases}$ $\begin{cases} y - 3z = -1 \\ \underline{-y + 5z = 3} \\ 2z = 2 \\ z = 1 \end{cases}$ $y - 3 = -1$
$y = 2$
$x + 2 + 1 = 2$
$x = -1$

Solution: $(-1, 2, 1)$

11. $D = \begin{vmatrix} 3 & -2 & 0 \\ 5 & 4 & 1 \\ 3 & 0 & 1 \end{vmatrix} = (-1) \begin{vmatrix} 3 & -2 \\ 3 & 0 \end{vmatrix} + \begin{vmatrix} 3 & -2 \\ 5 & 4 \end{vmatrix}$ $D_x = \begin{vmatrix} -17 & -2 & 0 \\ 8 & 4 & 1 \\ -2 & 0 & 1 \end{vmatrix} = (-1)(0 - 4) + (-68 + 16)$

$= (-1)(0 + 6) + (12 + 10)$ $= 4 + (-52)$

$= -6 + 22$ $= -48$

$= 16$

$D_y = \begin{vmatrix} 3 & -17 & 0 \\ 5 & 8 & 1 \\ 3 & -2 & 1 \end{vmatrix} = (-1)(-6 + 51) + (24 + 85)$ $D_z = \begin{vmatrix} 3 & -2 & -17 \\ 5 & 4 & 8 \\ 3 & 0 & -2 \end{vmatrix} = -(-2)(-10 - 24) + 4(-6 + 51)$

$= -45 + 109$ $= 2(-34) + 4(45)$

$= 64$ $= 112$

Solution: $x = -3; y = 4; z = 7$ or $(-3, 4, 7)$

12.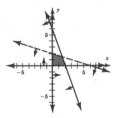

13. $(5, -4)$ **14.** $(10, 5)$
15. $(9, 3)$ **16.** $(\frac{13}{31}, \frac{14}{31})$
17. $(3, 0, -2)$

18. 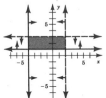   **19.**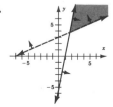

20. 25 mph

Chapter 9

Problem Set 9.1, Pages 288–291
1. Relation   **3.** Relation   **5.** Both   **7.** Both   **9.** Relation   **11.** Both   **13.** Both   **15.** Relation
17. $R = \{0, -2, 2, \sqrt{10}, -\sqrt{10}\}$; not a function   **19.** $R = \{0, 4, 10\}$; a function   **21.** $R = \{-2, 34, 208\}$; a function
23. $R = \{3, 8, -1\}$; a function   **25.** $R = \{3\}$; a function   **27.** $\{(1, 16), (4, 256), (10, 1,600), (16, 4,096)\}$
29. $d = 16t^2$; in $1\frac{1}{2}$ sec, $d = 16(1.5)^2 = 36$ ft; for a seven-story building this means each story is about 5 ft, which hardly seems likely.
31. Height at $t = 1.2$ sec is 106.992 ft; height at $t = 2.3$ sec is 164.588 ft; $D = \{t | 0 \le t \le 6.8\}$

Problem Set 9.2, Pages 294–296
1. a. 3   **b.** 1   **c.** 5   **d.** 18   **e.** 3   **3. a.** 2   **b.** 6   **c.** -3 **d.** -5 **e.** 15
5. $B(4) = -7$ **7.** $D(0) = 0$ **9.** $F(-4) = 32$ **11.** $H(-4) = 8$ **13.** $J(6) = 2$ **15.** $L(-7) = -1$
17. $N(1) = 5$ **19.** $R(3) = 7$ **21.** $T(x) = 8x + 3$; $T(-1) = -5$ **23.** $Y(u) = u + 1$; $Y(-13) = -12$
27. a. $x^2 - 3$ **b.** $x^2 + 2xh + h^2 - 3$ **c.** $2xh + h^2$ **d.** $2x + h$ **29.** 5   **31.** $2x + h$

33. $\dfrac{-2x - h}{(x^2 + 2)(x^2 + 2xh + h^2 + 2)}$

Problem Set 9.3, Pages 307–309
1. Functions: 3, 5, 7, 8, 11, 12, 13, and 14

3.   **5.** 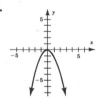   **7.**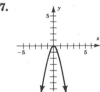

9.
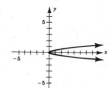

11.

13.

15.
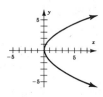

17.
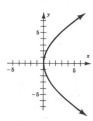

19. (5, −3); down; narrow
21. (5, −3); left; narrow
23. (−1, −2); left; narrow
25. (5, 0); up; standard
27. (0, 0); down; wide

29.
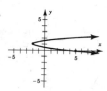

31.

33.
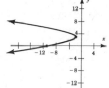

35.

37. $y = (x - 4)^2$; (4, 0)
39. $y = \frac{1}{3}(x - 3)^2$; (3, 0)
41. $x = (y - 1)^2$; (0, 1)
43. $x = \frac{1}{5}(y + 5)^2$; (0, −5)

45.
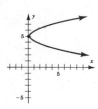

47. $x - 1 = (y + 4)^2$

49.
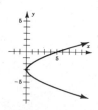

51. $y + 4 = -\frac{1}{4}(x - 2)^2$

53. (−8, 0), (0, 2), (0, −4)   **55.** (0, −2), ($\frac{2}{3}$, 0), (−$\frac{1}{2}$, 0)
57. (7, 0), (0, 3 + $\sqrt{2}$), (0, 3 − $\sqrt{2}$); approximate values: (0, 4.41), (0, 1.59)

59. $(0, 3), \left(\dfrac{3+\sqrt{3}}{2}, 0\right), \left(\dfrac{3-\sqrt{3}}{2}, 0\right)$; approximate values: $(2.37, 0), (.63, 0)$

61. $(10, 0)$

Problem Set 9.4, Pages 313–314

1. 5   **3.** $2\sqrt{5}$ **5.** $\sqrt{37}$ **7.** $\sqrt{(h+4)^2 + (k-3)^2}$ **9.** $x\sqrt{58}$

11.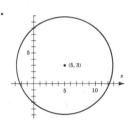

13.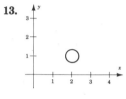

15.

17.

19.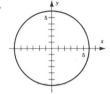

21.

23.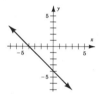

25.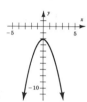

27.

29.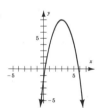

31.

33.

35.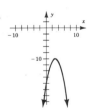

37.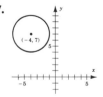

39.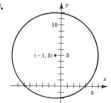

41.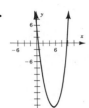

43.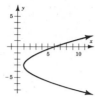

45.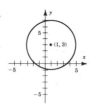

Problem Set 9.5, Pages 322–324

1. Line   **3.** Parabola   **5.** Circle   **7.** Hyperbola   **9.** Circle   **11.** Circle   **13.** Parabola
15. Hyperbola   **17.** Circle   **19.** Parabola

21.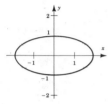

23.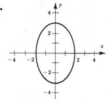

25.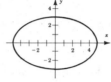

27.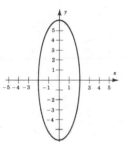

29.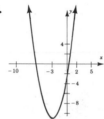

31.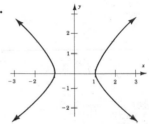

33.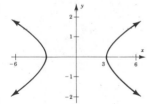

35.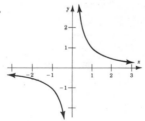

37.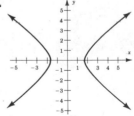

39.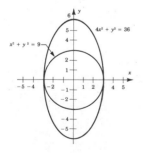

41.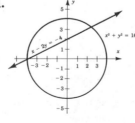

Problem Set 9.6, Page 327

1.

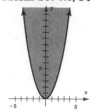

3.

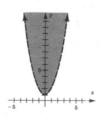

5.

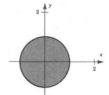

7.

9.

11.

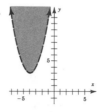

13.

15.

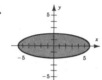

17.

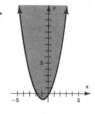

19.

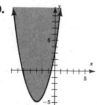

21.

23.

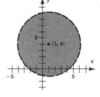

25.

9.7 Review Problems, Pages 328–329

1. associated with exactly one second component   **2.** domain   **3.** 'a. parabola   **b.** circle   **c.** parabola
d. ellipse   **e.** parabola   **f.** hyperbola   **g.** circle   **4.** vertex   **5.** distance; $\sqrt{(x_2 - x_1)^2 + (y_2 - y_1)^2}$
6. a. Both   **b.** Relation   **c.** Neither   **d.** Relation   **e.** Both   **f.** Relation   **7. a.** 0
b. 2   **c.** $1 - t^2$ **d.** $3t - 1$ **8.** $-2x - h$ **9. a.** 13   **b.** $\sqrt{13}$ **c.** $\sqrt{(h - 5)^2 + (k + 3)^2}$
d. $\sqrt{58}$ **e.** $\sqrt{(u - s)^2 + (v - t)^2}$

10.

11.

12.
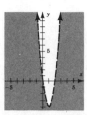

13.

14.

15.

16.

17.
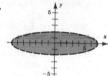

18.
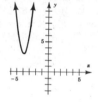

19. a. Line   **b.** Parabola   **c.** Parabola   **d.** Circle   **e.** Ellipse   **f.** Parabola   **g.** Ellipse
h. Hyperbola   **i.** Circle   **j.** Line   **20. a.** Circle   **b.** Hyperbola   **c.** Hyperbola
d. Circle   **e.** Parabola   **f.** Parabola   **g.** Hyperbola   **h.** Parabola   **i.** Parabola   **j.** Hyperbola

Chapter 10

Problem Set 10.1, Pages 336–337

1.
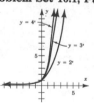

3.
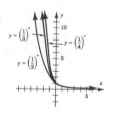

5.
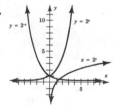

7. 4   **9.** $\frac{2}{3}$ **11.** 7   **13.** -3 **15.** $\frac{1}{3}$ **17.** -1 **19.** $\frac{1}{4}$

21.
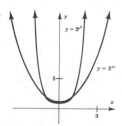

23.

25.
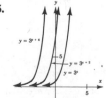

27.
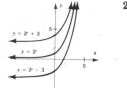

29.
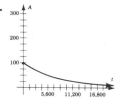

Problem Set 10.2, Pages 343–345

1. About 97 g remains.   **3.** About .45 g remains.   **5.** About .01 g remains.
7. Approximately 425,000 in 1995.   **9.** Approximately 169,000 in 1985.   **11.** Balance is $2,001.60.
13. Balance is $2,288.98.   **15.** Value at maturity is $13,742.19.
17. Compounded quarterly: $2,001.60 (Problem 11)
   Compounded monthly: $2,009.66 (Problem 12)
   Compounded daily: $A \approx \$2,013.6184$
   You would earn $12.02 more than the bank (Problem 11) and $3.96 more than the credit union (Problem 12).
19. $101.68   **21.** Population 2,950,000 in 1980 (actually, 2,950,059)
23. Population 560,000 in 1980 (actually, 561,943)   **25.** Estimated 660,000 in 1990 and 630,000 in 2000
27. 221 mg   **29.** 6.55 psi   **31.** About 7 days   **33.** His typing rate is 22 wpm.

35.
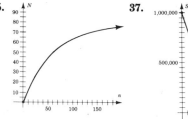

37.
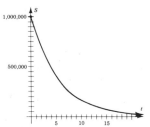

Problem Set 10.3, Pages 353–354

1. $\log_5 125 = 3$ **3.** $\log_3 \frac{1}{9} = -2$ **5.** $\log_4 8 = \frac{3}{2}$ **7.** $\log_{3/2} \frac{4}{9} = -2$ **9.** $\log_b a = c$ **11.** $2^3 = 8$
13. $10^{-2} = .01$ **15.** $4^{.5} = 2$ **17.** $(\frac{1}{3})^{-2} = 9$ **19.** $k^c = h$ **21.** 3   **23.** 2   **25.** $\frac{2}{3}$ **27.** 9
29. 2   **31.** 2   **33.** 3   **35.** $b^0 = 1$; $b > 0$, $b \neq 1$

37.
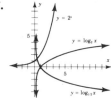

39.
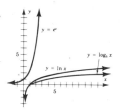

41. $\log_b 4 + \log_b a + \log_b c$ **43.** $\log \pi + 2 \log r$ **45.** $\log_b P + \frac{1}{2} \log_b Q$ **47.** $\log_b r + 2 \log_b s - \frac{1}{3} \log_b t$

49. $\ln P - rt$ (notice that $\ln e = 1$)   **51.** $t = \frac{1}{r} \ln \frac{P}{P_0}$ **53.** $a = \frac{-1}{.21} \ln \frac{P}{14.7}$ or $a = \frac{1}{.21} \ln \frac{14.7}{P}$

55. $h = \frac{t}{\log_{1/2}(A/A_0)}$ or $h = \frac{t \ln .5}{\ln (A/A_0)}$ or $h = \frac{t \log .5}{\log(A/A_0)}$ **57.** $n = 1 - \frac{1}{.11} \ln \left(\frac{P_n}{P_1}\right)$ **59.** $t = -\frac{L}{R} \ln \left(1 - \frac{IR}{E}\right)$

Problem Set 10.4, Pages 360–363

1. 1.658964843 **3.** −2.750435918 **5.** 4.29666519 **7.** −1.148853505 **9.** −9.500312916

11. 19.94019395 **13.** 2.90 **15.** 6.20 **17.** 10.50 **19.** 6.40 **21.** $2 \cdot 5^4\sqrt{3}$ or $1{,}250\sqrt{3}$ **23.** 25

25. 1 **27.** $\sqrt{2e}$ **29.** 10^8 **31.** $\dfrac{1}{\ln \pi} \approx .873568267$ **33.** $\dfrac{1}{\ln 3} \approx .9102392264$

35. $\dfrac{\ln 3}{\ln 1.03} \approx 37.16700973$ **37.** $\dfrac{\ln .000379}{\ln 1.44} \approx -21.60461574$ **39.** $\dfrac{\ln 2.63 \cdot 10^{11}}{\ln .569} \approx -46.63343313$

41. 30 decibels **43.** 107 decibels **45.** About 7.6 years (7 years 212 days)

47. About 3.2 years (3 years 84 days) **49.** About 14.1% **51.** 90°F **53.** 91°F **55.** 2 hr 20 min

57. $1.78 \cdot 10^{24}$ ergs

Problem Set 10.5, Pages 367–370

1. $4,714.37 **3.** About 16.6% **5.** Value is approximately $2,760.80 after 5 years

7. Approximately 3.6% 1950–1960; 1.1% 1960–1970; 1.8% 1970–1980

9. Population would have been approximately 573,000 in 1980. **11.** Population estimated as 1,160,000 in 2000.

13. 1964 population was approximately 545,000. **15.** $362.08 **17.** ~~$176.95~~ $194.63 **19.** $21.22 **21.** About .87%

23. 5 billion, 1989; 6 billion, 1999; 7 billion, 2007; 8 billion, 2015

25. Using the present rate of 1.8% (as given in the article), the estimated 2001 population will be 6,270,000,000 (6.2732488 billion)

10.6 Review Problems, Pages 371–372

1. exponential **2.** $x = y$ **3.** approaches **4.** $s^r = t;\ r = \log_s t$ **5.** $\log_b x$ **6.** sum of the logs

7. one; zero **8.** common **9.** scientific notation **10.** $x = y$

11. a.

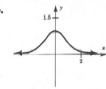

b.

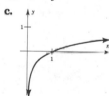

c.

12. a. 2 **b.** $-\frac{2}{3}$ **c.** $\frac{1.331}{1.000}$, or 1.331 **13.** $\log_2 8 = 3$ **14.** $8^{2/3} = 4$ **15. a.** 1.5010593

b. −2.1655793 **c.** 284.18424 **d.** .048794017 **e.** .87356852 **f.** .47369631 **g.** 8 **h.** 2^{-16}

i. 0 **16. a.** $\log a + \log b$ **b.** $\log_b c + \frac{1}{2}\log_b d$ **c.** $\ln k - ht$ **d.** $\log 5 + 3\log 6 - \frac{1}{2}\log 160$

17. a. 3.2380461 **b.** −4.13610826 **c.** 24.179582 **18. a.** $2,237.74 **b.** **c.** 5.78%

19. a. 126.1525, or 126 **b.** 114.8283, or 115 **c.** 48.4857, or 48.5

20. $947.89

Chapter 11

Problem Set 11.1, Pages 380–381

1. 17, arithmetic **3.** 96, geometric **5.** 85, neither **7.** pq^5, geometric **9.** 36, neither

11. 2, neither **13.** $\frac{5}{6}$, neither **15.** 216, neither **17.** 0, 3, 6 **19.** $a + d,\ a + 2d,\ a + 3d$

21. $0, \frac{1}{3}, \frac{1}{2}$ **23.** −2, 3, −4 **25.** $2, \frac{3}{2}, \frac{4}{3}$ **27.** −5, −5, −5 **29.** 303 **31.** 21 **33.** −7

35. $3, 1, \frac{1}{3}, \frac{1}{9}, \frac{1}{27}$ **37.** 1, 3, 4, 7, 11

Problem Set 11.2, Pages 386–388

1. $a_n = 4n - 1$ **3.** $a_n = 1 + 5n$ **5.** $a_n = -15 + 7n$ **7.** $a_n = 160 - 9n$ **9.** $a_n = nx$
11. $5, 9, 13, 17; 1 + 4n$ **13.** $-15, -7, 1, 9; -23 + 8n$ **15.** $100, 95, 90, 85; 105 - 5n$
17. $\frac{1}{2}, 2, \frac{7}{2}, 5; -1 + \frac{3}{2}n$ **19.** $5, 5 + x, 5 + 2x, 5 + 3x; 5 - x + nx$ **21.** $a_{20} = 101$ **23.** $a_{12} = 14$
25. $d = -2$ **27.** $d = 1$ **29.** $A_{10} = 845$ **31.** $A_{10} = -190$ **33.** $A_{15} = 480$ **35.** $A_{10} = 145$

37. $A_{25} = 400$ **39.** $A_{100} = 2,375$ **41.** $A_{20} = \frac{20}{2}[200 + (19)(50)] = 11,500$ **43.** $29\left(\frac{42 + 98}{2}\right) = 2,030$

45. $44\left(\frac{49 + 135}{2}\right) = 4,048$ **47.** $A_n = n\left(\frac{2 + 2n}{2}\right) = n(n + 1)$ **49.** $A_{87} = 87\left(\frac{1 + 87}{2}\right) = 3,828$ **51. a.** $\frac{9}{2}$
b. 4   **c.** -1 **d.** 84   **e.** 48   **53.** 55 blocks

Problem Set 11.3, Pages 393–395

1. $5, 15, 45, 135; 5 \cdot 3^{n-1}$ **3.** $1, -2, 4, -8; (-2)^{n-1}$ **5.** $-15, -3, -\frac{3}{5}, -\frac{3}{25}; -15 \cdot (\frac{1}{5})^{n-1}$ or $-3 \cdot 5^{2-n}$
7. $54, -36, 24, -16; 54 \cdot (-\frac{2}{3})^{n-1}$ or $(-1)^{n-1} \cdot 2^n \cdot 3^{4-n}$ **9.** $8, 8x, 8x^2, 8x^3; 8x^{n-1}$ **11.** $g_1 = 3, r = 2$
13. $g_1 = 1, r = \frac{1}{2}$ **15.** $g_1 = 3,125, r = -\frac{1}{5}$ **17.** $g_1 = 100, r = \frac{3}{2}$ **19.** $g_1 = x, r = x$ **21.** $g_n = 3 \cdot 2^{n-1}$
23. $g_n = (\frac{1}{2})^{n-1}$ or 2^{1-n} **25.** $g_n = 5^5 (-\frac{1}{5})^{n-1}$ or $(-1)^{n-1} \cdot 5^{6-n}$ **27.** $g_n = 100(\frac{3}{2})^{n-1}$ or $g_n = 2^{3-n} \cdot 3^{n-1} \cdot 5^2$
29. $g_n = xx^{n-1} = x^n$ **31.** $g_5 = 6 \cdot 3^4 = 2 \cdot 3^5 = 486$ **33.** $g_9 = 2^{10}(\frac{1}{2})^8 = 4$ **35.** $r = -\frac{1}{3}; g_7 = 3^{-3}$ or $\frac{1}{27}$
37. $r = \frac{\pm\sqrt{3}}{4}; g_5 = \frac{9}{32}$ **39.** $G_5 = \frac{6(1 - 3^5)}{1 - 3} = 3^6 - 3$ or 726   **41.** $G_9 = 2^{11} - 2^2$ or 2,044

43. $G_8 = 2^2 (3^8 - 2^8)$ or 25,220   **45.** $G_5 = \frac{3^5 + 1}{4 \cdot 3^5}$ or $\frac{61}{243}$ or .2510288066 (calc. approx.)   **47.** $G_6 = -\frac{21}{8}$ or -2.625

49. $G_8 = \frac{1}{3^6}(3^8 + 1)$ or $\frac{6,560}{729}$ or 8.9986283 (calc. approx.)   **51.** 3,905 letters   **53.** 11,110 letters

55. $r = 1.2; g_7 = 800,000(1.2)^5 = 1,990,656$

Problem Set 11.4, Pages 399–401

1. 2   **3.** 4   **5.** 2,000   **7.** $\frac{-40}{3}$ **9.** $\frac{1}{2}$ **11.** $\frac{4}{9}$ **13.** $\frac{3}{11}$ **15.** $\frac{27}{11}$ **17.** $\frac{923}{999}$ **19.** $\frac{1,394}{3,333}$
21. No sum $(r > 1)$ **23.** $13\frac{1}{2}$ **25.** $4 + 2\sqrt{2}$ **27.** $2 + \frac{3}{2}\sqrt{2}$ or $\frac{4 + 3\sqrt{2}}{2}$ **29.** $\frac{1,132}{225}$ **31.** 200 cm
33. 1,500 revolutions   **35.** 190 ft   **37.** $\frac{45}{2} + \frac{45}{8} + \frac{45}{16} + \cdots$

Problem Set 11.5, Pages 408–410

1. $X = 36$ **3.** $X = \frac{35}{8}$ or 4.375   **5.** $X = 93$ **7.** $A = 20$ **9.** $C = 49$ **11.** $E = 22$ **13.** $G = 2$
15. $I = 72$ **17.** $L = 132$ **19.** $N = 220$ **21.** $Q = 8$ **23.** $S = 28$ **25.** $T = 56$ **27.** $V = 70$
29. $Y = 10$ **33.** $\sum\limits_{k=1}^{7} 2^{-k}$ **35.** $\sum\limits_{k=0}^{4} 6^k$ or $\sum\limits_{k=1}^{5} 6^{k-1}$ **37.** $\sum\limits_{k=1}^{11} (10k - 9)$ **39.** $\sum\limits_{k=1}^{7} (\frac{1}{6} + \frac{1}{3}k)$

41. $\sum\limits_{k=1}^{9} 8\left(\frac{-\sqrt{2}}{2}\right)^{k-1}$ or $\sum\limits_{k=1}^{9} 9^{(2-k)/2}$ **43.** $a_1b_1 + a_2b_2 + a_3b_3 + \cdots + a_rb_r$

45. $\sum\limits_{j=1}^{r} ka_j = ka_1 + ka_2 + ka_3 + \cdots + ka_r$

$= k(a_1 + a_2 + a_3 + \cdots + a_r)$

$= k\sum\limits_{j=1}^{r} a_j$

47. $\sum\limits_{k=1}^{n} (a_k + b_k) = (a_1 + b_1) + (a_2 + b_2) + (a_3 + b_3) + \cdots + (a_n + b_n)$

$= (a_1 + a_2 + a_3 + \cdots + a_n) + (b_1 + b_2 + b_3 + \cdots + b_n)$

$= \sum\limits_{k=1}^{n} a_k + \sum\limits_{k=1}^{n} b_k$

49. $(2^k - 1)$st row, where $k = 0, 1, 2, \ldots$

Problem Set 11.6, Pages 412–413

1. $x^5 - 5x^4 + 10x^3 - 10x^2 + 5x - 1$ **3.** $x^8 + 8x^7 + 28x^6 + 56x^5 + 70x^4 + 56x^3 + 28x^2 + 8x + 1$

5. $x^6 - 6x^5y + 15x^4y^2 - 20x^3y^3 + 15x^2y^4 - 6xy^5 + y^6$ **7.** $x^5 + 10x^4 + 40x^3 + 80x^2 + 80x + 32$

9. $x^5 - 15x^4 + 90x^3 - 270x^2 + 405x - 243$ **11.** $\binom{11}{6} = 462$ **13.** $\binom{14}{4} = 1{,}001$

15. Term is $\binom{16}{4}x^{12}(-1)^4 = 1{,}820x^{16}$; coefficient is $1{,}820$

17. Term is $\binom{9}{4}r^5(2)^4 = 126 \cdot 2^4 r^5 = 2{,}016 r^5$; coefficient is $2{,}016$

19. Term is $\binom{8}{1}a^7(-2b)^1 = 8(-2)a^7 b = -16a^7 b$; coefficient is -16 **21.** $x^{15} - 15x^{14}y + 105x^{13}y^2 - 455x^{12}y^3 + \cdots$

23. $x^8 + 8\sqrt{2}\,x^7 + 56x^6 + 112\sqrt{2}\,x^5 + \cdots$ **25.** $x^{10} - 30x^9y + 405x^8y^2 - 3{,}240x^7y^3 + \cdots$

27. $a^{15}b^{15} - 30a^{14}b^{15} + 420a^{13}b^{15} - 3{,}640a^{12}b^{15} + \cdots$ **29.** $z^{22} + 55z^{20}k + 1{,}375z^{18}k^2 + 20{,}625z^{16}k^3 + \cdots$

31. $(1+1)^n = \binom{n}{0} + \binom{n}{1} + \binom{n}{2} + \cdots + \binom{n}{n-1} + \binom{n}{n}$; thus, $2^n = \binom{n}{0} + \binom{n}{1} + \binom{n}{2} + \cdots + \binom{n}{n-1} + \binom{n}{n}$

11.7 Review Problems, Pages 413–414

1. sequence   **2.** infinite; finite   **3.** difference   **4.** $n(n-1)(n-2) \cdot \cdots \cdot 3 \cdot 2 \cdot 1$ **5.** $\dfrac{n!}{r!\,(n-r)!}$

6. a. Arithmetic; $a_n = -9 + 10n$ **b.** Neither; $11{,}111$, $111{,}111$; one digit of one added to each term

c. Geometric; $g_n = 11^{n-1}$ **d.** Geometric; $g_n = 162 \cdot 3^{-n}$ **e.** Neither; 25, 36; $s_n = n^2$ **7. a.** $2{,}560$; 155

b. 5; 200 **8. a.** 2; 110 **b.** $\frac{1}{2}$; $1{,}023$ **9. a.** $3, 8, 13, 18$ **b.** 10^5, $5 \cdot 10^4$, $25 \cdot 10^3$, $125 \cdot 10^2$

c. $-1, \frac{1}{2}, -\frac{1}{3}, \frac{1}{4}$ **d.** $-1, \frac{1}{2}, -\frac{1}{8}, \frac{1}{24}$ **e.** $1, 2, 3, 5$ **10. a.** $\frac{24}{11}$ **b.** 200 **11. a.** $40{,}296$

b. 24 **c.** $1{,}680$ **d.** 2 **e.** 70 **12.** $A_{10} = \sum_{k=1}^{10} 2k$ **13.** $G_{10} = \sum_{k=1}^{10} 2^{10-k}$ **14. a.** 1 **b.** 35

c. $\dfrac{p!}{q!(p-q)!}$ **15. a.** 48 **b.** $20{,}300$ **c.** $59{,}048$ **16. a.** $\binom{n}{0} + \binom{n}{1} + \binom{n}{2} + \cdots + \binom{n}{r}$

b. $a^n + a^{n-1}b + a^{n-2}b^2 + \cdots + ab^{n-1} + b^n$ **c.** $\binom{n}{0}a^n + \binom{n}{1}a^{n-1}b + \cdots + \binom{n}{n}b^n$

17. a. $x^5 - 5x^4y + 10x^3y^2 - 10x^2y^3 + 5xy^4 - y^5$ **b.** $32x^5 + 80x^4y + 80x^3y^2 + 40x^2y^3 + 10xy^4 + y^5$

c. $7{,}920$ **18.** $2{,}046$ **19.** approximately $4.84 \cdot 10^{24}$ **20.** 625 cm

APPENDIX C | Glossary

Abscissa (3.2) The horizontal coordinates in a two-dimensional system of rectangular coordinates, usually denoted by x.

Absolute value (1.3) The absolute value of a number is that number if the number is nonnegative; it is the opposite of that number if the number is negative. Symbolically,

$$|n| = \begin{cases} n & \text{if } n \geq 0 \\ -n & \text{if } n < 0 \end{cases}$$

Addition method (8.1, 8.3) The solution of a system of equations in which we obtain coefficients of one of the variables as opposites and then add to eliminate that variable.

Addition property of equality (2.1) The same number or algebraic expression may be added to or subtracted from both sides of an equation to obtain an equivalent equation.

Addition property of order (2.3) The same number may be added to or subtracted from both sides of an inequality, leaving the order unchanged.

Additive identity (1.2) The number 0, which has the property that $a + 0 = a$ for any real number a.

Additive inverse (1.2) See Opposites.

Algebraic expression (1.4) Any meaningful combination of numbers, variables, and signs of operation.

Arithmetic progression (11.1, 11.2) See Arithmetic sequence.

Arithmetic sequence (11.1, 11.2) A sequence, each term of which is equal to the sum of the preceding term and a constant, written $a, a + d, a + 2d, \ldots, a + (n - 1)d$, where a is the first term, d is the *common difference*, and $a + (n - 1)d$ is the nth term. Also called an *arithmetic progression*.

Arithmetic series (11.2) The indicated sum of the terms of an arithmetic sequence. The sum of n terms is denoted by A_n and

$$A_n = \frac{n}{2}(a_1 + a_n) \qquad \text{or} \qquad A_n = \frac{n}{2}[2a_1 + (n - 1)d]$$

Associative property (1.2) A property of grouping: If a, b, and c are real numbers, then $(a + b) + c = a + (b + c)$ and $(ab)c = a(bc)$.

Axes (3.2) The intersecting lines of a Cartesian coordinate system. The horizontal axis is called the x-axis, and the vertical axis is called the y-axis. The axes divide the plane into four parts called *quadrants*.

Axis of a parabola (9.3) See Parabola.

Axis of symmetry (9.3) A curve is symmetric with respect to a line, called the axis of symmetry, if for any point P there is a point Q such that the axis of symmetry is the perpendicular bisector of the line segment PQ.

Base   (1.4, 4.1) See Exponent.
Base of a radical   (6.2) See Radical.
Binomial   (4.1) A polynomial with exactly two terms.
Binomial theorem   (11.6) For any positive integer n,

$$(a+b)^n = \sum_{k=0}^{n} \binom{n}{k} a^{n-k}b^k \qquad \text{where} \quad \binom{n}{k} = \frac{n!}{k!(n-k)!}$$

Braces   (1.1) See Grouping symbols.
Brackets   (1.1) See Grouping symbols.

Cartesian coordinate system   (3.2) Two intersecting lines, called *axes,* used to locate points in a plane. If the intersecting lines are perpendicular, the system is called a *rectangular coordinate system.*
Circle   (9.4, 9.5) The set of points in a plane that are a given distance from a given point. The given point is called the *center* and the given distance is called the *radius.* The equation of a circle with center (h,k) and radius r is

$$(x-h)^2 + (y-k)^2 = r^2$$

Closed   (1.2) See Closure property.
Closed half-plane   (3.5) See Half-plane.
Closure property   (1.2) A set is *closed* for an operation if whenever the operation is performed on elements from that set, the result is also an element of that set.
Coefficient   (1.4) Any factor of a term is said to be the coefficient of the remaining factors. Generally, it is taken to be the numerical coefficient of the variable factors.
Cofactor   (8.4) The cofactor of an element in a determinant is $(+1)$ or (-1) times its minor, as determined by its position in the array.
Common logarithm   (10.3) See Logarithm function.
Common monomial factor   (4.4) A monomial that is a factor of each term of a polynomial.
Commutative property   (1.2) A property of order: If a and b are real numbers, then $a + b = b + a$ and $ab = ba$.
Completing the square   (7.1, 7.2) Process applied to the solution of quadratic equations.
Complex fraction   (5.5) If a or b in a/b is a fraction, then a/b is called a complex fraction.
Complex numbers   (6.6) The set of numbers of the form $a + bi$, where a and b are real numbers and $i = \sqrt{-1}$. If $a = 0$, it is a pure imaginary number, and if $b = 0$, it is a real number.
Compound statement   (2.3) Equations or inequalities that impose more than one condition on a quantity. If two conditions apply simultaneously, the solution is the *intersection* of their individual solutions. If either of two conditions applies or both apply, the solution is the *union* of the solutions.
Conditional equation   (2.1) See Equation.

Conditional inequality   (2.3) See Inequality.
Conic sections   (9.5) The sets of points found by intersecting a plane and a cone. They include lines, circles, parabolas, ellipses, and hyperbolas.
Conjugates   (4.5, 6.5) Pairs of numbers that are the sum and difference of the same numbers; $a + b$ and $a - b$ are called conjugates. If conjugates are multiplied, the result is the difference of squares:

$$(a+b)(a-b) = a^2 - b^2$$

Consistent system   (8.1) If a system of equations has at least one solution, it is consistent; otherwise it is said to be *inconsistent.*
Contradiction   (2.1, 2.3) See Equation or Inequality.
Counting numbers   (1.1) See Natural numbers.
Cramer's rule   (8.2, 8.4) A determinant method of solving a system of linear equations.
Critical values   (4.6) The values for which each of the factors of a polynomial (inequality) is 0.
Cube root   (6.1) See Root of a number.

Degree   (1.4, 4.1) The degree of a term in one variable is the exponent of the variable or the sum of the exponents of the variables if there are more than one. The degree of a polynomial is the degree of its highest-degree term.
Denominator   (5.1) See Rational number.
Dependent system   (8.1) If any ordered pair satisfying one equation in a system of equations also satisfies the other, we describe the system as dependent.
Dependent variable   (3.1, 9.1) The variable associated with the second component of an ordered pair.
Determinant   (8.2, 8.4) The real number D, denoted by

$$D = \begin{vmatrix} a_1 & b_1 \\ a_2 & b_2 \end{vmatrix} = a_1 b_2 - a_2 b_1$$

Difference of cubes   (4.5) A polynomial of the form $a^3 - b^3 = (a - b)(a^2 + ab + b^2)$.
Difference of squares   (4.5) The product of a conjugate pair—that is, a polynomial of the form

$$a^2 - b^2 = (a+b)(a-b)$$

Direct variation   (7.4) See Variation.
Discriminant   (7.2) See Quadratic formula.
Distance   (9.4) One dimension: between points $P_1(x_1)$ and $P_2(x_2)$ is

$$d = |x_2 - x_1| = \sqrt{(x_2 - x_1)^2}$$

Two dimensions: between points $P_1(x_1,y_1)$ and $P_2(x_2,y_2)$ is

$$d = \sqrt{(x_2 - x_1)^2 + (y_2 - y_1)^2}$$

This result is also called the *distance formula.*

Distributive property   (1.2) If a, b, and c are real numbers, then $a(b + c) = ab + ac$ and $(a + b)c = ac + bc$.
Domain   (3.1, 9.1) The set of replacements for the independent variable.

e (10.2) See Natural base.
Elements   (1.1) See Set.
Ellipse   (9.5) The set of all points in a plane such that, for each point on the curve, the sum of its distances from two fixed points (called the *foci*) is a constant. The graph of $Ax^2 + By^2 = C$ is an ellipse if A, B, and C are all positive or all negative. The intercept form for an ellipse centered at the origin is

$$\frac{x^2}{a^2} + \frac{y^2}{b^2} = 1$$

The x-intercepts are $(\pm a, 0)$, and the y-intercepts are $(0, \pm b)$.
Empty set   (1.1) See Set.
Equation   (2.1) A statement of equality. If always true, an equation is called an *identity;* if always false, an equation is called a *contradiction.* If sometimes true and sometimes false, it is called a *conditional equation.* Values that make an equation true are said to *satisfy* the equation and are called *solutions* or *roots* of the equation. Equations with the same solutions are called *equivalent equations.*
Equation of a graph   (3.2) Every point on the graph has coordinates that satisfy the equation, and every ordered pair that satisfies the equation has coordinates that lie on the graph.
Equivalent equations.   (2.1) See Equation.
Exponent   (1.4, 4.1, 5.3, 6.1, 10.1) b^n, where b is any nonzero real number and n is any natural number, is defined as follows:

$$b^n = b \cdot b \cdot \ldots \cdot b$$
$$b^0 = 1 \qquad b^{-n} = \frac{1}{b^n}$$

$\setminus$ n factors

b is called the *base,* n is called the *exponent,* and b^n is called a *power.*
Exponential function   (10.1) $f(x) = b^x$, where b is a positive constant other than 1.
Extraneous root   (5.4, 7.3) A number obtained in the process of solving an equation that is not a root of the equation to be solved.

Factor   (4.1) Each of the numbers multiplied to form a product is called a factor of the product.
Factorial   (11.5) For a natural number n, the product of all the positive integers less than or equal to n. It is denoted by $n!$ and

$$n! = 1 \cdot 2 \cdot 3 \cdot \ldots \cdot (n - 1) \cdot n$$

Also, $0! = 1$.
Factoring   (4.1, 4.4) The process of determining the factors of a product.
Finite sequence   (11.1) See Sequence.
Finite set   (1.1) See Set.
Flowchart   (1.3) A device used to illustrate decision-making processes.
Fraction   (5.1) See Rational number.
Function   (9.1) A set of ordered pairs in which the first component is associated with exactly one second component.

Geometric progression   (11.1, 11.3) See Geometric sequence.
Geometric sequence   (11.1, 11.3) A sequence for which the ratio of each term to the preceding term is a constant, written

$$a, ar, ar^2, \ldots, ar^{n-1}$$

where a is the first term, r is the *common ratio,* and ar^{n-1} is the nth term; also called a *geometric progression.*
Geometric series   (11.3) The indicated sum of the terms of a geometric sequence. The sum of n terms is denoted by G_n and

$$G_n = \frac{g_1(1 - r^n)}{1 - r} \qquad r \neq 1$$

If $|r| < 1$, then

$$\lim_{n \to \infty} G_n = \frac{g_1}{1 - r}$$

If $|r| \geq 1$, then the infinite geometric series has no sum.
Graph of an equation   (3.2) See Equation of a graph.
Greater than   (1.1) If a lies to the right of b on a number line, then a is greater than b, $a > b$.
Grouping symbols   (1.1) Parentheses ( ), brackets [ ], and braces { }, indicate the order of operations and are also sometimes used to indicate multiplication, as in $(2)(3) = 6$.

Half-plane   (3.5) The part of a plane that lies on one side of a line in the plane. It is a *closed* half-plane if the line is included. It is an *open* half-plane if the line is not included. The line is the *boundary* of the half-plane in either case.
Horizontal line   (3.3) A line with zero slope. Its equation has the form $y =$ Constant.
Hyperbola   (9.5) The set of all points in a plane such that for each point on the curve the difference of its distance from two fixed points (called the *foci*) is a constant.

i (6.6) $i = \sqrt{-1}$ and is defined so that $i^2 = -1$. It is sometimes called the *imaginary unit*.

Identity (1.2) See Additive identity and Multiplicative identity.

Identity (2.1, 2.3) See Equation or Inequality.

Imaginary unit (6.6) The number *i*.

Inconsistent system (8.1) See Consistent system.

Independent variable (3.1, 9.1) The variable associated with the first component of an ordered pair.

Index of a radical (6.2) See Radical.

Inequality (2.3, 4.6, 8.5, 9.6) A statement of order. If always true, an inequality is called an *identity;* if always false, an inequality is called a *contradiction.* If sometimes true and sometimes false, it is called a *conditional inequality.* Values that make the statement true are said to *satisfy* the inequality. A *string of inequalities* may be used to show the order of three or more quantities.

Infinite sequence (11.1) See Sequence.

Infinite series (11.4) See Series and Geometric series.

Infinite set (1.1) See Set.

Integers (1.1) $I = \{. \,.\,. , -3, -2, -1, 0, 1, 2, 3, . \,.\,.\}$, composed of the natural numbers, their opposites, and 0.

Intercepts (3.3, 9.3) The point or points where a line or a curve crosses a coordinate axis. The *x*-intercepts are sometimes called the *zeros* of the equation.

Intercepts of an ellipse (9.5) See Ellipse.

Intercepts of a parabola (9.3) Given the parabola $y = ax^2 + bx + c$, the *y-intercept* is the point $(0, c)$; the *x-intercepts* are the points $(x_1, 0)$ and $(x_2, 0)$, where x_1 and x_2 satisfy the equation $ax^2 + bx + c = 0$.

Intersection (2.3) See Compound statement.

Inverse variation (7.4) See Variation.

Irrational number (1.1) A number that can be expressed as a nonrepeating, nonterminal decimal.

Joint variation (7.4) See Variation.

Least common denominator (LCD) (5.2) The smallest number that is exactly divisible by each of the given numbers.

Less than (1.1) If *a* is to the left of *b* on a number line, then *a* is less than *b*, $a < b$.

Like terms (1.4) Terms that differ only in their numerical coefficients.

Linear equation (3.2) A first-degree equation with two variables.

Logarithm function (10.3) For $b > 0$, $b \neq 1$, $x = b^y$ is equivalent to $y = \log_b x$. The logarithm to base *b* of *x* is the power *y* to which *b* must be raised to equal *x*. If the base is 10, *y* is a *common logarithm* and is written $y = \log x$. If the base is *e*, *y* is a *natural logarithm* and is written $y = \ln x$.

Members (1.1) See Set.

Minor (8.4) The minor of an element of a determinant is the (smaller) determinant that remains after deleting all entries in its row and column.

Monomial (4.1) A polynomial with one and only one term.

Multiplication property of equality (2.1) Both sides of an equation may be multiplied or divided by any nonzero number to obtain an equivalent equation.

Multiplication property of order (2.3) Both sides of an inequality may be multiplied or divided by a positive number, and the order of the inequality will remain unchanged. The order is reversed if both sides are multiplied or divided by a negative number.

Multiplicative identity (1.2) The number 1, with the property that $1 \cdot a = a$ for any real number *a*.

Multiplicative inverse (1.2, 5.1) See Reciprocal.

Natural base, *e* (10.2) A constant that is approximately 2.7182818 and is defined by

$$\lim_{n \to \infty}\left(1 + \frac{1}{n}\right)^n = e$$

Natural logarithm (10.3) See Logarithm function.

Natural numbers (1.1) $N = \{1, 2, 3, 4, 5, . \,.\,.\}$, the positive integers, also called the *counting numbers*.

Null set (1.1) See Set.

Number line (1.1) A line used to display a set of numbers graphically.

Numerator (5.1) See Rational number.

Numerical coefficient (1.4) See Coefficient.

Open half-plane (3.5) See Half-plane.

Opposites (1.2, 1.3) Opposites *x* and $-x$ are the same distance from 0 on the number line but in opposite directions; $-x$ is also called the *additive inverse* of *x*.

Ordered pair (3.1) A pair of numbers, written (x,y), where the order in which they are named is important.

Order-of-operations convention (1.1) If no grouping symbols are used in a numerical expression, first perform all multiplication and division from left to right, and then perform all addition and subtraction from left to right.

Ordinate (3.2) The vertical coordinates in a two-dimensional system of rectangular coordinates, usually denoted by *y*.

Origin (1.1, 3.2) The point designating 0 on a number line. In two dimensions, the point of intersection of the coordinate axes.

Parabola (9.3, 9.5) The set of points in a plane satisfying the equations

$$y = ax^2 + bx + c, \qquad a \neq 0$$
$$\text{or}$$
$$x = ay^2 + by + c, \qquad a \neq 0$$

The *axis of symmetry* is the *axis* of the parabola. The point where the axis cuts the parabola is the *vertex*.

Parentheses (1.1) See Grouping symbols.

Perfect square (4.5) A polynomial of the form $(a + b)^2 = a^2 + 2ab + b^2$.

Point–slope form of the equation of a line (3.4) $y - y_1 = m(x - x_1)$, where m is the slope and (x_1, y_1) is a point on the line.

Polynomial (1.4, 4.1) An algebraic expression that may be written as a sum (or difference) of terms. The *term* of a polynomial contains multiplication only.

Power (1.4, 4.1) See Exponent.

Prime numbers (1.1)

$$P = \{2, 3, 5, 7, 11, 13, 17, 19, 23, \ldots\}$$

Numbers with exactly two factors, 1 and the number itself.

Principal root (6.2) The positive nth root, $b^{1/n}$ or $\sqrt[n]{b}$.

Progression (11.1) See Sequence.

Property of exponentials (10.1) For nonzero real x and y and for positive real a, $b \neq 1$, if $a^x = a^y$, then $x = y$; or if $a^x = b^x$, then $a = b$.

Proportion (5.4) A statement of equality between two ratios.

Pure imaginary number (6.6) See Complex numbers.

Quadrant (3.2) See Axes.

Quadratic (4.2, 9.3) A second-degree polynomial.

Quadratic formula (7.2) If $ax^2 + bx + c = 0$ and $a \neq 0$, then

$$x = \frac{-b \pm \sqrt{b^2 - 4ac}}{2a}$$

The radicand $b^2 - 4ac$ is called the *discriminant* of the quadratic.

Quadratic inequality (4.6, 9.6) A region of the plane whose boundary is a quadratic equation.

Radical (6.2) For a natural number $n \geq 2$ and b a positive number, $\sqrt[n]{b} = b^{1/n}$. The symbol $\sqrt{}$ is called a *radical*, n is called the *index*, and b is called the *base* or *radicand*.

Radicand (6.2) See Radical.

Range (9.1) The set of replacements for the dependent variable.

Ratio (5.4) The quotient of two numbers or expressions.

Rational equation (5.4) An equation that has at least one variable in the denominator.

Rational expression (5.1, 6.4) A polynomial divided by a nonzero polynomial.

Rationalizing the denominator (6.4) The process whereby radicals are eliminated from denominators.

Rational number (1.1, 5.1) A number belonging to the set Q defined by

$$Q = \left\{ \frac{a}{b} \,\middle|\, a \text{ is an integer, } b \text{ is a nonzero integer} \right\}$$

a is called the *numerator*, and b is called the *denominator*.

Real numbers (1.1) The set of all rational and irrational numbers.

Real polynomial (4.1) A polynomial with coefficients and variables that are restricted to the real numbers. If the coefficients are restricted to a subset of the reals, it is a real polynomial *over* that set.

Reciprocal (1.2, 1.3, 5.1) The reciprocal of n is $1/n$, also called the *multiplicative inverse*.

Relation (9.1) A set of ordered pairs.

Rise (3.3) See Slope of a line.

Root of a number (6.1) An nth root (n is a natural number) of a number b is a only if $a^n = b$.

Roots of an equation (2.1) See Solutions.

Run (3.3) See Slope of a line.

Satisfy (2.1) See Equation or Inequality.

Scientific notation 1. (5.3) Writing a number as a product of a number between 1 and 10 and a power of 10.

2. (10.4) For any real number n, $n = m \cdot 10^C$, $1 \leq m < 10$, $C \in I$.

Sequence (11.1) An *infinite sequence* is a function whose domain is the set of counting numbers. It is sometimes called a *progression*. A *finite sequence* with n terms is a function whose domain is the set of numbers

$$\{1, 2, 3, \ldots, n\}$$

Series (11.2) The indicated sum of a finite or infinite sequence of terms.

Set (1.1) A collection of particular things, called the *members* or *elements* of the set. A set with no elements is called the *null set* or *empty set* and is denoted by the symbol $\emptyset$. All elements of a *finite set* may be listed, whereas the elements of an *infinite set* continue without end.

Similar terms (1.4) See Like terms.

Similar triangles (5.4) Two triangles are similar if and only if corresponding angles are equal. Corresponding sides are then proportional.

Simplified form for a radical (6.3, 6.4) A radical is in simplified form if it contains (1) no radical for which the radicand has a factor with a power greater than or equal to the index of the radical; (2) no radical as a denominator; (3) no fraction within a radical; and (4) no common factors (other than 1) between the exponent of the radicand and the index of the radical.

Simultaneous equations (8.1) Two or more equations that are conditions imposed on all variables that may or may not have common solutions. See System of equations.

Slope–intercept form of the equation of a line (3.3) $y = mx + b$, where b is the y-intercept and m is the slope.

Slope of a line (3.3) The slope of a line passing through (x_1, y_1) and (x_2, y_2) is denoted by m, is found by

$$m = \frac{y_2 - y_1}{x_2 - x_1} = \frac{\text{Vertical change}}{\text{Horizontal change}} = \frac{\text{Rise}}{\text{Run}}$$

and represents the steepness of the line.

Solutions (2.1, 3.1, 8.1, 8.3, 8.5) The values, ordered pairs of values, or ordered triplets of values for which an equation, system of equations, inequality, or system of inequalities is true.

Square root (6.1) See Root of a number.

Standard form of the equation of a line (3.2) $Ax + By + C = 0$, where A, B, and C are numbers, not all 0, and (x, y) is any point on the line.

Standard forms of a fraction (5.1) If p and q represent positive integers, then the standard forms for a fraction are

$$\frac{p}{q} \quad \text{and} \quad \frac{-p}{q}$$

String of inequalities (2.3) See Inequality.

Subset (1.1) A is a subset of B, $A \subseteq B$, if all the elements of A are also in B.

Substitution method (8.1) The solution of a system of equations in which one of the equations is solved for one of the variables and substituted into the other equation.

Sum and product property (7.2) If $ax^2 + bx + c = 0$ and has roots r_1 and r_2, then $r_1 + r_2 = -b/a$ and $r_1 r_2 = c/a$.

Summation notation (11.5) Sigma, the Greek letter, written Σ, is used to indicate the process of summing the first to the nth terms of a set of numbers a_1, a_2, a_3, . . . , a_n. The sum is written

$$\sum_{i=1}^{n} a_i$$

Sum of cubes (4.5) A polynomial of the form $a^3 + b^3 = (a + b)(a^2 - ab + b^2)$.

Symbols of inclusion (1.1) See Grouping symbols.

Synthetic division (4.3) An abbreviated algorithm for division of a polynomial, $P(x)$, by a divisor of the form $x - k$.

System of equations (8.1) A set of equations that are to be solved *simultaneously*. A brace symbol is used to show the equations belonging to the system.

System of inequalities (8.5) A set of inequalities that are to be solved simultaneously. The solution is the set of all ordered pairs (x, y) that satisfy all the given inequalities. It is found by finding the intersection of the half-planes defined by each inequality.

Term (1.4, 4.1) See Polynomial.

Theorem (1.2) A statement derived from more elementary results.

Trinomial (4.1) A polynomial with exactly three terms.

Union (2.3) See Compound statement.

Unit circle (9.4) Circle with radius 1.

Variable (1.1) A symbol that represents unspecified elements of a given set.

Variation (7.4) If variables x and y are related so that: **1.** $y = kx$, we say that y *varies directly* as x or that y is *directly proportional* to x. **2.** $y = kx^2$, we say that y *varies directly as the square* of x or that y is *directly proportional to the square* of x. **3.** $y = \dfrac{k}{x}$, we say that y *varies inversely* as x or that y is *inversely proportional* to x. **4.** $y = \dfrac{k}{x^2}$, we say that y *varies inversely as the square* of x or that y is *inversely proportional to the square* of x. If the variables x, y, and z are related so that $z = kxy$, we say that z *varies jointly* as x and y; z can be written as a combination of the other variation types.

Venn diagram (1.1) Diagram used to illustrate relationships among sets.

Vertex of a parabola (9.3) If $y - k = a(x - h)^2$, then the vertex is (h, k). Also, see Parabola.

Vertical line (3.3) A line with undefined slope. Its equation has the form $x = \text{Constant}$.

x-intercept (3.3, 9.3) The place where a graph passes through the x-axis.

y-intercept (3.3, 9.3) The place where a graph passes through the y-axis. For a line $y = mx + b$, it is the point $(0, b)$. For $y = ax^2 + bx + c$, it is the point $(0, c)$. See also Intercepts of a parabola.

Zeros of an equation (9.3) The roots of an equation. See Intercepts of a parabola.

Index

A study guide has been developed to assist you in mastering difficult concepts that you may encounter in this text. For each chapter, it provides a review, additional examples, and an extensive self-test. It is available from your local bookstore under the name *Study Guide for Intermediate Algebra for College Students, 2nd Edition.*

LINEAR EQUATIONS

Standard form: $Ax + By + C = 0$
Slope–intercept form: $y = mx + b$
Point–slope form: $y - k = m(x - h)$
Horizontal line: $y = $ Constant
Vertical line: $x = $ Constant
Procedure for graphing a line—see page 65
Procedure for graphing a linear inequality—see page 91

PYTHAGOREAN THEOREM

If a triangle with legs a and b and hypotenuse c is a right triangle, then

$c^2 = a^2 + b^2$

CONSTANTS

$e \approx 2.7182818284$
$\pi \approx 3.141592654$

FACTORS AND EXPANSIONS

Difference of squares: $a^2 - b^2 = (a - b)(a + b)$
Difference of cubes: $a^3 - b^3 = (a - b)(a^2 + ab + b^2)$
Sum of cubes: $a^3 + b^3 = (a + b)(a^2 - ab + b^2)$
Perfect square: $(a + b)^2 = a^2 + 2ab + b^2$
Perfect cube: $(a + b)^3 = a^3 + 3a^2b + 3ab^2 + b^3$

Binomial theorem: $(a + b)^n = \sum_{k=0}^{n} \binom{n}{k} a^{n-k}b^k$ where $\binom{n}{k} = \dfrac{n!}{k!(n - k)!}$

$n! = 1 \cdot 2 \cdot 3 \cdot 4 \cdot \cdots \cdot (n-1)n$
$0! = 1$
$1! = 1$

QUADRATIC EQUATIONS

Parabolas: $y - k = a(x - h)^2$
              $x - h = a(y - k)^2$

Circle: $(x - h)^2 + (y - k)^2 = r^2$

Ellipse: $\dfrac{x^2}{a^2} + \dfrac{y^2}{b^2} = 1$

Hyperbola: $\dfrac{x^2}{a^2} - \dfrac{y^2}{b^2} = 1$ or $\dfrac{y^2}{a^2} - \dfrac{x^2}{b^2} = 1$

QUADRATIC FORMULA

If $ax^2 + bx + c = 0$, $a \neq 0$, then

$$x = \dfrac{-b \pm \sqrt{b^2 - 4ac}}{2a}$$